Jim Hudgins

CENTRAL FLYWAY

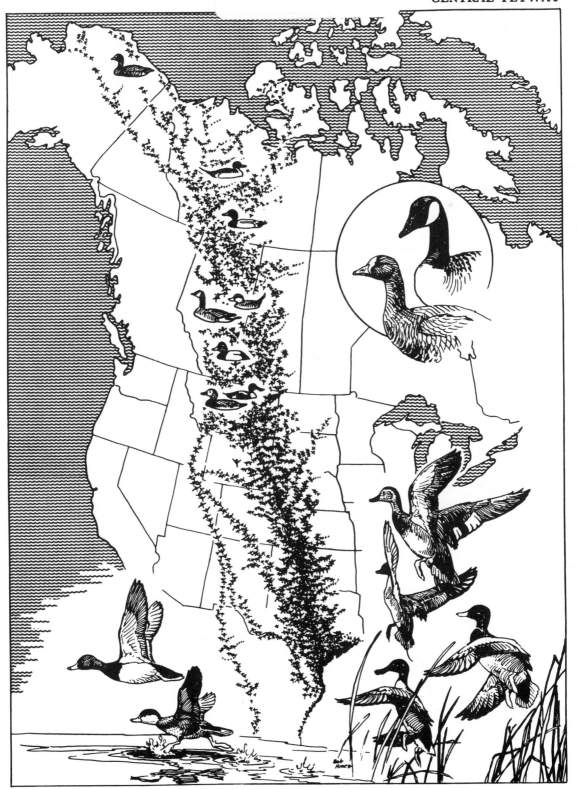

Flyways

For sale by the Superintendent of Documents, U.S. Government
Printing Office, Washington, D.C. 20402
May 1984

Flyways

Pioneering Waterfowl Management in North America

Published by

The United States
Department of the
Interior

Fish and Wildlife
Service

Edited by
A.S. Hawkins
R.C. Hanson
H.K. Nelson
H.M. Reeves

©D. Nelson

Foreword

Robert A. Jantzen

T.KELLEY '83

Waterfowl collectively constitute a treasure belonging to all North Americans, for their enjoyment and use now and in the future. Since the 1920s, however, the welfare of waterfowl has been threatened increasingly and will continue to be threatened in the years ahead.

The continued existence of healthy populations of ducks, geese, and swans in the future will depend on sophisticated management programs and dedicated people to carry them out. The successes of the past did not "just happen"; they were fashioned through tremendous efforts and the perseverance of dedicated laymen and professionals.

This book tells the story of some of the early work in waterfowl management as experienced by the people directly involved. There have been other published accounts of the development of the waterfowl management program, but none has told the story as it is told here. In *Flyways*, many of the fieldmen who developed present methods and gathered the information that serve as the basis for today's program are able to relate their experiences in their own ways. Many of the contributors are now in retirement, so we are particularly grateful to capture their recollections here.

It is apparent, as one reads these pages, that the task of managing North American waterfowl is never-ending. Some of the problems that nag us today were identified early on and will continue to challenge those who take over the waterfowl management program in the future. It is valuable to pause and reflect on the illustrious past of the waterfowl management business, seeing in it the basis for today's programs and tomorrow's challenges.

I am pleased to see this important historical account become part of the documented past and a guide to the future.

Robert A. Jantzen, Director
U.S. Fish and Wildlife Service

Preface

Editorial Committee
A.S. Hawkins
R.C. Hanson
H.K. Nelson
H.M. Reeves

Two decades age, 103 authors, scattered across Canada and the United States, pooled their knowledge about waterfowl to create a book called *Waterfowl Tomorrow*. According to its preface, the book dealt with the "needs of forty-eight species of ducks, geese, and swans that live on the North American Continent" and "the lands and waters that sustain this wildfowl." *Waterfowl Tomorrow* summed up the art of waterfowl management as it stood in the early 1960s.

Though *Flyways* is a different kind of book, it should be seen as a companion publication to *Waterfowl Tomorrow*. Much of its subject material is similar, and two dozens of its writers had articles in *Waterfowl Tomorrow*. In proper sequence, however, *Flyways* should have preceded *Waterfowl Tomorrow* since the purpose of this book is to tell the many stories that, put together, tell the overall story of the evolution of what fairly may be regarded as the world's most remarkable wildlife management program.

It is a program so young that many of the people involved in its beginnings are alive today. Many of these innovators were invited to dig into their notebooks and memories in order to submit articles on their early experiences. Fifty were able to respond, providing a unique behind-the-scenes glimpse of the birth of the flyway concept and all the programs we associate with it today. This is their story.

The seeds of the waterfowl management program were sown early in the twentieth century by a few creative individuals who are no longer alive to record their experiences. Yet, because they were trained scientists, they left careful records of their activities. From these we have drawn accounts of their contributions, trying more to emphasize their characters than to sum up all their accomplishments. We believe readers will find these accounts steeped in history and rich with the flavor of exploration and adventure.

On one hand, these early accounts forcibly demonstrate the vast differences between then and now in terms of manpower, equipment, funding, transportation, maps, guidelines, and experience. Yet they eloquently reflect the battles with mosquitoes and boggy terrain that are very much a part of modern day managers. All the scientists and administrators who have followed the earliest pioneers have, in a real sense, stood on these pioneers' shoulders. *Flyways* is dedicated to these trailblazers, whose dedication and innovation did so much to get today's program founded.

Acknowledgement of each contributor to *Flyways* is given in the "About the Contributors" section. Besides the authors, other individuals and organizations contributed in various ways. Ross Hanson and Art Hawkins conceived the idea of such a book after the Spring 1979, issue of *Naturalist* magazine, dealing with much the same topic, was so well received. Harvey K. Nelson and H.M. "Milt" Reeves joined them to form an editorial committee. John P. Rogers and Robert I. Smith of the Migratory Bird Management Office conducted the administrative review required by the Service and offered useful suggestions. Robert Putz, FWS Associate Director, arranged funding for final editing and printing. Arthur S. "Tex" Hawkins spent long hours on the preliminary editing of manuscripts. Steve Grooms whipped the collected manuscripts into shape, trying to achieve a degree of unity while preserving the distinctiveness of the voices of the authors. Tom Kelley, graphic designer, and Jim Ross, Public Affair Officer, designed and coordinated production of the book. Roosevelt McDuffie, Bob DeMarais, Randy Tate and Don Reilly assisted with graphics and layout. Nikki Des Rosier, Nathalie Raab, Lynn Kelley, Dianne Pearson, Patricia Percy and Sharon Amundson assisted with typing, proofreading and editorial review. Shirley Johnson and John Mullins, Contracting and General Services, handled all outside contracts in the production of the book.

All who have been involved with this project — and there are many more that could be named here — have been impressed with the importance of collecting and publishing these stories. The men whose work is described here deserve no less. Beyond that, we all believe it is important to make a record of the cooperative effort that has created today's waterfowl management program.

The accomplishments of the past are extremely remarkable. The dragons that needed slaying by the early pioneers were mostly awesome because they represented facts not known. After all, the North American waterfowl resource is one of the most diverse and complicated natural communities in the world, living in some of the most remote and impassable terrain on the continent. Yet, unfortunately, the dragons that face today's managers seem in many ways even more fearsome because they involve basic conflicts in social groups and social values. They will not be put to rest easily, as the final chapter of *Flyways* makes clear.

The highest hope of the editorial committee is that *Flyways* will make a worthy contribution to the effort to ensure continued strong waterfowl populations. Today's managers obviously owe a great debt to those who preceded them, for the number of facts unknown has dwindled remarkably. Beyond that, however, we are convinced today's managers can draw inspiration from these tales of the early years of the waterfowl management program. The legacy of knowledge left by the early figures is easily matched by a legacy of dedication and hard work for a good cause.

Introduction

Ten thousand years ago retreating glaciers built a paradise for waterfowl in North America second to none in the world. A century ago this national heritage remained largely intact, but a few decades later the picture changed abruptly.

White settlers trekking westward during the 1800s were too busy clearing away the forest and wresting a living from the soil to damage the waterfowl habitat. They even improved it some by planting small fields of grain relished by some species of ducks. They then plowed the prairies and, that obstacle conquered, launched larger projects such as building dams and draining marshes.

Rapidly developing technogical civilization and an exponentially increasing human population have rearranged the landscape to make it supply needs and satisfy escalating fancies. Wetlands interfered with development, so that at every opportunity they were drained or filled, causing a steady reduction of duck habitat. While duck habitat was declining, duck hunting areas became easier to reach as roads and transportation improved. The result was inevitable. Sooner or later waterfowl would be in trouble, and North America's waterfowl ran into serious trouble sooner than many expected.

Legislation for the protection of birds gained considerable support near the close of the 19th century as conservationists witnessed the demise of the passenger pigeon and the bison. Many suspected that waterfowl might be next to disappear. The obvious way to remedy the situation was through law, but each politicial unit had a different idea on which regulations to apply. Consequently, the first laws enacted to protect waterfowl as they moved through the flyways took on a crazy quilt pattern.

As one might expect, the states and provinces looked at migratory game differently than they did at resident game. All too often the goal was to "get our share" before someone else did. It soon became clear that a resource shared by more than one nation and many states and provinces had to be managed in a highly cooperative manner with the federal wildlife agencies taking the lead, but with much help from other wildlife agencies and the private sector. It also became clear that laws alone were not enough. Too little was known about the birds themselves — their year-round habitat requirements, numbers, productivity, major mortality factors, and longevity — to make responsible management decisions.

This enlightened concept for managing migratory birds led to the passage of the Migra-

A protective canvasback hen. USFWS photo by J. Stoudt.

tory Bird Treaty Act in 1916, which placed definite responsibilities on the federal governments of the United States and Canada regarding the welfare of waterfowl. But development of a fact-finding capability took time, since trained personnel, funds and equipment were all in short supply. It took the great drought of the 1930s to generate sufficient concern and pressure so the purse strings were loosened and investigations were broadened. Slowed temporarily by World War II, the waterfowl program took off in high gear after the war ended, powered by enthusiastic and dedicated people who were freed from the shackles of war and eager to work to ensure the future of a cherished natural resource.

North America's waterfowl management program is unique in the annals of world wildlife conservation efforts. No other program has spanned so many years, involved so many people, covered so much ground, or cost so much money. Behind present-day understanding and management of waterfowl by flyways lie stories never before told, stories of adventure, discovery, sacrifice, and plain hard work. In particular, the fascinating story of how the many pieces of the program were conceived, developed, fitted and implemented has gone untold. Further, the published material on North American waterfowl management has not been written from the viewpoint of the individuals actually involved.

Many of these trailblazers have taken the time to search their memories, notebooks and photo albums in preparing their eye-witness accounts for this book. Some who belong with this group of pioneers were unable to participate for various reasons. Others have passed on, but for them vignettes have been prepared, giving highlights of their careers as they related to waterfowl.

The editors regret that this volume could not be more complete. However, we believe that it accurately portrays the problems, the spirit of adventure and accomplishments of an era when waterfowl management in North America was in its early stages. In some ways, progress has been painfully slow, and in the final chapter examples are given of some of yesterdays' problems still unsolved today. Waterfowl management has come a long way in the past 60 years but still has some distance to go before the future of the waterfowl resource is secure.

The editors believe that this valuable collection of memorabilia, so high in historic content, should be preserved; hence this book.

Contents

XVIII

Crisis Along the Flyways

Waterfowl, perhaps more than any other group of birds, stimulate strong human responses. Admired by artists and poets for their beauty and grace, waterfowl are avidly pursued by hunters for their table and sporting qualities, hated by some farmers whose crops they destroy, and lovingly observed by a public that simply enjoys having them around. The goings and comings of waterfowl have even been a matter of life and death to some native North Americans. And always, the great migrations of waterfowl have inspired mankind while serving as a symbol of the passing of the seasons.

It is hardly surprising, therefore, that disputes and decisions regarding ducks and geese have often involved the highest tribunals and officials in the land. This chapter discusses some such proceedings, especially those leading to the passage of the Migratory Bird Treaty Act, the legislation that made possible today's extensive system of cooperative management.

Great benefits sometimes follow from simple inventions, and this chapter offers fresh proof. The invention that revolutionized our understanding of waterfowl was the leg band. Management of waterfowl by flyway came about largely because of the leg band, the history of which is traced in the following pages.

Game laws limiting the harvest of waterfowl have always been controversial, especially in the earliest days of legislation reflecting the new federal supervision of waterfowl populations. In a short period of time, hunters were denied the right to sell ducks and geese, to hunt them in spring, or to use live decoys or bait for taking them. This infringement on states' authority caused some states to mount vigorous legal challenges to the right of federal authorities to control waterfowl hunting. Not until such disputes were settled could productive cooperative management begin.

In both Canada and the United States, the primary responsibility for ensuring the future of waterfowl rests with the federal government. Yet that responsibility and the work necessary to support it are shared with the provinces and states. The resulting governmental machinery sometimes grinds too slowly to satisfy the public it serves, and sometimes too there are gaps or shortcomings in the system. These deficiencies have been met, at least in part, by initiatives from private groups, particularly Ducks Unlimited.

These stories, and others, are presented in this chapter.

The U.S. Response

Arthur S. Hawkins

Southward in fall and northward in spring, waterfowl have followed their ancestral travel routes or "flyways" since the retreating glaciers left landmarks and watery stepping stones as guideposts. Observers noted these bird migrations for centuries, but here in North America, not until the present century were the routes delineated and given names.

Flyways became apparent largely as a result of a technique called banding. John James Audubon, the great American artist, was credited with using silver wires to leg-band a brood of phoebes in 1803. Two of his banded phoebes returned the following year, completing the first banding study. Dr. Leon J. Cole, professor at the University of Wisconsin, used leg bands to mark pigeons he was studying and, with P.A. Taverner of Canada, was instrumental in organizing the American Bird Banding Association in 1909. In 1920 their records and subsequent administration of the banding program was turned over to the U.S. Bureau of Biological Survey (USBS), with Frederic C. Lincoln in charge.

Even before the banding technique was developed, much was known about bird migration. In 1915, Wells W. Cooke, Biological Survey biologist, published a government bulletin on bird migration, noting that "the survey has been collecting data on bird migration for more than 25 years." This information came from "more than 2,000 different observers," including "field naturalists" and "lighthouse keepers." Cooke presented maps showing migration routes of several species but lacked banding data to support his conclusions, conclusions that were remarkably accurate considering his handicaps.

Fredrick C. Lincoln — in 1935 and again in 1950 — updated Cooke's bulletin on migration, adding information strengthened by the new file on banded birds. A manual for bird banders issued in 1929 showed that more than 400,000 birds (all species) had been banded in Canada and the United States, producing 19,000 usable recovery records. The file had grown to "well over 2,500,000 entries" by 1935. A decade later "nearly 5,000,000 birds had been banded," producing "more than 300,000 usable return records." About twelve hundred ducks were banded on the Great Salt Lake marshes of Utah from 1914-1916 by Alexander Wetmore during his duck-sickness studies. Lincoln developed a waterlily-leaf trap that caught about two thousand ducks in Illinois River marshes during March 1922, the first large-scale banding of waterfowl.

According to Lincoln, "Recovery of banded ducks and geese accumulated so rapidly that by 1930 it was possible to map out the four waterfowl flyways' great geographical regions, each with breeding and wintering grounds connected by a complicated series of migration routes." Thus, the flyway concept was conceived at about the same time that the great drought of the 1930s spread over the land, parching the nesting grounds and leaving the waterfowl population in shambles.

Banding revolutionized the waterfowl managers' understanding of the birds they managed. USFWS photo by Rex Gary Schmidt.

The Dust Bowl days decimated waterfowl populations. This is the dry bed of Old Wives (Johnston) Lake, Saskatchewan, in 1937. USFWS photo by G. B. Saunders.

Most of us have heard about the "dirty thirties" and how the waterfowl resource was blighted by the prolonged drought. Only a few are aware that duck numbers were also perceived as slumping before the turn of the century. We are inclined to envision the "good old days" as a time when the woods, prairies and marshes abounded with wildlife, and all the waters teemed with fish. That might have been true, relatively speaking, but some old-timers who were keen observers saw it differently. Dr. Clarence M. Weed and Dr. Ned Dearborn, both highly educated and well-qualified professionals, were two such observers. In 1903 they wrote a book containing much information about waterfowl and the people who enjoyed them. As they saw it: "The stock of wildfowl has reached a low ebb through a long-continued and ever-increasing persecution and an ever-narrowing breeding range. Two different motive forces have pushed the persecution — the market and an inborn love of hunting, the one commercial (a matter of dollars and

cents) the other a natural instinct."

But in this dark hour the authors offered hope. "By care the stock may be replenished and the birds indefinitely preserved — a continued source of benefit to us and a worthy legacy to posterity."

Even in the first years of this century the roots of the problem were apparent. Migratory birds could not receive the protection they needed without more uniform harvest regulations. The Lacey Act, passed by the U.S. Congress in 1900, recognized this need. It prohibited interstate commerce of wildlife contrary to laws of the states involved. It prohibited the importation of foreign wildlife without a federal permit, and it gave the USDA new responsibilities concerning the preservation, distribution, introduction, and restoration of wildlife.

Weed and Dearborn gave examples of the dissimilar state hunting regulations. For example, ducks could not be taken in Iowa from April 15 to September 1, while in adjacent Minnesota the closed dates were January 1 to September 1, and in Missouri (also adjacent to Iowa), April 1 to October 1. From these and other similar cases the authors concluded, "This condition of things is manifestly wrong, and so long as it continues the laws in question are certain to be violated." Realistically, they pointed out, "If game laws do not meet the approval and have the hearty support of the masses, they are void."

Reacting to this lack of uniformity in game laws, Charles Hallock, as early as 1897, suggested to the National Game, Bird and Fish Protective Association that the United States be divided into three districts — Northern, Southern, and Pacific — within which similar game laws would be adopted. (Except for Arizona, which was placed in the Southern District, Hallock's Pacific District was identical to the Pacific Flyway as delineated a half-century later.) But Hallock was ahead of his time. States still were unwilling to relinquish their jurisdiction over the taking of wildlife.

George Shiras III, then U.S. Congressman from Pennsylvania but better known as an outstanding nature photographer, was among those convinced that the trend in waterfowl numbers would continue downward until migratory birds were placed under centralized federal control. The bill he introduced in 1904 supported this conviction but, like Hallock's idea, had little chance for passage.

After nearly a decade of intensive lobbying and salesmanship by conservation leaders, the Migratory Bird Act was signed into law by President Taft on March 4, 1913. It empowered the secretary of agriculture to set the dates for hunting migratory game birds, "having due regard to the zones of temperature, and to the distribution, abundance, economic value, breeding habits and times and lives of migratory flight of such birds." Among those most responsible for the Act's passage were John B. Burnham of the American Game Protective Association (founded in 1911); Dr. T. Gilbert Pearson, secretary of the National Association of Audubon Socie-

ties (founded in 1901); and Charles Sheldon of the Boone and Crockett Club. The Weeks-McLean Bill, which upon passage became the act, was guided through the House by Representative Weeks of Massachusetts and through the Senate by Senator McLean of Connecticut. It was patterned after the Shiras Bill but was broadened to include non-game migratory birds, as well as those classed as game.

These conservation-minded legislators had to overcome strong opposition to their bill not only from unrelenting state-righters, but also from market hunters whose income was threatened and sportsmen who enjoyed spring shooting. On a broader front, the act immediately came under fire from those who questioned its constitutionality. In 1914, a U.S. District Court judge at Jonesboro, Arkansas, at the trial of the *United States v. Harvey C. Shauver,* found the act unconstitutional.

Meanwhile, to counter the question of constitutionality (at the suggestion of Justice Elihu Root), a small group commenced drafting a treaty between the United States and Canada for the protection of migratory birds. A draft prepared by W.S. Haskell, legal council for the American Game Protective Association, was rejected. Then, Dr. T. S. Palmer of the Biological Survey wrote the draft that three years later in 1916, with few changes, was ratified by Great Britain for Canada and by the United States. In Canada, Dr. C. Gordon Hewitt, Dominion consulting zoologist, did most of the legwork that finally resulted in the treaty's acceptance. Other Canadians who deserve special credit for its passage were Honorable Martin Burrell, minister of agriculture; Clifford Sifton, chairman of the Commission of Conservation; J. B. Harkin of Canadian National Parks; James White, deputy head of the Conservation Commission; and several officers of Canadian railroads who took special interest in this project. In the United States, Dr. E. W. Nelson became chief of the Biological Survey in 1916, and it was his job to implement the provisions of the legislation.

Ratification of the Migratory Bird Treaty

removed the need for a Supreme Court ruling on the constitutionality of the Migratory Bird Act, but one important step remained: passage of an enabling act. This act was passed on June 6, 1918, giving the USBS responsibility for its enforcement. Opponents, however, still didn't accept defeat. In 1920 following a test case, *Missouri v. Holland* (the U.S. government's enforcement officer), the Supreme Court ruled in favor of Holland in a landmark decision read by Justice Oliver Wendell Holmes. This decision cleared the way for a new era in the appreciation, use, and management of the continent's migratory birds.

Early in the 1930s when hunting seasons were being restricted, a foundation called More Game Birds in America (the forerunner to Ducks Unlimited) complained that "in the past three years, the open seasons for migratory waterfowl have been changed five times, culminating in the highly unsatisfactory 30-day season for 1931 . . . Last year, in the neighboring states of Missouri, Illinois, Indiana, and Kentucky, there were four different seasons for waterfowl shooting fixed by Federal regulations."

Hallock's idea of thirty-five years earlier was resurrected and embellished with a series of maps showing temperature zones across the country on the first day of each month from October through January and the average date when the mean temperature dropped below 32 degrees Fahrenheit. These weather maps were then converted into three north-south "waterfowl season zones." Apparently in response to the foundation's suggestion, the three hunting season zones set by the secretary during the late 1930s corresponded closely to those of More Game Birds. After that they became increasingly complicated by exceptions and modifications, until the north-south format was dropped and an east-west flyway system was adopted in 1948.

Excellent scientific studies and biological literature on waterfowl and other migratory birds existed long before the Migratory Bird Treaty Act was ratified. However, the emphasis was changed by the treaty and its obligations, at least as far as the federal government was concerned. The American Ornithological Union deserves much credit for the establishment in 1884 of an office of Economic Ornithology in the USDA to study and publish the food habits and migration of birds and other wildlife. In 1905 this office became the USBS. Their publications dealt primarily with food and other habits of birds, their economic status (especially in relation to agriculture), and the new laws for their protection.

By 1918 the staff of the young Biological Survey had published at least two dozen free or inexpensive pamphlets on migratory birds. These pamphlets featured the results of several food habit studies and instructions for raising ducks or attracting birds with bird houses and food. Information about the migration and distribution of birds, and game laws also was available.

In the early years, the food habits laboratory was the busiest place in the Survey. Here most of the new generation of waterfowl biologists received their indoctrination. Soon the declining status of waterfowl and their habitats would require major attention, but not yet. This was the lull before the storm.

In a report recounting the progress made during the first decade under the Migratory Bird Treaty Act, an Audubon Society spokesman stated, "The number of wildfowl have so increased since 1913 as to astonish the country." Surprisingly enough, in this report from an organization often considered lukewarm toward hunting is the following statement: "Ducks exist in enormous numbers throughout the continent. . . We must think of them in terms of tens of millions and not feel alarmed that several million are killed each year. They are very prolific."

But this mood of complacency was soon shattered by Director Nelson of the Biological Survey. In the mid-1920s he wrote: "The danger to the perpetualism of the stock of wildfowl is so great and so imminent . . . that there is the most vital need for all conservationists and lovers of wildlife to sink petty differences of opinion as to the details and to unite in constructive work to insure the future of our migratory game birds."

Warnings such as those of Dr. Nelson had to be based on more than food habits studies on instructions on how to raise ducks. And they were. Fieldmen under his direction were beginning to look at waterfowl status and their overall well-being, as they were obliged to do by the Migratory Bird Treaty. The Audubon report of 1926 gave the Survey a high score in meeting this responsibility. "Congress has given complete administrative power to the Department of Agriculture, acting through the Biological Survey . . . It has fulfilled its responsibilities and produced satisfactory results." The report pointed out that "the supply can only be approximately determined by a detailed study of continental conditions by trained men . . . The Department has in the Biological Survey the only organization competent to solve these problems." This was a fine tribute to the fieldmen who soon would be known as "flyway biologists."

During the 1920s a start was made by Congress toward creating a national refuge system, with separate acts establishing the Upper Mississippi River Wildlife and Fish Refuge in 1924, and the Bear River Migratory Bird Refuge in 1929. The Migratory Bird Conservation Act, passed in 1929, authorized the appropriation of $7.9 million for the purchase or lease of refuges for waterfowl, and in the western provinces of Canada more than a dozen lakes and marshes were designated as inviolate sanctuaries.

Another major development in 1929 was the presentation by Chairman Aldo Leopold of his committee's report on an American Wildlife policy at the sixteenth American Game Conference. Regarding migratory game, the policy stated that "the management measures most needed are the public acquisition of habitats threatened with drainage, the establishment of a continental system of public and private refuges, and a more adequate program of fact finding." The report added, "There is pressing need to know more about the status, not only of the migratory game crop as a whole, but of each constituent species." Singling out defects in the current program, the report states that "its stock of facts is inadequate. Research must keep ahead, not lag behind the need for facts. Game yields can be greatly increased, and the costs and risks of management decreased, by more research."

This recognition of the need for research to make possible an improved management program, coming as it did from the leading conservationists of that day, couldn't have occurred at a better time. A drought was setting in on the western plains of North America that was to become the most severe in history. Concurrently, a major economic depression nearly paralyzed the nation.

Sometimes a near-catastrophe is a blessing in disguise. Such was the case, so far as waterfowl were concerned in the 1930s when dust blotted out the midday sun throughout the midlands of North America. Marshlands, parched from years of deficient rainfall, became mudflats that caked and crumbled and added to the rolling clouds as the dust bowl expanded. Even the casual observer knew that all wildlife that depended on wetlands was in serious trouble.

According to a USDA report published in 1934, "Serious drought conditions have arisen periodically throughout recorded history, always doubtless working hardship on waterfowl. But never, so far as is known, have there been so many destructive conditions and agencies at work at once upon a depleted waterfowl supply as during the past 5 years . . . The support and interest of all public-spirited citizens are now needed to repair the damage."

The great drought of the thirties was devastating because of its duration. According to Bell and Preble, writing in 1934:

> The long period of deficient precipitation over hundreds of thousands of square miles of the finest breeding territory in the North Central States and the southern parts of the Prairie Provinces of Canada began in 1915. With the exception of a slightly increased rainfall in 1920, this shortage continued til

Baiting ducks with corn was a common practice at duck clubs in the Illinois River Bottoms until outlawed in 1935. Photo by Bob Becker.

1934, when all available records for duration of time, extent of territory affected, and severity of drought conditions were broken. Serious drought conditions have arisen periodically throughout recorded history, always doubtless working hardships upon the waterfowl. But never, so far as is known, have there been so many destructive conditions and agencies at work at once upon a depleted waterfowl supply as during the past five years. During that period the number of waterfowl have fallen drastically. The support and interest of all public-spirited citizens are now needed to repair the damage . . .

So alarming was the situation facing waterfowl that J. Clark Salyer, also in 1934, wrote, "This nesting grounds now lies as a desert so far as its millions of waterfowl are concerned. The sturdy human stock of the prairie lands will endure. The herds will grow fat again. But can the earlier inhabitants, the winged millions, reestablish themselves in all their early abundance?"

But the dust clouds had a silver lining. Thanks to the leadership of people like Aldo Leopold and J. N. "Ding" Darling in the United States, and Hoyes Lloyd in Canada, the North American public responded as it usually does when the chips are down. A blueprint for action was ready in the form of the American Game Policy and, despite a depression, the money was available from President Franklin D. Roosevelt's emergency programs. Private interests rose to the occasion under the banners of the National Wildlife Federation, the Wildlife Management Institute, and Ducks Unlimited.

The 1930s were trying years in more ways than one for those responsible for managing the waterfowl resource. As conditions got tougher, tempers flared. Hunting regulations became progressively more restrictive, much to the dismay of hunters. But to the non-hunters and many conservationists, all hunting should have been banned for the duration of the emergency. The Biological Survey, which was responsible for the regulations, thus caught criticism from both sides of the issue.

Representing United States sportsmen, the More Game Birds in America Foundation reported on a survey they sponsored, and two years later the same organization conducted and reported on the *1935 International Wild Duck Census.* Their findings agreed with those of Biological Survey investigators, but the two organizations drew different conclusions. Whereas the Survey pointed to the shotgun as a major cause of the decline and saw tighter harvest regulations as a means of helping the situation, More Game Birds stated that "this is no time to experiment with substitutes or to squabble about petty, unpopular and unenforceable shooting restrictions presumed to provide the remedy." The Survey's position was weakened in the eyes of strict conservationists by permitting the continuance of two deadly hunting techniques, baiting and using live decoys. Nor did a faux pas committed by the USBS in 1934 escape the attention of the critics. A critic named Irving Brant pointed out that "the so-called 'staggered season' which the United States Bureau of Biological Survey established in 1934, actually wrote into the law the precise method of 'rest days' by which the heaviest slaughter of ducks is obtained on baited shooting grounds." Subsequent analysis of banding data showed that this criticism was justified, and the mistake was not repeated.

Lest the Biological Survey receive all the blame for questionable decisions on hunting regulations made during those crucial years, it should be pointed out that then, as now, decisions were influenced by recommendations of an advisory board. It has been claimed that this twenty-member board, during those years, was dominated by Eastern duck club members, a fact that explains the majority votes against shortening the season, lowering the bag limit, and abolishing baiting.

A major problem of that era was enforcement. Market hunting still flourished in parts of the country and general unrest among hunters led to a level of violations far beyond the capability of the two dozen federal law officers to combat. To make matters worse,

new automotive transportation was rapidly increasing the mobility of hunters. Meanwhile developers and farmers were taking advantage of the drought to drain wetlands previously too difficult to reach.

A shortage of funds had severely limited the activities of the young Biological Survey, but this situation changed rapidly for the better during the 1930s. The seed of an idea germinating for several years finally sprouted in the form of companion bills introduced by Congressman Richard Kleberg from Texas and Senator Frederic C. Walcott from Connecticut. These bills became the Migratory Bird Hunting Stamp Act of 1934. Roosevelt, who had just become president, had commenced concocting his "alphabet soup" series of programs aimed at putting depressed America back to work through public works programs. Suddenly millions of dollars became available for the acquisition and development of waterfowl habitat.

But the money did not come easily. It took a super salesman named Ding Darling, during the few months he served as Survey chief, to implement the program designed by a special committee appointed by President Roosevelt. Darling, Aldo Leopold, and Thomas Beck prepared this blueprint. Considerably fewer funds would have gone into wildlife projects without such a plan, which emphasized the need for waterfowl habitat and fact finding. Ding Darling was the Billy Sunday and Billy Graham of the conservation movement, all wrapped into one. Probably no conservation leader before or since has so effectively united the various conservation interests of the nation in a common cause.

As chief of the Biological Survey, Darling needed a strong personality to carry out his ambitious program — and in J. Clark Salyer he found the ideal man. Salyer was put in charge of the newly created Division of Migratory Waterfowl. With $8.5 million in emergency funds at his disposal, Salyer began the task of building a migratory birds refuge system, which became the world's largest.

Another positive and epochal development during the early 1930s was the publication of Aldo Leopold's classic book, *Game Management*. It heralded a new era in the outlook toward wildlife and the way it was managed. Two concepts Leopold introduced in that work were unknown outside the professional management community for four decades, but today "ecology" and "the environment" are everyday words. In 1933 Leopold described the same phenomenon for the word "conservation". He wrote:

> "Came then Theodore Roosevelt with the idea of 'conservation through wise use'. Wildlife, forests, ranges, and waterpower were conceived by him to be *renewable organic resources,* which might last forever if they were *harvested scientifically, and not faster than they reproduced.* Conservation had until then been a lowly word, sleeping obscurely in the back of the dictionary. The public had never heard it. It carried no particular connotation of woods or waters. Overnight it became the label of a national issue."

Leopold reinterpreted and added scope to the Roosevelt conservation doctrine. Leopold conceived of natural resources as one integral whole, conservation as a public responsibility, and wildlife management as the means for discharging that responsibility. In *Game Management* for the first time conservation leaders and students had a reference for exploring the principles and approaches that would make "conservation" and wildlife management interdependent. Above all, Leopold emphasized the role of science and the need for research.

The stage was now set for wildlife management to become a recognized profession and for the flyway system of managing waterfowl to become recognized as one of its towering accomplishments. Management has come a long way since Audubon first banded those phoebes, eighteen decades ago!

The Canadian Response

Victor E. F. Solman

North America was discovered by Europeans seeking the riches of the East Indies. Having encountered what later became Canada, they found great resources of fish, trees, and fur. They harvested those resources and transported the products to the markets of Europe. Beaver became symbolic of Canada because the pelts were one of the first export products to Europe. Wildlife was important from the beginning. Most of the people carrying out the exploitation of the resources came from Europe; to them, the stocks available in North America seemed almost without limit. That tradition of abundance lasted for a long time and, indeed, still persists in parts of Canada.

As Canada became settled and heavy use was made of wildlife in small areas, game laws were introduced. Some have been in effect in parts of Canada since the early 1700s. At the time the provinces were united under the British North America Act, provincial control of wildlife resources was well established and there was little federal concern. In fact, the whole matter was taken so much for granted that there is no mention of wildlife in the British North America Act.

This did not indicate a complete lack of federal interest, however, because there was federal activity on behalf of wildlife as early as 1887. The islands and shoreline at the north end of Last Mountain Lake, Saskatchewan, were made a bird sanctuary by Order-in-Council on June 8 of that year. That was one of the first activities of that kind in North America. On June 23, 1887 Canada's first national park was authorized under the Rocky Mountain Park Act. There were clauses in that legislation relating to wildlife protection, but the main intent was creation of a tourist resort and preservation of a group of hot springs and associated scenery rather than the management of wildlife. As the parks organization expanded, progressively more attention was paid to wildlife, but most national parks were created primarily to preserve other values.

Between 1850 and 1900 a number of influential persons in North America became concerned about the declining numbers of passenger pigeons and bison. When they looked ahead, they could see the end of certain species unless actions were taken. One bird group of concern to many people was waterfowl, including ducks, geese, and swans. They were being shot for food and sport and, indeed, were a part of the commercial food supply in many parts of the country. Although provinces and states had been legislating for the protection of wildlife for more than 100 years, they found they could not effectively deal with a migratory resource that seasonally moved between breeding and wintering grounds, and was harvested in each jurisdiction through which it passed. In that situation, it was easy to overharvest the stock. Not only was the annual increment being taken each year, but a part of the parent stock as well. There was also shooting in the spring and on the breeding grounds, which was very destructive to the resource. Farsighted people then tried to have the harvest reduced by encouraging the provinces and states to cooperate. Human nature being what it is, it was very difficult to bring about. When the birds were in a province or state, that province or state tried to secure the best possible opportunity for its citizens to harvest a "fair" share of the resource, knowing that other political entities would also be involved in the total amount of the harvest. Invariably each political entity took its full share of the harvest and perhaps a bit more, and the decline continued.

There was an attempt in the United States to impose federal control on the system, but that was challenged by some states as unconstitutional, and the matter was referred to the United States Supreme Court. It was clear that federal control in that way was unconstitutional in the United States and that a similar attempt in Canada would probably be unsuccessful for similar reasons. Farsighted people in Canada and the United States sought a solution that would be acceptable and workable in both countries. The solution finally arrived at involved a treaty between the two countries. It worked simply, because both the British North America Act and the United States Constitution have provisions for implementation of the terms of an international treaty as a federal responsibility.

After several years of preparatory work, the Migratory Birds Convention (Treaty) between Canada, represented by Great Britain, and the United States was signed in 1916. Following that, each country passed legislation implementing the treaty and began to promulgate regulations for the control of migratory birds. Signing the treaty, and the act based upon it, put the federal government squarely into the wildlife management business for the first time.

An Advisory Board on Wildlife Protection was created by Order-in-Council on December 28, 1916. That organization had been recommended by J. B. Harkin, the commissioner of Dominion Parks, and had as its members James White, D. C. Hewitt, R. M. Anderson, and J. B. Harkin. One of the first jobs the members of the board did was draft the Migratory Birds Convention Act and suggest the appointment of an officer to administer the act and regulations. They also drafted a Northwest Game Act and concerned themselves with caribou in the Northwest Territories, pronghorn, elk, wolves, and other wildlife, as well as special habitats such as Point Pelee, Bonaventure Island, and a number of areas of importance for birds in western Canada.

Because of the passage of the Migratory Birds Convention Act, there was a need for an official to be appointed to carry out the terms of the act. By 1918 there was an active and growing national parks organization in the Department of the Interior. It seemed logical that an agency dealing with wildlife should be located within the national parks organization. Accordingly, the official charged with responsibility for the Migratory Birds

Harrison F. Lewis, Chief Federal Migratory Bird Officer for Quebec and Ontario, checks a pile of geese and ducks bagged in 1940 along James Bay. USFWS photo by H. Peters.

Convention Act, Hoyes Lloyd, reported for duty to that agency on December 11, 1918. His job title was ornithologist, and he started at a yearly salary of $2,200. Lloyd's basic responsibility was administration of the Migratory Birds Convention Act, but he had an added responsibility involving the Northwest Game Act. In 1919 the protection of wildlife in national parks was added to his duties and his title was changed to supervisor of Wildlife Protection. He had a secretary and, as you can imagine, he and the secretary were kept pretty busy trying to cope with migratory birds and their problems throughout Canada, game in the Northwest Territories, and wildlife in national parks. It was not long before he was able to convince his superior, J. B. Harkin of the National Parks Branch,

that he needed some help to carry out a job that covered such a large area and involved so many wild creatures of a wide range of species.

His pleas for assistance resulted in the creation of additional positions in the summer of 1920. Competitions were held for the two positions of chief federal migratory bird officer for Ontario and Quebec, and for the western provinces. James A. Munro of British Columbia was the successful applicant for the western position and Harrison F. Lewis for the position involving Ontario and Quebec. Prior to these appointments, R. W. Tufts of Wolfville, Nova Scotia, had been appointed on November 19, 1919, as officer for the maritime provinces.

As can be seen from the record thus far,

although the Commission on Conservation had functioned since 1911 and the Advisory Board on Wildlife Protection since late 1916, work by qualified professionals in wildlife conservation did not begin in the federal government until 1920, and only then because of the responsibilities under the Migratory Birds Convention. As the years passed, there were further subdivisions of Canada in terms of staffing in the federal service; eventually J. A. Munro restricted his activities to British Columbia, and J. Dewey Soper was added to deal with migratory bird problems in the prairie provinces.

By Order-in-Council in April 1921, Lloyd was appointed secretary to the Advisory Board on Wildlife Protection to ensure that his work as superintendent of Wildlife Protection would be fully coordinated with that of the advisory board, which continued until the late 1940s. In 1947 the director of the Lands, Parks and Forests Branch of the Department of Mines and Resources deemed that a separate federal wildlife agency should be created, to be called the Dominion Wildlife Service. It became the Canadian Wildlife Service in April 1950.

Starting with the Commission of Conservation, which involved the provincial governments as well as federal government officials, there was a tradition of increasing federal and provincial cooperation in the wildlife field. With termination of the work of the Commission of Conservation, and because of the need for close cooperation with regard to migratory birds conservation, a series of conferences was begun in 1922 at which federal and provincial officials came together. They discussed migratory birds and differing approaches to the use, conservation, and control of those resources by the two levels of government. They also dealt with other matters of interest to both federal and provincial wildlife officials. The Federal Provincial Wildlife conferences, begun in 1922, were initially held at irregular intervals but eventually became annual forums for the exchange of ideas throughout the wildlife field; the one held in July 1953 was the forty-seventh in the

series. Over the years the conferences have been extremely helpful in sorting out differing approaches to wildlife conservation when perceived from the federal and provincial points of view.

As a case in point, and one that has been debated frequently, the federal government, under the migratory work of the Migratory Birds Convention Act and Regulations, is responsible for safeguarding the migratory bird resources by whatever means are appropriate. Provincial governments, on the other hand, look upon migratory birds as resources that annually pass through their jurisdictions and are harvested by their citizens; and from which, through the sale of licenses and other means, they secure revenue for operating at least a part of their wildlife management activities. Because of the differences in approach there are annual discussions about what harvests should be allowed and under what conditions. As federal and provincial officials cooperate in annual studies of the resources, there is usually no argument about the data on populations and distribution, which are the key to decisions about allowable harvests and where, when, and by what means they should be conducted. There are complicating factors, including those related to the damage migratory birds may do to agricultural crops (largely as a result of the technology used in harvesting those crops.) To put it bluntly, the grain farmers would like to see fewer ducks, the duck hunters would like to see more, and the provincial and federal governments are in the middle of the perennial debate about how many harvests there should be and where they should occur. Enforcement of provincial and federal regulations regarding the harvest of waterfowl by hunters is carried on jointly by the Royal Canadian Mounted Police and the provincial conservation officers.

Major responsibility for migratory birds has always been the responsibility of the Canadian Wildlife Service. Over the years, through cooperation with provincial governments and private industry, the Service has also become involved in a variety of other projects, ranging from controlling the reproduction of raptors, preventing the extinction of such birds as peregrine falcons, studying animal diseases (sometimes involving both wildlife and humans, e.g., rabies), to increasing the Service's involvement in recent years with toxic substances in the environment. Toxic substances in all parts of Canada may have detrimental effects on migratory birds and, in many cases, on fish, other wildlife and people.

Cooperation has always been good between the federal Canadian Wildlife Service and its provincial counterparts, and with other agencies in wildlife work including those in the private sector of the economy. Cooperative studies of joint importance have gone on for more than thirty years. To bring a measure of legislative authority to such arrangements, Parliament passed the Canada Wildlife Act in July 1973. This made it easier to justify to the Treasury Board expenditures for cooperative work with provinces which, in any case, had been going on for a very long time. The Act has one rather unique feature in that it defines wildlife as any nondomestic animal. With that definition, it can deal with any kind of wildlife in the country. The new act has not yet resulted in research on the wellbeing of frogs or snails or some of our smaller invertebrate friends, but it looks as if there is the authority to do just that if there is ever the need.

Federal activity in the wildlife field naturally brought the Canadian Wildlife Service into contact with the original Canadians. Many of the treaties that were signed between the Government of Canada and the Indian tribes deal with the right of access to wildlife. When the Migratory Birds Treaty was signed, it set limits on when migratory birds could be taken. Applied to native populations in remote areas, the limits would have created hardships and real difficulty. The application of the regulations had to be tempered with the reality of human survival, and so it was for many years. With the increased concern over native rights in recent years, the native-

Eskimos living off the land were no serious threat to the vast waterfowl resource. USFWS photo by F. Dufresne.

land-claim settlements in the James Bay area, and those under negotiation in the Mackenzie Valley and other parts of northern Canada, it is probable that native use of migratory birds will come under a different sort of control. It may be necessary to modify the Migratory Birds Treaty to spell out more clearly the application of the act based on that treaty to native peoples throughout Canada. That matter is under study.

Public reaction to wildlife as shown by federal government action has changed from a complete lack of concern for supposedly infinite stocks 100 years ago to the current great concern for wildlife and its habitat. Canadians now examine the potential impact on wildlife of almost any large construction project proposed. Public awareness of the worth of wildlife resources now seems to ensure wildlife a continuing place in the Canadian way of life.

When the world human population reaches a sufficiently high level, decisions will have to be made between using land for production of human food or production of wildlife. It is possible that many hungry persons will not opt for the preservation of wildlife habitat, given those alternatives. Nevertheless, until we in this fortunate country reach that unhappy state of affairs, there will be ample land not required for food production. Wildlife, if properly managed, can be produced and can continue to offer to Canadian citizens and their guests all of the rewards we normally associate with being able to observe, photograph, and harvest wildlife resources.

Man evolved as a hunter. Hunters had to know a lot about wildlife to be successful. Although we no longer must kill wildlife to survive, we are still hunters. As hunters and naturalists, we find it rewarding to know where to find wildlife, how to observe it, and how to pass along our knowledge and capacity for outdoor pleasure to succeeding generations.

This bait trap, placed in the Laguna Madre along the south Texas coast, caught mostly redheads which, after banding, were released. USFWS photo.

14

The first extensive census of American waterfowl was conducted in 1935 by the More Game Birds in America Foundation. Participants shown here are (left to right): C. S. Bedell, Cecil McNeal, A. C. Camerle, Carl Yule, J. C. Huntington, and A. M. Bartley. Photo by Ducks Unlimited.

Response of the Private Sector

William G. Leitch

The first comprehensive waterfowl-breeding-ground survey was carried out in 1935 by the More Game Birds in America Foundation. This private organization, the progenitor of Ducks Unlimited, was formed in 1930 by concerned sportsmen in response to a general decline in game birds in America. By 1935 it had produced two publications dealing with the decline of waterfowl during the then-current drought. *More Waterfowl by Assisting Nature* appeared in 1931, and *The Duck Decline in the Northwest* in 1933. These were stepping-stones to *The 1935 International Wild Duck Census.* Arthur Bartley, John Huntington, and Alexander C. Camerle of the foundation staff and Edward B. Pitblado, a keen sportsmen and conservationist from Winnipeg, Canada, compiled these reports and organized the aerial and ground surveys for the 1935 census which followed.

Further preparatory work for the 1935 census was carried out in 1934 when experimental flights were made over the Lake Winnipeg and Saskatchewan River Delta marshes of Manitoba. They confirmed that censusing waterfowl by aircraft was possible and practical. While the 1935 census was organized and coordinated by the More Game Birds in America Foundation, there was some financial assistance from the arms and ammunition industry. The Chrysler Corporation supplied Dodge automobiles for the United States portion of the census.

Ground counts were made in Minnesota, North and South Dakota, and the three prairie provinces of Canada in August 1935. In the United States, these were organized on a county basis; in Canada a similar municipal basis was used. A coordinator was appointed in each area. In western Canada it was the municipal secretary-treasurer who then appointed a volunteer in each township of the municipality to collect the data. These data were subsequently forwarded to the provincial committee, composed of executives of the respective fish and game associations, natural history associations, and government personnel. It is particularly interesting that in Manitoba even the Canadian Bankers Association was involved, and rural branch bank

©H. A. Hochbaum

managers helped in the survey. In all, several thousand people participated.

Using prepared forms and township plats (blank charts with sections and quarters outlined), the following data were compiled:

(1) Counts of ducks, by species wherever ascertainable.
(2) Counts and sizes of broods, by species if possible.
(3) An estimate of ducks present in addition to those actually counted.
(4) The main causes of duck and nest losses.
(5) Information on duck breeding places that might be improved or restored by building dams or dikes.
(6) Recommendations for improving duck breeding conditions.
(7) Exact location of area investigated, and name, occupation, and address of investigator.

Coordination was supplied in each of the three states by individuals hired for that purpose. In western Canada, Huntington in Manitoba, Camerle in Saskatchewan, and Bartley in Alberta played a similar role.

Aerial surveys were made of the important waterfowl areas north of the agricultural fringe as far as the edge of the Pre-Cambrian Shield and extending down the valley of the Slave River as far as Great Slave Lake. Observers were the members of the foundation staff mentioned above, and William Vogt of the National Audubon Society. Estimates were made of the number of ducks per acre for individual marshes and lakes. Records were also kept of the general nature of the terrain and the character of waters, marshes, and streams along the route.

Although bush flying had emerged from its infancy, it was still in its unpredictable adolescence. There were few navigational aids, maps were unreliable, and gasoline availability and quality often doubtful. All of which made for an adventuresome trip! Unfortunately, no personal diaries or logs of this first aerial waterfowl survey have survived. The fact it was safely and successfully accomplished can be credited directly to the skill and experience of the bush pilots employed by the aerial survey crews.

A final amusing comment from the report illustrates the state of bush aviation at the time: "Cabin planes which permit good visibility all around are far superior to open cockpit machines for this work."

The results of the census, which were published in the foundation pamplet, *The 1935 International Wild Duck Census,* were as follows:

In the entire census area there were at least 42,700,000 ducks during August, 1935, distributed as follows:

Totals by provinces:

Alberta ...	16,400,000	
Saskatch-ewan	12,000,000	
Mani-toba	7,500,000	
Portion of MacKenzie District ..	4,600,000	40,500,000

Total by states:

North Dakota ..	1,200,000	
South Dakota ..	350,000	
Minne-sota	650,000	2,200,000

It was also estimated, based on these results, that the continental wild duck population was probably about 65 million.

The report is an outstanding document, not only for its demonstrated understanding of waterfowl habitat, but also because subsequent surveys would confirm that the estimate of waterfowl numbers was likely within striking distance of reality or, in modern vernacular, "in the ball park." Regrettably the authorship is unacknowledged and remains unknown, although Pitblado is known to have helped edit the original draft. Undoubtedly the final draft was prepared by Bartley, Huntington, and Camerle.

Arthur Bartley subsequently became executive director of Ducks Unlimited Inc. when it was formed by More Game Birds in America Foundation in 1937. Edward Pitblado was closely involved in the organization in 1938 of Ducks Unlimited (Canada). Alexander Camerle, a Hungarian, is important because it is believed that he first introduced the concept of censusing waterfowl on the breeding grounds by aircraft. He may have brought the idea from his native land.

©W. Koelpin

Remembering How It Was

Few living persons can recall the condition of waterfowl and waterfowl habitat in the early third of this century. The six authors of this chapter can and, for our benefit, have. Their memoirs make colorful reading, and at the same time serve to remind us how much change has come to waterfowl hunting and waterfowl management in a relatively brief time.

In the early 1900s, waterfowl hunters exerted far less pressure on the resource, largely because of the difficulties of transportation. When the only way to reach the hunting grounds was by train, fewer people hunted. The increased popularity of the automobile changed that, but even so in the early days wet weather made transportation impossible on many roads.

Problems of that sort afflicted game wardens, as well. In the early days, federal game agents were poorly equipped and badly outnumbered by violators.

Transportation was nowhere more difficult that it was in the trackless north country, yet that country was vitally important as a waterfowl breeding grounds.

The logic of using airplanes in such country, and other wild places inhabited by waterfowl, seems so strong now that it is amusing to discover how difficult it was to convince early administrators of their value. The history of modern waterfowl management almost, but not quite, begins with the first use of airplanes in biological survey work.

It is also surprising to learn that it was once a novel idea to apply the lessons of biology to waterfowl management. The first biologists working with waterfowl had little in the way of previous lessons to guide their work. Everything was improvised. Much the same was true of the early teachers of the embryonic science of waterfowl management.

This chapter, then, contains the recollections of a duck hunter, game warden, field biologist, pilot, teacher, and surveyor. We can see far more readily how far the waterfowl management program has come by seeing where it began, not so long ago.

Pure contentment. Frederic Leopold and Spud share a duck blind at the Crystal Lake Club near Burlington, Iowa. Courtesy of F. Leopold.

A Duck Hunter

Frederic Leopold

The Crystal Lake Club lies in Illinois, across the Mississippi River from my home in Burlington, Iowa. My family's involvement with the club began in 1886 when Charles Starker, my maternal grandfather, purchased a membership in the one-year-old organization. He remained a member until his death in 1900. My father was an early member. I am pleased to relate that my daughter, Margaret Barker, and my niece, Dolores Collins, represent the fourth generation and ninety-second year of our family's continuous membership in the Crystal Lake Club.

My own recollections date back to about 1903 or '04 when I was eight or nine years old. I would sometimes accompany my father on duck or jacksnipe hunts in early autumn.

At that time there were three hunting clubs along the main line of the Chicago, Burlington and Quincy Railroad east of the river: Crystal Lake Club (called Bass Lake on the railroad signboard); Lone Tree Club, two miles east; and Sand Lake Club, several miles beyond that. All three clubhouses were similar in style. They were built up on pilings level with the railroad embankment and were painted yellow with red trim. They were highly ornamented with fancy scroll work and wood brackets plus balconies, dormer windows, and flagpoles on the peaks.

Access was provided by local trains, of which there were several daily each way. The fare was two cents per mile, or about ten to twelve cents each way. There were no station houses, since the clubs were only flag stops, and the conductor pulled his signal cord if he had club passengers aboard. To stop the train for the return trip, the club steward hung out a stop sign by day or a kerosene lantern at night as a signal.

Our membership list carried the names of many prominent Burlington citizens. It was

Crystal Lake Club House, Burlington, Iowa.

This is the Crystal Lake Clubhouse, built in 1885. The small shed at the left is an icehouse. Courtesy of F. Leopold.

almost a "Who's Who" roster of our city's foremost families. This included officials of our great railroad, who on occasion would have the most important through trains (like number one westbound or number six eastbound) stop at Crystal Lake to discharge them or take them on board if they were in a hurry to get home.

Social activities in the early days of the club were simple. Members and guests could get meals served by the steward and cooked by his wife. The usual menu was a choice of eggs in several forms or fried ham or pork chops with potatoes, usually American fried or sometimes boiled, plus a piece of apple pie. The men usually had beer, sometimes in huge quart bottles seldom seen today.

The beer was cooled in the ice box. Crystal Lake Club, like other clubs, maintained an ice house, filled each winter with ice from the adjacent lake. When the ice reached suitable thickness the members, assisted by hired workers and a team of horses, cut the ice into blocks of convenient size. The blocks were

then slid up a chute into the storage house, which was elevated above the high-water mark in case of a spring flood. The ice was packed under a couple feet of sawdust from the local pine mill. This insulated it enough to last through the summer.

Quite often groups of members came to the club on the noon train to spend an afternoon of leisure when there was no hunting. They might try their hand at fishing or socialize over a bottle of beer, with a game of penny-ante poker or pitch to spice the occasion. They usually stayed for an early supper and took the 6:30 train back to town. There was also a later return train called "The Dolly" at about 8:30. This train made a daily round trip to Monmouth and Keithsburg and returned to accommodate farmers and tradesmen. On Saturday night the train was usually loaded with young farmers coming to town to celebrate and carouse in Burlington's many saloons and other places of entertainment. I never knew how those young men got back home the next day, since most local trains did not run on Sunday and there was no other means of transportation.

In the days of the old clubhouse there were no women members, and women visitors were unusual. Not that there was any rule; it was just the custom. By the early years in the new house, members occasionally brought their wives to join the summer fishing. The next appearance of women at the club was for skating, and they often joined in the sport. Roasting hot dogs over a campfire was a favorite pastime between rounds of skating. In the prohibition years the local "Mississippi River dew" and "bathtub gin" were frequently brought along to warm up the chilly skaters while they toasted their shins and backsides at the campfire.

During the pre-levee days, the club's boathouse was a roofed floating platform moored along the railroad embankment. Our boats were made of wood and were kept afloat except during the winter. Then they were turned bottom-up on the shore. The extreme variations in water level obliged us to float the boathouse, and for some years after our first on-shore boathouse was built by the picnic grounds, the old floating boathouse was maintained. It was supported by empty barrels. Fish found shelter beneath the barrels, so most fishing concentrated there.

In summer low-water stages, bass fishermen in boots successfully used Skinner Spoons or minnows to fish the lake on both east and west shores and from the railroad embankment. This type of fishing took place when the water was lower than we have seen it for many years. The lake was less than a hundred yards wide in front of the clubhouse. Prior to the creation of the drainage district and the building of the river levee, the midsummer water level often receded as much as three feet below what we have since considered a low stage.

The fishermen did not generally use reels or fancy tackle, but had long cane poles with a line length to match the pole length. I recall watching one of our former members, Dr. Frank LaForce, who fished this way. He got so excited when a bass struck that, instead of playing the fish, he just turned tail and ran toward shore while dragging the butt end of the pole behind him until the bass lay floundering on dry land.

The club maintained a register of all game and fish taken, and members were required to make detailed entries of each day's take. Since everyone came and went by train there was plenty of time to enter the record while awaiting the train's arrival. Our old register books are still kept as valuable historical records.

The original club area was approximately twice its present size, extending eastward from Buck Brush and Willow more than a mile to include Eagle Swamp and Big Eagle Lake, plus the fine big old timber to the east of these swamps. Our east boundary was approximately where the present drainage ditch runs north from Lone Tree railroad crossing. Across the tracks from Eagle lay Lone Tree Clubhouse on the south side of the tracks. This club leased its area rather than owning its grounds, as Crystal Lake did.

Before my time the railroad ran on trestles for five or six miles from the river bridge to a point beyond Lone Tree. To protect this wood trestle work, a watchman using an "Irish Mail" handcar patrolled this section to put out fires started by burning coals dropped by the steam locomotives. By the early twentieth century the solid fill was completed except for a short bridge where our lake drained to the south. Just south of this bridge, Running Slough, which drained Lone Tree Lake, came in from the east and the two followed the present drainage ditch to Carthage Lake.

In times of flood Crystal Lake was a flowing part of the Mississippi River. A strong current would run through Main Lake then and keep it swept clean of silt and fill, creating a very deep, narrow channel. Then when the floods receded, our lakes became landlocked; only the deeper lakes retained water in times of drought. Before the canalization of the river, the river stage at times went down to the official zero-low-water stage or even below that. Not infrequently our newspapers contained accounts of men wading across the river.

In most summers our Main Lake became very narrow and extended only a bit beyond Schlapp's Point. Under these conditions the dried lake beds often grew up in weeds, such as smartweed, pigweed, sedge, and wild millet. These, when flooded in autumn, became prime duck feeding areas. There were no cattails and little hibiscus, since flooding while in bloom will kill both. We thought ourselves extremely lucky when the first cattails appeared. They were such a pretty decoration and made such fine blinds and muskrat houses. These plants only became a problem after our present stabilized water levels had existed for a decade or longer.

In spring it was a custom of the railroad section gang to set fire to our east prairie on a day when there was a brisk south wind. As a result, our area was burned clean as a billiard table right up to the series of lakes and ditches which kept most fires from reaching the Big Timber. These frequent fires prevented the growth of trees in our prairie and maintained the sod of native prairie grasses on the ridges. Unfortunately, we later destroyed our largest prairie area when we decided to convert it to crops. This program resulted in some cash income in about half the years. The remaining years were too wet to allow a crop to be raised. Our unique prairie is now gone forever.

I mentioned that the club originally owned an area east of our present east boundary. For about a half-mile east lay a broad prairie ridge that was dry except during flood stages. Further east lay Eagle Swamp and Eagle Timber. This swamp area ran north more than half a mile from the railroad on the south. On the east and on the north of the swamp lay Eagle Timber. This was typical bottomland timber except for three cottonwood trees which towered well above the surrounding woods. In the top of the northernmost cottonwood a pair of eagles had built a huge nest. The body of the nest was, my father said, as large as a wagon bed, and I'm

sure that was no exaggeration. The area, of course, got its name from this nest. The eagles were gone before my day, but the nest remained for years.

On the north of Eagle Timber lay a narrow lake running from west to east named Big Eagle Lake. Since the entire swamp and lake area was a good duck feeding area, it was a favorite hunting ground for my dad. Muskrat houses were plentiful in much of the marsh. We had a family story about a traveler on a passing passenger train who, on seeing the rat houses surrounded by water, remarked, "Some poor farmer has lost his hay crop this year." It was true that neighboring farmers often asked permission to cut prairie hay on our ridges, to use as winter feed for their cattle. Our Hay Ridge got its name from the fact that it was a favorite area for farmers to cut. Now it has grown up in brush and blackberries and badly needs spring burning to bring it back to prairie grasses.

For me a typical waterfowl hunting day was on a Saturday when we were out of school. By the time I was old enough to accompany Father, my two older brothers had gone east to school, so I went alone with him. We arose very early and dressed by gaslight, our clothes and boots having been laid out the night before. We walked, or more or less stumbled our way, in darkness to the railroad station where we had breakfast.

How fine the hotcakes and syrup looked and smelled, but they weren't for me. Father was something of a Spartan who felt that a meal that would "stick to our ribs" should consist of things more substantial such as baked pork and beans. Of course, in the morning the big baking pans of pork and beans, a standard item at ten cents a serving at all lunch counters, were leftovers from the night before. So at 5:00 A.M., we dined on milk, cold pork and beans, and perhaps a baked apple. The diet must have been good for us since we often walked most of the day with only a light midday lunch.

We caught the local passenger train that

made up at Burlington, a small one consisting of a noisy little steam engine followed by two or three coaches. Local trains radiated out of Burlington early each morning, returning late in the day on every branch line from town. The cars were lighted by shiny brass kerosene lamps swinging from ceiling brackets. Heat came from a pot-bellied coal stove, and all was supervised by a resplendent conductor in shiny blue serge with brass buttons, gold braid and a round military cap. All this gave him an air of splendid authority, for was he not the master of this noisy conveyance? As we neared our stop at the clubhouse, the conductor pulled the signal cord at the peak of the car to tell the engineer that he should stop to let us off.

Father preferred to duck hunt Eagle Swamp east of our grounds instead of hunting Crystal Lake, so we usually got off at Lone Tree Club just across the tracks. He also enjoyed hunting jacksnipe, and for that game Lone Tree was superior because the terrain there was just right, consisting of hundreds of acres of cattle-grazed swamp. To my mind jacksnipe are the most delectable of all game birds. We dressed them, leaving the neck and head attached and the hazelnut-size morsel of brain intact.

We would detrain in utter darkness on the elevated right-of-way. As the train departed, the taillights of the back platform gradually diminished as they grew more distant. The weather was often cold and windy, which augered well for a good day's hunt. Father would note the wind direction and decide where to hunt that day. Then we started off down the steep embankment to the edge of the swamp. In the darkness we sometimes heard ducks calling ahead of us or heard the whistle of passing wings above our heads. We needed no boat in Eagle since boots were sufficient for the shallow water.

Father used no decoys except the ducks he bagged, which were set out in preparation for pass shooting. Neither did he use a duck call, although he did urge me to try to learn to call. He seldom killed more than a dozen or fifteen ducks a day although the legal limit, seldom enforced, was set at about forty or fifty birds.

There were no permanent or established blinds in Eagle Swamp, so dad's shooting stand was wherever he felt the ducks might pass within shotgun range. He seldom took long shots since he recognized that his choke-bored sixteen-gauge gun had an effective range not to exceed forty-five yards. He was very proud of his L.C. Smith double barrel, for which he had a set of twenty-eight-inch choked barrels and also a set of twenty-six-inch open quail barrels. I still hunt with this same gun, which is now well over seventy years old and still in nearly perfect condition.

His blind for the day was very simple. Usually he kicked a foot hold in the edge of a full-size muskrat house so he could have a firm base to stand upon. He selected the upwind side of the rat house, for most chances would be coming upwind. Then he gathered an armful of rushes that he stuck into the top of the rat house. By leaning forward with elbows on the house, he had enough concealment to allow the birds to come into range before they saw him. In fact, he tried to get in his first shot before the ducks flared. This made the shot a bit more deadly. The blind offered no protection from bad weather. As there was room for only one person in such a blind, I usually watched from the edge of nearby brushy cover and could sometimes enjoy the warmth of a tiny fire during the early morning hunt.

When the morning flight slowed up Dad would join me, and we often did some jump shooting or perhaps made a sneak on a puddle where father had observed mallards alighting earlier in the day. Usually we were near enough to Eagle Timber that we could try an hour or so of squirrel hunting before or after eating lunch. When I became big enough to shoulder a shotgun he turned the squirrel hunting over to me, keeping a watchful eye on my manner of handling the gun to be sure I was taking proper safety precautions. His primary rule was "never allow the gun to point at any object you do not want to kill." Loaded or not, we observed this rule; it

1977-78 Ross' geese *by Martin R. Murk*

took precedence over reliance on a safety catch.

Our duck hunting was usually confined to the pursuit of what we called "using ducks." Using ducks are birds that have temporarily ceased their migration, having found an area where they can subsist comfortably. These ducks had found food of acceptable quality and quantity plus resting areas where they felt reasonably safe from predation by both man and beast.

There were, of course, big days when the flight included a procession of large flocks of migrants, one after the other. These birds usually passed quite high in the sky — poor prospects for swamp hunters without open water or a spread of decoys. But the number of birds migrating was impressive. Flock after flock followed each other in a never-ending stream, sometimes throughout the day. Occasionally flocks of geese or double-crested cormorants, which we called loons, joined the procession, and I looked longingly at the geese in hopes that someday I might get a chance to bag one.

The most productive part of our day's hunt was usually the forenoon. Afternoon might be spent in leisurely pursuits such as squirrel hunting or jump shooting if conditions favored, but more often we spent those hours wandering through the woods and marsh observing what was about us.

Once we found signs of a recent evening's raccoon hunt where hunters had made a campfire while they sought means of bringing their quarry to ground so the dogs could kill the critter. The hunters would, at times, cut and lean a climbable sapling against a large tree, allowing a climber to reach the limbs and club the raccoon off his perch. There were no flashlights to assist hunters in those days. On another occasion, I recall father pointing out a probable mink den in a hollow willow. Here we would find bits of the remains of animals or birds. And there were always raccoon scats full of purple grape stain and bits of bleached crayfish shells.

Toward evening father sometimes tried for a late chance at mallards if the flight looked promising. But he was always careful to stop duck shooting early enough to recover any birds that fell to his gun in the twilight.

By dark we were usually at the clubhouse where supper was being prepared. And how good those pork chops did smell to my youthful appetite! Dad would register our kill for the day and we would chat with other hunters.

After supper the steward hung out his lantern to signal the train to stop for passengers. We boarded in a hurry when the train pulled up amid screeching brakes, sparks, and escaping steam, adding its noise to the general excitement of the day.

The train ride to town always seemed too short, and the rumble as we crossed the big river bridge was the signal that we were nearly home. The noisy exchange of boisterous remarks by farm boys coming to town for a spree was a bit mysterious to me, but I could understand that they were excited at the prospect of things to come.

At the big station we passed through the bright lights and were soon on South Main Street walking toward home. The arc lights at each intersection stretched on for blocks ahead as we trudged along. Finally we arrived at Clay Street corner and turned up toward home, with just one final uphill block to go. Usually I asked to carry our duck stringer on our walk home, so by this time I was really aching with weariness on this final uphill stretch.

The carbon arc street light was behind us as we climbed. As we walked up the center of the street our shadows grew longer and longer before us. Finally the tips of our shadows overtopped the bricks on the hill's crest, and then I knew we had at last reached home, tired but happy.

Mother welcomed us with enthusiasm. Our bag would be exhibited on the living room rug in front of the grate fire and examined with appropriate exclamations of appreciation of the beauty of each bird. This often led to an explanation of just how and where a bird had been killed. As keeper of the game strap and chief game carrier, I often took pains to smooth and clean the plumage of each bird carefully to enhance its beauty.

There was no such thing as cold storage or freezing game in those days, so the string was carefully hung in the cool interior of our huge barn where there was shade and ventilation high enough to be well out of reach of our dogs or stray animals.

Game was always served sparingly at father's table. We had no dinners where each guest received a whole mallard, leading to satiated diners who wished after dinner that they had eaten less. Wild game was considered a special privilege to be savored. A duck served at least two people, and the breast meat was carefully carved into thin wafers by father as he served us. So we usually left the table wishing we could have had just a bit more of that delightful meat.

Father had stopped spring shooting before my earliest memories. What I recall as days of high duck population looked like much less than that to Father. He had been a hunter since boyhood in the 1860s and thus had observed a great decline in duck population. He realized that we had better reduce our kill or, inevitably, we would lose our sport. These things he observed and recognized over seventy years ago, while many of us, even today, do not admit that the bitter end with nearly duckless skies is coming ever closer and closer!

Father died in 1914, having brought up three boys to love things wild and natural. Although we were all hunters, we recognized that temperance must be a part of continued enjoyment of nature's bounty. He also taught us to observe what went on in the wild world and to try to understand the meaning of what we saw. Ernest Thompson Seton called this faculty the "ability to read sign." A real love of nature is the basis for proficiency in this ability.

Aldo, my brother, expressed his appreciation of our inheritance from father in his book, *Game Management*, with this dedication: "To My Father, Carl Leopold, 'Pioneer in Sportsmanship.'"

After my father's death, I was no longer eligible to hunt on Crystal Lake grounds. My brother, Carl, received father's share in the club. I was busy away at college and later in the army until my return in 1919. I finally became a full-fledged club member in 1927. This is my fifty-fifth year of membership.

Larry Merovka, one of the first U. S. Game Wardens, examines confiscated birds and firearms. Courtesy of L. Merovka.

A Federal Game Warden

Larry Merovka

Ever since my boyhood days I have had an avid interest in hunting. I was born and reared in a small southern-Illinois town overlooking the Mississippi River bottomlands where there were a lot of duck hunters. I killed my first wild duck when I was sixteen years old, and quickly developed a keen interest in waterfowl hunting. By the beginning of the 1930s I was reaching maturity and was already an ardent and successful duck hunter.

By that time there had already developed a great deal of public concern for the future of our priceless heritage of migratory waterfowl. Foremost was ever-increasing commitment by conscientious sportsmen to see the end of the deplorable practice of hunting waterfowl during their spring migration. I got caught up in the fervor to stop spring hunting and, soon after the Migratory Bird Treaty Act became law in 1918, I was acting as guide and informant to federal game wardens. Because the ban on spring hunting was very unpopular in my home community, I was often threatened, berated, and vilified by fellow townsmen for the assistance I contributed toward its enforcement. My cooperation led to my being appointed as a U.S. deputy game warden in 1924.

In those days we considered the greatest threats to waterfowl to be spring hunting, baiting, the use of live decoys and punt guns, trapping, market hunting, and similar unethical methods of decimating the waterfowl supply. By the mid-1930s public sentiment and a serious duck shortage brought about the adoption of federal regulations prohibiting these practices.

But laws and regulations are not self-enforcing. There was much defiance and apathy toward enforcement in some areas. Some hunters in Missouri and Illinois were diehards with respect to the ban on spring waterfowl hunting, so federal enforcement activities were concentrated in those two states over a long period of time. The attorney general of Missouri challenged the efforts of the federal government to enforce its ban on spring waterfowl hunting, filing a lawsuit that resulted in a decree by the U.S. Supreme Court upholding the constitutionality of the challenged law. Even so, spring waterfowl hunting was not prohibited by state law in Missouri until 1937. Fortunately, attitudes change. Today Missouri has one of the most progressive and effective wildlife management programs in the nation.

During the 1920s federal game wardens concentrated their enforcement activities in Missouri and Illinois in localities where illegal waterfowl hunting was most prevalent. While on such an assignment one spring along the Illinois River, wardens Kenneth Roahen and Marquis Charlton were shotgunned at close range and severely wounded by murderous market hunters. The alleged assailants were later arrested and tried before a jury in state court in an area where there was strong sentiment against the ban on spring waterfowl hunting. The accused assailants were not convicted. Why was the case prosecuted in state court? At the time, the federal statute pertaining to assault of federal law enforcement officers did not cover game law enforcement personnel. It has since been amended to correct this oversight.

During the spring months, unimproved roads leading through river and creek bottoms where duck hunting was most prevalent were so muddy and rutted that they were often impassible for even the light autos used by enforcement personnel. Wardens were adept at getting over bad roads, but sometimes they became so deeply mired they had to get pulled out by a team of stout horses or mules. People living in isolated areas were quick to take advantage of conditions that enabled them to kill ducks out of season with

impunity because wardens could not get to them.

But they were not always immune to arrest. Once while on spring patrol in northern Missouri I heard a lot of duck hunting was being done in a wooded, flooded river bottom. Reaching the area by auto was out of the question, and so was walking to it from the nearest town. But I learned that I could use a local train that would let me off and pick me up at a flag stop about seven miles from the illegal hunting area. I was young and robust, and so decided to take that train one Sunday when I was confident the hunters would be out in force. It was a patrol experience that will always live in my memory as one of the most arduous and rewarding I ever experienced during my long career. I encountered many hunters, most of them so sure they would not be accosted by game wardens that they were hunting over decoys. I made eleven arrests that day, though I missed more than I caught because I couldn't get into deep water areas without a boat. It was amusing to see the astonishment on the faces of those I apprehended, and I've often wished that I could have made a photographic record of their reactions to my unexpected appearance.

I got back to my hotel after a night train ride. I don't think I ever had a more exhausting experience, before or since. It was noon before I got up the next day, but I was highly elated over the results of my efforts. So was my boss, who was generous in his praise of my initiative and achievement. All the hunters I arrested were prosecuted and assessed heavy fines. This had a salutary effect, not only in the area where the arrests were made, but elsewhere in Missouri because of the heavy publicity the cases received. The federal courts in Missouri gave strong support to enforcement of the Migratory Bird Treaty Act, and our cases also fared well in the federal courts of Illinois, especially with respect to the more serious violations. We wardens were deeply grateful for this morale-raising support because the going was tough for us in the early days, and we needed all the

Wm. J. Koelpin © 1980

©W. Koelpin

help we could get.

Bad roads were only part of our woes. The federal ban on spring waterfowl hunting generated a lot of animosity in Missouri and Illinois toward the officers who enforced it. Because of the many threats of bodily harm, wardens commonly carried buckshot-loaded shotguns for defense while on patrol. One Sunday a federal warden carrying a shotgun arrested a hunter in southeast Missouri for killing ducks out of season. The hunter was a good friend of the county attorney, who later filed a complaint against the warden for violating an ancient blue law that prohibited hunting on Sunday . . . even though the warden was only hunting outlaws. Only intervention by the U.S. District Attorney's office in St. Louis brought about dismissal of the trumped-up charge.

There were other unhappy examples of poor judical support of our efforts. Once in Arkansas a man who had pleaded guilty in federal court to a game law violation was told by the judge to leave the court room and "get lost." In another southern state a group of hunters who had pleaded guilty in federal court to illegal killing of a large number of doves were fined a penny each. I once made a strong case against a notorious market hunter at Reelfoot Lake, in western Tennessee, who had made sales of wild ducks to me. The jury in his trial hastily returned a "not guilty" verdict. This shameful miscarriage of justice so incensed the fair presiding judge that he rebuked the jury and dismissed the members from further service.

All too often, federal wardens had good reason to wonder who was on trial, they or persons they had brought charges against. Harassment of wardens was done in many ways. They were often taunted and reviled by ignorant and strongly prejudiced persons with no conception of wildlife conservation principles. Tires on patrol cars were slashed; fine sand or emery dust was poured into car motors with devastating results; and boats and other marine equipment were damaged, destroyed, or stolen.

An extreme example of enmity toward game wardens came to light when I was helping to put strong pressure on a notorious gang of market hunters. They removed and sharpened the saw-toothed cutting bar from a discarded hay mower. This they embedded in a narrow dirt forest road mostly used by themselves and game wardens. The sharpened cutter bar teeth were slanted forward so that any incoming car would have all its tires cut. All the outlaws using the area were told about this game warden booby trap. But poetic justice prevailed. The only person to have a set of tires ruined was a relative of one of the men who had planted the mower blade. We wardens had already been tipped off by the disgruntled stepdaughter of one of the conspirators.

It took a lot of courage, fortitude, tenacity, and dedication to endure the abuses and hardships that were the lot of federal game wardens in the early days. But it was a good cause and one deemed worthy of endurance of such adversities. Although I was threatened with firearms on numerous occasions, I was never seriously injured. On two occasions while on night patrol in rice fields frequented by market hunters, I was shot at and hit hard enough by shotgun pellets to raise painful welts on my skin. My assailants escaped under the cover of darkness.

Two situations stand out in my memory as the most unconscionable and disgusting slaughter of waterfowl I ever witnessed. The scene of the worst carnage was the Tindall Green Tree Reservoir located near Stuttgart, Arkansas, in the rice growing belt of that state. The time was the early 1930s. The reservoir covered a large wooded area where vast numbers of mallards collected after feeding at night in the nearby rice fields. For a while no hunting was permitted on the reservoir, but hunters kept pressing for permission to hunt there until those in control finally yielded and let them in for a fee of ten dollars per hunt. The hunters gathered early in the morning and, at a given signal, were permitted to enter the shooting area en masse. Pandemonium reigned as the horde of trigger-happy hunters started shooting

A pen of live decoys placed in front of a hunter's blind attracted wild ducks to within easy shooting distance. This practice was outlawed in 1935. Photo by Bob Becker.

ducks milling through the timber in numbers resembling large flocks of blackbirds. Soon the water was littered with dead and crippled ducks. In time all hunters picked up and culled a limit of fifteen birds apiece and departed. They left behind a great many more ducks to rot, be picked up by nonhunters, or be eaten by predators. Game wardens could not cope with the deplorable situation because, with many hunters shooting and birds falling at the same time, it was difficult to bring charges of bag limit violations that would hold up in court.

But a strong flare-up of public revulsion over this despicable slaughter succeeded in bringing the carnage to an end. During the first week of April 1932, a special committee of the U.S. Senate held public hearings in Washington, D.C. on the serious shortage of waterfowl existing at that time, with a view to determining the causes and appropriate remedial measures. One committee witness stated:

> Judge Miles of Arkansas can tell you of the most deplorable conditions that exist in his state, where commercial hunting has been developed to its most aggravated degree.

You know we thought we had gone a long way when we stopped market hunting about a generation ago by prohibiting the sale of waterfowl. Today we are developing a new form of market hunting through the commercialized shooting of birds on the wing, which, in time, I think will exceed the evils of the old market hunting. I understand that in 1930 on Tyndall's Lake in Arkansas, which is a commercial hunting area, there were duck carcasses found estimated to be 40,000 in number washed upon the shore, that were not recovered by those fellows who went down to shoot at so much per gun and who were not sportsmen enough to retrieve their birds.

The other repugnant event I recall took place along the Illinois River and involved what was called "field pen" shooting. Mesh wire pens were built in fields and large numbers of live mallard decoys were placed in them. A pool of water was provided, along with tons of corn scattered around the perimeters of the pens. Thousands of wild mallard ducks poured into these death traps where unscrupulous hunters killed limits of fifteen birds each for a charge of ten dollars. As soon as one group of hunters moved out another moved in, and the carnage continued. Fortunately this disgraceful commercial activity was stopped when federal regulations were amended in the mid-1930s to outlaw the taking of migratory waterfowl by aid of bait or live decoys. It was a timely and laudable action.

The Depression posed many problems for game wardens. It brought about a strong upsurge in out-of-season and market hunting. Wild rabbits became common table fare, and people facetiously referred to them as "Hoover hogs" because they held President Herbert Hoover responsible for their plight. Negroes in the South where I worked during the Depression were particularly hard hit because they had long depended on white plantation owners to furnish them food and housing in return for sharecrop farming. Many turned to living off the land as much as possible, and there was no point in arresting them for illegal hunting or fishing activities because they could not be convicted in local courts. Moreover, we game wardens were sympathetic to the plight of both whites and blacks and were little inclined to add to the woes of people already under severe stress. Nevertheless, I and other wardens could not allow people to commit serious violations of the game laws with impunity.

Often when I caught people taking game out of season or in excess of bag limits they would plead hunger as a justification. Often enough, they were truly suffering from hunger. I once apprehended a family man who was shooting ducks out of season. He pleaded with me not to file charges against him, saying that all the food he had in his house was a small jar of rice. I accompanied him to his home, which was a cabin made of rough lumber. So was the little bit of furniture it contained. Pallets on the floor served as beds. It was a touching situation, and the man had told me the truth about having no food except a small quantity of rice. I took him into a nearby town and bought him a good supply of staple groceries. I shall never forget the depth of his gratitude nor the warm glow it generated in me for having done a kindly deed for a person well worthy

of it. On many other occasions I acted the part of a Good Samaritan toward poor and illiterate rural people in dire need who did not know how to go about getting on relief rolls. No one who experienced the Depression will ever forget it, and I recall with satisfaction the many times I was able to show compassion toward people involved in game law violations during that traumatic period. It was during these trying times that I learned the true meaning of Christianity.

The first undercover operation against waterfowl market hunters was conducted by U.S. Game Warden John E. Perry out of Peoria, Illinois. The time was about 1930. Perry, who was a big, handsome, and well-groomed individual, posed as an alcoholic bum who bought and sold wild ducks to support himself and his booze habit. He looked the part, too. He went around unshaven and dressed in shabby clothes, looking like a typical skid row character. He bought ducks from a lot of well-known market hunters along the Illinois River who later could hardly believe their eyes when he appeared in federal court to testify against them, clean shaven and dressed like a Wall Street banker. They all pleaded guilty to illegal sale of wild ducks and were assessed heavy fines.

The highlight of my forty-one year career in federal game law enforcement was the period from 1933 to 1940, when I was in charge of that activity in Louisiana. It was a challenging assignment that tested my mettle and law enforcement talents to the utmost. Political corruption was rampant, and there was a general breakdown in respect for law. Market hunting of migratory waterfowl was thriving when I arrived on the scene. Ducks and geese as well as other game species, could be bought throughout the coastal area at restaurants, night clubs, markets, and from individual hunters.

Our main enforcement thrust was directed against known market hunters, and ultimately our vigorous and unrelenting efforts met with a high degree of success. I called on the U.S. district attorneys and federal judges

The first Manitoba waterfowl survey team visits an Indian camp in the Netley Marshes of Manitoba in 1935. The non-Indians pictured (left to right) are: Tom Gibson, Manitoba Game Guardian; Larry Merovka, U. S. Game Agent; and Clarence Aldous, biologist. USFWS photo courtesy of L. Merovka.

and made strong pleas for their support of our enforcement efforts. This produced very gratifying results. The days of small "slap on the wrist" penalties came to a sudden end. Jail sentences of from thirty days to six months were imposed in all cases involving market hunting and other commercial traffic in ducks, geese, and other migratory game birds. This had an inhibiting effect so that by the time I left Louisiana in 1940, upon my promotion to the position of regional supervisor of Law Enforcement for what was then an eight-state southwestern administrative region of the USFWS, we had succeeded in making the sale of migratory game birds in Louisiana a risky venture. Also, as market hunting activity decreased, we were able to devote more attention to bag-limit violations, motorboat shooting, baiting, night hunting, and similar infractions committed in connection with sport hunting.

The deplorable political corruption that existed during my seven-year stay in Louisiana was dealt with quite effectively by a reform government that took office in 1940. Although investigations conducted by the new regime revealed that the Louisiana Department of Conservation had been deeply involved in the past corruption, something I well knew, it pleases me to now reveal that there were a good many honest people in that department who covertly gave me information that greatly aided our enforcement efforts.

Over the years there have been many changes in the official titles of game law enforcement officers, both state and federal. The first such officers employed by the U.S. Bureau of Biological Survey (now USFWS) were hired to enforce the Lacey Act of 1900, which restricted interstate transportation of wild birds and mammals. These officers were called Lacey Act inspectors until passage of the Migratory Bird Treaty Act in 1918, when they were given the additional responsibility of enforcing that law. Their title was then changed to U.S. Game Warden. The next change was to U.S. Game Protector, followed by U.S. Game Management Agent. Presently the title is Special Agent. State game law enforcement personnel have mostly been called game wardens, game protectors, game rangers, game inspectors, and conservation officers. In the early days of game law enforcement, many people bestowed other titles on us, including: rabbit shepherd, brush cop, catfish gestapo, coonservation agent, peckerwood sheriff, cornfield constable, duck marshal, varmint protector, and cat killer.

I always understood that laws and regulations are only one wildlife management tool — a tool that by itself is inadequate to maintain high population levels. I knew that research and application of research findings were important to game management. Consequently, I gave research personnel unstinting support and was always glad when I could furnish equipment and personal services to help them attain their project objectives.

I have been fortunate enough to make a comfortable living doing what I most wanted to do. My keen and abiding interest in my work allowed me to take in stride the long hours, little vacation time, long absences from home and family, physical hardships, assaults, oral abuse, and other adversities. Now well along in years and enjoying an active and very pleasant retirement, I look back at what has been a most rewarding life and draw satisfaction from having been able to help take care of God's wild creatures. Also it has always been a source of satisfaction to me to be able to report that no boss of mine ever asked me to pull punches or in any other way act dishonestly. We early wardens were always told to enforce the law in an honest, fair, and impartial manner. And this was the rule we adhered to. We old-timers bequeathed this tradition to our successors upon retirement with a fervent hope that it will always be honored.

All line drawings (unless noted) by H. A. Hochbaum.©

John Lynch, in a Coast Guard seaplane on May 15, 1939, discovered two young whooping cranes and thirteen adults in the White Lake marshes of Louisiana, confirming the existence of a resident colony. Photo courtesy of J. Lynch.

A Field Biologist

John J. Lynch

I was a student of the eager category. As a youngster I haunted a grass airstrip at Newport, Rhode Island, in hopes that some veteran pilot would notice me. According to the script, this pilot would give me an airplane ride and thus initiate me into the mysteries of flight. Unfortunately, nothing of consequence came of this.

But just a few years later I found myself not only airborne, but trying to learn new ways of identifying birds, other wild animals, and plants from the air. These life forms looked strange indeed when viewed from a fast-moving aircraft. The standard manuals of biology were not very helpful in this regard.

After completing a tour of duty in the Dakotas in the winter of 1935 and early 1936, the U.S. Bureau of Biological Survey (USBS) transferred me to the Atlantic Coast. My primary function there was to scout the Atlantic seaboard from the Canadian border south to Chesapeake Bay, looking for areas that could be purchased and developed into wildlife refuges. This was a large enough assignment in itself. But as the work progressed into the spring of 1936, new assignments were added to the list.

There was the matter of destruction of birds and wildlife habitat by oil pollution. There was also the disappearance of eel grass. This marine aquatic plant is very important to many water birds and other forms of marine life in the tidewaters of the Atlantic Coast. It seemed as though new chores were being added to my list faster than I could do the jobs I already had.

One July morning in 1936 I found myself driving toward the southern tip of New Jersey, wondering how I was going to get three months of work done in the next three weeks. I noticed a sign along the highway that said "U.S. Coast Guard Air Base, Cape May, NJ." On a sudden impulse, I entered the gates, produced my credentials, and asked if I might see the skipper. As it turned out, the skipper was very interested in my problems.

When I told the base commander that I was trying to do a great deal on the North Atlantic coast in a very brief time, he asked how I had been going about it. I told him that as far as the coastal marshes and lagoons were concerned, it was no trouble working the landward side. I could always catch a ride out with local fishermen and oystermen, duck guides, and federal game agents when they happened to be in the vicinity. But covering the ocean side of those big lagoons was a different matter.

I had hit upon the expedient of getting in touch with Coast Guard surf stations. These stations were located at intervals along the Atlantic beaches. I would get to one of them, then walk up or down the beach toward the next one, making side trips into the marshes and shoal-water portions of the lagoons on the inner side of the beach. Sooner or later I would meet the patrol from the next surf station. They would bring me back to the next station and feed me; and if night was approaching, they were always able to find an extra bed. If I happened to miss the patrol, an old beachcomber like myself, born and raised in that country, never went hungry. There was always enough to eat if you knew where to look.

The air base skipper was shaken by my story. He said, "You're doing all this the hard way. Let's jump in an airplane and see if we can't find an easier method."

Late that evening we came back to the Coast Guard air base after putting in over five hours in an ancient, single-engine amphibian. The skipper looked a little bit gray from riding in that airplane all day, and I resembled a barn owl from the helmet and goggle marks on my face. But I was gratified by the amount of ground we had covered. In one day I had managed to get a very good look at areas that would have taken weeks to evaluate from the ground. I had also scouted some areas that were previously inaccessible and found ways to reach them by boat. I now faced the happy prospect of getting my three or four months' work done in a week or two.

The Coast Guard skipper, seeing that I was really fired up, gave me a list of Coast Guard and Navy air facilities on the Atlantic Coast, and told me that I would be welcomed there anytime. From that day on I became a staunch advocate of air power for wildlife studies.

During the rest of 1936 and into January of 1937 I was able to arrange plane coverage of much of the upper Atlantic Coast, thanks to the naval air stations of Salem, Massachusetts; Gould Island, Rhode Island, and a number of other points. Perhaps the high point of that experience was the week I spent at the naval air station in Lakehurst, New Jersey, where the so-called LTA (lighter-than-air) enthusiasts did business. These people flew dirigibles, blimps, and other "airships."

For an observer, a ride in a blimp is really going first class compared with flying in an open-cockpit airplane. You can get up, walk around, and look out the window whenever you feel like it. Of course, there are some disadvantages. Blimps aren't very fast, so you can't be in much of a hurry to get anywhere in particular. It also helps to have the wind going the same way that you want to go. Otherwise, you'll never get there.

It was especially interesting to see the reaction of birds to one of these "gas-bags" (as the LTA critics called them). Different birds react in different ways to the sound of an aircraft engine. Some would get up and fly away. Some of the sea birds would dive, and the most accomplished diver along the Atlantic coast is the old squaw duck. When you approach a flock of old squaws in a standard aircraft, they immediately start diving and are able to stay underwater for an incredible length of time. Usually they don't surface until the aircraft is gone. But after they dove at the approach of the blimp, they would surface later to find the slow-moving airship directly *overhead*. Their second crash dive was usually quite comical.

In March 1937 I was transferred to the Gulf Coast to investigate ways of managing some recently purchased refuges, including Delta, Lacassine, and Sabine refuges in Louisiana, St. Marks in Florida, Aransas in Texas, and others up the Mississippi Valley.

These Gulf Coast marshes were so extensive there was no way that I could cover them all on foot or in a boat. I had to get into the air to get a better understanding of their importance. Fortunately, there was another Coast Guard air base at Biloxi, Mississippi, not very far from my Delta National Wildlife Refuge headquarters. Soon, in response to my phone calls, Coast Guard planes were picking me up along the Gulf Coast, flying me over country I needed to see, and returning me to their base.

One of the most ambitious things I tried during this period with flyway biologist Charlie Gillham was to fly the midwinter inventory of waterfowl between Biloxi, Mississippi, and Brownsville, Texas, with the help of Coast Guard pilots. In January 1939 we worked the outer edge of the Gulf Coast marshes by amphibian aircraft. After spending the evening in Matamoros, Mexico, just

Pilots John Ball and Walter Crissey plan their flight into Mexico at the beginning of the 1951 midwinter waterfowl survey. The plane is a Grumman Widgeon. USFWS photo courtesy of J. Ball.

across the Rio Grande from Brownsville, we somehow made it back to the airport the following morning and covered the salt flats, rice fields, and inner marshes of Texas and Louisiana on the way back to Biloxi. It was quite an experience, even if a bit over-ambitious.

Another trip made with help from the Coast Guard involved the report of a colony of whooping cranes residing in Louisiana and nesting on the vast marshes north of White Lake. In May 1939 the Coast Guard furnished a pilot and sea plane and we flew the White Lake marshes. During that flight we did see thirteen whooping cranes on the White Lake marshes. Of those thirteen, two were young-of-the-year, about one-third grown. These birds *had* to be resident cranes. They certainly could not be part of the migrant group that spent the winter in Texas and the summer in the Northwest Territories of Canada, not with two young-of-the-year the middle of May. I got some photos of those cranes. Unfortunately, the pictures had to be shot through the salt-stained window of the sea plane and were not very good. None-theless, our 1939 flight established the fact that there was a flock of whooping cranes residing and resting in Louisiana. In 1940 the flock was nearly destroyed by a summer cloudburst and flood.

About six birds survived that tragedy. One was picked up near the town of Ville Platte, Louisiana, and was moved to Audubon Park in New Orleans, where she spent many years. The captive crane became known as Jose-phine. The other five resident whooping cranes remaining in the wild dwindled to a single bird that we managed to capture with a helicopter in 1950. Again, we demonstrated that aircraft could be useful in getting new jobs done for wildlife on the flyways.

My rewarding connection with the Coast Guard air base at Biloxi continued. Then in January 1940 the U.S. Army Air Force Barksdale Base at Shreveport helped us fly some of the midwinter inventories. At this time all of the southern part of the Missis-sippi Valley and the Gulf Coast marshes were in the grip of an extraordinary period of cold weather. It seemed as if the whole lower Mississippi Valley was frozen over, including the lakes and flood bottoms and many of the marshes ordinarily used by the waterfowl. Suddenly, we discovered an enormous concentration of ducks on Catahoula Lake just north of Alexandria, Louisiana.

Charlie Gillham and I were in a rather primitive twin-engine bomber. I happened to be in the bombardier seat way out in the nose of the ship. It looked to me as if all the ducks in the world were on Catahoula Lake, in an area free of ice that was approximately eight-een miles long and about one-and-one-half miles wide. Those that were not actually in the water were standing on the ice waiting their turn to get into the water. Estimating that number of birds was quite out of the question; we tried to make a guess. There might have been 8 or 10 million (or perhaps 100 million). No one could be sure how many ducks were concentrated there.

When we got back to the air force base at Shreveport we asked about trying to get a photoreconnaisance aircraft over Catahoula to take pictures of that enormous flock to better estimate their number. Approval for the photoflight came through in *April* of 1940. By that time the ducks were on their way to Saskatchewan and points north.

In the summer of 1940 I was fortunate enough to make a trip to the far north with Charlie Gillham (see the story of that trip in Chapter 4). There we met a famous bunch of bush pilots. They were a colorful lot. At first they seemed to take very lightly the rules of God, man, the agency they worked for, and the government authorities who regulated matters pertaining to aviation. Upon closer observation, however, I noticed that there was one set of laws these pilots never played loose with. These were the laws of aerody-namics. Flying, in that group, was not a ball-game. You didn't get three strikes; just one. They took their flying very seriously.

Each pilot knew precisely the capabilities of his aircraft and his own ability to handle his machine. Yet all were equally aware of the limitations of their equipment and of their own skills. Of course, I will have to admit that some of the things these bush pilots did with aircraft back in 1940 made a lasting impression on my own flying in subsequent years. To them, the marginal seemed to be routine, and the impossible was worth a try. But any time they ran a calculated risk with an airplane their calculations were very thorough.

Shortly after that experience, our nation got involved in World War II, and I wound up in the U.S. Navy. Once there, I tried to convince the brass that I knew enough about flying airplanes for them to sign me up for pilot training. I should have known better. They informed me that I was being signed aboard not to fly airplanes, but to teach the pilots who did fly what to do if their planes got shot down in combat or they got lost and ran out of gas.

I spent the war setting up survival-training courses at the various air stations in the United States and in the Pacific. This included training in the use of oxygen, flotation devices, parachuting, and eventually air/sea rescue. Needless to say, I didn't do very much waterfowl work during that period, although I mentioned in my notes that one female pintail duck was seen in Majuro Atoll in the middle of the Pacific Ocean. That pintail looked as if she didn't have the faintest idea how she got there or what she was going to do next.

In 1947 I got rid of my navy uniform and was back in the old mud-stained khakis. That summer I found myself in Canada with an International panel truck, running ground surveys in the province of Saskatchewan. This was really interesting work, but I wondered if there might not be a better way to do it. Fortunately, biologists Bob Smith and Dave Spencer of the USFWS dropped into Saskatchewan every so often with their aircraft, and we tried going over some of my ground transects by airplane. Of course, this stunt had been used with a great success some years previously in the Dakotas.

Our work in 1947 showed so much promise that when I returned to Saskatchewan in the summer of 1949 I was at the controls of an old World War II L-5 airplane. This was when I really started having fun. Aircraft were perfectly suited to cover vast areas in a very short time, like our joint Canadian-United States summer operation in the prairies and the far north. However, when it came to doing more detailed work, aircraft obviously had some limitations. Planes were useful for extensive study but not for intensive work. While an enormous amount of information could be collected on terrain by trained pilots flying suitable aircraft at low altitudes, it was hard to get enough information from any one flight.

We therefore had to decide specifically what information was most useful and concentrate our efforts. Also, our methods of getting information had to be standardized because various parts of that vast country would be covered by different pilots. We had to learn how to interpret the information gotten from aerial surveys. Finally, somebody had to add up all the pieces to generate a picture for all of the northern states of the United States, prairie Canada, Alaska, and the Far North. This consolidated information was needed desperately by Washington and Ottawa. These matters took a little working out, but gradually our work evolved into the aerial surveys that are being used today.

Subsequently, in the late 1950s, I worked with Bob Smith in the Far North trying to develop the same sort of aerial surveys for the Arctic that had worked so well for the prairies. We found out, as we had suspected, that the Far North was a different ball game. It turned out later that much of the information about birds that nest in the Arctic region could be obtained during the winter period in the States.

Through our Canadian operations, we discovered new uses for aircraft. Fixed-wing (conventional) aircraft and, later, helicopters were employed in special studies involving comparison of aerial data and information gathered by ground observers. Planes were also used in surveying very large chunks of habitat and in helping isolated banding and special-study crews maintain contact with the outside world. Every summer a couple of pilots were assigned to do reconnaissance work and fly in supplies for banding crews. Airplanes were also used for educational purposes such as flying visitors around on what came to be known as the "show me" tours.

One additional chore for aircraft in Canada was photographic work. In 1952 I got involved in an attempt to photograph the nesting grounds of the whooping crane. Rex Gary Schmidt, the USFWS photographer who was to have done that job, found that the Audubon Society had decided that there should be an air-space reservation over the Wood Buffalo Park. Schmidt then decided to turn his movie equipment over to me when he was called back to Washington. Bob Smith and I later "got lost" trying to find Fort Smith, "accidentally" flew right over the whooping crane nesting grounds, and photographed the area. We got the job done, and nobody ever bothered to fuss at us for getting lost.

A Pilot

John N. Ball

The decade of the 1930s began with a great and growing depression, a great and growing drought, and a great and growing realization that our once-abundant waterfowl were fast becoming endangered. These were interrelated problems of international significance.

The New Deal launched programs and appropriated what then were fantastic sums to remedy the first two problems. J. N. "Ding" Darling, the new and dynamic chief of the Biological Survey (USBS) of the Department of Agriculture, had a direct line to the president. Darling was quick to recognize that what was good for the first two could be of mutual benefit to all three. President Roosevelt was convinced.

A sandy-haired dynamo by the name of J. Clark Salyer II was added to the Biological Survey staff to plan and direct a waterfowl refuge program of unprecedented magnitude. This refuge system would be based on the ecological needs of the many species of ducks and geese, applying the principles of wildlife management espoused by Aldo Leopold on a national scale for the first time.

The reorganization of the Biological Survey to launch the envisioned program included a fact-gathering group of flyway biologists whose realm covered the breeding grounds of Alaska, Canada, and the United States flyways, and the wintering grounds of Mexico and Central America. Frederick C. Lincoln headed this section of the Branch of Wildlife Research. Annual hunting seasons would be based on information the biologists gathered on duck and goose populations, and conditions they found on the breeding and wintering grounds.

An important part of management, the setting of regulations and their enforcement, was assigned to the Branch of Game Management. W. E. Crouch was placed in charge. He also served as the Washington office liaison with the Alaska Game Commission,

This is "Icarus." Owned and operated by John Ball of the U. S. Biological Survey, it was the first plane used for wildlife and habitat investigations in the United States. Photo courtesy of J. Ball.

which set and enforced the game regulations for the then Territory of Alaska.

By 1934, under Ding Darling's guidance, the rejuvenated Biological Survey went into action. Submarginal land acquisition money was made available for purchasing waterfowl refuges. Civilian Conservation Corps (CCC) camps were assigned to develop the newly acquired lands, as were Works Project Administration (WPA) work crews, with funds allocated through state administrators.

Still other money for the construction of buildings and dams under contract came available through the Public Works Administration. Economic Recovery Administration and resettlement administration monies, together with other relief allocations, were directed to help man and bird. Frequently, the availability of moneys had a deadline, so time was of the essence.

Because limited personnel needed to cover vast areas, it became increasingly apparent that a new wildlife management tool — the airplane — would be needed.

Fred Lincoln, I believe, deserves credit for being the first in Biological Survey to recognize the potential of the airplane as a tool in waterfowl management and to do something about it. In the fall of 1931 he arranged with the Army to take him on a waterfowl reconnaissance flight over duck concentrations on the Potomac River out of Washington, D.C. The pilot was Lt. David W. Goodrich; Andrew E. Matos, an army aerial photographer, took pictures. This flight convinced Lincoln of the value of the airplane and aerial photography in waterfowl survey work.

photography in waterfowl survey work.

Three of Lincoln's staff later came to be known as flyway biologists. They were Charles E. Gillham, Dr. George B. Saunders, and Harold S. Peters. They also felt the need to use aircraft as a tool to increase research productivity. Their jobs took them into the hinterlands of Canada and Mexico where no other access would enable them to cover vast breeding and wintering grounds within waterfowl migration cycles.

Arrangements were made for the Coast Guard, Navy, and Army to carry Lincoln and other survey observers on some of their routine flights over coastal marshes for annual winter waterfowl inventory. From 1936 or 1937 until the end of World War II the flyway biologists made occasional and limited use of chartered aircraft and pilots to cover otherwise inaccessible areas in Canada and Mexico. At the same time, there was some chartering of bush pilots and their aircraft in Alaska by enforcement agents under the Alaska Game Commission. These experiments sold the flyway biologists and enforcement field people on the advantages of small aircraft. However, administrators and some senior field people were not yet ready to abandon the backpack, canoe, and horse.

During the thirties there were few aircraft or pilots outside the military and the airlines. A dwindling number of World War I biplanes were still in use. They were used by former military or self-taught pilots barnstorming about the country in an effort to keep body, soul, and flying machine together.

This breed and their craft were being eliminated by the threat of starvation and by the well-publicized but not fully understood tailspin. Neither these pilots nor their machines were well adapted to the needs of wildlife management.

The so-called bush pilot of the back country was doing somewhat better. His craft, although usually old, was better suited to his missions, and he served an economic need. He too operated, for the most part, on a shoestring.

Toward the end of the decade, two and four-placed aircraft with performance characteristics that could be adapted to wildlife management were introduced by Stinson, Fairchild, Cessna, Monocoupe and others. So while some adaptable aircraft had reached the marketplace, there were no pilots with wildlife management qualifications available to fly them. Hiring a professional pilot for each field biologist or agent who needed this new tool was not feasible within available funds. Another impediment came from USBS administrative restrictions; the bureau's appropriation language did not include authorization for the purchase or operation of aircraft. Congress even limited the number of passenger automobiles the survey could operate. Administrators were not about to go after aircraft.

I came into the picture at this point. After graduating from the University of Pennsylvania with a bachelor's degree in economics in 1930, I was hired by the Game Research Division of E.I. duPont deNemours and Company in Wilmington, Delaware. This division was charged with keeping abreast of the developing techniques in the new field of game management and promoting their use wherever possible. A field staff of six was assigned to multi-state regions, working with wildlife agencies, sportsmen's associations, farm organizations, schools, colleges, wildlife groups, and similar groups.

After a brief orientation at the home office under the guidance of Major L.W.T. Waller, Jr. and his assistant, C.M. Palmer, Jr., I was assigned respectively to John Otterson in the New England Region, A.C. Heyward in the South Eastern Region, Henry P. Davis in the South Central Region, and Earl Feitz in the North Central Region. Further indoctrination came with my assignment to the Madison, Wisconsin, office of Aldo Leopold in 1931.

Upon completion of this training, I was headquartered in Madison and placed in charge of the North Central Region, which included the lake states, Ohio, Indiana, Illinois, Iowa, Nebraska, and the Dakotas. In 1932, the duPont field staff and the game research activities, along with operating funds, were turned over to the American Game Association, headed by Seth Gordon. My territory remained the same.

My work in late 1933 and 1934 was concentrated on the promotion of drought-control impoundments in North and South Dakota. This led to collaboration with J. Clark Salyer II and the Biological Survey on the waterfowl refuge program. In 1934 Salyer suggested I go over to the Biological Survey payroll at a somewhat better salary to take on the job of coordinating refuge program activities in South Dakota, Nebraska, Wyoming, North Dakota, Minnesota, and Iowa. The headquarters were in Pierre and, later, Mitchell, South Dakota.

From 1934 through 1937 major refuges were acquired, developed, and operated out of the Mitchell office. These included Sand Lake, Waubay, Lake Andes, LaCreek, and Bear Butte in South Dakota; Arrowwood Lake in North Dakota; and Valentine, Niobrara, and Crescent Lake in Nebraska. Many other projects and activities required periodic attention. Travel was by personal car at five cents per mile. Distances were great. Roads were gravel at best and gumbo or wagon tracks at worst. At that time no paved road extended across South Dakota, and the Nebraska sandhills had no roads. This was the time of drought and dust storms.

I worked a twelve-hour day and a seven-day week, with administrative time spent in the office, supervisory and planning time spent in the field, and after-hours time spent driving between projects, ingesting dust all the way. Fortunately, I was a bachelor and the work was interesting, so the extra hours didn't bother me. The dust was the only really unpleasant part of the routine.

As time went on and more road travel was required, it became obvious that a small aircraft would save a lot of travel time, wear and tear, and perhaps enable me to do a better job. Still, aircraft were so expensive there would be no possibility of the government furnishing one when it wouldn't even furnish a car. Besides, I didn't have the time or money needed to learn to fly. Forget it!

I had been aloft in a small plane only twice. The first trip was in one of those World War I barnstorming biplanes in a pasture near Swarthmore, Pennsylvania, at five dollars per ride in about 1928. The second flight (at no cost) was with Stewart Stetson, of the hat family, in his Velie-powered Monocoupe from Philadelphia to Wilmington, Delaware. I held my breath and pulled leather as the little Monocoupe dropped over the power lines that bordered all airports in those days. It rolled to a stop with hardly a bounce. What better terrain than prairie country for landing an airplane! I resolved to explore the possibilities sometime.

One day in the summer of 1936, after a gritty 240-mile drive from Mitchell to Jamestown, North Dakota, I arrived at the hotel in time for dinner but too late to go on to the Arrowwood Refuge. I went to the local airport to browse. They were operating a Piper Cub and a Rearwin. The former seemed a bit short on cruising range and capacity. It had suffered some from a puff of wind a day or two earlier. The Rearwin was unfamiliar to me, but seemed to have more suitable features. I was intrigued with the notion a plane might be purchased for about a year's salary and that eight hours of dual instruction would bring an average individual to solo under favorable conditions. Not beyond the realm of possibility! The wild oat was sown.

I bought two books on the airplane and how to fly it, and one on weather. Next came some research on small aircraft that might be suitable and affordable. The collection of brochures was impressive; the economics, discouraging. There was no chance that the Biological Survey would take an interest in such a venture. I felt able to make a good case for reimbursement on the same mileage basis as that allowed for a personal car. Any attempt to get an advance committment, I felt, would only result in a flat negative response. However, the administrators might give my proposal consideration if it were submitted as a *fait accompli*. I was willing to take the risk if the original cost of the machine and learning to fly it could be kept within bounds.

I sent a few letters to manufacturers of potentially suitable aircraft suggesting what a nice and novel thing it would be for one of their flying machines to be used to advance the Biological Survey's waterfowl program. Might even give them some useful publicity. The Rearwin Aircraft Company of Kansas City, Kansas, nibbled.

En route to Mitchell from the St. Louis Game Management Conference of mid-September 1936, I kept an appointment with Mr. Rearwin at the Kansas City factory. He offered the airplane at 10 percent off list. At no additional cost he would give me the dual instruction necessary to solo with sufficient competence to get back to Mitchell (with a bit of luck). Instruction would be on my plane; I would provide gas, oil, and any necessary repairs. The cost of the plane would be just under twenty five hundred dollars, with delivery about March 20, 1937. I was hooked. There was no mention of my plans to the folks back in Washington. My request for two weeks leave to begin March 19, 1937, elicited the following reply from A. C. Elmer, the Assistant Chief, Migratory Waterfowl Division:

> Your application for leave for the period March 19 to April 3 is being returned to your office approved.
> Surely you do not anticipate leaving Limbo again for this extended period unless it would possibly be to acquire a wife. If congratulations are in order they are herewith duly transmitted.
> You are entitled to enjoy yourself to the best of your ability during this period.

Limbo, it should be noted, was my Irish Setter and worthy assistant.

I showed up at the Rearwin factory on the morning of March 20. They rolled out a beautiful, shiny-red Rearwin Sportster NC 18009. It was tandem two-seat, high-winged, cabin monoplane, equipped with a wood propeller, speed ring, tail skid, and ninety-horsepower air-cooled, radial, five-cylinder LeBlond engine. It was started by standing in front of the plane and spinning the propeller. It was equipped with brakes, a carburetor, heater, and carburetor air filter. The instruments included a compass, tachometer, altimeter, back indicator, gas gauges, oil pressure and temperature gauges, and (soon to be added) outside thermometer. There were no wing flaps, battery, lights, radio, or cabin heater. There was room for a reasonable amount of baggage behind the rear seat. Controls were provided for each seat, but the

pilot normally flew from the front. Cruising range was about five hours at a speed of 110 miles per hour, plus or minus the wind. Stalling or landing speed was 38 miles per hour. I was pleased and signed the necessary papers.

That same day my log book shows 2.4 hours of dual instruction. On March 26, following a total of 8.8 hours of instruction, came my first solo flight. After another 14.8 hours, of which 7.4 were cross-country practice, the Rearwin folks thought that if they pointed me north I would eventually get home.

On April 4, 1937, armed with student pilot license #37341, I thanked the Rearwins for their patience. They wished me luck; NC 18009 and I headed north. After a gas stop at Council Bluffs, Iowa, and a total of 5.8 hours after losing sight of Kansas City, I spotted Mitchell. It was disconcerting to see the half-section of prairie that served as the Mitchell airport covered with fresh snow. Landing on that would be a new experience, but there would be many more as time went on. It took only two or three more bounces than usual to stay down. The few waiting at the airport were more surprised at a "show" than they would have been at a "no show."

Rearwin NC 18009, now christened "Icarus," set out on more substantial than Icarian wings to convince the USBS that an airplane was a practical and economical wildlife management tool whose time had come.

The first flight on official business by an employee-owned-and-operated aircraft was launched from Mitchell, on April 8, 1937. Destination: Sand Lake National Waterfowl Refuge near Aberdeen, South Dakota, 172 road miles north. Icarus landed on a mowed strip adjacent to the refuge CCC camp 1.7 hours later. Reconnaisance flights over the eighteen-thousand acre refuge quickly documented progress of development work and provided planning data. Icarus was put to bed for the night with lines, metal stakes, a scout axe, engine, and propeller covers — gear that had become permanent security equipment. The driving time from Mitchell would have been at least four hours, and the reconnaissance would have taken a full day without Icarus. The return to Mitchell next morning took 1.5 hours, leaving me a full day for administrative work in the office.

Icarus' performance surpassed expectations. The Plane's construction was sturdy enough for non-airport landings and take-offs. The long fuselage and location of the center of gravity well aft of the wheels, while making the plane quite heavy in the tail for turning manually or taxiing, proved an asset in preventing nosing over in mud, high weeds, grain fields, or (as I would later learn) taking off across plowed furrow and flying through barbed-wire fences.

The flights of April 8 and 9 set the operational pattern from the Mitchell office until my transfer to the Washington office on September 3, 1937. Flights extended as far west as Lander, Wyoming, and, upon my transfer, east to Washington, D.C. Many of the flights had our CCC engineer, Arthur F. Miller, WPA administrative assistant Harold J. Regan, or some other survey employee as passenger. From April 8 until my arrival in Washington, I logged a total of 103 hours of flight time, spread over thirty-five days, on Biological Survey business.

Field trips went on schedule with minimum delays due to weather and none due to breakdown of equipment. Only twice was the plane damaged, and then not sufficiently to make it inoperative. Once it failed to clear a dam core trench on takeoff. The plane staggered, bounced, and stayed airborn. The landing gear needed some attention later, but it was not necessary to abort the trip. On another occasion, Icarus flew through a steel-posted barbed-wire fence when I was forced to land in a pasture during a storm and overshot the first attempt. Sparks flew, the top fence wires parted, and a post was bent ninety degrees. Icarus came around a second time and successfully landed with no more than a slightly nicked propeller, minor damage to one wing strut, and small rips in the fabric.

That night the storm continued, so I was obliged to spend it with the farmer whose fence I had damaged. Since there was no phone, I couldn't notify the office of my whereabouts. A couple of concerned friends in Mitchell decided that no airplane could have survived the storm, and that a wake was in order. When I flew in to Mitchell the next day, I was not popular for having caused the morning-after condition of the mourners.

After a few months, I felt that there was enough data to demonstrate the practicability and economy to the government of aircraft operation on a road-mile basis of five cents, as was allowed for a personal car on government business. On August 19, 1937, I submitted a claim at that rate for the use of personal aircraft, supporting my claim with thirteen pages of justification. In due season, the answer came back from the administrators in Washington: "Claim for aircraft mileage disallowed." This was hardly unexpected. I still felt that it was worth my while to use the aircraft. And they would consider a claim for actual gas and oil expenses, although I unfortunately did not have the necessary receipts. So those first few flights were charged to experience, with no regrets. Future receipts were saved and reimbursed.

In December 1938 I concluded a refuge inspection trip in the Dakotas by picking up Margaret, my bride of the previous year, and Limbo our dog, at Mitchell; we then returned to Washington, D.C. This trip logged 32.8 hours of official flying time. I submitted a gas and oil claim in the amount of $92.94, which the government paid.

That was the last flight Icarus made on government business, but the plane continued to provide enjoyable transportation for Margaret, Limbo, and me. While I received very little in the way of monetary reimbursement for the use of Icarus, I gained valuable experience. I believe Icarus accomplished its mission by demonstrating to the Biological Survey that a small airplane is a practical, economical tool that can help ordinary employees enhance their contribution to the field of wildlife management.

The 1940's

The Alaska Game Commission had recognized the airplane as a necessary tool for conducting its wildlife management responsibilities in the territory and had done something about it. Two or three of their game agents had been "bush pilots." The commission had scraped together a little money, and in the fall of 1939 it requested the USBS to purchase a small two-placed aircraft on its account.

Because I was the only pilot of any sort on the Washington staff, I had been consulted to some extent on the procurement specifications. The bid of the Monocoupe Corporation, St. Louis, Missouri, was accepted for delivery about the middle of January 1940. It covered a two-place, side-by-side, high-wing monoplane that was powered by a ninety horsepower, five-cylindered, raidal Lambert engine. Performance was quoted as: top speed, 130 miles per hour; cruising, 110 miles per hour; landing, 40 miles per hour; range, 600 miles; service ceiling 16,000 feet; rate of climb at sea level, 900 feet per minute. The Monocoupe was painted dark green with three narrow, white, longitudinal stripes and the Alaska Game Commission logo on the fuselage. "USDI" and the Civil Aeronautics Administration (CAA) number, "NC 19435," were emblazoned on the wings. It would be equipped with skis or floats after arrival in Alaska.

After paying for the plane there was little money left over for delivery. Part of this problem could be met by shipping the plane from Seattle to Alaska on the survey vessel "Brown Bear," which regularly transported supplies to the territory. Still, St. Louis was a long way from Seattle.

I was due to make a refuge inspection trip through the Northwest early in 1940, so I suggested to W. E. Crouch, the chief of the Branch of Game Management, that I would be willing to help them by ferrying the Monocoupe to Seattle if I could make a couple of refuge stops en route. I thought

Clark Salyer might agree to cover my personal expenses if the commission would cover the aircraft expenses. Crouch was reluctant to trust his first-born airplane to such a novice. He conferred with the Alaska people. Because funds were tight the agreement was accepted, all be it.

When I arrived at the Monocoupe factory that January, the plane was ready and beautiful. Everything seemed in order, and the necessary paperwork was completed. Soon I was ready to be checked out in the Monocoupe. I had never flown one, nor had I flown a plane with flaps, a radio, and all of that deluxe equipment. A check flight was certainly desirable, particularly since hanger talk reputed the Monocoupe to be a little tricky. But it was not to be. The taxiways were covered with deeply rutted ice, the runways were icy, and it looked as if there would be little improvement the rest of the winter. I thought conditions would permit a takeoff but certainly not a landing. I had the wheel pants removed and stowed aboard, for they would be an impediment in the snow. Finally I made the decision to go. Taxiing over the rutted ice presented difficulties. A suitable takeoff position was finally reached and off we went. There was no problem and, fortunately, no necessity to return to the field.

After a number of wintery days of flying that included snow-covered airports, dust storms, and extreme turbulence, my flight ended safely at the Sand Point Naval Air Station, Seattle, Washington. It is often said that delivery of the first-born is the most difficult.

Clarence Rhode, a handsome young Alaska game agent who was learning to fly, met me at the airport to take charge of the Monocoupe. The plane was partially dismantled, placed aboard the "Brown Bear," and taken to Alaska by Douglas Grey. It was reported to have arrived in the territory without a scratch and to have performed admirably.

Clarence Rhode, whose prime interests were aircraft, flying, Alaska, and wildlife conservation, went on to become Alaska's outstanding regional director. In that capacity he planned and supervised the development, operation, and maintenance of the USFWS major aircraft fleet. In late August 1958, a Grumman Goose he was flying with his son Jack and Alaska game agent Fredricksen as passengers disappeared somewhere in the Brooks Range. A massive air search failed to find the plane or the men. Twenty-one years later two backpackers found the plane, fifty-five miles northwest of Arctic Village. It had missed the pass by two hundred feet, crashed, and burned.

My knowledge of pre-World War II history of FWS aviation ends with the purchase for the Alaska Game Commission of two four-placed Fairchilds during the summer of 1940. Two Alaska game agents, Sam White and another whose name I do not recall, came to the Fairchild factory at Hagerstown, Maryland. They brought the planes to the Washington Hoover Airport, where the Pentagon now stands, for all to see. After a few days they were off to Alaska. The Fairchilds, too, served well on wheels, floats, and skis. Aircraft were increasing the productivity of the Alaska game agents.

A second Monocoupe was purchased for Alaska in 1941, I believe. A call to active duty in the Naval Reserve in February, 1941, ended my direct knowledge of the FWS's flying activities until my return in January, 1946, when a formerly reluctant agency was more than ready to go flying.

The research staff of the Bureau of Biological Survey held a conference in St. Louis, Missouri, in 1937. Members working with waterfowl were (left to right, by number): front row, 1 Logan Bennett, 2 Clarence Cottam, 4 Frederick C. Lincoln; second row, 2 C. S. Williams, 9 Charlie Gillham, 12 Luther J. Goldman; third row, 2 William H. Marshall, 4 John J. Lynch, 6 George B. Saunders, 8 A. L. Nelson, 9 C. Sperry, 10 Edward R. Kalmbach, 13 Harold S. Peters, 14 E. Horn. USFWS photo.

Aircraft for Wildlife Management

After World War II, the USFWS was anxious to acquire surplus aircraft. FWS Director Albert M. Day supported the development of an air capability.

The Branch of Wildlife Refuges wanted light aircraft to keep abreast of refuge populations and to help with maintenance, enforcement, and planning throughout the system. They wanted to use aerial spraying to control undesirable aquatic and terrestrial vegetation, and insects, and for seeding. Potential refuge reconnaissance in Alaska could be effectively accomplished only from the air.

The Branch of Predator and Rodent Control considered the airplane an efficient means of setting out and checking bait stations, locating predators, and running trap lines as part of their predator control program in the western range states and Alaska.

The Branch of Commercial Fisheries needed aircraft for fish reconnaissance, law enforcement in the salmon fisheries of Alaska, and for transporting personnel and supplies to remote stations.

ment, and planning throughout the system. They wanted to use aerial spraying to control undesirable aquatic and terrestrial vegetation, and insects, and for seeding. Potential refuge reconnaisance in Alaska could be effectively accomplished only from the air.

The Branch of Predator and Rodent Control considered the airplane an efficient means of setting out and checking bait stations, locating predators, and running trap lines as part of their predator control program in the western range states and in Alaska.

The Branch of Commercial Fisheries needed aircraft for fish reconnaisance, law enforcement in the salmon fisheries of Alaska, and for transporting personnel and supplies to remote stations.

Types of aircraft suitable for the contemplated uses varied widely from twin-engined amphibians to single-engined, two- and four-placed planes on wheels, floats, or skis.

Biologists Begin to Sprout "Wings"

The military ended World War II with a conglomeration of excess aircraft and equipment. The War Assets Administration (WAA) was set up to expedite disposal of all surplus. Legislation gave both the WAA and the military services authority to transfer surplus to governmental agencies without cost and on a priority basis. The FWS went after those aircraft and parts like a poor relative descending upon the estate of a rich uncle.

The first to act was flyway biologist Harold Peters, who by this time had become an enthusiastic pilot in search of something to fly. He visited the Camden, South Carolina, WAA disposal yard in 1946, and came away with five two-place, 190-horse power, single-engine Stinson reconnaisance planes (military designation "L-5"), and two, five-or six-place Nordyne Norsemen single-engine planes.

Hard on Peters' heels was flyway biologist Dr. George B. Saunders, who had located a Navy Grumman Goose amphibian powered with two 450-horsepower Pratt and Whitney engines in Brownsville, Texas. Dr. Saunders hoped to use this Grumman on the Mexican winter-waterfowl inventory.

The USFWS air fleet had jumped 200 percent over night from the four Alaska planes acquired just before the start of World War II. This was only the beginning.

Clarence Rhode, a first-class scrounger, was adding to the fleet in Alaska. Planes in even better condition than those early discards were found, still in the hands of the military and Coast Guard. In July 1950 a Grumman Goose, destined for flyway biologist Bob Smith, came straight from a major Navy overhaul to the FWS in perfect condition. This Goose, "N-749," was to become recognized all along the Pacific Flyway, from Mexico to Arctic Canada.

Predator and Rodent Control wanted two planes capable of carrying loads of bait for setting out stations. A five-place, 450-horsepower, single-engined Howard GH-2 and a 165-horsepower, four-place Cessna were available for the asking. Four three-place, 100-horsepower Cessnas were what the FWS needed. We took them. Alaska latched onto four or five "L-1s" and about the same number of "YL-15s." The USFWS wound up with the world's largest fleet of amphibious, twin-engined Grumman Gooses and Widgeons, mostly acquired directly from the Navy and the Coast Guard. Engines and spare parts to support the fleet of Grummans were picked up wherever available. Alaska acquired a twin Beechcraft "C-45" and a "DC-3" to add versatility to its fleet.

By the end of 1948, the FWS operating fleet had grown to thirty-six planes, divided among the Branches as follows:

Game Management	13
Alaska Fisheries	8
Predator and Rodent Control	5
Wildlife Research	4
Wildlife Refuges	4
Fishery Biology	1
Federal Aid	1

The FWS's fleet stabilized at about fifty-two by 1957, a number exceeded, I believe, only by the military and the CAA among government agencies.

Administrative and Technical Guidance

It soon became obvious that not all surplus military aircraft were suitable for wildlife work. Nor were all licensed pilots qualified to fly all types of aircraft on all wildlife missions.

Director Day was concerned that the program was burgeoning without technical guidance or control. In April of 1946 he issued a memorandum designating me to "handle details concerned with operation of the airplanes insofar as the Chicago office is concerned." I would be responsible for supervising the maintenance and operation of our fleet of airplanes.

The aircraft duties would be extra curricular to my regular job as chief of operations, Branch of Wildlife Refuges. This was awkward, as Refuges was paying my salary but supervising aircraft would take much of my time. Clark Salyer, the branch chief, was patient. There would be some benefits for Refuges too, such as combining branch business with the ferrying of aircraft for other branches. It was particularly advantageous when planes were destined for Alaska.

This somewhat informal arrangement remained in effect until October 1948, when I was reclassified and given the title "supervising airplane pilot," with 40 percent of my time allotted to agency-wide air operations and 60 percent to refuge operations. My desk remained in Refuges but now the 40 percent of my salary and expenses on air operations was taken up by the benefitting branches on the basis of their number of planes.

In April 1955 the position was placed in the Branch of Engineering and retitled, "supervising airplane pilot-safety engineer." Forty-five percent of the time was allocated to air operations, with the duties remaining the same; 30 percent was allocated to service-wide safety; and the remaining 25 percent went to service-wide automotive and vessel operations, with radio communication liaison thrown in later. The functions under Engineering were financed by assessment against the branches.

In the fall of 1957, the USFWS was reorganized into the Bureau of Sport Fisheries and Wildlife, the Bureau of Commercial Fisheries, under the authority of the Office of the Commissioner of Fish and Wildlife. I was transferred to the Office of the Commissioner, with responsibility for the Safety Program. Ed Wellein was assigned the duties of supervising airplane pilot for the Bureau of Sport Fisheries and Wildlife, under the chief of the Branch of Game Management.

Maintenance and Operations

Government aircraft were not required to meet the CAA's (later Federal Aeronautics Administration) licensing and maintenance requirements. Since the agency was not staffed to perform these functions, it was USFWS policy to require all aircraft to be licensed and periodically inspected as prescribed by the CAA for civilian aircraft. In this way the USFWS was able to take advantage of a trained and existing inspection staff.

All aircraft acquired from surplus were in flyable condition suitable for ferrying but needing varying amounts of reconditioning before they could be licensed and placed in operation. Bids were solicited for standing contracts to perform this work on a labor and parts basis.

In the continental United States, the newly reconditioned aircraft were assigned to pilot-biologists or pilot agents. Maintenance, in accordance with CAA standards, was the responsibility of the pilot, using commercial facilities and licensed private mechanics.

Alaskan operations were handled somewhat differently since commercial maintenance was not readily available. Regional Director Rhode pooled the aircraft assigned to his region and set up a maintenance and operation base at Anchorage under supervising pilot-mechanic Theron Smith. Thanks to the efforts of Director Day and Regional Director Rhode, Congress appropriated some $600,000 to construct a suitable hanger facility on the shore of Lake Hood adjacent to the Anchorage International Airport. The hanger was finished in 1950. Without it, the maintenance of the agency's aircraft fleet could not have been sustained.

A small satellite hanger-shop facility at Fairbanks, with pilot-agent Ray Woolford in charge, along with a shop in Juneau, with Bob Meek and later Elba P. Kropf in charge as pilot-mechanics, provided a satisfactory distribution of maintenance personnel and aircraft to service the needs of the operating branches. By the end of 1951, Alaska had five full-time mechanics in addition to Theron

Smith, Tom Wardleigh, Bob Meek, Elba Kropf, and D. B. "Buck" Harris, who were pilot-mechanics available for field dispatch in emergencies.

Alaska maintenance and operations were coordinated by a territory-wide, USFWS radio network that enabled all stations, aircraft, and vessels to communicate. Credit for this network, developed from surplus electronic equipment, belongs to Regional Director Rhode. It greatly enhanced the safety of Alaskan operations.

Pilot Personnel

Many of the USFWS's aircraft missions were performed at low levels, requiring the pilot to divide his attention between the airplane and surface activities. Precision, skill, and good judgment were prerequisites for Service pilots. From the beginning, the concept of a hybrid pilot-agent or pilot-biologist was uppermost. Alaska "crossed" some pilots with mechanics and obtained a highly useful hybrid.

By the end of World War II, flyway biologists Harold Peters and Bob Smith had obtained their CAA pilot licenses, as had game management agent Roy Ferguson. In Alaska, there was Clarence Rhode, Ray Woolford, and one or two others. A number of military-trained pilots who had premilitary wildlife management degrees or experience in law enforcement were now seeking employment with the Service. Veterans with wildlife backgrounds took advantage of the GI Training Bill to learn to fly. Similarly, war pilots desiring employment in the wildlife field used the training bill to acquire this skill.

The minimum prerequisite was a CAA private license with appropriate ratings. Each prospective pilot was given a flight check and, upon meeting the higher standards required by the Service, was issued a "Letter of Authorization to Pilot Fish and Wildlife Service Aircraft." This letter of authorization spelled out the equipment and the types of missions authorized, based on the pilot's demonstrated capabilities and experience.

Senior pilots, with experience as instructors, were authorized to give flight checks and refresher training as more advanced requirements were needed. Each branch indicated the prospective pilots it would like qualified and the types of missions that might be assigned. Some would have occasion to fly only rarely, perhaps using chartered aircraft. In any case, the Letter of Flight Authority was required to pilot on official business. By the fall of 1957, approximately one hundred Letters of Flight Authority had been issued.

New Aircraft Replace War Surplus

The first new World War II aircraft was purchased by the Branch of Game Management and delivered July 15, 1947, for use in Alaska. It was a promising new design that marked the Republic Aircraft Corporation's switch from fighter to private and commercial aircraft. The "SeaBee" seemed made to order for the USFWS — a four-place, single-engine, amphibian powered with a 215-horsepower Franklin engine mounted aft of the cabin. The propeller was controlled and reversible. A retractable water rudder was a valuable adjunct to the controls. The cabin was spacious. Visibility forward, to either side, and up or down was wonderful. Performance as a boat was excellent. Everyone was enthusiastic. We bought two more.

Alas, however, the SeaBee was underpowered and slow to climb out of the ground effect, particularly when operating from fields above sea level. It's gliding range with the power off was little more than straight down, a characteristic of many military aircraft that was not to the USFWS's liking. Pilots' compensations for its shortcomings, however, made the SeaBee highly useful for both enforcement and flyway assignments.

New two- and four-place Pipers and four-place Cessnas outperformed the various single-engine planes acquired from surplus through 1948. They were better adapted to floats and skis. The single-engine military surplus planes were gradually sold and the proceeds were applied to purchase Pipers and Cessnas.

On October 22, 1948, the USFWS was given a nearly new four-place Fairchild-24 by an ardent conservationist and industrialist, William Sweet of Attleboro, Massachusetts, for use on Atlantic Flyway work. It proved to be a valuable addition to the Service's fleet.

In addition to previously mentioned planes, Alaska purchased two used commercial planes, a Gullwing Stinson and a Waco, to supplement its surplus equipment.

Grumman Gooses and Widgeons continued to be acquired from surplus well into the 1950s. Several of the Widgeons were converted from Ranger in-line engines to more powerful and reliable Lycoming radials.

By 1957, the Service's aircraft fleet had reached maturity. Practically all single-engine planes were now of post-war vintage. Only the multi-engine aircraft remained from the war surplus acquisitions.

USFWS aircraft prior to 1955 could be identified by their orange-and-black color scheme. Thereafter, an international orange and white pattern was adopted to improve the visibility of the plane both on the ground and in flight.

USFWS pilots in the postwar years covered the hinterland from Alaska to Arctic Canada, along the United States flyways, through Mexico, Central America, and the Caribbean. They pioneered "agricultural flying" as a wildlife management tool. They flew where weather information was lacking, navigational aids were few, and maintenance facilities were inadequate. They accomplished their missions with skill and dedication.

The USFWS pilot corps included men such as Clarence Rhode, Bob Smith, Dave Spencer, Leon Cool, Theron Smith, Walt Crissey, Ed Wellein, Ted Ball, Fred Glover, Al Kropf, Buck Harris, Harvey Hedlund, Jim Hickey, Ross Hanson, Ray Woolford, Tom Wardleigh, Al Noltemeir, and Alaska's Governor Jay Hammond.

A Teacher

William H. Marshall

Several experiences early in my career will always be vivid in my memories because they involved exposures to some of the men who revitalized waterfowl programs in the 1930s.

In June 1935 I reported to the U.S. Forest Service in Amherst, Massachussetts, as an assistant conservationist. This was a cooperative project with the U.S. Biological Survey (USBS). I was to review plans and accomplishments of wildlife projects in Civilian Conservation Corps (CCC) camps. Soon I was sent to Washington to receive instructions and advice from the USBS. I reported to Ira N. "Gabe" Gabrielson, who had just transferred in from the Portland office and who obviously had been selected by J. N. "Ding" Darling as his heir apparent.

After a day or two of discussion with Gabe, Art Einarson, Leo Couch, Clarence Cottam, and others, Gabe took me to meet Ding Darling. We went down the long, crowded halls of the Agriculture Building and right into Ding's office. He gave me a hearty handshake and we talked for about ten minutes. It was a truly exhilarating experience; his acuteness and dedication to wildlife conservation showed brilliantly.

Another vivid experience of a different kind came soon after. The New Jersey Mosquito Extermination Commission (MEC), a very powerful organization in that state, had eighteen new CCC camps strung along the coast from Hoboken to Cape May. My immediate boss, Crosby A. Hoar, called me into his office one day and said, "Here are eighteen annual work plans, two-and-a-half pages long, which just say we are going to ditch all of the salt marshes in such and such an area — that's not enough, and looks dangerous to me. You are to meet Clarence Cottam in Trenton and try to find out what this is all about."

I drove to Trenton and met Clarence, known for his dynamic personality and drive. "Mac" MacNamara, superintendent of game for New Jersey, joined us. Mac was a wise and dedicated Irishman who knew not only the ins and outs of politics in New Jersey, but also had a tremendous knowledge of Jersey wildlife habitats, especially the salt marshes.

We spent four days driving from camp to camp (they were already occupied and geared up with tools, trucks and other supplies) and visited many salt marshes. It was obvious that, come hell or high water, they were going to ditch every salt marsh in the state. After the second day, Mac pointed out to me that a car with a couple of MEC employees followed us wherever we went, and they undoubtedly were reporting back to Trenton on whom we talked to and where we went. This was before the FBI.

At a final, long, evening session in a Trenton hotel, we decided that we really did not have enough information to block programs of already-established camps. But neither did the MEC have any information as to what ponds or other valuable wildlife habitats they would drain. Our strategy was to report that, since the work plans had no maps and no hydrological information which would even indicate where the ditches would go or what ponds they would drain, the MEC plans were incomplete. Further, we would point out that much valuable wildlife habitat would be damaged.

I returned to Amherst to recommend against approval of the work plans, which my boss then sent back to the MEC with a request that maps and water-level data be supplied before they would be approved. The type of information we sought has, in recent years, been referred to as an "environmental impact statement." Ultimately I had to return to Trenton to face the music — without Clarence or Mac. I was ushered into the executive director's office with a distinct lack of cordiality. There was no sparring; he just lit into me for blocking progress and depriving citizens of the great state of New Jersey of their rights. Besides, he went on, asking for *maps* of salt marshes was just nonsense. I hung tight, quoting Mr. Hoar's letter. Finally the director stood up, pounded on his desk and said, "Mr. Marshall, I know both U.S. Senators from New Jersey, and unless you persuade Mr. Hoar to approve these plans tomorrow, you will be out of a job in twenty four hours." He obviously meant it.

However, after telephone conversations with Gabe and Ding, Mr. Hoar stood fast. I did not lose my job, the ditching was delayed for several months, and much of the most damaging ditching was ruled out. Ding obviously had political "clout" that he used in Washington when necessary for the sake of waterfowl. And Clarence, as he did again so many times afterward, fought with distinction for waterfowl habitat.

Soon afterward, I was fortunate to spend a month working for and learning from two other waterfowl greats who were building the federal waterfowl refuge system: J. Clark Salyer II and "Doc" W. B. Bourne. One day after office hours in Washington the three of us left by car for the Outer Banks of North Carolina. It was typical of Clark's energy that although he had already spent ten hours in the office, he was ready to drive that night to Norfolk, Virginia in a heavy rainstorm. He wanted to get an early start the next morning. Also, fairly typically, he had no reservations, so we spent the night in a raunchy hotel discussing plans for the Pea Island Refuge.

We spent the next two days driving along the beaches almost to Cape Hatteras, and drove back to Washington late at night. We got stuck in wet sand up to the running boards twice (Clark did not always like the long way around). Luckily we were pulled out before the tide came in. All of the greater snow geese were on the Pea Island flats, and we were able to outline the desired refuge boundaries. Being there at the very beginning was a thrilling experience.

Later, Clark sent me south to get information on the Okefenokee Swamp, which he wanted for a refuge. At Folkston I met the manager of the Hibbard Lumber Company, which owned the land, and he arranged for a "local" to take me into the swamp for three weeks. Within a half hour of leaving the Folkston canal, I was lost. But Harry Chesser, who was born and raised on Chesser Island, knew the swamp. He poled our pirogue through miles of alligator trails and across the "prairies," as Harry called the open marshy areas. We camped on small islands and spent two nights at his house, a two-room log cabin with an adjacent shelter for the cows, pigs, and chickens. The only light was from a large open fireplace where we cooked and ate black-eyed peas, eggs, and sow belly.

I kept track of waterfowl, mostly ring-necks and woodies (locally called "screamers"). I also saw two or three flocks of Florida sandhill cranes. We didn't see a gator or a snake until the last day.

After coming out, I drove to Jacksonville and arranged with the Coast Guard for a flight over the swamp. We covered all the open "prairies" at low level, rising to clear the cypress hummocks. When I indicated I'd seen enough we headed back to Jacksonville. Then I learned the real reason for the flight.

The pilot spotted a still in a cypress swamp and kicked the biplane into a tight circle at perhaps three hundred feet. He held up his note board on which he had written me a note saying, "Draw a map of how the road comes into the house." I was busy doing this when air sickness overtook me and I had to hang my head over the side. To add to the excitement, a man came out on the porch and started shooting at us. We left and I tidied up the sketch map. Two cars with armed men met us at the Jacksonville airport. About three hours later they came back after destroying the still, telling me, "It was a fine map, but 180 degrees off is a bit confusing."

Remembering my stint at the Bear River Marshes is pleasant for me since it was my first permanent job. I reported on the refuge July 1, 1936, as a junior biologist in the Research Division of the Biological Survey. Frankly, I didn't know beans about "ducks in the marsh." However, I had spent a little time with Miles Pirnie in Michigan and Clarence Cottam in New Jersey, and I was armed with the available books and references of the time.

My reception at headquarters was not overjoyous. After all, I was a college kid from a different division. However, for lodging I had a one-room frame house on the river-bank, and I was assigned office space in the new but empty laboratory building. When it got cold I moved into one of the lab rooms for the winter. This was heated, had a rest room, and was far more handy than the shack, which was a hundred yards away and across two spillways via unplowed roads. A boat and motor were available until I burned up the motor in a greenhorn accident.

H. M. Wight, of Michigan, had drilled into me that the first step in wildlife research was learning the habitat. I spent many hours on the dikes and in the marshes and salt flats. My work regimen was eleven days "on" and three days "off," with infrequent trips to town (seventeen miles away).

That fall I did a lot of hunting with George Jorgensen, a temporary worker who had grown up as a market hunter near Bringham City. George knew his ducks as few men ever did. Before going into the marsh we would decide what species and, in the case of mallards and pintails, what sex we would shoot. Accordingly, George would pick the spot for a blind and tell me how to set the decoys. He always shot a "crossing double" —two crossing birds with one shell. In fact he only took five shells with him, as the limit was ten!

The only maps available then were engineering maps, which were excellent but which stressed dikes, spillways, and borrow pits. My graduate training had involved a lot of cover mapping, and I enjoyed that kind of work. I began to map the area. Before freeze-up the marshes were tough to get around in because the bottom was soft and the channels were tunnels lined with walls of six- to eight-foot high bulrush and cattails. After freeze-up I could use skis, so I began running section and forty lines from known corners on the dikes. I marked this grid by stakes and then ran lines, sketching in channels and emergent vegetation. The beauty of the

marshes was unforgettable — as it was some-times well below zero, the great expanses of open ice interspersed with brown vegetation had the spectacular Wellsville or Promon-tory mountains as a backdrop. I finished the map by mid-February, but what would I do with it?

Fortunately, on March 1, Cecil S. Will-iams came to Bear River to initiate nesting studies. He had spent the two previous sea-sons with E. R. Kalmbach on the prairies and so knew how to go about it. The map, to him, was an excellent base, and we checked plants and areas again.

About that time the first Canada geese showed up to begin establishing territories. We decided to pool our efforts to find as many nests as possible, locate them on maps, and follow up on nest success. Three CCC enrollees were assigned for the work. As a crew, we combed the vegetation at about ten-day intervals, tagging the nests, locating them on the map, and recording the data. The going was strenuous, as the marsh was soft, the sun hot, and the mosquitos abun-dant.

By late July we had tallied 95 goose nests and 2,410 duck nests, locating them on the map. We followed 84 duck nests and 1,560 goose nests through to their success or fail-ure. We also kept records of vegetation, dis-tance to open water, and height above the bottom. The piles of data sheets were pretty high, even when sorted by species.

When things wound down in August we resolved that our information would not gather dust, so we did more sorting, review-ing, and categorizing. Luckily, we did have a hand-operated adding machine. The ulti-mate result was two publications on water-fowl nesting habits printed in the *Journal of Wildlife Management* in October 1937 and April 1938.

One interesting facet of this research dem-onstrates the rigidity of the Biological Survey at that time. Cec and I worked together as a team. Using the maps I'd drawn and his experience in nesting studies, we were able to fit things together to our satisfaction. Cec

decided he wanted to spend the rest of his career on Canada goose studies, and since this was a joint endeavor, we agreed that all goose data would be published as "Williams and Marshall," while the names would be reversed on the duck manuscript. There would be a short paper on Canada goose goslings appearing in the *Journal* in July 1938. Actually, I had discovered that the broods were roosting on dikes at night and could be counted shortly after dawn as they swam away. Since I was sleeping at headquarters and Cec was living in town, it was easier for me to be out early, so I made nearly all the counts.

Soon after the three manuscripts were sent to Washington for approval they came back with editorial comments and suggestions. Since Cec was an assistant biologist and I was a junior biologist, the edict was that he would have to be listed as the senior author. Cec fought this by mail and we talked over the phone about it one day, but to no avail. Civil service status could not be violated. We gave up and parted friends when I moved on

to study fur bearers in Idaho.

During my Bear River days I had some experiences censusing waterfowl from the air. United Airlines pilots, required to lay over at Salt Lake City for twenty four hours while on flights from Chicago to San Francisco, could retain their commissions by flying Air Corps planes based nearby. The airline's aircraft were Ford tri-motors and, of course, "stunting" with them was forbidden. On the other hand, the Air Corps planes were PT-9s, the same single-engine, canvas-covered biplane in which these men had received their training as fighter pilots.

The regular Air Corps captain was glad to be able to assign these reserve officers a definite mission every two weeks. By driving to Salt Lake City airport, signing a two-page liability release in case of a crash, and strapping on a parachute (which would be useless at low altitudes), I could accompany the mission.

We had a regular route north to marshes near Ogden, then around the refuge, and finally west to the Locomotive Springs State

Waterfowl Management Area. Convinced that the pilots were excellent, I peered over the edges of the open cockpit and marked waterfowl concentrations on county maps. We flew a straight course at five hundred feet, communicating by hand signals or with a note pad, as the noise was deafening. There was no intercom.

The excitement began when I raised both hands to indicate mission completed. The seventy miles back to Salt Lake were anything but routine. These ex-fighter pilots had fun diving at wild horses on Promontory Point or at the Southern Pacific trains crossing the Great Salt Lake on the Lucin cutoff trestle.

From my aerial census figures, I projected a total of two million ducks for the entire Great Salt Lake Basin. Later, when I attended a meeting of USFWS biologists, Fred Lincoln made it clear that air censusing was the job of flyway biologists, not mine. At this Denver meeting in 1937, I met all the flyway biologists and was particularly impressed by Luther Goldman.

After two wonderful years at the Bear River Refuge, I moved to Idaho for a stint as

fire warden in the Sawtooth Mountains, working toward a PhD degree at the University of Minnesota. In 1945, following service in World War II, I joined the staff at the University of Minnesota, teaching courses in wildlife management.

Soon after I became a teacher, GIs returned from the war in full force and, since many were interested in waterfowl, I became directly involved in waterfowl again. My early experiences with these birds began to bear fruit. These students, fresh from their military duty, were eager to pursue new careers. In those days the demand for trained waterfowl specialists was strong, and many of our students became leaders in the new field of waterfowl management. It is with great satisfaction that I look at a list of leading waterfowl professionals of the past two or three decades and find among them the names of many of my former students.

It was my privilege to introduce many of these young men to waterfowl field work. My own early FWS work in the Bear River Marshes were a fine background for university teaching.

A Surveyor

Gerald W. Malaher

It was over six decades ago — in 1922 — that I first went north. I travelled by train from Winnipeg to The Pas, a trip lasting twenty-four hours. At that time the Hudson Bay Railway was completed only to Gillam, and Port Nelson was still supposed to be its terminus on Hudson Bay. Once a week the Muskeg Special, as the train was known, would run as far as Mile 214. If a railway car jumped the tracks, all the passengers turned out to jack it back on with poles cut from the bush. Though the Mandy mine had been staked some years before, Flin Flon did not yet exist, and it was to be another six years before the railway from The Pas extended that far. Snow Lake, Lynn Lake, and Thompson mines were still dreams. Transportation north of The Pas, apart from an unfinished railway, was by canoe in summer and by dog team in winter.

In the fall there was always an influx of lumberjacks on their way to logging camps 100 miles up the Carrot River. Each spring these same lumberjacks invaded The Pas with their winter earnings in their jeans, ready and anxious to paint the town red. Many were the ladies of pleasure who came from down south to entertain them and relieve them of their hard-earned wages. It fell to Sergeant Grennan of the Royal North West Mounted Police to shunt the ladies southward again; but in the meantime, the lumberjacks were queued up in the long corridor upstairs in the Derby House, each with a dollar bill in his hand, waiting his turn.

Such was the north country as I first knew it. The saying, "There ain't no law of God nor man goes north of 53 degrees," was common among northerners in those days. They were almost a subspecies of the genus *Homo,* living by their own standards and somewhat contemptuous of the south and southerners. But I was destined to live in a very different atmosphere.

Gerry Malaher believed a natural resources department director should spend as much time as possible in the field. Here he is shown in the Turtle Mountains of Manitoba. Photo by Manitoba Department of Natural Resources.

The McKay Indian Boarding School, some six miles upstream on the Saskatchewan, was run by the Indian Eskimo Commission of the Church of England in Canada. In my letter of appointment it had been suggested I

57

might "take up a course of instruction under Reverend E. Minchin, Principal of the School to fit you for a wider sphere of usefulness later on." This I suspected would lead to a clerical collar and I had no intention of that. I was to be the farm instructor and conduct a mixed farming operation to produce milk, beef, pork, and vegetables to feed 100 Indian children and to help make the school self-supporting.

During my stay at the school I got to know many Indian people and to like them. One who befriended me was John Harris, a kindly old man, short of stature, pigeon-toed, with long, black hair plaited over his shoulders, a bit stooped but full of vigor, and a renowned hunter. He used to come to the school to sell moose meat. It took fifty pounds of meat per meal to feed the Indian children. We got to know each other and, since I had no small canoe, John offered to teach me how to hunt out of his small birchbark craft, beautifully made by himself. It was only twelve-feet long, but had a wide beam and was so light it could be hooked on one elbow and carried over a portage. It was also very tippy. John accepted me as a senior partner in duck hunting since I had a double-barrel, hammerless shotgun, while he had only an old muzzleloader.

It was fascinating to watch old John reloading that muzzleloader. Before the cloud of black smoke had cleared away, out came the ramrod and down the barrel it went to remove any sparks before the next charge of black powder was put in. Wads cost money, and John didn't have very much, so the wad to cover the lead shot was made from the pith in the stem of the soft-stemmed bulrush. A wad was kept inside his left cheek ready for use. In his right cheek was the next charge of shot. Saliva would hold the shot together, said John. Standard procedure was to spit the shot down the barrel, out of the right corner of his mouth, swing over to the left, spit, and in went the wad to be plunged down with the ramrod. Long practice had made this a surprisingly quick operation.

For three years we hunted together and enjoyed each other's company. John was one of nature's gentlemen, quiet but full of humor and quick to smile. But in the hunting of moose he could be stern and a hard taskmaster.

I often used to visit John and his wife in their small plaster-covered log home on the Indian reservation, and was welcomed with courtly ceremony. We would drink tea together and talk of hunting and the nature of the hunted. The house, with its adzed-pole floor and little curtains at the windows, was always scrupulously clean but carried a faint and delicate odor of skunk. Tracing this down I found a bottle of skunk oil kept on the windowsill. It was John's firm belief that skunk oil was better than white man's medicine for any and all human afflictions.

I was intending to return to England for a visit. John heard this and came over to the school to see me.

"I hear you are going across the big water," he said. "Yes, John, I am." "You will come back?" "I'm not sure, John, but I think so." "I hope so," he said, as he reached into his haversack and produced a Bull Durham tobacco bag. It contained kinnikinik, his homemade tobacco made from the inner bark of the red osier dogwood — or red willow as it was generally called.

Bowing, he handed it to me with the words, "Here, take this. Don't smoke it all at once, but when you do, think of me." With these words he turned and left me, not willing to show any emotion.

From Halifax I sent him a picture postcard of the S.S. *Andania* on which I was to cross the big water.

It was eighteen years before I returned to The Pas. My old friend John Harris had long gone to his happy hunting ground. Gone, but never to be forgotten! He taught me many things.

After less than three years at the school I had become disillusioned with the program that kept Indian boys away from home during their formative years when they should have been learning how to earn a living from the natural resources in their home territory. Instead they returned home at age eighteen knowing little about it. When I was given the opportunity to join an exploratory canoe survey charged with mapping the two-thousand-mile shoreline of Reindeer Lake, I left the school to experience and enjoy the real north.

With the twentieth century almost one-quarter gone, there were still few detailed maps of Canada's north country. Main rivers had been traversed by geologists, topographers and men of the Dominion Lands Survey, and their actual canoe routes plotted with some accuracy; but detail within sight on either side was only sketched in, and was often highly inaccurate. In between these traversed rivers huge areas on the maps were blank and merely marked "UNEXPLORED."

World War I had hastened the development of aircraft, and the Royal Canadian Air Force was formed shortly thereafter, many of the first pilots being veterans of the R.A.F. Now aerial photography was to be tried in conjunction with ground surveys to fill in all detail of land and water. In the summer of 1924 an exploratory shoreline survey of Reindeer Lake was to be made by ground survey. An aircraft, a Vickers Viking amphibian, was to fly up from The Pas in midsummer and photograph the islands. The ground survey party was to freight five thousand gallons of gasoline by canoe from Cumberland House, where it was delivered by a stern-wheeled riverboat to Brochet, the trading post and Indian village at the north end of Reindeer.

The flight to Reindeer was considered with almost the same detail and seriousness as a flight to the moon today. The pilot, Basil Hobbs, had every item weighed in to the aircraft. Bob Davidson, the navigator, thought it might be pretty cold flying that far north in an open-cockpit aircraft and was wearing two pairs of pants. When the pilot discovered this, Davidson was compelled to remove one pair to reduce weight!

Since existing maps were very inadequate, there was fear that the village of Brochet would not be located. The ground survey party, therefore, was instructed to see that a large bonfire was built and an Indian hired to listen and watch for the aircraft which would be like a *gitche seeseeb* — a big duck that flew in the sky. He was then to throw gasoline on the log pile and make as much smoke as possible.

It was a Sunday morning in August. Everyone except our Indian fire-watcher was at Mass, for Father Egenolf was a stern disciplinarian. It was a lovely job for our old Indian hired to start the fire. All he had to do was to sit by the log pile all day and listen, then look. He didn't even have to go to Mass! He lay there on the shore with his hat over his eyes, half asleep, for it was a warm, sunny day. Mosquitos bothered him a bit, and one seemed to make an unusually loud buzzing noise. He flipped his left ear, he flipped his right ear, but still the buzzing kept on and grew even louder. Could this be the *gitche seeseeb?* He opened one eye and looked down south. There in the sky was a small black dot. He watched it; it grew bigger and the noise grew louder. Indeed, it must be the *gitche seeseeb!* Forgetting all about the fire he jumped up, ran to the church and whispered through an open window, *"Gitche seeseeb* coming." Around the church echoed the whisper *gitche seeseeb — gitche seeseeb — gitche seeseeb.*

Father Egenolf was at the altar with his back to the congregation, intoning his prayers. One by one the Indians picked up their tin-can spittoons kept between their mocassined feet, and quietly pussyfooted out of church. When Father Egenolf turned around his church was empty!

Meanwhile the entire settlement — men, women, and children — had gathered at the lake shore and excitement was high. The pilot of the aircraft was jubilant; he had found Brochet easily, fire or no fire, smoke or no smoke. Forgetting that none of those people below had ever seen an aeroplane before, he dove straight at the crowd, pulling out only at the last minute. Excitement turned to terror, and everyone disappeared in the bush. It was ten minutes before the men began sheepishly to reappear, and a full half-hour before the women and children returned.

Father Egenolf was angry, both with his congregation and with the pilot. It was necessary to placate the priest, and curiosity soon got the better of his anger. He was soon dressed up in flying helmet, goggles, and life jacket, seated in the copilot's cockpit, and encouraged to manipulate rudder, ailerons, and elevators. This he did like a child with a new toy.

But his anger at his flock was not as easily assuaged, for on the next Sunday morning he stood in the door of the church and refused entry to those who had deserted him a week earlier.

In the summer of 1925 activity shifted to the territory east of Lake Winnipeg. The settlement of Little Grand Rapids on the Berens River, near the Manitoba-Ontario border was to be the operation's air base. Five-thousand gallons of gasoline had to be freighted by canoe 110 miles inland from Lake Winnipeg, over fifty-three rapids and falls. An Indian crew was hired, and five trips made up the Berens. We had three 2½ horse-power, Evinrude outboard motors, but none of the Indians knew how to run them, much less get them started again if anything went wrong. As the only member of the party who knew anything about those early outboard motors, I had first to select and teach two Indians how to start, steer, and slow down or accelerate the motors. When we started out — and throughout the five trips up river — I had to hang behind the canoe flotilla ready to change places with anyone with motor trouble, get his motor running, and then catch up.

My bowman was John Ross, and at first I relied completely on him to determine what course to follow and when to run ashore and track the canoe up a rapid. It seemed to me there were many places we could use the motor, but I said nothing while John signalled every move we should make. The third time up the river John had gained some confidence in me and my engine. On one occa-

sion he was asleep in the bow as we approached a rapid which I felt sure we could cross with the engine, so up I went. With the unusual motion of the canoe John woke up. A look of terror crossed his face and, grabbing his paddle, he pulled for shore. The engine was stronger than his paddle, and I kept on. After that he was more content to let me run other rapids. John always took his shoes off when in the canoe and went barefoot, as he had no socks. With new confidence he lay back against a packsack and put one foot over the gunwale on either side. If at any time I was in doubt just where to steer and called out, "Which way, John?" one or the other big toe would waggle, indicating the way to turn. In swift water he no longer grabbed his paddle but lay back watching the shoreline. As long as he could see we were making some headway, however slowly, he would not move.

Whenever possible we spent the weekend at Little Grand Rapids with Johnny Moar, the Hudson Bay Company post manager. He had four daughters and played the fiddle. Saturday night dances to the tune of the "Red River Jig" and "Little Drops of Brandy" were a wonderful break from portaging gasoline.

The year before, in 1924, the Department of Indian Affairs had decided to use aircraft in making treaty payments at remote reservations. Johnny Moar told me the story of that first attempt. There had been no trouble in finding Little Grand Rapids, the first stop, as it was easy to follow the Berens River upstream from Lake Winnipeg. The next port of call was to be Deer Lake in northwest Ontario on another watershed. The plane took off but maps were of little use, and the party could not find Deer Lake. With half their fuel used up they returned to Little Grand Rapids. That night they consulted Johnny Moar about the route. Now Johnny knew every canoe route within a hundred miles, for he had spent his whole life in the area. He merely shut his eyes, lay back in his chair, and described in detail the whole canoe route to Deer Lake. "If you know it that well," said the pilot, "why not come with us tomorrow and show us the way?" Johnny agreed, though he had never been in an aircraft. Indeed, this was the first one he had seen.

They took off, with Johnny sitting in the open-bow cockpit. Johnny pointed out the way to start, but within half an hour they had travelled as far as a canoe could go in a whole day. Johnny's mind could not keep up with the speed of the aircraft, and he too became hopelessly lost. Again, with half their fuel gone, they had to turn back. But this time they didn't find Little Grand Rapids. With only a few minutes' fuel left they were forced to land, not knowing where they were. Johnny knew every large lake in the country but, dropped out of the sky, he couldn't recognize this one. He decided to walk the shoreline looking for something he could recognize and found an Indian grave. He knew every Indian who had died in the past fifty years. If he could just think of the right name he would know where he was and, if necessary, find his way home. He sat by that grave for three days repeating to himself the names of dead Indians, but still the right name would not come to him.

Unknown to all was the fact that a party of moose hunters from Little Grand Rapids had been on the lake when the aircraft landed. The Indians saw the plane go down behind an island, heard the hull hit the water, and thought it had crashed. They were too afraid to go and see, so they hightailed it back to Little Grand Rapids and told the Hudson's Bay Company clerk of their fears. Emergency food and a first-aid kit were loaded in the canoe and back they went, the clerk with them, to search for survivors.

Johnny was sitting by the grave when he saw a canoe rounding a point a mile or so away. He waved his shirt, and the canoe approached. As soon as it was within hailing distance Johnny shouted, "Whose grave is this?" Across the water came the reply, "Josiah Partridge." "Oh, hell!" said Johnny, "This is Dogskin Lake," and immediately he knew the way home.

After he had told me this story he said flatly, "They'll never get me in a plane again, not as long as I live." When it was suggested that air travel was the coming thing and would get him in to Winnipeg in a couple of hours instead of a week by canoe and lake steamer, he finally relented with the words, "Well, not unless they allow me to take five pounds of shingle nails, a crooked knife, and enough canvas to make a canoe. Then I don't care where they drop me. I'll make a canoe and find my way home."

We had met Little Grand Rapids canoes coming down to Berens River Post for freight on our first trip up the river. The clerk at the post had ordered a radio, which the freighters later delivered. No one had ever seen a radio before and no one knew how to install it. By this time our freighting was finished, the photographic crew had arrived, and the surveyor and I were waiting for the finished aerial photos from which to pick out the best canoe route cross-country to Hudson, Ontario. With time to spare, I volunteered to install the radio. The bright copper aerial strung between the shore and the dwelling house caused much consternation among the natives. It was thought to contain an evil spirit that would harm the settlement, and they didn't like walking underneath it.

Later at my suggestion one of the older Indians was brought in to listen, and the earphones were clamped on his head. There was no change of expression as he listened to music. When told in his own language that the music was coming through the air, not even from Canada but from far to the south in another country, he merely shook his head in disbelief. Pressed for an answer as to where the music came from, he pointed to the radio and said, "out of the box." He thought it was the same as the old Victrola with the cylindrical records, which the Indians knew.

Finally, through an interpreter, I asked how he could be convinced I was telling the truth. After some thought he replied, "Tomorrow I hunt moose. If this machine is as wonderful as the young white man says it is, let it tell me where I shall find a moose — then I shall believe."

The aerial photos taken were flown out to Kenora, Ontario, shipped to Ottawa, developed, printed, and three big suitcases of pictures were sent back to us. Our job then was to sort out the pictures showing the best canoe route diagonally across the area photographed. These we took with us to travel by, and sent the bulk of the pictures back to Ottawa.

We were to put in the ground control as we travelled by triangulating between points identifiable on a picture, and thus providing an accurate scale for plotting the final map. At forty to 50 mile intervals latitude and longitude observations on time stars were taken to determine exact locations that would enable any plotting errors to be distributed across the map, instead of accumulating as plotting progressed.

The load of instruments, photographs, tent, bedding, and supplies was too much for one seventeen-foot, semi-freighter canoe; so we hired two Indians with a second canoe to accompany us and help with the portaging. We promised to take them to *Gitchi Karweagamuk* (Big Round Lake), a lake on the Bloodvein River from which they knew the regular route home. All went well for the first week until we noticed the Indians were uneasy. They said they thought we were lost. To prove otherwise, I showed them a picture of the lake on which we were camped, pointed across the lake and told them that over there was a short portage to the next lake, as shown on the picture. They talked this over, then off they went to see if I was telling the truth. They came back satisfied and on we all went. Two days later at an ungodly early hour we awoke to hear the Indians making breakfast. As soon as we appeared they said they were going home, nor could we dissuade them. They were given enough grub to get them home, and a pay chit on the Hudson Bay Company; and off they went in a hurry. We knew not why. There was a one-mile portage immediately ahead of us to be scouted and then cut. Beyond was some fifty miles of country with

dance, and it all seemed strange to us. not an axe mark, portage trail, old camp fire, or other human sign to be found. Beaver, otter, and other fur animals were in abundance, and it all seemed strange to us.

Two years later when back at Little Grand Rapids, I asked Johnny Moar if he could explain why the Indians left us and why no one was trapping the unusual abundance of fur animals. He laughed and told me this story.

Many years ago a party of Indians left Little Grand Rapids for their spring trapping, taking their canoes along on the dog toboggans. They camped on the shore of a narrow lake on the opposite side of which was a high rock cliff.

One night, soon after break-up of the ice, there was a violent spring thunderstorm. A rift in the top of the cliff had been widened through the years by ice forming in the cleft and gradually pushing the rock forward. Reverberations of the thunder had been enough to topple the delicately balanced rock, and huge masses of the cliff plunged into the lake. The resultant tidal wave swept through the Indian camp, drowned some of the people, drowned most of the dogs chained to trees along the shoreline, smashed some of the canoes, and generally wrecked the camp.

Believing that the *Weetigo* (evil spirit) was responsible, the survivors hurriedly salvaged what they could and hightailed it home. Word of the tragedy soon spread and none of the Indians of Little Grand Rapids, Pikangicum or Red Lake would enter the area. We were going to pass right through it, and that was why our Indian companions had deserted us.

The next spring we started out from Hudson, again taking five-thousand gallons of gasoline into the back country, this time to Lac St. Joseph. The route lay up Lac Seul to the east end, and then up the Root River to its headwaters, from where there was a half-mile height of land portage over to Lac St. Joseph. This was a well-established Hudson Bay Company freight route, and to our joy we found pole-rails laid like a railroad track

©M. Anderson

across the portage and an iron-wheeled flat-car ready for our use. Tumplines and canoe ropes were attached to the flatcar, and the gasoline was loaded. With the entire crew pulling on the ropes, short work was made of the portage.
the ropes, short work was made of the portage.

Several more trips were made before the job was completed. On the final freighting trip we took in all the summer's supply of food for ourselves and two air crews. With our Indian crew paid off and sent back to Hudson, we built a log shack as a cache for the supplies.

Our next job was to scout the west end of Lac St. Joseph for a good campsite and air-craft harbour. An excellent sheltered base-campsite with sand beach was located some miles up the lake. The air crew was expected shortly and was to look for us in that vicinity. While waiting, we moved gasoline from the height of land portage to the campsite. As soon as the planes were heard we ran our canoe out to open water and kept circling around until we were spotted. The aircraft landed beside us, and we led them to the chosen campsite.

While air photographs were being taken we made sorties in every direction and trav-elled the full length of Lac St. Joseph to Osnaburgh Hose. There we made an obser-vation of the rapids tumbling from the lake to form the Albany River.

Every week or so one aircraft was flown to the railway to take in exposed film, pick up mail, and bring in fresh meat, oranges, grape-fruit, and vegetables. The tent camp was improved by building a unique structure using material at hand. One wall was made from upright poles stuck in the sand and chinked with moss. The opposite wall was made from the wooden cases that had each held two four-gallon tins of gasoline. These cases also supplied the nails. An end wall was made of the tins, cut up and overlapped like shingles. At the opposite end an automobile-type tent was erected; the front flap was used to partially form the roof, the rest being covered with a canvas tarpaulin. The tent became the storehouse and inside the walls were the kitchen and dining room.

We were sorry to leave all this luxury and return to trail grub and the nightly pitching of a new camp but, when prints of the air photos arrived, perforce we departed to make the ground control survey, travelling north up the Cat River and beyond to the headwaters of the Severn River.

With snow behind us we arrived back in Hudson, Ontario late in the fall. There was time only to quickly store material before the train left for Winnipeg. Prospectors and trappers had cleaned the store out of pants and shirts, so we boarded the train in dirty trail clothes. There had been no time for supper and we were hungry. The surveyor was reluctant to go to the dining car in his dirty garments, but finally consented if I would lead the way. The waiter virtually threw the menu at us while looking down his nose (and probably holding his breath). He had to be told to bring us serviettes, but after that looked after us better. When he brought the finger bowls I felt like drinking out of mine — just in spite.

The use of aircraft to detect and suppress forest fires in Manitoba began in the early 1920s. The base for the eastern portion of the province was first established at Victoria Beach, Lake Winnipeg. This proved to be a poor harbour and in 1927 the air base was moved to Lac du Bonnet. From there we patrolled the Whiteshell area and northward on the east side of Lake Winnipeg to Poplar River. Natural resources were still under control of the federal government, with the flying being done by the Royal Canadian Air Force (RCAF). I was now employed by the Dominion Forest Services.

Air-to-ground radio was still experimental and seldom worked more than ten miles from the base. Most aircraft used carried no radio equipment. Open-cockpit flying boats were the type generally used.

A large flock of racing pigeons was kept at the base with a pigeoneer on staff to train and look after them. His office was with the

Royal Canadian Signal Corps, which operated radio between Lac du Bonnet, Winnipeg, and northern bases such as Cormorant and Norway House.

Every flight leaving the base on forest patrol carried two pigeons. These were brought to the dock in a wicker container by the pigeoneer and placed aboard. A pocket inside the lid held a message pad of rice paper, carbon paper, pencil, and two leg clips with a small aluminum message tube attached. Birds were used for two general purposes. If a fire was spotted, its location and spread would be noted together with the time spotted, and the message clipped on the leg of one of the birds. It was not necessary to land if the bird was properly released. The drill was to slow the aircraft to just above stalling speed, hold the bird on its back with head forward and throw it downward over the side. To release it in any other way would probably have resulted in a broken wing.

The second general use for birds was in case of engine failure or accident. In this case the cause of engine failure or result of accident would be reported together with time and location. If two birds were still available a carbon copy would be made and used for the second bird. There were two cardinal rules to observe in making a release: never release both birds together, as companionship might lead to dawdling along the way; and never release a bird unless it could easily reach base before sunset. To stop and roost on the way was dangerous to it.

When birds were sent out with a patrol flight the pigeon cote at base was closed, but there was a little vestibule-type trap that an incoming bird would enter in trying to join the other birds. Its weight on a treadle both shut the door behind it and rang a bell in the Signal Corps office. The pigeoneer removed the message capsule and delivered it to the duty officer, saluting smartly as he did so. If it concerned a fire, it was then brought over to us at the Dominion Forest Service. Information on fires was only sent in by pigeon when the aircraft was outward bound. I kept a complete record of pigeon service flights in

1928, and in every instance one or the other of the birds came safely back to base.

Flying in those early days was an adventure. All aircraft seemed to be underpowered. On a calm day or when the air was soggy it was often necessary for the RCAF crash boat to run out at full speed and create a wave; the aircraft would follow behind to take off on its wash. Many were the times we sat out on the wings to let the engine cool down after trying to take off when away from base.

The observer's cockpit was a round hole in the nose of the Vickers Viking and Vickers Vedette flying boats. If you stood up, you were out in the wind from the waist up. If you were wise, you kept your toes tucked under a small, inside nose brace to prevent being ejected should the aircraft be subjected to a sudden downdraft, often wrongly spoken of as an air pocket. You had to be careful too on take-off, particularly in cold weather, as spray frequently came in over the nose. A piece of canvas was kept in the front cockpit and you ducked down, throwing it over head and back, and holding on tight until airborne. Flying suits, warmly lined, helmets, and fur-lined goggles were provided for all flights. Even at that, long flights in fall weather would leave you half-frozen.

The carburetors on some of the engines — particularly, as I remember, the Lynx radial engine — were not designed for use in cold weather, so sometimes we were forced down to the tree tops or even to a forced landing and warm-up before the engine would function properly. On one occasion the engine quit cold when halfway over a fifteen mile dry hop east of Lake Winnipeg. The utter silence was frightening while the pilot jiggled the throttle and I looked over the side trying to decide whether it was better to stick with the ship or parachute to the muskeg before we got too low. It seemed an eternity but I don't suppose it was actually more than twenty seconds before the engine spluttered, caught, and returned to normal revs.

Magnetos, too, were often a source of trouble. One day when on patrol with Pilot Officer Hickson at the controls of a Cyrus

Mark II Moth, the whole aircraft started to shake and shudder, until I thought it would fall apart. A glance below showed Happy Lake a few miles to the north. With throttle pulled back, we glided down toward it; but it soon became evident that we would end up in the trees before reaching the lake. The only alternative landing was a small, normally very unattractive muskeg lake, and in this the aircraft was safely set down. Getting out on the pontoons we found the lake to be shallow and so full of muskeg muck that even by paddling hard we could only move forward by inches. The muck merely spread out in a brown mass behind us. A paddle, pushed straight down and followed by my arm did not reach bottom. There was no more resistance to the effort than if it had been made through water only.

There was only one small rock point on the lake; toward it we struggled, but made mighty little progress until we reached a large bed of water lilies. Feeling for the roots and pressing on them, we finally reached shore after taking over half an hour to make a quarter mile.

The trouble determined, the appropriate message was written in duplicate and the two pigeons released, the second twenty minutes after the first. In the message we said we would walk over to Happy Lake and await rescue there.

Next morning a Vedette flew in with the Lac du Bonnet commanding officer aboard. When he saw the situation of the aircraft he sent the pilot back to base with instruction to bring in Sergeant Pilot (Egghead) Elliot — the lightest pilot at the station. In the meanwhile everything movable was taken out of the Moth until only five gallons of gasoline remained in the tank. The Moth was then pulled along the shore to the bottom of a small bay, pulled back against the muskeg, and tied by the tail to a small spruce. A new magneto was installed and the engine tested.

The far shore of the lake looked ominously close, and we all wondered how Elliot could safely make the take-off. When he walked over from Happy Lake he obviously didn't like the look of things, but orders were to "fly it out." Elliot climbed aboard, the prop was swung over, the engine started and warmed up to take-off temperature. At full throttle, while still held back by the tail rope, the pontoons lifted high in the water. At a given signal from Elliot, the rope was cut and away went the Moth. We watched with hearts in our mouths while the pontoons seemed to refuse to leave the water. Finally the plane was airborne and gathering speed low over the lake. At the last minute, Elliot jerked back on the stick and jumped the plane fifty feet to skim safely over the muskeg spruce and land in Happy Lake — a happy but trembling man.

Indians from Little Grand Rapids were frequently called on to turn out and fight forest fires on the east side of Lake Winnipeg. As late as 1927 no Indian would fly. They insisted on travelling by canoe, whch generally meant a large fire by the time they reached it. Time and again I tried to persuade them, but to no avail.

Then a small fire was spotted within twenty-minutes flying time from the settlement. To reach it by canoe would take almost three days. We landed at Little Grand Rapids, and as usual everybody came down to the dock to watch the plane come in, including Johnny Moar. Jumping out on the dock, I shook hands and explained the need for quick action to him. "Can't we possibly get these men to fly?" I asked. Johnny smiled and said, "There's one man over there who was telling everyone he wished he had the chance." Then he addressed the crowd, saying, "You all heard Moses Owen boasting. Now is his chance."

Now Moses was a man of some substance in the community. He was the official dog-killer when feasts of dog meat were organized. He looked most uncomfortable as everyone turned to look at him. If he now refused he would permanently lose face, and this he feared more than the risk of flying, so reluctantly he agreed to go. We could only carry one extra man plus tools and supplies. Moses was put in the front cockpit with instructions to crouch down and cover himself during take-off as it was quite rough. We took off, but at five-hundred feet there still was no sign of Moses. I nudged the pilot, pointed forward, and spread my hands to indicate "What has happened to Moses?" The pilot grinned, pulled back the throttle and put the aircraft into a short but steep dive. Up came Moses like a jack-in-the-box looking very scared, but my smile quickly put him at ease and he began to look around. A few minutes later he pointed downward and excitedly mouthed words to me I could not hear; he had recognized Night Owl Rapids on the Berens River. Within a few minutes he was leaning so far out of the cockpit we were afraid we might lose him.

He had been told we would leave him and the equipment at the fire and go back for more men. Then the horrible thought came to me that if we returned without Moses and with no message from him, all the Indians might think he was dead or had been spirited away and would never return. I found a birch tree, cut some bark, took out a pencil and handed both to Moses saying, "Musiniagan nithce," which roughly meant "Write a letter, brother." The birch bark was covered with writing in the Cree syllabics and handed back to me. Armed with this, I handed it out back at Little Grand Rapids, and it was passed around for everyone to read. What Moses had said I never knew, and often wished I had obtained a translation of it. It must have been good, because there was then no difficulty, and never was again. Every man wanted to fly. Today, no one will travel by canoe if flying is possible.

In the summer of 1928 there was a bad fire east of Lake Winnipegosis. The ranger had no experience with using aircraft and persisted in using the forestry patrol boat, wasting much valuable time. I was sent in to correct this situation.

Pilot Officer Hickson and I left Lac du Bonnet early on a Saturday evening, flew to Victoria Beach, topped up the fuel tank, and stayed the night. We took off again at 5:00 A.M. Sunday morning. As we passed over the Meadow Portage between Lake Manitoba and Lake Winnipegosis, I leaned out of the front cockpit to look at the ground. It was a beautiful sunny morning with not a cloud in the sky, but as I leaned out my goggles were spattered with moisture. This was a puzzle, and I began looking for the source. Out from under the engine cowling there was a long red streak from which drops of ethyl gasoline were torn off into the wind. I hastily wrote a note to Hickson, "Bad gasoline leak, better land," and gestured toward the red stain. We landed at a little sand beach on the first island in Winnipegosis, pulled the aircraft up on the sand as far as we could, lifted the engine cowling, and found the leak.

There was a small gasoline lead passing directly from the fuel tank to the engine primer. This had broken as a result of long vibration in the wind, and a thin stream of gasoline was pouring out. The broken pipe was pinched shut with pliers, and we both contributed our wads of chewing gum to plaster over it as added protection against further leak.

Next, we measured the remaining gasoline in the wing tank by thrusting a stick down through the filler opening. There was approximately two inches of fuel in the bottom of the tank. It was only some ten miles further to the air station on Snake Island, our destination, and Hickson thought the two inches of fuel would suffice. We pushed off and drifted away from the island to save fuel. When we were in position for take-off, I climbed down on the float, swung the prop, and away we went.

Neither of us had landed at Snake Island before. The water in the bay looked shallow and there appeared to be scattered rocks below, so we circled to look. The rocks turned out to be underwater weeds, so we passed upwind over the island to circle again and come in for a landing.

By this time there was a fair breeze blowing. About half a mile north of the island, at about two-hundred feet, Hickson began a steep turn to starboard. Halfway through the turn, with the wind on our beam, the engine quit. We stalled, the aircraft dropped, and there was insufficient height to recover from the stall — so into the lake we crashed. There was actually a little gasoline left in the tank, but in making the steep turn it had all run from the fuel line to the carburetor.

The starboard float broke in half, the port float was leaking badly, a main strut of the undercarriage had broken, and the jagged broken end had come up through the fusilage between Hickson's knees to neatly take a piece out of his Air Force breeches. Had it been two inches to the right, his knee would have been smashed. As it was, neither of us was really hurt. I was waist-deep in water in the front cockpit, but Hickson was high and dry behind. Fortunately, there was a crash pad on the front edge of the cockpit, or I would have had a split forehead at least.

We expected the aircraft to sink at any moment and watched the shore of the island for signs of rescue activity. It was still very early on that Sunday morning. When we had passed over the island everyone was still in bed. The air base was on the south side of the island, and we were on the north side. It was a long way around the shore, and might be some time before a rescue boat could reach us. Then, joy to behold, a group of pajama-clad figures dragging a big skiff emerged from the bush and launched the skiff. There was a narrow neck in the middle of the island, and to save time the boat had been dragged over.

We both had been wearing life jackets. I had always been impressed that a jacket should be blown up by mouth and the cylinder of compressed air only pierced in case of emergency. Apparently, I had not considered this an emergency as I had blown up the life jacket by mouth!

Hickson and I were taken ashore, and I returned to help tow in the aircraft while he deflated the jackets and opened up the parachutes to dry. When we returned to shore Hickson was laughing and said to me, "There's nothing wrong with your lungs; your lifejacket was as hard as a football!" It was an A-1 crash, and the little Moth aircraft never roamed the sky again.

In 1930 the federal government transferred the authority for managing natural resources to the provinces, and the RCAF then ceased flying forest patrols in Manitoba. In 1931 Western Canada Airways did the flying on contract. In the meantime, formation of a Manitoba government air service was being considered. The federal government transferred four Vickers Vedettes to the province, and on June 2, 1932, Jim Ulman arrived at Lac du Bonnet with the first of these flying boats. The spring fire season was bad. Roy Brown of Wings Limited had been hired to fly on forest protection until the Manitoba Government Air Service arrived, and was still flying for us because of the number of fires.

On June 11, Brown and I were flying east of Lake Winnipeg and stopped at the ranger station on Sasaginnigak Lake for lunch. On taking off again, we spotted a small smoke near the Manitoba-Ontario boundary, and flew over to investigate. The fire was in Ontario, on a portage along the Dogskin River. It had obviously just started, the result of a campfire left burning. A short distance downstream we located two canoes travelling toward Little Grand Rapids. There was nowhere to land so we flew on to Little Grand Rapids, where I instructed Al Disbrowe, fire ranger, to go to the mouth of the Dogskin River and apprehend the canoeists when they reached that point.

On return to Lac du Bonnet I telephoned the Ontario Department of Lands and Forests, Kenora, advised them of the fire, and asked if they wished to prosecute the offenders. The answer was yes, so arrangements were made. Two Little Grand Rapids Indians, John Flatstone and John Bones Flatstone, were to be held under house arrest at Little Grand Rapids. They would be brought to Boundary Island on Moar Lake (Eagle Lake), east of Little Grand Rapids, at noon, June 16. There we would meet the Ontario officials and turn over our prisoners.

On the morning of June 16, Corporal Stewart of the Royal Canadian Mounted Police was flown to Little Grand Rapids, where he picked up the Indians. We all then continued to Moar Lake, landing almost exactly at 12 o'clock. As we taxied toward Boundary Island the Ontario plane came in sight through the smokey atmosphere and landed behind us.

Magistrate Dyner (Ontario) then selected a good rock on the boundary line on which to sit. Ontario officials lined themselves behind him. The Manitoba prisoners were marched up to the boundary line by Corporal Stewart and turned over to H. S. Johns, Ontario Provincial Police. The court was called to order and formally declared open. The charge was read to the accused and interpreted by Alf Disbrowe. A plea of guilty was entered. The facts of the case were given by Roy Brown and myself, and we explained that as John and John Bones Flatstone were the last to leave the portage (their course was some distance behind the lead canoe) they were responsible for leaving the campfire burning.

Both men were sentenced to three months in the common jail at Kenora, put into the Ontario plane, and taken south. This we thought would be a good lesson to the people of Little Grand Rapids. Little did we realize that the men would become romantic figures in their community.

At that time, in 1932, the Indians of Little Grand Rapids were not used to the white man's world nor his modern conveniences. When, three months later, John and John Bones returned to the settlement via Lake Winnipeg and the Berens River, they held the people enthralled by their stories, acted out with many a gesture, of how when it got dark they pulled a string and — presto — the sun shone up on the ceiling. Were they thirsty or did they want to wash, they merely walked over to a tub on the wall, turned a little handle — thus — and out flowed water. Most wonderful of all, when nature called there was a bowl to sit on, with water down below. When finished you pulled a chain with a little handle on the end of it, and with a roar like Night Owl Rapid, down came a

flood and everything — but everything — disappeared.

Thus was the white man's penalty thwarted, and the two men became the heroes of the day. There is little doubt they received many presents of tobacco for telling and retelling their story for many moons thereafter.

These stories of northern Manitoba, northeast Saskatchewan, and northwest Ontario are just a few of those that can be told about working conditions and the local inhabitants in that era of half a century ago. The airplane was just coming into use in detailed mapping of remote territory by aerial photography. Forest fire protection through use of aircraft had begun. The ancient method of canoe travel and transport of goods was still in vogue but was soon to give way to aircraft and the Caterpillar tractor.

A decade slipped by before I was again north of 53 degrees, this time as supervisor of Game and Fisheries for the province. Even in that time many changes were taking place as the north was opened up.

Today many settlements have their own landing strips, carved out of the forest. Some have regular telephone and radio-telephone communication. All-weather roads are reaching far into the north, mining towns have sprung up, railways have been extended, schools have been built, and nursing stations established. The mighty Nelson and Churchill rivers have been harnessed for electricity. Many changes are for the better, but in some respects change has been too rapid. Old customs and the old way of life are disappearing fast. Much of the real romance of the north is gone.

A chapter in history covering this transition period in the north has been largely neglected. Those who recall that period have reached their three-score years and ten. Time is running short if firsthand accounts are to be gathered, recorded, and preserved.

©J. Raedeke

Remembering the Pioneers

The early files of the Bureau of Biological Survey and the infant U.S. Fish and Wildlife Service were deposited in the Smithsonian archives in the Arts and Industries Building on the Mall near the nation's capitol. Here are some forty-four cubic feet of carefully catalogued and preserved unpublished reports, field notes, and photographs that describe the early investigations in the United States, Canada, Mexico, and other countries.

This material is anything but a pile of dull, dusty records. In these pages can be found evidence of the monumental contributions of men who are no longer alive to tell their stories.

And what stories they are. If you glance through these pages, your perceptions might include:

Smell
- the tangy coastal breeze over a New Jersey saltmarsh
- the pungence of mesquite smoke from a Mexican campfire
- the stench of whale blubber being rendered over an Eskimo fire

Taste
- hot biscuits from a reflector oven
- tamales, frijoles, tortillas, and tequila
- boiled beans — and more boiled beans

Sound
- the hiss of a canoe cutting through Canadian water
- the deadening drone of a Grumman Goose's twin engines
- the picturesque cadence of Louisiana Cajun speech

Touch
- the warmth of a downy gosling being banded in Oregon
- the vibration in a pilot's stick of a plane flying transects
- the icy chill of Chesapeake Bay water topping hip boots during canvasback banding

Sight
- an Arctic whiteout
- mallards pitching into an Alberta grain field flattened by hail
- scaup sweeping over a South Dakota duck pass

All this, and more, still lives in the pages of those who advanced the early work of managing North America's waterfowl. For their field notes, as well as their pioneering work, we are deeply in their debt.

On January 25, 1935, Frederick C. Lincoln conducted the first aerial census of a wintering duck population. Here, Lincoln (in coveralls) stands with photographer Andrew E. Matos and pilot David W. Goodrich of the U. S. Air Corps prior to takeoff. Photo by U. S. Army Air Service.

Portraits

Frederick C. Lincoln

Henry M. Reeves

Frederick Lincoln is generally regarded as the father of waterfowl flyways in North America. However, Lincoln, in his landmark report, *The Waterfowl Flyways of North America,* generously recognized the contributions made by W.W. Cooke and others in gathering and examining data on North American waterfowl migration. He identified Cooke as the father of bird migration studies in North America, noting that although Cooke's migration routes were delineated "necessarily of more or less general nature, . . . in some cases he presented the data in remarkable detail." Lincoln also recognized Alexander Wetmore's pioneering studies of waterflow banded in Utah.

Unlike Cooke, Lincoln had a vast accumulation of banding and recovery data at his command. Lincoln clearly identified and enounced the importance of the flyway concept to waterfowl conservation by stating:

> Conservationists now know that the birds have a strong attachment for the ancestral flyways and they recognize the significance of this fact . . . It indicates that if the birds should be exterminated in any one of the four major flyways now definitely recognized, it would at best be a long time before that region could be repopulated, even though birds of the species affected should continue over other flyways to return to their great breeding grounds of the North.

He further elaborated: It is a matter of common knowledge that migratory birds follow certain definite routes on their journeys to and from breeding and winter quarters, but it is not generally understood that these routes are followed by the same groups of individual birds during successive years. Migration studies by the banding method have shown that by adhering more or less rigidly to any particular flyway the ducks and geese tend to perpetuate not only that ancestral route but also the groups of individuals that use it. The significance of this discovery to problems of administration is obvious.

Lincoln carefully defined the term "flyway," noting that in the past it had been used more or less indiscriminately with "migration route." He described migration routes as "the individual lanes of avian travel from breeding grounds to winter quarters," and flyways as "those broader areas into which certain migration routes blend or come together in a definite geographic region." Thus, waterfowl flyways are comprised of the composite migration routes of all ducks, geese, and swans that share common breeding, migration, and wintering locales.

Nevertheless, Lincoln recognized that waterfowl flyways based solely on biological data tended to overlap, and that only their ocean boundaries were clearly defined. Even this statement is not strictly true, as we now know that some species, such as brant, may migrate long distances over the open sea from Alaska to Mexico or from Arctic Canada to Ireland. Lincoln further observed that the waterfowl flyways tended to become more sharply defined from about 45 degrees latitude southward to the Gulf Coast. He recognized the significance of this phenomenon by explaining that much of the sport hunting of ducks and geese take place at about 45 degrees and southward.

Lincoln's four flyways — Atlantic, Mississippi, Central, and Pacific — were formulated largely on the results of banding data. Initially the use of discretely numbered bands was the only means of marking individual birds; color marking was later employed to mark discrete population segments or individual birds. Color marking permitted the gathering of sight observations without the mortality usually associated with the recovery of banded birds.

Lincoln cited the results of banding pintails and wigeons at Lake Merritt, in Oakland, California, to illustrate the fidelity of ducks to their flyway. Several hundred birds of each species had been banded there since 1926. He noted that of the 550 recoveries, nearly 97 percent occurred within the Pacific Flyway. During 1933-34 more than half the ducks trapped at Lake Merritt were carrying bands attached there in previous years. This example may be somewhat extreme, as results from bandings of other species or in other areas (especially in prairie Canada and more northerly areas) generally illustrate a lesser degree of fidelity.

The supreme test of Lincoln's flyway philosophy involved the capture of pintails and other ducks wintering at Avery Island, Louisiana, near the southern extremity of the Mississippi Flyway. The birds were shipped by express to six widely distributed locations in the Atlantic and Pacific flyways, and released after banding. The succeeding year found them back in their original wintering quarters, despite the fact that other ducks of their own species were relatively common at the locations and in the flyways where they were released.

The flyway concept developed by Lincoln forms the foundation of the biological administrative units implemented in 1948 by the USFWS for developing flyway-oriented regulations. Surprisingly few modifications have been made over the years in the four flyway boundaries. Lincoln's flyway concept has been applied with notable success to various management populations of Canada geese, and, in some instances, flyways have been divided into lesser units to facilitate the management of ducks. The High and Low Plains units of the Central Flyway and the Columbia Basin of the Pacific Flyway are such examples.

Lincoln came to Washington, D.C. from his position as curator of birds at the Colorado Museum of Natural History in Denver, Colorado. Entering on duty with the Bureau of Biological Survey (USBS) in 1920, he was assigned the formidable task of organizing the new bird-banding program recently taken over by the federal government from several ornithological organizations which had recognized the need for a single, centrally located banding program. Much of Lincoln's earlier career was directed to this effort, analyzing the results of the banding program and espousing the concepts of waterfowl management as revealed by banding and surveys. He also worked closely with his Canadian counterparts as that nation became a full-fledged cooperator in the North American banding and survey programs.

In 1926 Lincoln wrote the first publication describing methods of capturing and banding waterfowl in North America. He categorizes traps as being either "automatic," functioning without the presence of an operator, or "nonautomatic," requiring more or less continuous observation and manipulation by a concealed watcher. Lincoln described three basic types of automatic traps: the raft trap, the water-leaf trap; and the McIhenny pen trap developed by E.A. McIlhenny, a pioneer duck bander in Avery Island, Louisiana. Nonautomatic traps included the spring-pole trap and the cage trap, which were triggered or closed from distant locations by rope. While Lincoln does not so state, unpublished correspondence and reports suggest that several of the trap designs used by the pioneer waterfowl banders were copies or modifications of traps long used by market hunters and poachers. Evidently these early traps were relatively efficient even though crude materials, such as saplings and chickenwire, made their construction difficult and time consuming.

Lincoln recommended that banders utilize live decoys borrowed from gun clubs as means of enticing ducks into traps, and that banders capture the ducks in the trap by "grasping them around the neck." Neither practice is recommended today! He also instructed banders to submit their records daily to the Biological Survey if they banded during the waterfowl season. In-season banding of migratory game birds is strongly discouraged today because of the biases it interjects into the analysis of band recovery data. Despite our minor criticisms of procedures in these early days, Lincoln was truly the father of the North American waterfowl banding program.

In 1927 Lincoln recounted some of the incidents associated with the abbreviated mailing address inscribed on bird bands. He noted, after describing the various inscriptions in use:

> Any of these legends is however, sufficiently complete to insure delivery of a letter, as the post-office officials have been fully advised of the work and have delivered promptly envelopes bearing such enigmatical address as: "Mr. Biol. Surv., 23171, Wash. D.C."; "Biol. Survey Co., Wash. D.C."; and "Boil Service, Wash. D.C.". The word "boil" in the last example was due to a curious misprint in one lot of bands whereby the "o" and "i" were transposed. In addition to complicating matters for postal employees, this error caused many humorous comments from bird-banding cooperators, one of whom was fearful that the legend would be misunderstood as cooking instructions, since the bands plainly stated: wash, boil and serve.

Lincoln's booklet, *The Migration of North American Birds,* first published in 1935 as USDA Circular 363 and periodically revised, has long been one of the most popular of all government publications. It was revised by Steven B. Peterson in 1979, and reissued as *Migration of Birds.* Lincoln wrote a book in 1939 titled *The Migration of American Birds,* and contributed generously to a number of authoritative books on waterfowl and waterfowl hunting. Notable among these was *American Waterfowl, Their Present Situation and the Outlook for Their Future,* written in 1930 with John C. Phillips, a renowned authority on waterfowl of the world, and especially North America. Their tome reigned as the best overall book on North American waterfowl written up to that time, and it held that position for many years. Lincoln died in 1960 after an illustrious federal career of forty years.

Wetmore examines a mallard and cinnamon teal made helpless by "duck sickness" (avian botulism). Photo courtesy of Smithsonian Institute.

Alexander Wetmore

Henry M. Reeves

Both intellectually and physically, Alexander Wetmore was a giant among men. His prodigious energy, innovative views, and steadfast determination enabled him to rise from the ranks of a field biologist to the highest levels of American ornithology and science. He served as president of the American Ornithologists' Union and later was awarded the title of honorary president on his ninetieth birthday. His professional and administrative capabilities eventually led to his appointment as secretary of the Smithsonian Institution, perhaps America's most prestigious scientific position. He held that post with great distinction, eventually requesting that he be permitted to resume his beloved ornithological studies at the Smithsonian.

Space does not enable us to list the many honors and awards which were conveyed upon Dr. Wetmore, nor list the hundreds of scientific and popular aritcles he authored. Wetmore remained active at the Smithson-

ian until near his death. About two years before his death his wife, Beatrice, lamented that Alex's *daily* output had declined to but a half-dozen pages of scientific manuscript. Few biologists today meet that standard! His last monumental undertaking was the writing of *Birds of the Republic of Panama,* a four-volume treatise, of which about three-fourths was completed before his death.

Our attention now shifts to Wetmore's assignments on waterfowl in the Great Salt Lake Basin of Utah during the period of 1913 through 1916. His may have been the first of countless thousands of field assignments given federal waterfowl biologists. Some of the following information was gleaned from Dr. Wetmore's papers filed in the Smithsonian Archives and from three landmark publications.

"Duck Sickness" Studies

Wetmore, then an assistant biologist with the Biological Survey, was detailed in August 1913 to the Bear River marshes of Utah to investigate serious losses of waterfowl caused by an undertermined agent or organism. Only twenty-seven years old, Wetmore had already completed a number of important biological assignments for the USBS. Sick and dead ducks had been noticed in the Bear River marshes at the north end of the Great Salt Lake for many years, but it was not until 1910 that the numbers reached epidemic proportions. In 1910 water levels were well below normal. Based on accounts given him. Wetmore wrote of this outbreak: "Many thousand wild ducks died on both the Jordan and Weber [rivers] while on the great mud flat in the Bear River delta the mortality is said to have been almost beyond belief. Dead birds rotting in the sun dotted the water in shallow bays, and long windrows of bodies were blown up on the shorelines and against the rushes. The birds died in such great numbers, and the causes of the mortality were so obscure, that a strong prejudice arose against killing and eating ducks that were apparently healthy."

Conditions ameliorated with fall rains and

rising water levels. Mortalities the following year were far less serious but worsened again in 1912. Some 30,000 carcasses were retrieved from the Weber River flats, and 44,462 dead ducks were gathered from the Bear River delta alone during the period of August 22 through September 22.

Wetmore pursued his studies of the perplexing malady during August of 1913, the late summer of 1914, and during the summer and fall of 1915 and 1916. His final report, *The Duck Sickness in Utah*, was published as USDA Bulletin No. 672 on June 21, 1918. It was the federal government's first comprehensive study of disease among waterfowl.

A thorough scientist, Wetmore gathered much information from other regions of the West where the same or similar malady had caused massive waterfowl mortality. During November of 1914 he visited Tulare Lake and Owens Lake, California, where losses to a similar agent had occurred, and in 1915 he visited afflicted areas of Montana. Wetmore quickly noted that in all cases the losses were associated with lowering water levels during the late summer and fall.

Wetmore's investigations entailed long hours in the field under most arduous working conditions, including high temperatures, a scorching sun, soft marsh bottoms and shallow water, lack of shade, shelter, and water, and insects. On May 15, 1916, he

Alexander Wetomre and A. K. Fisher gathering sick ducks on the Bear River Marshes in September 1914. Photo courtesy of Smithsonian Institution.

activated the Bear River Field Laboratory, indeed an impressive name for a most unimpressive building by today's standards. He also constructed pens for holding the sick or control birds needed for pursuing his disease studies by means of the classic scientific approach.

Wetmore began by describing the symptoms characteristic of "duck sickness." The following excerpt from his description illustrates Wetmore's attention to close observation and detail:

> One important external symptom, easily overlooked, remains to be mentioned. Besides upper and lower eyelids birds possess a third eyelid, or nictitating membrane, that lies concealed at the lower angle of the anterior corner of the eye. In winking, this membrane is drawn rapidly back across the eyeball to the posterior corner. In birds with duck sickness paralysis early affects the muscle (the pyramidalis) controlling this third eyelid, so that its action is more or less weakened. Winking is very slow at first, then the nictitating membrane can come back only part way across the rounded eyeball. Gradually the action of the muscle lessens, until finally the third lid lies motionless in its normal position at the anterior canthus of the eye. To test the activity of this membrane it is necessary only to hold the bird's head firmly and then with some slender object, to touch gently the eyeball near the posterior corner and observe the action of the third lid. When this is unaffected it will spring back at once, perhaps several times, in an effort to protect the sensitive surface of the eyeball. In birds with the duck sickness it operates as has just been described. This one reaction serves as a ready means of distinguishing the duck sickness from any other diseased condition of waterfowl known to the writer.

Wetmore eventually determined that duck sickness was fatal to at least thirty-six species of birds inhabiting the Bear River marshes, and that at least sixteen other specimens may have died of the same sickness. At least ten species of waterfowl fell victim to the disease. Wetmore determined that the green-winged teal was the most vulnerable, followed closely by the pintail, and in turn by the mallard, spoon-bill (shoveller), and cinnamon teal. Sick gadwalls and widgeons were seldom found.

When recognized medical means of transmitting the malady from a sick to an apparently healthy bird failed, Wetmore concluded that the sickness was not contagious. Nor could he isolate any visible disease organism.

Controlled experiments led him to eliminate several suspected causes of duck sickness. These included: sulphurous or sulphuric acid arising from smelters near Salt Lake City, waste water from the settling ponds of nearby sugar factories, sewage, parasitic nematodes, and arsenic poisoning.

Unfortunately, Wetmore's investigations led him astray at this point, and he unequivocally concluded that "the duck sickness in Utah is caused by the toxin action of certain soluble salts found in alkali. In other words, it may be said that it is due to poisoning by alkali, as that term is used in the West. By actual experiment it has been found that the duck sickness may be caused by the chlorides of calcium and magnesium."

Wetmore went on to state that he could predict the timing and location of an outbreak by observing strong winds that caused flooding or exposure of mud flats.

While Wetmore was correct in identifying the environmental situation conducive to an outbreak of duck sickness, he failed to find the causative agent known as *Clostridium botulinum* Type C, which thrived in the same environment and whose toxin causes the disease widely known to today's waterfowl biologists as botulism.

Wetmore's experiments led him to find an effective means of treating sick birds. He states, "Birds with duck sickness recover in a short time (unless too far gone) when placed on water that is moderately fresh." Of 1,211 sick ducks of seven species placed on fresh water, 77 percent recovered. Anxious to determine whether the apparently recovered birds would survive in the wild, Wetmore banded them with aluminum bands bearing the bureau's designation and address. This leads us to the second pioneering waterfowl investigation undertaken by Wetmore at Bear River.

1979-80 Green-winged teal *by Kenneth L. Michaelsen*

Of the 994 ducks banded, recovery reports were eventually received for 174, or 17 percent. Wetmore reported upon the results of his pioneering efforts in USDA Bulletin No. 1145. His analysis of resulting data focused upon the recovery locations and times, and implied routes of migration of the ducks banded at Bear River. He noted, for example, that many of the banded green-winged teal evidently wintered in California; many pintails also wintered in the Central Valley of California, but others were reported from widely distributed locations including Arizona, New Mexico, Texas, Oklahoma, Nebraska, Missouri, Montana, and Saskatchewan; and that although the banded redheads were harvested heavily near the banding location, others were taken in southern Idaho and a few east of the Rocky Mountains, including one from Texas. Wetmore cautioned, "In considering these records it is to be borne in mind that many of the birds banded at the mouth of Bear River, Utah, were individuals that had not bred there."

Wetmore noted that the proportions of birds that were recovered and reported varied by species. The recovery notes are summarized as follows: mallard, 30 percent; redhead, 21 percent; gadwall, 24 percent; shoveler, 19 percent; pintail 15 percent; green-winged teal, 15 percent; and cinnamon teal, 11 percent. Although Wetmore did not observe that these differences may have reflected differences in shooting pressure and vulnerability to hunting, he did forsee that the distribution of recoveries by years following banding reflected survival.

Wetmore modestly reported that his work indicated that "results may be obtained from work in banding birds of this family." Little did he imagine at that time that banding would become one of the most important tools available to biologists in ascertaining the population characteristics of North American waterfowl. Banding was eventually to provide vital information on waterfowl migration and movements; homing; harvest distribution by time and place; differential vulnerability by age and sex cohorts; survival and harvest rates; and, when used with harvest and band-reporting information, a means of indirectly estimating population sizes. George Jonkel, chief of the Bird Banding Laboratory, reported that as of August of 1979, 3,181,952 mallards alone had been banded in North America, and from these, 485,314 recoveries had materialized. Altogether, more than 34 million birds of all species had been banded by August of 1979.

Lead Poisoning

While others, including W. L. McAtee of the Biological Survey in 1908, had written about the poisoning of waterfowl from ingesting lead shot, it again fell to Alexander Wetmore to undertake the first investigations of the malady using a scientific approach.

In his classic report *Lead Poisoning in Waterfowl,* published in 1919 as USDA Bulletin No. 793, Wetmore stated:

> "Lead poisoning in various species of wild ducks and other waterfowl has recently attracted attention among persons interested in game birds in the United States. Though for a number of years this disease has been reported in periodicals devoted to sport, and from other sources, it is little recognized and understood, and few sportsmen have knowledge of it. Already it has caused the loss of a considerable number of waterfowl each year, and there is no doubt that as time goes on it will assume greater importance. Lead poisoning in waterfowl has its origin in the large quantity of expended shot that from year to year is deposited in the mud about shooting points and blinds in marshes, shallow bays, and lakes. Many birds find and swallow these leaden pellets while searching for food, and become seriously affected by the poison thus taken. Present knowledge indicates that the mallard, canvasback, and pintail ducks and whistling swans have suffered most, but a number of other species will probably be included in the list when the matter is more fully investigated."

Banding Studies

In 1914 the federal government had not yet become involved in the banding of birds, and the relatively little banding activity that was underway then was being coordinated by various ornithological organizations on a regional basis. Recognizing the potential of banding techniques for waterfowl, Wetmore arranged to have aluminum bands, which had originally been manufactured for poultry use, stamped with the designation and address of the Biological Survey. Each band carried its own serial number. During the period 1914-16, Wetmore banded 1,241 birds of twenty three species. These included 336 green-winged teal, 239 redheads, 221 pintails, 72 mallards, 48 shovelers, 45 cinnamon teal, 17 gadwalls, and 2 ruddy ducks. All but the redheads had recovered from duck sickness before being released.

About the redheads, Wetmore wrote: "Though like some other children in their lack of respect for parental guidance and opinion, young redheads are gregarious and seek others of the season's hatching, so that they ordinarily travel in company. These inexperienced birds, as they passed the duck pens where birds convalescent from the duck sickness were confined, came over in search of company, and clambered out on shore in an attempt to join the ducks in the cages. Trapping them when they were still unable to fly was an easy matter, so that in 1915 many were captured and 239 were banded and released."

Unfortunately, the poultry bands were subject to wear so that after two years they became thin and friable. Wetmore speculated that most of the bands had been lost after three years. Thus he recommended that the bureau obtain bands having twice the thickness of those employed for poultry. His recommendation was accepted when bands were ordered specifically for use on wild birds.

Wetmore undertook studies of lead poisoning as an adjunct to his duck-sickness studies then under way at Bear River. There he found mallards and pintails, chiefly males, afflicted from June through September. The number that died was considerable, though insignificant when compared with the numbers dying of other diseases.

With characteristic thoroughness, Wetmore reviewed the previous history of lead poisoning in North American waterfowl, the species affected, and described the symptoms in detail. Part of his description of the early symptoms follows:

> A prominent indication of this malady is a paralysis of important muscles, which increases steadily as the ailment progresses. This paralysis seems first to affect the nerves supplying the great muscles of the breast, and in a very short time the birds are unable to fly. Following this the wings begin to droop from the sides. In many cases the extensor muscles supporting the wing tip, that portion of the fore limb homologous with the hand, are seriously affected, and the wing hangs from the carpal joint, a symptom strikingly like 'wrist drop' found in many cases of lead poisoning in man. The wings float loosely on the surface when the affected birds are in the water, and in several cases the tips of the primaries may drag as the bird walks about on the ground. Other muscles are affected as well. When the bird is standing, the breast is depressed and the tail droops.

During routine examinations of gizzards of twenty-eight mallards and ten pintails which had died of lead poisoning at Bear River, Wetmore found a total of 939 lead shot, ranging from fifteen to forty pellets, averaging about twenty-five pellets per bird. He noted that where shot had been in the gizzard for a considerable time it was much worn and in many cases ground down to flattened disks by the action of the stomach muscles and abrasion with grit.

Wetmore initiated controlled studies of penned ducks by inserting lead pellets down the esophagus using a funnel. He found that a dosage of six pellets of number six shot was always fatal, and that two or three pellets sometimes caused death. In one experiment, two mallard were each given one number six shot. One died nine days later while the other eventually recovered. Inasmuch as shot in those days contained small quantities of arsenic as a hardening agent, the question remained as to whether death resulted from the lead or the arsenic. Consequently, Wetmore undertook additional studies involving granulated lead doses, lacking arsenic, in quantities equal to the lead pellets. These experimental ducks died in characteristic fashion, proving that lead was the active agent causing the poisoning. Wetmore suggested that the effects of lead upon female reproduction and virility of offspring might

be of even greater importance than direct mortality, but he was unable to initiate the necessary experiments.

Wetmore then went into the marshes to determine the prevalence of lead shot. He systematically sampled the marsh bottom around a duck blind which had been in use for at least twenty hunting seasons. About ten quarts of silt were examined at each site by filtering through a sieve mesh which retained number seven and larger shot. He found from one to thirteen pellets in samples collected from 200 to 230-yard distances from the blind. At other stations, twenty to twenty-two shot were taken from three samples. He noted that the mass of the shot had settled through the upper layers of soft mud and lay at a depth of ten to twelve inches. Most of the shot recovered was "soft" although the shot type then in current use was "chilled." This observation suggested that spent shot remained in the marsh for long periods of time, and that its prevalence would increase with time. Wetmore speculated that lead poisoning among waterfowl would increase, and likely would be detected in new locations. His predictions have been substantiated.

Wetmore was unable to recommend a practical remedy to lead poisoning. He noted that ducks sometimes feed in soft mud at depths of twelve to sixteen inches, thus negating harrowing as a means of causing lead shot to sink beyond their reach. Sometimes he successfully treated poisoned birds with a solution of sixty grams of magnesic sulphate in ten quarts of water, but large-scale application of this technique was not feasible. Apparently the use of a nontoxic shot substance did not come to mind or else was dismissed as not being possible because no suitable alternative material was available. Nonetheless, Wetmore's lead shot studies at Bear River marked the beginning of the third major area of waterfowl investigation which continues to this day.

Early Inventory and Survey Work

The observant and industrious Wetmore

even found time to write of the number and abundance of waterfowl, their food supplies, and the general conditions under wich they lived at Bear River marshes. His studies during 1914-16 surely represent the most careful field studies up to that time of waterfowl on those marshes, and perhaps in other local areas of the United States, if not North America.

During the period May 15 through June 26, Wetmore and his assistant, T.E. Griesa, attempted to inventory the numbers of waterfowl pairs on their area. They estimated that about 3,650 pairs of ducks of eight species bred in the Bear River marshes. Nearly half were redheads (1,725 pairs), followed by cinnamon teal (800 pairs), mallards (300 pairs), shovelers (250 pairs), gadwalls, ruddy ducks, pintails, green-winged teal, widgeon, and blue-winged teal. They also estimated that about 100 pairs of Canada geese bred there as well. Was their systematic inventory of breeding ducks the first undertaken on a North American marsh? Surely it was the first such breeding population estimate to be accompanied by confidence limits — as Wetmore states, "allowance being made for not more than 40 percent of error."

Not content with these estimates, Wetmore proceeded to calculate the numbers of waterfowl produced. He estimated that from 25,000 to 30,000 ducks were raised in an average season, as in 1916. Was this our first waterfowl production estimate for a discrete unit of habitat? Despite the impressive numbers, Wetmore stated that the Bear River marshes attracted even greater numbers of waterfowl that flocked there from far distances to molt. Male pintails were particularly evident among the early arriving molters. He wrote, "In 1916 pintails appeared even earlier in the season; on June 7 about 100 drakes were found in South Bay, while on the following day their numbers had been augmented to about 1,000."

Wetmore estimated that only 2-3 females were among a flock of nearly 3,000 males observed on June 14. Wetmore recorded many other interesting aspects of waterfowl movement, migration, and behavior during his Bear River days.

His 1921 report also contains much information on the plants at Bear River having value to waterfowl. Among these, he identified four submerged aquatics, three floating aquatics, and forty-three "shore and marsh plants." He regarded sago pondweed *(Potamogeton pectinatus)* and "bayonet grass" *(Scirpus paludosus)* as the two most important seed-producing plants for waterfowl. Further, he recognized that although cattails *(Typha* spp.) and cane *(Phragmites* sp.) had value as cover they had no food value. In general, Wetmore's assessments of the value of plants to waterfowl at Bear River remain valid today.

Edward R. Kalmbach

Henry M. Reeves

As we have seen, Alexander Wetmore attributed large-scale loss of ducks on western marshes to "duck sickness," which he correctly attributed to a toxin. However, he mistakenly concluded that the alkalis so prevalent in western marshes produced the toxin. As time elapsed, others began to suspect that the alkalis were not the true source of the virulent toxin. To clarify the uncertainty, the Biological Survey renewed its study of the disease in 1927 and during 1929-31. In 1927 Charles C. Sperry was assigned to the new investigation and he established a field station at Klamath Falls, Oregon, near the fabulous marshes of the Klamath Basin. In 1929 cooperative investigations began as scientists of the Bureau of Animal Industry (USAI) and the USBS sought to find the true cause of duck die-offs.

Late July and early August of 1930, unexpected results were attained by experimentally feeding gulls on the body tissues of birds dying of duck sickness. It became evident that a malady akin to duck sickness could be produced by feeding such material after it had undergone decomposition. By early October, L. T. Giltner, of the USAI, was able to identify a bacterium, *Clostridium botulinum* type C, from material supplied by Klamath Falls laboratory. All types of *B. Clostridium* are saprophytes, which live and produce toxin in the presence of dead organic matter. The bacteria, washed free of toxins, are harmless to birds. It is only the preformed toxin, developed outside the body of the bird, which is harmful. Botulism is not contagious as it cannot be passed from one living thing to another; it can be contracted only through the assimilation of food and water.

The type C disease organism had been known in the United States as a frequent cause of "limberneck" in poultry and forage poisoning in livestock.

Work at Klamath Falls then shifted to determining the relative susceptibility of the different species of ducks to the disease, the suitability of various body tissues as incubating media, the effects of physical and chemical agencies on the toxicity of the laboratory cultures, and learning what factors appeared to favor production of the toxin in marshes frequented by ducks. The type C bacterium forms spores that may persist from one season to the next for years, to develop, multiply, and produce toxin again when environmental conditions are suitable.

E. R. Kalmbach was the key Biological Survey scientist who carried on detailed studies of botulism once the causative organism had been discovered. During the summer of 1931, Millard F. Gunderson, a bacteriologist, was employed by the Bureau to work with Kalmbach in Klamath Falls. Together they extended laboratory findings to waterfowl habitats of the western marshes. Information gleaned from many sources indicated that diseases like those found at Bear River and in the Klamath Basin had been reported from broad areas of the western United States, prairie Canada, and central Mexico. Wetmore, during travels in Uruguay, found dead and sick water birds which appeared to be afflicted with botulism. He also gathered additional information on the magnitude of duck losses. These frequently numbered in the tens of thousands, with perhaps the largest being the quarter-million waterfowl that perished in the Bear River marshes in 1932. Kalmbach and Gunderson increased the number of species known to be susceptible to botulism from thirty-six to sixty-nine species of twenty-one avian families.

Laboratory tests indicated that the domestic pigeon was about 175 times as susceptible to botulism as the green-winged teal, which was the most susceptible of all duck species tested. Consequently, pigeons were used by Gunderson in his laboratory experiments. In general, shallow-water feeding species of ducks were more vulnerable than diving duck species which usually frequent deep waters. Redhead ducklings were an exception, probably because they usually fed in shallow waters. The investigators found that as few as ten small dead sarcophaged larvae, weighing together only one-tenth of a gram, contained enough toxin to kill a male pintail four days later. Fifteen somewhat larger sarcophaged larvae fed to each of two mallards caused death in nineteen and thirty-six hours, respectively.

Fortunately, ducks that died of botulism were not harmful to humans. As Kalmbach wrote, "In the days of market hunting in California, it was common knowledge that unscrupulous hunters made it a practice to gather birds affected with or recently dying of the disease, fire lead shot into their bodies, and offer them for sale."

Kalmbach and Gunderson described the symptoms of botulism in waterfowl, analyzed the pathology of the disease, demonstrated the disease in both experimental and wild waterfowl, identified the factors causing or influencing the disease in the wild, and discussed remedial measures for preventing or reducing an outbreak. They found that the environmental factors conducive to an outbreak were quite complex. These factors included, besides the presence of the causative organism, the prevalence of dead organic matter, alkalinity and salinity, temperature, water level and water movement, abundance of waterfowl, and species of potential waterfowl victims.

Major remedial measures included water manipulation to prevent the development of micro-environments required for the production of the toxin, frightening waterfowl from areas conducive to toxin production, and removing carcasses of dead birds which became hosts to the botulism organism.

The latter recommendations have been applied widely by waterfowl managers of western marshes used by waterfowl. The numbers of water birds saved by these preventive measures is not known, although the total must be enormous in the half century since biologists determined the true cause of western duck sickness.

With the advent of the drought over the prairie pothole region in the 1930s, attention shifted to various factors contributing to the demise of North American waterfowl. In those early days of wildlife management, undue emphasis was often placed on predation as the cause for reduced wildlife numbers. Consequently, considerable attention focused on the crow as a predator of waterfowl nests and young. Accordingly, E. R. Kalmbach was assigned the task of evaluating the relationship of the crow to waterfowl. Kalmbach was a natural choice because earlier he had published his comprehensive food habit studies of the crow in the United States and had recently completed definitive studies of botulism on waterfowl.

Kalmbach initiated his field studies in 1934 in three locations in Alberta and Saskatchewan. These areas were selected because of the presence of both crows and waterfowl, and because they had different habitat conditions. At Waterhen Lake, Saskatchewan, crows were very abundant and waterfowl nesting was chiefly confined to ditch banks, thus the duck nests were concentrated and very vulnerable to crow predation. In the Cooking Lake District, southeast of Edmonton, Alberta, waterfowl nested about the periphery of small islands, while crows nested in trees on the same islands. In the Prince Albert District, Saskatchewan, the study area was situated in typical pothole country, where both crows and nesting ducks were widely distributed, in contrast to the concentrations on the first two study areas. Field observations were continued through the 1935 season.

During the course of his studies, Kalmbach recorded data from several hundred nests, compared the breeding ranges of several species of waterfowl with the range of the crow, and identified specific conditions influencing crow predation on waterfowl. He noted that crows tended to occur in greatest numbers in the areas of extensive agriculture, and that in the northern forests they existed only around settlements and clearings.

During the two field seasons, Kalmbach obtained data on 512 duck nests. His study was the second of many waterfowl nesting studies that have been undertaken on North

American ducks (Logan Bennett began his nesting study of blue-winged teal in Iowa in 1932). Included were 188 mallard, 94 lesser scaup, 76 blue-winged teal, and 52 pintail nests, with the remainder from nine other species. Kalmbach noted that 250 nests, or 49 percent, hatched successfully. Overall, 156 nests (31 percent) were destroyed by crows. The intensity of crow predation varied by study area. It was greatest where duck nesting was concentrated and crows were abundant, and lowest in the pothole study area.

Kalmbach also found that crow destruction of duck nests decreased from 47 percent during the first half of the duck-nesting season to 22 percent during the second, possibly due to declining food requirements of nesting crows. Somewhat surprisingly, "poorly" concealed duck nests were 63 percent successful in producing young, while nests whose concealment was rated as "fair", "good," or "excellent" were less successful. Kalmbach speculated that hens which conceal their nests poorly may be more aggressive in defending them from predators.

Kalmbach also examined stomachs of crows, finding that seventeen of twenty-five stomachs of adult crows contained shell fragments that in at least four instances (and probably twelve others) were of duck eggs. Shell remnants were found in twenty-five of forty-three nesting crows; of these, seven were definitely and five tentatively identified as duck eggshells. Downy feathers of ducklings were also found in three instances. Kalmbach was extremely careful not to assign guilt to the crow unless the evidence was conclusive.

While Kalmbach recognized that crows were detrimental to waterfowl production in local areas, he also knew that waterfowl are subject to a number of other decimating factors, and that their annual production usually offsets natural losses. He recommended that if any crow control were to be exercised, it should be confined to federal, state or privately managed areas to which crows have been attracted in unduly large numbers by the presence of nesting waterfowl and on which the consequent delicate problem of control might be kept in experienced hands.

Ed Kalmbach was a self-made man who inspired others by the excellence of his work and his leadership. Despite the lack of a formal education (he never went to college), he became director at the Denver Wildlife Research Center and was awarded a PhD degree from the University of Colorado.

Waldo L. McAtee

Henry M. Reeves

One of the major areas of investigation undertaken early by the Biological Survey dealt with the food habits of migratory birds. Thus it was only natural, when increasing concern for waterfowl after the turn of the century led to passage of migratory bird protection legislation in 1913 (Federal Migratory Bird Act) and 1918 (Migratory Bird Treaty Act), that there would be renewed interest in the foods of waterfowl. A number of federal biologists, including Clarence Cottam, Neil Hotchkiss, Douglas C. Mabbot, Alexander C. Martin, Franklin P. Metcalf, Arnold L. Nelson, Harry C. Oberholser, Fran M. Uhler, and Alexander Wetmore made great contributions to our knowledge of waterfowl foods and plants useful to wildfowl. The dean of this group of specialists, however, was undoubtedly Waldo L. McAtee.

McAtee was from the old school of field naturalists, whose interests ranged widely through the animal and plant kingdoms. An extremely prolific writer, McAtee's technical writings have been estimated to number between 1,200 and 1,300, plus some 6,053 abstracts written during his editorship of the *Wildlife Review*, the first sustained periodical summarizing current wildlife literature. In addition, he edited some fourteen books, including several early standards in the burgeoning field of wildlife management, and for several years served as technical advisor for all publications of the USBS. He was a key organizer of the Wildlife Society, and fell heir to editing the new society's *Journal of Wildlife Management* for five years. His booklet, *Local Names of Migratory Game Birds*, illustrates his versatile knowledge and served as the standard reference in the early years following passage of the Migratory Bird Treaty Act, when waterfowl were locally known by many names. Between his serious writings he found time to write of American folklore and even compose poetry. He was indeed a man of the pen and book.

McAtee began his food habit studies in 1903 while a summer employee of the Biological Survey in Washington, D.C., between his junior and senior years at Indiana University. In 1916 McAtee was chosen to head the new Division of Food Habits Research. His early food habit studies, especially of songbirds, required that he learn to identify various insects, usually by bits of wings, tibia, and other fragmented parts. In the process, he became an expert entomologist. Alone, or in conjunction with collaborators, he described some twenty genera and 466 species of insects previously unknown to science. A few new fishes were thrown in for good measure! In recognition of his services to taxonomy, thirteen species and two genera of insects, plus a plant, were named for him. Aside from his duties with the Biological Survey, McAtee served as acting curator of Hemiptera (the "true" bugs) for the U.S. National Museum. He was equally proficient in identifying plant items in birds' diets, and it is said that his phenomenal knowledge of seeds and fruits was a never-ending source of wonder to his colleagues.

But it is to McAtee's contributions to waterfowl that we direct our attention. Although wild rice *(Zizania aquatica)* and wild celery *(Vallisneria spiralis)* had long been recognized as important waterfowl foods, especially along the Atlantic Coast, the value of the pondweeds *(Potamogeton* spp.) had more or less been overlooked until McAtee's studies. In his initial report, he determined that the pondweed seeds comprised 14 percent of the food items found in the stomachs of several hundred ducks of sixteen species. They, along with the seeds and sprouts of wild rice and the seed pods and tubers of wild celery, provided one-fourth of all the food material found in the ducks' stomachs. The proportions of foods, of course, varied by duck species, locations, and times of collection. McAtee observed that because wild rice seed often has a germination of up to eighteen months, young shoots and germinated seed may be found in the duck stomachs at practically all seasons. He noted that wild celery, whose scientific name has the same derivation as the canvasback's *(Athya valisneria),* comprised about one-fourth of the food consumed by cans.

Interest in the first report on waterfowl foods prompted the USBS, personified by McAtee, to embark upon a series of additional reports on aquatic foods of waterfowl. These included a 1914 study of five duck foods, a 1915 study of eleven duck foods, a long report on the food habits of the mallard in 1918, and a manual on the propagation of duck foods. His book, *Wildfowl Food Plants,* probably the first on the subject in North America, appeared in 1939.

The food habits and plant propagation information published by McAtee and his associates was extremely useful in the intensive management of waterfowl on the many new federal and state refuges, and hunting clubs. Knowledge of the importance of various aquatic plants to waterfowl enabled biologists to assess the values of marshes and wetlands for waterfowl and, where possible, to manage those habitats more intensively for ducks and geese. McAtee is credited with raising the study of food habits of vertebrates from a primitive beginning with an uncertain future to a status of scientific excellence.

One biographer, John K. Terres, writes that McAtee often paraphrased the lines of Thoreau from *Walden,* in reference to apparent biological truths, "What everybody echoes or in silence passes as true today may turn out to be falsehood tomorrow, mere smoke of opinion . . ."

Late in life, McAtee was asked to comment on the future of the professional naturalist, who once represented the bulk of the biologists employed in the Biological Survey and its predecessor organizations. One senses that McAtee lamented the passing of the "naturalist" and his replacement by "specialized" biologists in his letter to Terres in 1956: "In this technical age there are many niches into which biological specialists can fit. But for [those] with a hankering to be an old-fashioned naturalist, it appears to me that museums offer the only hope. Even there, the candidate will have to specialize more or less, but in time may be able to make the job over to his heart's desire . . . A general naturalist can be as much at home as anyone in the living world and can lead the happiest life possible to man."

McAtee's colleagues were prolific in their praise of his talents. E. A. Preble, his field companion of fifty-one years said, "Mac is better informed on more groups of organisms than any man in the history of the Bureau of Biological Survey and its successor the Fish and Wildlife Service . . ." Perhaps no compliment is higher than that of Dr. Ira N. Gabrielson, then retired director of the USFWS, who stated that McAtee was the most versatile biologist he had ever known.

Wells W. Cooke

Henry M. Reeves

Wells W. Cook was America's foremost student of bird migration for several decades spanning the turn of the century. Born in Massachusetts in 1858, his preacher father moved to Ripon, Wisconsin, six years later. There young Cooke grew up and went to college. His interest in birds grew with him and continued wherever he went. His first teaching job was on the White Earth Indian Reservation in Minnesota, where he published a paper on bird nomenclature of the Chippewa Indians. Again teaching at an Indian school, he moved to Oklahoma and published on the winter birds of that state. During the next sixteen years Cooke served as a lecturer and professor of agriculture at colleges in Vermont, Colorado, and Pennsylvania as his interest in and knowledge of bird migration increased.

In 1881-1882, Cooke invited some 170 bird observers to send him records of wintering birds and dates of spring arrivals, and in 1885 he published a report on bird migration in the Mississippi Valley. He also published articles on agriculture during the next few years. When the American Ornithologist's Union was established in 1883, a committee was set up to assist Cooke in broadening his migration studies continent-wide. On July 1, 1901, an appointment in the U.S. Biological Survey permitted him to work full-time on his first love, bird migration and distribution.

The government's first publication on bird migration was printed in 1888. Wells W. Cooke's *Report on Bird Migration in the Mississippi Valley in the Years 1884 and 1885,* represented a cooperative endeavor between the Division of Economic Ornithology, of the USDA, and the Committee on Bird Migration of the American Ornithologists' Union. The American Ornithologists' Union organized in September of 1883, recognized bird migration as one of the most fertile fields for study. Much of Cooke's report presents information on bird migration in the Missis-

ippi Valley as recorded by some 170 observers during the two years, while the remainder addresses additional special studies and theoretical questions relating to bird migration.

Cooke believed that bird migration initially represented "intelligent movements which through repetition became habitual, and the habit was transmitted from parent to offspring until it has become as we see it now, the governing impulse of the bird's life." Cooke further states: "In the study of the yearly cycle of migrations there are two movements for which we must seek the cause — the restless pushing northward in the spring, in spite of cold, rain, sleet, and snow; and the southward journey in the fall. We have already stated that the northward movement is caused by a strong home love — an overpowering desire to be once more among the familiar scenes of the previous summer. The return movement is obviously the result of two causes — the approach of winter and the failure of the food supply."

Of the two, Cooke believed that food supply was more important than winter weather. He offered as evidence, observations of ducks (and snipe) remaining throughout the winter in Wyoming, near hot springs, whose warmth keeps the neighboring waters and ground from freezing. Nonetheless, Cooke recognized that weather influenced bird migration, and that each species exhibited characteristics of when, where, and how fast it migrated.

H. W. Henshaw, acting chief, of the USBS, wrote the following on July 10, 1906, to the Honorary James Wilson, then secretary of agriculture:

> Formerly abundant over the whole of the United States, waterfowl are steadily diminishing in numbers, and some species appear to be threatened with extinction in the near future. Their value for food is great, and they have formed in the past, and for all future time should continue to form; a valuable asset and an important source of revenue to the several States which harbor them. The preservation of the numerous species of ducks, geese, and swans is becoming an important matter of legislative enactment, and the present report is intended to furnish information as to present

©F.L. Jaques

range, abundance, and migration of the several species with reference to practical legislation.

With these remarks, he transmitted Wells W. Cooke's *Distribution and Migration of North American Ducks, Geese, and Swans,* published in 1906 by the Biological Survey as Bulletin Number 26. Cooke's monumental undertaking is notable in at least three respects. First, it summarized the vast accumulation of waterfowl migration and abundant data which hundreds of cooperators had reported to the Biological Survey, plus published records, thus forming the foundation necessary to support legislation aimed at improving the welfare of waterfowl. In addition, it provided information regarding the overall status and trend of the waterfowl resource, and factors affecting it. And finally, it apparently was the federal government's first major scientific publication limited solely to waterfowl.

Cooke identified the principal causes of the diminished numbers of waterfowl as "market hunting, spring shooting, and the destruction of the breeding grounds for farming purposes." He believed that the major destructive force up to about twenty years of his report was market hunting. After about 1885 the loss of wetland habitat became more important, due to the settlement of the extensive waterfowl breeding area west of the Great Lakes stimulated by the "invasion" of the railroads. He observed that the human population of North Dakota had increased many fold from 1880 to 1900, while the vast prairies of Canada were being changed to wheat fields. Although Cooke's recommendations included strict prohibition of shooting during the spring and during the breeding season, he stopped short of advocating total prohibition of the sale of waterfowl — just its transport to other states for sale.

In commenting on bird migration in 1906, Cooke stated: "Probably in no other region in the world do so large a proportion of the birds migrate approximately north and south as in North America north of the Gulf of Mexico. The outlines of the coast, the courses of the large rivers and the trend of the mountain chains united to make northward and southward migration easy and natural. In the case of ducks, however, there is a factor that causes thousands of individuals of several species to take a northwest and southeast route."

Cooke's latter comment referred chiefly to redheads, canvasbacks, greater scaup and, to a lesser extent, seven other duck species that breed in the mid continent but mostly winter along the mid-Atlantic Coast. He believed that their southeasterly fall migration was influenced by the corridor of marshes, lakes, and rivers through the Great Lakes Region. Lakes Region.

Cooke also observed that some blue-winged teal nesting in the prairie region of North America crossed the equator to winter in central South America; some pintail ducks from Alaska and Asia wintered in the Hawaiian Islands; and brant of the Atlantic Flyway returned north by a different route than the one followed in southward migration. These accurate conclusions are notable by their early date, especially when one considers that banding data were not yet available.

Cooke methodically classified the seventy-one species of waterfowl he attributed to North America by distribution patterns. Today's ornithologists would modify those tallies because of changes in avian taxonomy (for example, Cooke recognized two forms of the black duck but only four subspecies of Canada geese), and because of more recent information on the distribution of waterfowl in North America.

Nonetheless, Cooke's contributions are significant. They marked the beginning of systematic classification of North American waterfowl by distributional and migrational patterns, elements so essential to the development of enlightened domestic legislation and international agreements.

Edward A. Preble

Henry M. Reeves

E. A. Preble was one of the Biological Survey's early biologists assigned the task of gathering comprehensive biological information from remote and relatively little-explored areas of the United States, Canada, and Mexico. Our interest in Preble stems from his early travels and observations in the Hudson Bay region in 1900, and in the Northwest Territory of Canada during 1901, 1903, 1904, and 1907. Preble returned to the Northwest Territory in 1934 with Luther J. Goldman, and thus was able to compare the status of waterfowl with the levels he had observed some three decades earlier. He was often accompanied by a younger brother, Alfred E., who served as his assistant.

Preble's observations in the Hudson Bay region during the summer of 1900 were reported in *A Biological Investigation of the Hudson Bay Region,* published by the USBS as North American Fauna No. 22 (Preble 1902). His bulletin describes earlier biological findings there from travels and reports by Edwards, Hutchins, Hearne, Franklin, Parry, Swainson, Richardson, King, Rae, Gray, Murray, Mackenzie, Bell, Macoun, and others. Ornithologists will recognize among these individuals the source of several common names of North American species and subspecies of birds.

Preble explained the justification of the investigation as follows: "As time went on, however, less attention was given to the fauna of this region, while most other parts of North America were ransacked for natural history material, so that the close of the nineteenth century found Hudson Bay one of the most neglected fields of modern zoological research. Some specimens, originally described as poor specimens, and in the loose and inaccurate style of a hundred years ago, were known by these descriptions alone, while others were represented in museums only by poorly stuffed and faded specimens, entirely inadequate to meet requirements of modern scientific methods."

Preble, his brother, and two Indian guides and boatmen, paddled from Norway House, at the northern end of Lake Winnipeg, down the Nelson River to York Factory, on Hudson Bay, where they exchanged their canoe for a sailboat. This they sailed to Fort Churchill, exploring the "Barren Grounds" enroute. They hastily retraced their route as autumn approached, arriving at Norway House on September 19, 1900, after a water journey of more than twelve hundred miles. Preble summarized his observation of birds seen during the expedition by species. His following note on the mallard illustrates how these records were assembled:

> Anas boschas Linn. Mallard.
>
> First seen near Pine Lake June 28, where a female followed by a brood of young was noted, and one of the brood collected. An adult female was taken near Oxford House July 3, and between this point and York Factory the species was several times observed. One was seen on the marsh at Beacon Point, near York Factory, July 13, one on a small pond on the Barren Grounds north of Seal River August 18, and a female with a brood of unfledged young on Steel River August 31. During the first half of September the species was seen almost daily. A large flock was noted on Trout River September 9, and many were observed on the Echimamish September 14 and 15. During the first part of the journey, when we were going north, we saw several females with broods, and it was noticeable that the young, when startled, invariably took to the woods, where they easily concealed themselves. On our return we started up several large flocks, but more commonly found just three in a flock. The name given to this duck throughout the whole region visited is "stock duck." The catalogue of birds in the U.S. National Museum collection shows that specimens were collected at Moose Factory in 1881, and the bird undoubtedly occurs throughout the wooded portion of the region.

Preble noted that the first man to enter the Mackenzie region was Samuel Hearn, of the Hudson's Bay Company, in 1770-71. He was followed by Alexander Mackenzie of the Northwest Company in 1789, and Sir John Franklin's expeditions, the first occurring in 1820. In 1859, the Smithsonian Institution sent Robert Kennicott to the Mackenzie region for three years, during which thousands of specimens were collected and forwarded to the National Museum. Preble observed that one reason for his own assignment to the region in 1901 was to obtain representative collections of its mammals, birds, and plants. Preble noted, "This was the more necessary since the early material, consisting mainly of alcoholic specimens [sic] or skins without flesh measurements is not now in a condition satisfactory for comparison."

Preble's accounts of long, arduous days of canoeing, portaging, collecting and preparing specimens, and writing field notes leads one to consider whether there should not be a new Olympic event established. Possibly it could be called Naturalists Afield, and contestants would attempt to duplicate the physical accomplishments of northern field biologists — without the plague of mosquitoes, green-headed flies (locally called "bulldogs"), and "no-see-ums".

Preble wintered at Fort Simpson during 1903-04 but this persevering soul failed to tell us of any particular hardships. In reviewing his field notes, characteristically written with the flourish of most early naturalists, one quickly observes that scientific Latin names of birds and mammals are used throughout to the exclusion of common names.

Preble's notes contain extensive information on the description, distribution, status, and other comments on the many waterfowl species he observed in the Far North. The following quote on lesser snow geese used for food by Eskimos at Fort McPherson may be of interest: "While at Fort McPherson early in July I saw numbers of these geese in possession of the Eskimo. They had been killed on their breeding grounds, about the mouth of the Mackenzie, in June, and preserved by being kept in the water, hanging in bunches from the bow of the boat. When the birds are desired for use the feathers are scraped off and the birds roughly drawn. On account of their high condition at this stage only a slight amount of cooking is required, but during the brief process close proximity to the kettle is undesirable."

Preble reported that although the whistling swan *(Olor columbianus)* was formerly abundant, it was seen then only in small numbers. He relates:

> While the birds were still abundant swan skins formed an important article of trade. I was told that sixty or seventy years ago about 500 were annually traded at the Hudson's Bay Company post at Isle a la Crosse, and that an annual average of 300 skins was obtained at Fort Anderson during the five years of its existence.
>
> MacFarlane states that between 1853 and 1877 the Hudson's Bay Company sold a total of 17,671 swan skins. The number sold annually ranged from 1,312 in 1851 to 122 in 1877.
>
> From 1858 to 1884, inclusive, Athabasca district turned out 2,705 swan skins, nearly all of them from Fort Chipewyan. Mackenzie River district, according to a statement in my possession, supplied 2,500 skins from 1863 to 1883. From 1862 to 1877 Fort Resolution, Great Slave Lake, contributed 798 thereof. For 1889 Athabasca traded but 33, as against 251 skins in 1853. In 1889 and 1890 Isle a la Crosse, headquarters of English River district, sent out two skins for each outfit.
>
> The rapid decrease in numbers of this magnificent bird is well illustrated by these figures.

Preble and Goldman colorfully describe the glaciation of North America which ultimately created the prairie pothole region of western Canada and the north-central United States:

> Let us consider briefly the natural forces that made northern North America the waterfowl nursery to which the shooters of southern North America must always look for the bulk of their supply.
>
> One of the results of the grinding and scouring that took place during the unnumbered centuries of the Ice Age, when almost the entire surface of northern North America, including parts of most of our Northern States, was worked over and subjected to profound alterations, was to convert that great region into one of the most fruitful areas on the globe for the production of waterfowl. Innumerable basins were scooped out of the existing terrain, and the debris that resulted was carried and laid down in irregular mounds and ridges that enclosed and bounded other hollows and potholes. New drainage systems were established . . .
>
> Since the disappearance of the Great Ice sheets [sic], Nature has worked incessantly to plant the land and water areas then left

naked. The shallower lakes have been filled with vegetable mold, and have formed myriads of mossy swamps, or by the action of the sediment-carrying rivers have become vast estuaries. Thousands of large areas, after discharging their surplus waters, hold the residue throughout the summer in their mossy basins — huge sponges that avidly absorb and hold water, but dispense it reluctantly.

In these myriad ponds and marshes, aggregating an area almost beyond calculation, the majority of our most esteemed species of waterfowl nest, a few exclusively, the others in part. The southern fringe of this great nursery has been settled and has suffered from drainage, and the conversion of water areas to planted fields, so that it long ago lost much of its significance as a breeding ground. The part extending from 54 degrees north latitude to the Arctic Ocean remains much in its original state, unvexed by settlement, agriculture, drainage, or drought.

This great area, as I have said, is a vast waterfowl nursery. The main reason is found in the great proportion of the surface that is covered by lakes and marshes that produce a superabundant wealth of food, made possible by the influence of the long hours of sunlight in summer, a factor that speeds up the rate of plant and invertebrate development to a point that seems incredible to one accustomed only to the relative slowness that one obtains in temperate climates. The same favorable conditions of food supply are undoubtedly an important factor in influencing the majority of our shorebirds in their choice of breeding grounds. The principles behind many of these facts, of course, are not new. They were ably pointed out by Sir John Richardson, who was among the first of scientific observers to visit North America, and even before that time were known to students of European botany and zoology.

Following his return to the Northwest Territory, which he had visited three decades earlier, Preble wrote of the decline of waterfowl in the area, based on his personal observations as well as those of natives. He wrote:

When civilized man first entered the region, in quest of furs, scarcely a hundred and fifty years ago, he found waterfowl to be one of the important sources of food for the scattered tribes of natives who had long lived there. The descendants of these people still inhabit the region, but they number so few, considering the vast extent of country available, that their utmost efforts have never constituted a deterrent effect on the waterfowl worth considering. With the increasing advantages that commerce has brought, the natives, as well as the few whites who conduct the trading stores and the missions, have depended from year to year less and less on waterfowl. It is fortunate that this has been possible, for among those who give serious thought to the subject the conviction is universal that there has been a steady and serious diminution in all species.

The fact that formerly it was the custom about the delta [Athabaska Delta], as it was at all favorably situated northern posts, to kill as many ducks and geese as possible toward the close of the autumn migration, and to salt and freeze them for winter consumption, emphasizes the decline in abundance. Up to within a few years, geese and ducks were commonly taken for winter use, though in greatly decreased numbers, but the practice is now almost abandoned, for the simple reason that the results do not repay the expenditure of labor and ammunition. The birds thus obtained were drawn in part from stock locally raised, but mainly from those that were migrating southward from the vast untouched nurseries farther north. The reason for this very evident local diminution, of course, is found in the tremendous general decrease that North America's waterfowl have suffered, especially during the past 30 years, in large part because of the ever-increasing numbers of those who hunt for sport and profit, mainly in the United States. This general diminution is so well known as not to require further emphasis.

[Nonetheless, Preble continues:] After carefully considering all the circumstances attending our present study, such as the stage of water, the relative shortness of our stay, and the extent of our facilities for visiting the actual haunts of the birds, I am convinced that waterfowl as a whole are now not more than 40 percent as numerous in this region as they were 30 years ago. In general, those species that have the large breeding ranges — the mallard and the pintail for instance — have held up their numbers better than the others.

It might be thought that valuable testimony on this point might be gotten from the older residents. But these are now few in number, and the number who are in position to give valuable testimony is smaller still. Many are unobservant; others so far fail to grasp the signficance of one's inquires that they can render no help. A great proportion of the residents, of course, are too young, or have so recently come to the region, that their opinions are worthless. Anyone who realizes the lack of knowledge possessed by the average gunner of our own land regarding the comparative status of the birds of his own locality, will not be surprised at this statement.

Of those with whom I discussed the matter I would consider Pierre Mercredie the best qualified to speak. He was born on Lake Athabaska nearly 80 years ago, and has lived practically all his life at Fort Chipewyan. About 50 years were passed in the service of the Hudson's Bay Company, and for a long period he was in charge of the local post. His reading has been fairly wide, his memory is excellent, and his probity unchallenged. He attests to a great diminution of both ducks and geese, especially during the last 30 to 35 years, but would not hazard estimates, except that he is certain that between 1913 and 1929, when he was away from Lake Athabaska, geese of all kinds diminished 75 percent about Fort Chipewyan. He based his judgement on the rate of decline in the results of the fall hunt. He says that very few birds are now obtained, and that many families make no attempts in this direction.

Preble, long before systematic waterfowl and harvest surveys were available, commented on the relative importances of Canada and the United States as waterfowl production and harvest areas:

> A careful study of the conditions known to remain in the various parts of this vast northern area has led me to the conclusion that Canada and Alaska produce at least 85 percent of North America's waterfowl, of which less than one-sixth comes from Alaska. In making this calculation I have largely discounted the areas in extreme southern Alberta and Saskatchewan, sections that up to about 50 years ago were enormously productive, but where settlement and drought have long ago tremendously reduced the waterfowl population. Furthermore, I believe that at least 75 percent of the Canadian and Alaskan-bred waterfowl that are shot, meet their end in the United States.

One must wonder what information led Preble to the above conclusions, which are remarkably similar to present evaluations based upon comparatively sophisticated and extensive surveys. For example, 82.9 percent of the average fall flights of ducks during 1975-79 originated in Canada and Alaska (from files of Office of Migratory Bird Management, Laurel, Maryland, supplied by R. Blohm). In 1972 Geis and Cooch estimated that the United States accounted for 76.8 percent of the North American duck harvest during 1967-69. While some minor differences other than years cause the estimates to be not strictly comparable, Preble's understanding of the general roles of the United States and Canada as duck producers and harvesters is undeniably impressive.

Although Preble's experience with waterfowl was largely limited to northern areas which were still in essentially pristine condition, he did offer the following observation of more southern breeding habitats:

> No one even moderately informed on waterfowl habitat would wish to minimize the extent of the harm that drought imposes on the nesting waterfowl of a region. It must necessarily be serious. But to lay undue stress on a drought that concerns a relatively small part of the habitat of such wide-ranging breeders as the mallard, pintail, scaup, scoter, widgeon, shoveler, green-winged teal, and the various geese, is not reasonable. We must further consider the fact that many of the areas most affected by drought have long ago lost much of their significance as important breeding areas. It should be understood that I am speaking in broad terms, as is due a problem of continental concern, and not one of local or even of national importance alone. The time has come when we must give consideration to our waterfowl species in a broad way, and give the fullest possible consideration to the adequacy of the supply that comes south each year, and of the extent of the demands that are made upon it. By all means we should protect and improve to the utmost as many breeding areas as possible, but we must not allow ourselves to believe that by conferring benefit on a small proportion of any species that we are settling the problem of its survival.
>
> I will not here allude to the reasons that in the past have been mainly responsible for the disinclination of conservationists to face squarely the issue now presented, except to say that it has been due, in part, to indifference on the part of those who kill our birds, to the source from which the supply comes, and to ignorance of the effect that exploitation may exert on the numbers of even the most abundant of species. Those who wish to continue the disastrous killing practices of past years are quick to seize on any pretext to account for the lessened supply. Thus the damage done by natural enemies, drainage, settlement, diseases, and drought, all admittedly serious deterrent causes, have been over-emphasized in accounting for the shortage of waterfowl, while the effect wrought by the gun has been minimized.

Preble then offered his solution to the deteriorating waterfowl resource of North America:

It is my belief that, with the promulgation of suitable measures, and with the whole-hearted support of the consuming public, North America's supply of waterfowl could be built up gradually to any reasonable degree of abundance, with the exception of a few species whose breeding habitats lie mainly in semiarid section that are already largely out of the picture because of settlement, aided by drought or other natural causes. All such species, as well as those now known to be headed toward extermination from any cause, should be removed at once from the list of game birds. I have shown that most of our species still have ample areas within their breeding ranges that are unimpaired by drought, drainage, or settlement. The myriad lakes, marshes, and streams of middle and northern Canada and of Alaska lie there, stocked with an abundance of food, but not one-tenth occupied. These almost boundless breeding places await resettlement by ducks and geese. There is no source from which we may obtain the necessary stock unless we spare it from the flocks that come south each year to their natural winter homes, mainly in the marshes of the United States and Mexico. It is necessary, therefore, that we do our utmost to protect the birds on their migration and wintering grounds.

Therefore we must not continue to demand from these flocks, bred largely in northern lands and our guests for a few months in fall and winter, the tremendous toll that we have long exacted. If we are to restore the depleted stocks to a reasonable abundance adequate refuges on wintering grounds must be furnished, and there must be instituted, and enforced, drastic regulations for numbers and methods of kill. We must banish commercialism of all kinds, as well as the numerous destructive practices by which we lure and kill creatures that this generation now has in its power, but to which it holds no title. Baiting, live decoys, automatic and pump guns, sink boxes, tanks, and the selling of kill privileges on ponds to which the birds have been attracted, are among the methods that have no legitimate place in a worthwhile program of waterfowl restoration. When all unduly destructive practices are banned, and when we have learned to content ourselves with a reasonable take, we can reasonably expect an increase in our ducks and geese.

U. S. Biological Survey staff members photographed here at an annual shad bake in May 1943 were: standing, P. G. Russell, A. L. Nelson; left side of the table, M. Davis, W. M. Mann, E. A. Goldman, A. Wetmore, I. N. Gabrielson, F. C. Lincoln, and J. E. Benedict. Photo courtesy of Smithsonian Institution.

Edward Alphonso Goldman

Henry M. Reeves

The names Edward A. Goldman and Edward W. Nelson are synonymous with the descriptor "biological explorers of Mexico." During the turn of the century the two ventured into virtually every nook and cranny of Mexico, carrying on broad biological investigations of Mexico's mammals, birds, plants, and topography. Hartley H. T. Jackson, in his prefatory note to Goldman's *Biological Investigations in Mexico*, wrote of the inseparable pair: "The results of the biological explorations made by Nelson and Goldman in Mexico from 1892 to 1906 are among the most important ever achieved by two workers for any single country. These results should be appraised not only by the biological collections procured, including more than 17,400 mammals and 12,400 birds, but also by the vast fund of information obtained and preserved in thousands of pages of manuscript reports in regard to physiographic features, fauna, and flora of the country, at that time so little known. Immeasurable information

that was never preserved on paper vanished with the passing of these two great field naturalists."

Although primarily a mammalogist (he described more than three hundred new forms of mammals, and at least fifty taxa were named for him), Goldman had extremely broad interests in all matters biological, including waterfowl. He returned time and again to Mexico following the death of his mentor, Nelson, in 1934. The Smithsonian Archives contain many unpublished Goldman reports on waterfowl populations and habitats in Mexico. Also, Goldman served as the United States' chief technical advisor during the framing and negotiation of the bird and mammal treaty with Mexico (Convention Between the United States and Mexico for the Protection of Migratory Birds and Game Mammals). E. A.'s brother, Luther J., was to become the Biological Survey's first Pacific Flyway biologist, and a son, Luther C., was to accompany him into Mexico before becoming a refuge manager and photographer. It is appropriate to present some background of this remarkable family.

The ascent of the Goldman triumvirate

95

perhaps arises from the "broken singletree" incident, when E. A. first met Edward Nelson. The Goldman family in 1888 moved from Nebraska to settle in Tulare County, California. At the conclusion of a USBS expedition to Death Valley, California, Nelson (who was eventually to become the third chief of the bureau) and his party disbanded at Visalla, also in Tulare County. Nelson departed by buckboard through the San Joaquin Valley but experienced trouble with a broken singletree, and sought to have it repaired at the nearby Goldman ranch. As he discussed his problem with Jacob, E. A.'s father, it became apparent that the two had deep mutual interests in natural history. When Nelson mentioned that he was seeking an assistant, Jacob replied, "Maybe my son Ed would do." At that time, Ed was 18 years old.

E. A. was signed on in October of 1891 as Nelson's personal assistant at a salary of thirty dollars a month plus board. Nelson paid this sum from his own salary, which was then $1,800 per annum. This was the beginning of a forty-year friendship, during which government assignments carried them to distant locations in pursuit of biological knowledge. On March 1, 1892, Goldman received his first federal appointment, a temporary field assistant's position, which paid seventy-five dollars a month, plus "pay your own expenses." To Nelson, Goldman was virtually a son. Together they spent fourteen years in Mexico.

Later, during the construction of the Panama Canal, Goldman led a faunal survey which covered the Isthmus, and which was cooperatively supported by the Smithsonian Institution and the War and Agriculture departments. For six years he was in charge of the USBS Division of Biological Investigations and for three years, the Big Game and Bird Reservations; both assignments were in Washington. With the advent of World War I he became a sanitary officer, with the rank of major, in charge of rodent control work with the American Expeditionary Force in France. In 1928, in order to devote all his

energies to scientific research and writing, he was appointed an associate in zoology on the staff of the Smithsonian Institution, continuing as a collaborator in the USFWS Section of Biological Surveys. In this capacity he resumed his field investigations in Mexico.

Goldman's role in furthering the migratory and wildlife treaty with Mexico is described by Stanley P. Young, senior biologist with the USBS: "His expertness in ornithology was recognized when he received the assignment to journey to Mexico City to assist in handling the technical phases in the negotiations with respect to the convention between the United States and Mexico for the protection of migratory birds and game mammals. This treaty was concluded on February 7, 1936, in the City of Mexico. As a result of Goldman's untiring efforts in behalf of the treaty, and following its final adoption, the U.S. ambassador at Mexico City officially stated to Cordell Hull, then Secretary, the following:

> I have the honor to inform the Department that Major E. A. Goldman, Senior Biologist, United States Biological Survey, rendered invaluable assistance in connection with signing of the Convention for the Preservation of Migratory Birds and Game Mammals. Major Goldman was recognized by the Mexicans, with whom the negotiations were conducted, as an authority on Mexican fauna and as one who was more familiar with this subject than were the Mexicans themselves. His interest and cooperation were particularly useful in connection with technical matters relating to the convention. It is respectfully suggested that the Department of Agriculture be informed of the Embassy's appreciation of the help rendered by Major Goldman throughout the negotiations."

Goldman's records of the negotiations were characteristically modest and to the point. Some emotion is apparent, however, in the entry for February 7, 1936: "An exciting day spent working closely with the Embassy under rather high pressure, conferring with Dr. Eduardo Hay and other officials of the Mexican Foreign Office in completing final details to permit the treaty to be signed in time for announcement at the closing session of the North American Conference in Washington."

One cannot but sense that although Goldman fully recognized the importance of the treaty, he regretted the prolonged negotiations which prevented him from being afield earlier in Mexico to continue his biological investigations. One notes that the treaty, according to Goldman's records, was signed at 7:45 P.M. on February 7, the very last day of the first North American Wildlife Conference, called by President Franklin D. Roosevelt in Washington, D.C. Tentative plans had been made to announce the treaty signing at the conference, but evidently time had run out a few hours before. This treaty, has, for over four decades, provided the foundation upon which the two nations cooperatively conduct their programs to further the welfare of North American waterfowl.

Field work in Mexico was not without peril. Travel was often begun in the very early morning hours to avoid the scorching heat of midday, and it was difficult to maintain even a minimum supply of food. These problems are described by Goldman:

> At 4 A.M. on September 13 we left San Francisquito in brilliant moonlight and traveled 10 miles easterly, following the wagon road down a low-walled canyon heading to the King Richard mine. This was a gold mine, worked by an Englishman named Dick Daggett. To our surprise the camp was deserted, every house was locked, and there were no signs of recent occupation. This left us in a serious position, for we had less than a pound of flour and no beans, rice, sugar, or bacon, and were many days' travel from any supply point.
>
> We had seen Daggett several weeks before at San Quintin, and he had agreed to sell us provisions. It was, therefore, necessary to find him or face a trip of several hundred miles to the next supply point, subsisting on such small game as we might shoot. Several used trails radiated from the camp, one leading down the canyon toward the Gulf showing the most recent tracks. We followed this for about 6 miles, through a series of small canyons and over dividing ridges in a broken granite and slate hill country, and came out into the broad, gently sloping Calamahue Valley, through which a dry rocky wash, like a broad river bed, wound its way. The trail led us on down the valley about 9 miles to the mouth of the wash on the shore known as Calamahue Landing. This was one of several places along the Gulf coast where supplies ordered from Guaymas, Sonora, were occasionally landed for mining companies. We were much relieved to find a group of small brush shelters by a shallow well, where Daggett and his miners were camped. Daggett welcomed us hospitably and said that, through a misunderstanding, his supplies failed to arrive on time from Guaymas, and he and his men were forced to close the mine, come down to this point, and subsist for more than a month solely on sea turtles and fish caught along the shore of the Gulf, supplemented by wild honey taken from cavities among the rocks in the neighboring hills. Bees introduced by the missionaries found the habitat favorable and spread in the wild state throughout the peninsula. Fortunately, the night before our arrival the boat had come in, and the supplies were lying on the open beach at the mouth of the wash. Supplies were purchased, and as there was no feed for our stock we turned back up the valley about 3 miles and made a dry camp.

> The day had been extremely hot, and as we traveled up the smooth sandy flat just after sunset we saw two 'side-winder' rattlesnakes lying in the warm dust of the trail. On our approach they slid diagonally sidewise, as is their peculiar habit, and forward about 15 feet to one side of the trail. There they stopped and sounded their low warning rattles as each animal of our outfit passed. Many others were seen along our route through the central section of the peninsula. About 50 traps were set by me under bushes in the moonlight, the location of each marked by a small wisp of cotton twisted around the tip of a branch. The traps were recovered again by the same brilliant moonlight at 2 o'clock in the morning, when we wished to move on, and were found to contain 17 small mammals representing 3 species.

On another occasion, Goldman was arrested and thrown into a filthy jail because he had shot a bird on Sunday near the limits of a small Mexican hamlet. Only after presentation of United States credentials and lengthy harangue was Nelson successful in securing the release of his companion. At another time, while returning from the field late one evening, Goldman was attacked by three men. In the struggle he was struck on the head by a rock and knocked unconscious. Upon recovering he found that the prized tools of his trade — a bag of traps, altimeter, and shotgun — had been stolen. To his death,

Goldman carried the scar of the blow on his left temple.

Stricken by a thrombosis the afternoon of August 30, 1946, Goldman nevertheless made plans for future field work, discussing these with his wife and a son until nearly midnight on September 1. Within five hours he was dead. Burial, with full military honors, took place at Arlington National Cemetery on September 6, 1946. His published works, covering a span of forty-four years (1902-1946) included 206 titles.

Goldman possessed the personal qualities necessary for high professional accomplishments under adverse conditions and in forbidding regions. He wrote and spoke Spanish fluently, and as Young notes, "True was this also with respect to English." His understanding, generosity, intellect, perseverance, and an almost saintly even temper were among the many qualities admired by his colleagues. E. A.'s brother, Luther J., carried on the Goldman tradition, focusing on waterfowl in the land of our neighbor Canada.

Ira N. Gabrielson

Henry M. Reeves

Ira N. "Gabe" Gabrielson was raised in northwestern Iowa in the southernmost extremity of the prairie pothole region, a region which today still produces most of our game ducks. Gabe saw firsthand the destruction of the prairie wetlands. That experience caused him to recognize these enormously productive habitats and the values they had for many forms of wildlife, particularly waterfowl. This background was of inestimable value as Gabe rose through the ranks of the Biological Survey, eventually to become the first director of the new U.S. Fish and Wildlife Service in 1940.

Gabe grew up in a country of black soils, remnants of tall grass prairie, potholes, and shallow lakes abounding in waterfowl. After a teaching stint of three years, Gabe joined the USBS. During the next twenty years he traveled extensively throughout the United States conducting various wildlife investigations. Much of his early experience was in the western states in fields of predator and rodent control, food-habits research, economic ornithology, and game management. He recognized the relationships between game abundance and land use; throughout his career Gabe was an apostle of soil, water, and habitat stewardship.

The dynamic Ding Darling, chief of the Biological Survey, called Gabe to Washington in 1935 to head up the new Division of Wildlife Research; but shortly afterwards Gabe succeeded Ding as chief of the bureau. In those days the infant federal wildlife refuge system was just getting under way. Gabe devoted much of his effort to implementing this new system, created in response to the drought of the 1930s and the sharp decline of migratory waterfowl.

Durward Allen, in his obituary for Gabe, wrote: "Gabe's administrative tenure in the federal service brought significant developments toard scientific management. In many appearances before congressional committees, his vast fund of knowledge, his familiarity with 'backyards' of representatives from far-flung areas, and his genial manner made suitable friends in the right places. He had the confidence of President Rossevelt and Secretary Ickes."

During the time he directed the USBS and the new USFWS, Gabe was involved in many landmark accomplishments. Those included the rapid growth of the National Wildlife Refuge System; tightening federal water-USFWS's law enforcement arm; unmitigated opposition to wetlands drainage; establishment of the Patuxent Research Refuge (now the Patuxent Wildlife Research Center); and implementation of the Cooperative Wildlife Research Unit and Pittman-Robertson programs. The Patuxent program gave impetus to formal training of wildlife managers, researchers, and ultimateley administrators. The Pittman-Robertson program provided means for greatly increasing state wildlife programs, especially research, management, and habitat acquisition and management.

Both programs contribute greatly to the welfare of the waterfowl resource.

Gabe's broad interests and knowledge in wildlife management were evidenced by two important books he authored, *Wildlife Conservation,* which appeared in 1941, and *Wildlife Management,* published in 1951. Between these he found time to write the first definitive book on the wildlife refuges of North America, appropriately titled *Wildlife Refuges.* Probably his two most significant contributions to ornithology are *Birds of Oregon* and *The Birds of Alaska.* A long series of technical papers, articles, speeches, notes, and reports were issued from the mid-1930s and continued nearly to his death. Gabe's interest centered in the western states, and in 1936 Orgeon State College conferred upon him an honorary doctorate degree. This was the first of several such degrees he was to receive.

In 1946 Gabe resigned his directorship of the USFWS and became president of the Wildlife Management Institute in Washington, D.C. He served as chairman of the institute's board of directors from 1970 until his death on September 7, 1977. While with the institute, Gabe continued to exert a strong influence over wildlife and environmental programs of national and international scope.

The several buildings comprising the Patuxent Wildlife Research Center are named after past leaders of the Biological Survey and its predecessor agencies. Among these are the Merriam, Nelson, and Henshaw laboratories. Only Snowden Hall, the original headquarters of the Snowden Plantation, upon which the Patuxent Wildlife Research Center is located, retains its name. Tradition was broken in 1966 with the decision to name the new laboratory to house the migratory bird program staff after Dr. Gabrielson. Gabe reportedly quipped after the dedication that either someone thought he was dead when he wasn't, or he was dead and didn't know it!

Gabe was a persistent collector of birds when he was afield, and seldom was his collecting gun distant. His colleagues were often amused at how he always managed to gather a group of eager disciples to help prepare the skins. His collection of some eight thousand bird skins was eventually deposited at the Patuxent Wildlife Research Center for reference and use by other ornithologists. Gabe's voluminous papers were deposited at the Denver Conservation Library, where they are available to the public.

In a real sense, the world was his turf and good husbandry his mission.

Clarence Cottam

Henry M. Reeves

Clarence Cottam, stalwart biologist and adminsitrator of the USBS and the USFWS, was born on New Year's Day, 1899, of Mormon parentage, in St. George, Utah. He pursued his university studies at Dixie College, the University of Utah, and Brigham Young University. His federal career began in 1929 when he was appointed a junior biologist with the Biological Survey. Cottam's abilities came to the attention of Ding Darling soon after the latter assumed the position of bureau chief. The two became close friends, and Ding made free use of Cottam's many talents in furthering the bureau's programs in waterfowl management and research.

Cottam successively served as chief of the Section of Food Habits and chief of the Division of Wildlife Research. His *Food Habits of North American Diving Ducks,* published in 1939, was a monumental undertaking that involved his personal study of some seventy-thousand waterfowl gizzards. When he was once asked whether he had personally examined each of the gizzards, though he was not prone to profanity Cottam replied, "Every D-A-M one!" Cottam reportedly applied the same expletive nearly as often to his ill-fitting false teeth as to those who abused wildlife or its environment!

Cottam's scientific presentation before the American Game Conference in 1934 focused

Clarence Cottam held many different positions with the Biological Survey and later with the USFWS: field biologist, research chief, and finally assistant director. After retiring from the Service, he became director of the Welder Wildlife Foundation. Photo courtesy of Welder Wildlife Foundation.

on the status of brant and the species' major food, eelgrass. At the second North American Wildlife Conference he and J. E. Shillinger reviewed the significance of lead poisoning in waterfowl, concluding that "we must look upon the deleterious effect of lead poisoning in waterfowl as of major importance in maintaining an adequate supply of these birds." In 1938, speaking before the conference, Cottam addressed the effects of mosquito control on wildlife and the food habits of furbearers. In 1939 he and Warren S. Bourn reviewed the effects of lowering water levels on marsh wildlife. Cottam and Francis

M. Uhler evaluated at the 1940 conference the role of birds as a factor in controlling insect depredations. Other appearances before the Conference demonstrated his expertise. Consider the breath of knowledge that made it possible for him to speak on these topics: the role of impoundments in postwar planning for waterfowl, factors limiting the present knowledge of waterfowl, the dependence of waterfowl's future on management, effects of drainage and drought on coastal marshes, and progress in wildlife research and training.

Cottam chaired some eighty-five public hearings relating to the development of annual hunting regulations. In that official capacity he rigorously protected the waterfowl resource from abuse. His vast knowledge, total integrity, scornful wit, and scowl (accentuated by scraggly eyebrows and piercing gray eyes peering through wire framed glasses) made him a respected and usually successful adversary of those wishing to exploit the waterfowl resource.

Perhaps one of the most candid evaluations of Clarence Cottam is that of Ding Darling, who described Cottam as "the most competent, efficient and courageous member of the present staff," as was J. C. Salyer, II, "who should be accorded an equivalent rating." Upon hearing of Cottam's departure in 1954 from the position of assistant director of the USFWS, Ding wired his friend to say, "I know of no man in the service . . . who has rendered more valuable services in the field of conservation or whose talents have been less rewarded."

Cottam assumed in 1955 the position of director of the Welder Wildlife Foundation, at Sinton, Texas. This privately endowed foundation not only owned a substantial acreage upon which wildlife research could be conducted, but also provided funds to deserving students for undertaking wildlife research. During his tenure of nearly twenty years, to his death in 1974, nearly 150 graduate students from thirty-nine North American universities obtained degrees under the Welder Foundation's program. Naturally, a substantial number of these investigations concerned waterfowl.

Hoyes Lloyd

Victor E. F. Solman

Hoyes Lloyd was born in Hamilton, Ontario, on November 30, 1888. His mother's maiden name was Moore. The family moved to Toronto in 1899 where, in due course, Hoyes attended Harbord Collegiate Institute and the University of Toronto, specializing in chemistry. He received a B.A. in 1910 and an M.A. in 1911.

From 1912 to 1918 he was chemist in charge of milk control in the Health Laboratories of the city of Toronto. But his avocation was ornithology. In 1909 he had won the Canadian National Exhibition gold medal for a collection of bird skins, and in 1916 he was elected an associate member of the American Ornithologists Union.

The Migratory Birds Convention between the United States and Great Britain on behalf of Canada was signed in Washington, D.C. on August 16, 1916. The convention was ratified and confirmed in Canada by Act of Parliament which received assent on August 29, 1917. The first regulations under the act were authorized by Order-in-Council on April 23, 1918. A position was created in the Dominion Parks Branch, Department of the Interior, to deal with Canadian responsibilities under the convention. It was filled, after competition under the Civil Service Act, on November 27, 1918, by Hoyes Lloyd. He reported for his new duties on December 11, 1918. His title was ornithologist, and his annual salary was $2,000. In 1919 he was given the additional responsibility for administering the Northwest Game Act and protecting wildlife in Dominion Parks. His title then became Supervisor of Wildlife Protection. His staff consisted of a secretary.

Lloyd had to administer two new acts and develop public information to explain them. He had to establish cooperation among officials of nine provinces and the United States.

He had to begin developing a migratory bird sanctuary system and an enforcement system that provided convictions and penalties as examples that the new legislation was effective. Additionally, he did much letter and pamphlet writing and public speaking, and arranged for production of movies and slides to be used to improve public understanding of the new legislation. Late in 1919 and in 1920, Lloyd was able to recruit and place on duty three chief federal migratory bird officers (Robie Tufts, Harrison Lewis, and James Munro) for the maritime provinces, Ontario and Quebec, and the western provinces.

On April 12, 1921, Lloyd was appointed secretary to the Advisory Board on Wildlife Protection, which had been set up in 1916 to furnish the government with opinions and recommendations on wildlife matters. The board had drafted the Migratory Birds Convention Act. It dealt with proposals for migratory bird sanctuaries to manage wildlife in the territories, matters coming under the Northwest Game Act, and a wide range of other matters. Lloyd was made a member of the board in 1928.

Throughout his period of employment, Lloyd continued to lecture and write and distribute pamphlets on migratory birds. He travelled widely in Canada to familiarize himself with conditions and to support his growing staff. Migratory bird sanctuaries were created, including ten along the north shore of the Gulf of St. Lawrence. Problems involving wildlife, including crop damage by migratory birds, were studied and dealt with.

In 1922 Lloyd was given responsibility for setting up a system in the Dominion Parks Branch to record data on all birds banded in Canada, in cooperation with the United States Biological Survey in Washington.

The first Federal-Provincial Wildlife Conference in Canada was held December 6-8, 1922, with Lloyd as secretary. At that conference Lloyd was asked to improve the migratory bird regulations that dealt with damage to agricultural crops and fisheries interests. The second to ninth Federal-Provincial Wildlife conferences, held between 1924 and 1942, all found Lloyd active as secretary.

Lloyd was a member of the council of the Ottawa Field Naturalists Club for many years. In 1925 he was president of the club. In the February 1925 issue of the club publication, *The Canadian Field Naturalist,* a letter from Dr. Francis Harper was published questioning the biological wisdom of proceeding with a planned transfer of several thousand plains bison into Wood Buffalo National Park. Lloyd, as president, forwarded a copy of the issue to the minister of the Interior, affirming club support for Dr. Harper's stand. In return, Lloyd was given the choice of resigning from his official position or from the field naturalists club. He decided on the latter. His wisdom in publishing and supporting the Harper letter was born out by later problems.

Lloyd in 1927 began planning for a continental waterfowl census — in cooperation with the U.S. Biological Survey. The census was first taken in 1928 and repeated annually. The wildlife unit, under Lloyd's supervision, also supported work in the Arctic by J. Dewey Soper, who in 1929 discovered blue geese breeding grounds on southwest Baffin Island. Lloyd was vice chairman of the United States National Game Conference in 1934 and chairman in 1935. He worked hard to have the Game Export Act passed in 1941.

Hoyes Lloyd resigned from his position as superintendent of Wildlife Protection effective December 31, 1943. He had been responsible for federal protection of migratory birds for more than twenty-five years and for various other federal wildlife protection. He had carried responsibility for the principal federal wildlife conservation work through early difficulties and crises. He had expanded the work in migratory birds by adding a fourth chief federal migratory bird officer in 1934 to deal only with the prairie provinces. In 1938 he had expanded the abilities of his staff by adding a mammalogist and, in 1941, a limnologist. These experts provided continunity to special studies of mammals and fisheries resources carried on from time to time under contract by university professors. During his period of official duty, December 11, 1918 to December 31, 1943, Mr. Lloyd held many prestigious professional positions.

After retirement, Lloyd continued to live in Rockcliffe (Ottawa), keeping up his interests and contacts with the wildlife field. Until the 1960s, he regularly attended North American Wildlife and Natural Resources conferences, meetings of the Wildlife Society, the International Association of Game, Fish and Conservation Commissioners, and the American Ornithologists Union. He received the Seth Gordon Award of the International Association in 1974. He passed away on January 21, 1978.

Aldo Leopold

Arthur S. Hawkins

Known widely as the "father of wildlife management" in North America and for his many essays on land and resource use, Aldo Leopold was also a major contributor to modern waterfowl management. His hunting experiences as a boy in the Mississippi River bottoms across from Burlington, Iowa, taught him many lessons about ducks and wetlands. Then came years spent in the southwest, where his wildlife experience centered around deer.

Starting in 1928, Leopold conducted a game survey of eight north-central states sponsored by the sporting arms and ammunition manufacturing industry. Vividly impressed on him by that experience was the impending plight of waterfowl. Wetland drainage was progressing at an alarming rate, destroying excellent nesting grounds for ducks. Even so, the remaining marshes were sparsely occupied, which indicated that local breeding stocks had been depleted. Leopold was able to note only a few encouraging developments: three marsh restoration projects, one or two cases of carp control to improve waterfowl foods, recognition among duck clubs that "rest areas" (refuges) were effective, and an increasing public awareness that drainage was not always desirable. On the negative side, Leopold noted the increasing commercialization of waterfowl hunting, accompanied by distasteful practices such as live decoys and baiting. He found a lack of cooperation in some areas among state and federal officers in the enforcement of migratory bird regulations and a complete absence of surveys and plans for waterfowl conservation programs.

The survey strengthened Leopold's convictions that habitat was the key to waterfowl's future, and that preserving the necessary habitat would require major changes in land-use philosophy. He wrote:

> By and large, the cumulative shrinkage in breeding grounds cannot, however, be reversed, either by more science, or by more appropriations for public acquisition. The only fundamental remedy is to recognize the fact that undrained, ungrazed private marshlands perform a public service in producing migratory birds, and to give the owners an incentive for keeping, continuing, or restoring that service by according them a preferential tax status, such as is now accorded in some States to private forests, on the same principle of public service. The public can never acquire enough of the small marshes to offset the ones which are being taxed out of existence, nor can science show how to grow ducklings in a cornfield. The steam-roller of economic self-interest must somehow be steered so that it will work with, not against, the feeble palliatives so far employed to avert that spiritual calamity — a duckless America.

By the late 1920s, Leopold had gained national recognition and was named chairman of the American Game Policy Committee. The report of that committee was presented to the seventh annual American Game Conference in December 1930. One section of the report dealt with migratory birds. It identified four major needs: 1) a continental system of refuges, 2) better state cooperation in migratory bird management, 3) more international cooperation in migratory bird management, and 4) more fact finding.

The report pointed out that "the present man-power of the game conservation movement is almost wholly self-trained and accidental. The administrative man-power is usually without experience in management or administration. Moreover, the supply of man-power is short, as evidenced by the large number of men without either science or experience holding responsible administrative positions."

The report, which reflected Leopold's thinking, made a strong pitch for scientific training, asking that "the financing and training should be undertaken jointly by state conservation agencies and universities, with the technical guidance of the U.S. Biological Survey." Public-relation needs also were emphasized, as in the observation that "the public now knows of only one way to conserve game: restrictive legislation." The report scolded sporting magazines and conserva-

Aldo Leopold, the father of modern game management, cultivated his ecological concepts through frequent field trips. Photo by R. A. McCabe.

tion associations for catering to existing ideas rather than stimulating new ones. It called for the reorganization of conservation departments to accept the new responsibility "as public leaders of a highly technical form of applied biology." In short, the new game policy, largely authored by Leopold, identified the situation as it existed in 1930 and mapped a new scientific approach to wildlife management including waterfowl.

A golden opportunity to implement parts of the new policy came sooner than Leopold could have imagined. Early in 1934, President Franklin Roosevelt summoned three men to serve on a committee to devise a wildlife restoration program to supplement the administration's "submarginal land elimination program." Tom Beck — editor of *Collier's* magazine, member of the Connecticut State Board of Fisheries and Game, and president of More Game Birds of America, the forerunner of Ducks Unlimited — was appointed chairman. Jay N. "Ding" Darling — nationally famous conservation cartoonist, member of Iowa's Fish and Game Commission, and instigator of the first Cooperative Wildlife Research Unit — was a surprise second member because he was an outspoken critic of President Roosevelt. The third member was Aldo Leopold, a professional forester who had recently moved to the chair of game management at the University of Wisconsin, and who was the only technically trained person on what became known as the "Beck Committee."

Beck had proposed to President Roosevelt in 1933 that an allotment of some $12 million be made available for a new "wildlife restoration" program to be administered by a new agency. The Biological Survey was asked to evaluate the Beck proposal. Beck judged this evaluation totally unacceptable because, in his view, Survey personnel were "neither scientific nor acquainted with the problems of waterfowl management." He recommended abolishing the Survey. The president therefore broadened his instructions to the Beck Committee to include an evaluation of the Biological Survey and its leadership. The

Survey survived, thanks to both Leopold's and Darling's disagreement with Beck on this issue. And in 1934 Darling became its new director, thus solving the leadership problem.

Press accounts, such as one appearing in the *Chicago Tribune,* announced the appointment of the Beck Committee in glowing terms. Coming from the committee, according to the *Tribune,* would be a "gigantic national project to increase game birds in this country under the direction of the government to provide rural employment, utilize 20-to-50 million acres of land to be taken out of crop production, generally increase healthful recreation for million of outdoor fans, and provide a source of income for farmers." Mail commenced to pour into the offices of the three members, giving all sorts of advise and asking favors.

The committee's task proved to be difficult in more ways than one. It soon became apparent that the ideas of Beck and Leopold were poles apart. Beck was a successful editor and avid sportsman who was well known in political circles, but he had not caught up with the advanced ideas articulated in Leopold's classic book, *Game Management.* Darling's job was to mediate the disputes and to make the most out of this great opportunity to serve conservation interests.

At one point in negotiations, Leopold became so frustrated that he wrote to Darling to say "if we could be sure of a qualified administrator, with this broad conception of his duties, I would not care what the report said or whether we submitted any at all." The "broad conception" he had in mind can be seen in the changes he thought the administrator of the new program should consider:

(1) The delegation to the states of the present federal police function of enforcing the migratory bird regulations.
(2) The delegation to states of the administration of most federal game lands.
(3) The delegation to states of as much of the research function as possible, using the federal agency as a clearing house and coordinator, rather than a doer (as other agricultural research bureaus now do, and have always done).
(4) The use of funds thus released for a system of federal aid to states, to be allotted to stimulate good state cooperation and penalize bad. The possible differential use of regulatory powers to the same end.

Leopold went on in the same letter to present more of his thoughts on solutions to the threats facing waterfowl:

The present impasse on such questions as baiting, seasons, and bag limits is due to the lack of flexible localized regulations, and of effective cooperation by states in enforcing them. The states are "passing the buck" and the whole present federal wildlife structure is designed to encourage it.

The present program will either vastly augment this tendency, or abolish it, depending on the wisdom with which the administrator does his job.

The present willingness of the states to join the stampede for federalization of game does not mean they want it. They merely have their eye on the purse now open, and they know enough not to rock the boat while the emergency money is being passed out. Their complaints will be heard later.

To sum up: we must not delude ourselves by seeing this job as merely a heaven-sent chance to buy some game lands. It is, whether we will or not, the chance to make or break federal leadership in wildlife conservation. Every step has far-reaching implications. The fact that the rank and file of conservation enthusiasts are unaware of those implications makes us all the more responsible for foreseeing them. Hence my solicitude over what may seem trivial details in our report.

The hard-headed realism of these comments might surprise those who only know Leopold from his essays. He furthered reflected, in the same letter to Darling:

"The more I think about the committee's job, the more I am convinced that our success depends not on the report we write, but on the man who is chosen to execute the program. I am sure that any attempt to do the job by ourselves with only the help of the remnant of the Biological Survey would be hopeless."

Leopold's suggestions were hardly what Beck had in mind, to judge from Beck's pointed remarks to him in a letter dated February 1, 1934:

"I have the utmost confidence that our report, when ready, will meet with your approval, but, in reading and considering it you must bear in mind that after all you have spent four days working with us at Washington, where we have been at work continuously since January 6, and, therefore, feel that we have a pretty fair and sound picture of the situation that must be helped and improved."

Despite its internal divisions, the Beck Committee accomplished a great deal. It initiated a national wildlife refuge system chiefly designed to further the welfare of waterfowl. It led to a revitalization of the Biological Survey. Finally, it furthered the concepts of a federal aid program to improve state research and management of wildlife resources.

But, as his letter to Darling indicated, Leopold was particularly concerned about the quality of leadership of the USBS. That was assured when the president appointed Ding Darling as the Survey's new chief.

Leopold's contributions to waterfowl management didn't end there, as I know from many years of personal association with him. He helped establish the Delta Waterfowl Research station in Manitoba, and Albert Hochbaum, one of his students, became its director. I was another of Leopold's early students, and it was largely due to his encouragement that I pursued waterfowl management as a career. After World War II, as a flyway biologist with the USFWS, I shared office space with him. Leopold's essays, with their distinct blend of poetry and moral urgency, reflect his appreciation of waterfowl. His many speeches expressed his concern that progress toward assuring the perpetuation of waterfowl was far too slow.

The Darling-Salyer Team

Philip A. Du Mont
and Henry M. Reeves

Jay N. Darling, known as "Ding" to millions of Americans for his cartoons that appeared in more than a hundred newspapers across the country, is unique among the individuals featured in this history of the early days of the waterfowl program. He was neither a biologist, nor an administrator by choice, but he was a conservationist without peer who waged a ceaseless battle for conservation against an often indifferent American public. Recently, Professor David L. Lendt of Iowa State University researched Darling's life and wrote an excellent biography of this talented fellow Iowan.

Ding worked long hours and played with enthusiasm. His vigor and vitality knew no bounds, although he had many frustrating moments. He ate pie for breakfast. He visited Russia at the invitation of Stalin. He cavorted with Herbert Hoover. He knew Will Rogers, Henry Ford, Edna Ferber, Bernard Baruch, Robert Ripley, Ring Lardner and scores of other luminaries from the first half of the twentieth century.

A product of the midwest's prairie region, Ding came to know and love the prairies, their marshes, and their abundant wildlife. His hometown, Sioux City, was, in 1900, on the fringe of the frontier. Lendt writes: "Jay Darling, a child of the centennial, had seen that just one generation of indifference, neglect, and needless abuse of national riches could short-change every generation to follow. He saw the results of despoliation. He was a witness to waste."

Deeply disturbed by such observations, Darling developed a philosophy bordering on religion about conservation that was to become his guiding light henceforth. His early career began as a reporter-cartoonist for the Sioux City *Journal.* After six years with *Journal* he reached the monumental

Jay N. "Ding" Darling was the man of the hour when, during the mid-1930's, the waterfowl resource faced its gravest crisis of this century. Photo courtesy of Wildlife Management Institute.

salary of $27.50 weekly. He later moved to the *Des Moines Register and Leader,* for $50 a week. Many of his early cartoons featured activities of his idol, President Theodore Roosevelt. Darling was eventually enticed to New York City to work for the New York *Globe,* but he found the "Big Apple" not to his liking and after two years he returned to his native Iowa and the *Register and Leader.* However, he maintained ties in New York and through syndication in the *Herald Tribune* his cartoons became increasingly familiar to Americans. "Ding" eventually became a household word. His hastily conceived and executed "Long, Long Trail" memorialized Teddy Roosevelt's death and became one of his best known and beloved cartoons. His caricatures and misadventures of the New Deal were to bring reflective thought and humor to the public during the trying early days of Franklin Roosevelt's administration.

Ding helped organize the Iowa Division of the Izaak Walton League of America, and his influence in the conservation movement grew. He became a member of the non-partisan Iowa Conservation Commission, and was instrumental in organizing the Iowa Cooperative Wildlife Research Unit (the first in the country). He personally pledged $9,000 to help the new program get underway.

Conservation became a recurrent theme of his cartoons. All aspects of natural resource conservation, including soils, waters, forests, and wildlife, were subjects of his visual essays. Twice he was awarded Pulitzer Prizes for his excellence. A hunter himself, he campaigned against poor hunting ethics through cartoons such as in "The Annual Migration of Ducks Is On." More often, he focused his sharp pen upon the misuse and exploitation of natural resources.

The Ding Darling works that appear in this book are reprinted from *DING: THE LIFE OF JAY NORWOOD DARLING* by David L. Lendt, © 1979 by permission from the Iowa State University Press, 2121 South State Avenue, Ames, Iowa 50010.

Editoralizing through his cartoons, Darling showed his strong opposition to President Franklin D. Roosevelt's "New Deal," yet FDR asked Ding to serve on his "duck committee." According to co-author DuMont, "It was a surprise to many when Ding accepted the appointment but not to me because I knew how deeply committed he was to conservation, and how badly he wanted a chance to do something big about it." A few months earlier, having recently completed work on *A Revised List of the Birds of Iowa*, DuMont visited Ding in his Des Moines office. Ding knew he was looking for a job, and so offered to hire him to find lands and waters in northwestern Iowa that might serve as waterfowl nesting areas. Until he could convince the Iowa Fish and Game Department to continue DuMont's employment, Ding willingly paid his salary out of his own pocket.

President Roosevelt's Duck Committee owed its existence to the record-breaking drought that was spreading across North America, causing hunters and conservationists to demand that something be done to save the waterfowl. Joseph P. Knapp, owner of Crowell Publishing Company in Philadelphia and founder of the More Game Birds in America Foundation (forerunner to Ducks Unlimited), owned *Colliers Weekly* and some other magazines, giving him considerable national prestige. He was well acquainted with President Roosevelt, and he kept pressing him to do something for waterfowl. Finally he succeeded in getting the President to form a committee to draw up a program for acquiring land for waterfowl and other wildlife. Some of these lands were drainage projects requiring only a plugged drainage ditch to impound water. Knapp's managing editor for *Collier's,* Tom Beck, was given the chairmanship of the Duck Committee (thereafter called the Beck Committee). The other two members were Ding Darling and Aldo Leopold.

The committee was supposed to work closely with the Bureau of Biological Survey, but some Survey leaders resented this arrangement and failed to cooperate. Beck wanted to abolish the Survey then and there, but Leopold and Darling were unwilling to go that far, although they too resented the lack of cooperation received and agreed that changes were in order.

The committee (in conducting its work) sought and received suggestions from sportsmen's groups and game department officials. One of the best suggestions came from Burnie Maurek, former commissioner of fish and game in North Dakota, later to become a regional director of the revamped Biological Survey.

Despite disagreement within the committee itself on various points, Ding's power as mediator held it together until an action program was developed which, after a considerable delay, was approved by President Roosevelt.

Probably due to the Beck Committee's criticism of the Bureau of Biological Survey, President Roosevelt asked Darling to accept the position of chief. At first he refused but after being promised funds with which the Survey could carry on an expanded program, and being assured that he would be spared political interference, "Ding" accepted. He was appointed Chief in March 1934, by his fellow Iowan and friend, Henry A. Wallace, then Secretary of Agriculture. The position paid $8,000 annually, far less than Ding had been making on the newspaper. Even that small salary Ding refused, returning his paycheck to the U.S. Treasury.

One of the honors accorded Ding was the opportunity to purchase the first federal duck stamp, at $1; ironically, he had sketched the illustration, featuring a pair of mallards, several months before. This new series of stamps provided revenue to be used for the purchase of waterfowl refuges. Today these proceeds remain one of the major sources of funds for the acquisition of waterfowl habitats.

Ding quickly learned that no agency head in Washington, D.C., was ever afforded the luxury of protection from political pressure, and even FDR could not assure him that funds for the Biological Survey would be forthcoming. Consequently, Ding resorted to pleading and cajoling FDR and Congress for funds so urgently needed by the infant agency, particularly for waterfowl habitat to be included in the new national wildlife refuge program. Evidently Roosevelt did not make good on all his fiscal commitments that Ding considered inviolate, as Lendt writes:

> "Whenever Darling complained to the President that he had not received the $1 million he had been promised, FDR would write an I.O.U. for $1,000,000 and tell Ding to hand it to Harry Hopkins. Hopkins, recognizing the President's humor at work, would ignore the chit and suggest that Darling make his pleas to Ickes or Wallace."

Years later in a two-part article in *National Parks Magazine*, entitled "The Story of the Wildlife Refuge Program," Darling called this farce a "cat and mouse game" being played by the President to satisfy duck hunters who were pressuring him to do something for waterfowl.

When FDR finally admitted that he couldn't, or wouldn't, do anything further for the duck program, Darling turned to Congress for financial help, with far better results.

One of Ding's favorite stories centered around the duck stamp and Senator Norbeck. The vote on the Migratory Bird Hunting Stamp (Duck Stamp) Act was underway when Senator Peter Norbeck of South Dakota rose to ask unanimous approval for a rider to be added to the bill. Senator Norbeck, who had a reputation as a dedicated conservationist, pulled from his pocket a piece of paper on which he had written his resolution. As Ding told the story later, on that morning Senator Norbeck had left his upper plate on the table in the washroom because of a slight gum infection, and that, together with his emulsified Swedish and English diction, made it impossible for anyone to understand him.

Hunting on the J. Clark Salyer National Wildlife Refuge in October 1952. Shown (from left) are: J. Clark Salyer II, D. Gray, F. Gillett and L. Kirsch.

But because of his long record of integrity, the Senate voted unanimously to accept his resolution. The President was preparing for a fishing trip when the bill reached him for his signature. He read the title but not the amendment and signed the bill. Three weeks later an aide noticed the rider calling for the transfer of $6 million of unexpended funds to carry out the waterfowl program. Harry Hopkins promptly tied down the money, but Harold Ickes was too slow and the $6 million came out of his budget, much to his consternation.

FDR, a master politician himself, admired anyone who could outsmart him. Evidently he credited Darling with the coup that netted another six million for his duck work. "This fellow Darling is the only man in history who got an appropriation through Congress, past the budget, and signed by the President without anyone realizing that the Treasury had been raided . . . Nevertheless, more power to your arm! Go ahead with the six million dollars and talk to me about a month hence in regard to additional lands, if I have any money left."

Ding was quick to acknowledge that his phenomenal success as Director of the Biological Survey was due in large measure to the tireless efforts of his staff, and particularly of two members, J. Clark Salyer II and Clarence Cottam. Later he wrote that Cottam "is the most competent, efficient and courageous member of the present staff" along with Salyer "who should be accorded an equivalent rating."

The tremendous responsibility for implementing Darling's new program fell on Salyer's broad shoulders. Darling, while a member of the Iowa Fish and Game Board, had hired Salyer to work on one of the artificial lakes being constructed in southeastern Iowa. There he had demonstrated expertise at building underwater structures to encourage fish breeding. Ding, impressed by Salyer's energy and knowledge, was convinced that here was the man to put in charge of the new refuge program.

When Ding became director, he found that a limited refuge program already existed but with inadequate funding and manpower to implement a program such as the Beck Committee envisioned. Salyer quickly changed the picture. He reviewed all the reports and plans on file to see the proposed projects firsthand. There were days and nights when he would drive 600 and 700 miles if it meant getting to a project area or meeting the next day.

Salyer feared flying and was never known to have been in an airplane. One can only speculate what our refuge program would have been like if he had been able to fly over the many areas not reachable by ground transportation.

He became intimately acquainted with all the National Wildlife Refuges except those in Alaska, Hawaii, the territories, and offshore islands. When he visited a refuge, the manager would always invite him in for dinner. Salyer would always make it a point to talk with the manager's wife to find out what things were needed there. Sometimes he made promises impossible to fulfill. The assistant chief of refuges at that time was Art Elmer. It became a saying among refuge managers that "Salyer giveth and Elmer taketh away," because Elmer had his finger on the purse strings and many times had to write to the refuge and explain that the promised funds were unavailable.

There were six refuge protectors in the field and two refuge employees in Washington when Salyer arrived. This group worked together in developing a program involving thirty-eight Civilian Conservation camps that significantly aided refuge development in the late 1930s.

Clark Salyer was chief of the national wildlife refuge program for nearly thirty years. Ultimately he had health troubles and began to lose his sight. For the last two years of his life he was blind. It was amazing to see him function during that time. He would talk about projects and would know, for instance, what the water levels should be on every lake of Valentine National Wildlife in Nebraska. The Lower Souris National Wildlife Refuge in North Dakota, one of his favorites, was renamed the J. Clark Salyer National Wildlife Refuge in his honor.

Many activities and programs got underway or foundations were laid during Ding's short tenure with the Biological Survey. Perhaps the impetus he gave the wildlife refuge program was his greatest achivement. During Ding's tenure, a new revenue source for funding wildlife refuge acquisition was established with funds provided by the new federal Duck Stamp. Furthermore, the seeds were sown back in Iowa for the Cooperative Wildlife Research program and the Federal Aid to Wildlife Restoration program. Despite numerous setbacks, the Biological Survey was improved organizationally and funded much better than in the past. It was revitalized and prepared to tackle its many challenges with a new insight and direction.

Ding successfully prevailed upon President Roosevelt to call the North American Wildlife Conference, to be held in Washington, D.C., in 1936. It was to be the first of the annual conferences which continue to this day (the 49th North American Wildlife and Natural Resources Conference will be held in Boston during the spring of 1984). The first Conference resulted in the formation of the National Wildlife Federation, and Ding was selected to become its first president.
its first president.

After twenty months Ding resigned, feeling that he had contributed as much as possible as Chief of the Bureau of Biological Survey. As he put it, "As soon as I thought I had the machine well-greased and all the wheels on the rails and going places I came back home and started again to draw cartoons." This did not mean that his influence was to wane, however, Ding recommended as his successor Ira N. Gabrielson, who had joined the Bureau as an assistant biologist in economic ornithology in 1915 and whose activities had been chiefly confined to the western states.

In 1952, Ding, unable because of illness to attend the North American Wildlife Conference and annual meeting of the National Federation held at Miami, sent a message to him. A portion of the message read:

> "I regret to say that the battles for the great cause of conservation in good old U.S.A. are not being won and, further, that they will continue to be lost until the thousand and one independent and competing conservation organizations get together for unified national objectives and throw their massed strength against wasteful and ignorant exploitation. . . We will continue to go down to defeat and the natural resources of our country will continue going down a rat-hole with us until we are willing to join together in one mighty surge for the great cause whch I have so futilely tried to serve."

Even after his death on February 12, 1962, Ding continued to exert a strong influence on the conservation movement in the United States. Ding's farewell appropriately was in the form of a cartoon which had been sealed in an envelope to be opened only upon his death. It's caption read, "Bye now — It's been wonderful knowing you." It reflects his appreciation of America's natural resources, and the joys and privileges of being an American. One token of Darling's many contributions is the J. M. "Ding" Darling National Wildlife Refuge on Sanibel Island, Florida.

"Bye now — It's been wonderful knowing you."

The Patuxent Team

Matthew C. Perry

With the conclusion of World War I, many Americans began taking a closer look at our dwindling natural resources. The drainage ditch, plow, and market hunt were having a devastating effect on wildlife, especially waterfowl. The time was right for a change. The calls of alarm from naturalists, bird lovers, hunters, and scientists finally began to turn the tide on the dwindling wildlife habitats and populations.

The United States Biological Survey (USBS), the one government agency responsible for studying our wild resources, was the leading wildlife conservation organization of the 1920s. The Survey evolved in 1896 from the Division of Economic Ornithology, which was formed in 1886 by an act of Congress.

The work of the Survey in the first two decades of this century was similar to that of the previous years: to emphasize economic ornithology. Biologists sought to determine whether birds were beneficial or detrimental to agriculture. Scientists observed the birds in the field and analyzed their gullets and gizzards to determine what food organisms they had consumed. Based on these studies, advice could be given to farmers to enable them to decrease their losses.

In the early 1920s, universities and colleges had not yet formulated programs in wildlife biology or conservation, so scientists who worked for the Survey had degrees in curricula like botany, medicine, entomology, ornithology, and general biology.

The diverse backgrounds of the men who worked for the Survey contributed to the successes of the program. The field investigations and laboratory food habits research conducted between 1920 and 1940 were important in the formation of many U.S. Fish and Wildlife Service (USFWS) national wildlife refuges.

One of the young and energetic biologists of that period was Francis Morley Uhler. He started his employment with the Survey in 1924 after graduating from Gustavus Adolphus College in St. Peter, Minnesota, with a degree in biology. Uhler reported to work in Washington, D.C., but did not stay there long. He became a fieldman, charged with making reconnaissance surveys on various wetland areas to determine their value for migratory waterfowl refuges, and investigating troublesome problems confronting the Survey.

One of his earliest assignments was to investigate at Stump Lake, North Dakota, complaints of fishermen that the consumption of fish by cormorants was reducing their commercial fish harvest. A sample of cormorants was collected and analysis revealed they were feeding on tiger salamanders and five-spined sticklebacks, not on commercially harvested fish. Further study revealed that the water level in the lake had been decreasing in recent years, causing excessive alkalinity of the water, so Uhler concluded that natural ecological changes had caused the reduction in commercial fish. The cormorants had been vindicated, and in the process information was gathered about the economic and ecological relationships of fish-eating birds to man.

Uhler conducted other studies on fish-eating birds on the Mississippi River in 1925. During some of these investigations he was accompanied by the veteran biologist Charles C. Sperry, who gave him firsthand advice on how to conduct food-habits studies. Biologists were spread thin, however, and Sperry soon left for the Southwest and Mexico to conduct his own studies.

In 1924 the son of Congressman Will Dilz drowned in a boating mishap on the Mississippi River. The congressman wanted a national fish refuge created in memory of his son. Although there were national wildlife refuges at that time, there was no precedent for a national fish refuge. On June 7, 1924, however, precedent was established by act of Congress with the formation of the Upper Mississippi Wildlife and Fish Refuge. This unique refuge, first and last of its kind, includes 284 miles and 195,000 acres of wetland areas extending from the Chippewa River in Wisconsin to Rock River in Illinois. Fran Uhler and his colleagues conducted numerous field investigations on this extensive refuge.

In 1927 Uhler had a memorable experience while in the field with his colleague Neil Hotchkiss. They were conducting a botanical survey at the mouth of the Chippewa River where it enters the Mississippi River at Lake Pepin. Their small johnboat was on the lee side of a point of land protected from high winds of a developing storm. When Uhler and Hotchkiss rounded the point the wind flipped their boat, completely soaking them and their equipment. They paddled to shore safely and hailed a man in an old clamming boat who was "boiling out" water from the dredging operation. He took them to his house, where they got dry clothes. Then he let the biologists spread their blotters from the plant presses on his lawn to dry. The clammer, whose name was "Dad" Curdew (of French, Indian, and English descent), was apparently fascinated by this bedraggled pair of biologists. He provided them dinner and a place to sleep for the night.

The soaking and the friendliness that followed it were not forgotten. Uhler and Hotchkiss returned to the same area the next year, this time somewhat wiser. They persuaded their friend, the clammer, that he and his boat were needed for government reconnaissance surveys. The team went to work, with Curdew's sixteen-foot clam boat towing a small Arkansas-built pirogue for use in shallow water areas. Dad Curdew knew the river thoroughly. He was able to put the biologists where they wanted to go for the nominal fee of some "spirits," of which he was reputedly fond.

Sometimes when Uhler and Hotchkiss returned to their base station after a day afield in their pirogue, they found that their skipper had overimbibed. To say the least, their trips home were often eventful as Dad attempted to navigate the river.

Dad Curdew had a very close call one day when he was left to take care of the boat and gear. While trying to light a gas stove, he leaked gas on a drawing board used as a table. It was instantly a blaze. He tried to move it off the boat, but in the process the flaming gas spilled on the bed mattress from the settee and burned a large hole down its length. When the biologists returned they found Dad sheepish but unhurt.

The close working relationship that developed between Uhler and Hotchkiss in the mid-1920s was to last many years. Although they were often assigned to work in different parts of the country, their interest in botany repeatedly brought them together to compare notes. The botanical sampling that they did on the Upper Mississippi River Refuge from 1926 to 1928 had much impact on the management plans and development of this large refuge.

In 1929 Congress appropriated $1 million to purchase more wildlife refuge areas, an unusually large sum of money in those days. All biologists working with the USBS were committed to the best use of this money. An increased effort was made to find appropriate areas to purchase. Three teams were established, and in the spring of 1929 they dispersed to conduct their surveys.

Neil Hotchkiss, originally from New York and with an excellent botanical background, was given responsibility for the eastern third of the country. Fran Uhler, the veteran of many surveys in his home state of Minnesota, was assigned to the middle third of the country. The western third was given to Charles Sperry, who was assisted by Alex Martin in 1929. Martin later became an important scientist in food-habits studies.

Hotchkiss, Uhler, and Sperry had a great responsibility and a lot of territory to cover. Hotchkiss had the greatest amount of academic training in botanical work but the least amount of field experience. The drive and enthusiasm of the three men made up for any possible shortcomings in backgrounds. They set off to find the best possible wildlife areas in the country.

Much of the actual planning and organization of the surveys was done by W. L.

McAtee, Frederick Lincoln, and Edward Preble in Washington, D.C. McAtee, the immediate supervisor of the three fieldmen, assisted by making arrangements. He wanted the work to be conducted during the summer and fall when the men could see the plants at their best food production stage.

Travel throughout the country at that time was mostly by train. The few official vehicles assigned to the Biological Survey were assigned to law enforcement personnel. When the biologists arrived at the depot nearest their destination they were met by game wardens, who then provided local transportation during their working visit. The wardens acted as gracious hosts to these itinerant biologists and were a great asset to the reconnaissance program. The wardens also usually provided boats and field assistance.

The biologists got food and lodging in towns nearest their study areas. The meals and accommodations often left much to be desired. Later, when biologists had their own automobiles, they could be more selective. In the early years, the government paid for all expenses. Biologists later received per diem expenses, which is still the policy for traveling biologists.

During the autumn and early winter of 1933, Uhler conducted a very important investigation in the Illinois River area. He found that there was a surprisingly large amount of field-pen shooting with live decoys and bait. During a two-hour aerial survey with a federal game protector over Mason and Tazewell counties of Illinois, he counted 250 pens where live decoys were being used for hunting. Most of the pens were located within five miles of the Illinois bottomlands.

A typical field-pen consisted of a small aritificial pond equipped with a flock of live mallards to lure wild birds within gunning range. The areas were heavily baited and blinds were located near the ponds. Some shooting areas did not have a pond, but would have small water receptacles where the decoys could drink. Many of these areas were operated as commercial venture. One successful shooting area had four pens with twenty-five live decoys in each pen. They fed 1,400-2,500 bushels of corn per season and paid only fifty cents for each live decoy. Such an investment could possibly return several thousand dollars in one season. That profit was gained at the expense of enormous damages to waterfowl populations.

Uhler's report demonstrated the extent to which live decoys and baiting were being used by hunters in Illinois, and substantiated the heavy mallard kill that resulted. These techniques, moveover, were used in many other areas of the country. Thanks to Uhler's report, baiting and live decoys were prohibited everywhere after 1934.

Although Uhler spent a great amount of his time during his early years in the Mississippi Valley area, he also investigated waterfowl habitats closer to Washington, including Chesapeake Bay and its Susquehanna Flats.

Few areas in Chesapeake Bay have received as much biological attention as Susquehanna Flats. Due to its tremendous populations of diving ducks, especially canvasbacks, this area was a mecca for market hunters ten years before and after the turn of the century. The birds were attracted by the lush stands of wild celery and other aquatic plants that thrived in the nutrient-rich fresh water entering the bay from the Susquehanna River. The area is circular in shape and roughly six miles in diameter. Most of the area is shallow with a soft sandy mud bottom.

When Neil Hotchkiss investigated this area in July 1929, with the cooperation of E. Lee LeCompte, state game warden, he reported that practically the whole area was vegetated with wild celery. He believed it would make an excellent refuge but noted that a strong regional hunting tradition might make its establishment as a refuge difficult.

Hotchkiss surveyed two other areas in 1929. In July he was in the Elk River, not far from Susquehanna Flats and reported that the coves in the river were filled with an abundant growth of wild celery. He recommended that this area not be considered as a refuge, but that the Bohemia River, which flows into the Elk River, should receive further consideration based on reports of thousands of waterfowl using the area.

Another nearby area surveyed by Hotchkiss was the Aberdeen Proving Grounds, a large military base. He felt that the shoal waters off the shore would make an important refuge for resting and feeding waterfowl. A phosphorous dump near Mulberry Point was still a a hazard to the ducks, however, and he recommended that it be dredged to avoid future phosphorous poisoning.

Many biological field trips are done on weekends or holidays when most people are resting. Like mailmen taking a walk on their day off, biologists often spend their recreational hours in the field conducting bird and vegetation surveys. Such a trip was taken on November 13, 1932, by Fran Uhler in the company of his good friends, Dr. and Mrs. Arnold Nelson. They walked along the northeast side of the Susquehanna Flats, making detailed notes of the vegetation along the beach and the birds on the water. Wild celery was the dominant plant in windrows and was recorded as very abundant. The group recorded considerable numbers of scaup, ruddies, canvasbacks, and pintail, but unfortu-

nately no estimates of their population size were made. Dr. Nelson later became the director of Patuxent Wildlife Research Center and was managing editor of the classic book *Waterfowl Tomorrow.*

Reconnaissance teams went to all states in search of potential refuges. Little Rhode Island was no exception. Neil Hotchkiss and his assistant made a trip there in August 1929 to survey the coastal ponds of Washington County and to inspect ponds and salt marshes between Narragansett Pier and Watch Hill. Although they found good amounts of vegetation and reports of waterfowl abundance, they recommended against forming refuges there because of the summer resorts being constructed along the coast, and because of the nearness to Long Island and Cape Cod where other refuges were proposed.

In July 1936, Rhode Island was again investigated by federal biologists. This survey involved a new biologist, John J. Lynch, and a new area, Prudence Island. Lynch recommended against acquiring any of the marshes on Prudence Island because they were broken into small areas and too much valuable high land would have to be procured to obtain the marshes. Poor Rhode Island was passed over for refuge acquisition.

1981-82 Ruddy ducks *by John S. Wilson*

Frederic Lincoln conducted one of the first aerial surveys of birds and habitat in 1931 with an army plane. The trip convinced him of the advantage of aircraft in waterfowl work. Another aerial survey was conducted by Lincoln and Clarence Cottam in separate navy airplanes on March 4, 1935. Lincoln surveyed the northern part of Chesapeake Bay, including the Susquehanna Flats. Cottam surveyed the southern portion from Annapolis to Hooper Straits, reporting that the weather was warm and water conditions calm. He complained, however, that his pilot knew nothing of ornithology, that he flew too high, and that he did not cover the best territory.

Cottam was convinced that aerial surveys should be made, and that with more practice these surveys would give the best index of bird populations. He also reported that while flying near Cedar Point, in Talbot County, he observed large beds of small bivalves and much eelgrass and wigeon grass.

During the early years when Uhler and other biologists were scouring the country in search of potential refuge lands, their administrators were often worried on how they could pay their biologists' salaries. The resource dollar was spread as thin as it could be, and Congress was not always sympathetic to the biologist's needs. During the 1932 appropriation hearings, one congressman snidely remarked, "We don't care who killed cock robin"!

During the late 1930s, field biologists were near the end of another productive fiscal year, and funds were running low. Their supervisor, fearing that he could not meet payroll expenditures, requested an $8,000 extra appropriation from Congress. A congressional messenger arrived within a few days with the appropriate papers. The supervisor was instructed to sign the documents and submit them to the budgeting office. Before submitting the papers, however, he must have been overcome by the zealotry of a true resource administrator. Without the knowledge or consent of anyone else, he added another zero. Thus the small budget was bolstered, not with $8,000, but with $80,000.

All of Mr. Uhler's colleagues from those exciting early days have now either passed away or long been retired. Fran Uhler, however, is presently in his fifty-seventh year of remarkable service to the USFWS. His dedication and hard work have benefited all of us by helping to conserve our natural resources so that many generations of Americans will be able to see and appreciate the beautiful world of nature.

1982-83 Canvasbacks *by David A. Maass*

4

Foursomes of the Flyways

In 1927 the newly appointed chief of the U.S. Biological Survey, Paul G. Redington, asked: how many wild ducks are there? No one could provide an answer, so Harry C. Oberholser was authorized to enlist the help of observers scattered across the United States and Canada to perform the first extensive wild duck census.

Oberholser's observers generated a vast array of data, but the limitations of it were soon apparent. Virtually no trained observers were involved, and the skills of the volunteers were highly varied. There were gaps of coverage and many turnovers in their ranks, all of which added up to a huge headache for those who tried to work with the data. Better methods had to be devised.

Then, in the crisis of the Dust Bowl days of the 1930s, public concern for the welfare of waterfowl increased sharply. Suddenly the need for reliable information was felt much more keenly. The new chief of the Biological survey, J. N. "Ding" Darling, saw that new techniques would be needed to survey a mobile bird population whose activities spanned three nations.

From 1934 to 1936, five field parties were sent to Canada to learn what they could about nesting conditions. O. J. Murie and C. L. Fretwell went to British Columbia; W. H. Ransom and M. J. Furness went to southern Alberta and Saskatchewan; L. J. Goldman and C. Gillham went to northern Alberta and the Mackenzie district; C. M. Aldous and L. J. Merovka went to Manitoba; and N. Hotchkiss and L. F. Brackett went to the Maritime Provinces.

This approach proved so fruitful that in 1936 four flyway biologists were appointed to head up future wildlife investigations. They worked under Frederick C. Lincoln, the father of the flyway concept. The original foursome were L. J. Goldman, Charles Gillham, Harold Peters, and George Saunders.

In this chapter, John J. Lynch, who performed all the duties of flyway biologist without being named one, recounts experiences with Gillham. H. M. Reeves adds to that account, working from Smithsonian Institution archives. Reeves also provides information on the other deceased member of the original foursome, L. J. Goldman, augmenting archival information with an interview with Goldman's nephew, Luther.

Two other of the original four speak for themselves here, Harold Peters and George Saunders. Robert H. Smith, the first "second generation" flyway biologist, replaced Gillham in 1942, so his experiences are also reported here.

The duties assigned these men can only be described as awesome. As their stories tell, however, they found ways of rising to the challenges.

In Canada, another foursome with similar but more localized duties made an equally distinguished contribution. This group included J. A. Munro, J. D. Soper, H. F. Lewis, and Robie Tufts. All are now deceased, so material on their lives has been collected by Victor E. F. Solman.

©D. Nelson

The first Central Flyway Biologist was George B. Saunders, shown here in 1968 shortly before his retirement. Photo by Gainsville Sun.

The U.S. Team

George B. Saunders

I was one of four original flyway biologists hired by the U.S. Bureau of Biological Survey (USBS) in the mid-thirties to ride herd on the waterfowl populations of the North American continent. Our section chief, headquartered in Washington, D.C., was Frederick C. Lincoln, father of the flyway concept. We were a diverse group from varied backgrounds.

Atlantic Flyway biologist Harold S. Peters,

an avid bird student, hailed from Ohio and majored in biology at Ohio State University. As flyway biologist, he conducted surveys in the Maritime Provinces, Quebec, Newfoundland, the James Bay Region, and the eastern Arctic. His book, *Birds of Newfoundland*, written with Tom Burleigh and published in 1951, is a tangible reminder of those trips and tells of his keen interest in nongame birds as well as in waterfowl. During the winter months, he conducted waterfowl surveys in Cuba and other islands of the West Indies and along the south Atlantic Coast. As a pilot, he was among the first to use slow-flying aircraft in census work.

The third generation of Flyway Biologists, shortly after World War II: (left to right) Al Smith, Hortin Jensen, Art Hawkins, Ed Addy, and Jerry Stoudt. USFWS photo.

Mississippi Flyway biologist Charles E. Gillham was the most colorful of our group, an authentic adventurer who was as much at home in an Eskimo igloo as on his farm in southern Illinois. Some of his exciting experiences are detailed in his book, *Raw North*. Although he spent a little time in Mexico in 1936, his main waterfowl survey work was in the north country from Lake Athabaska to the Arctic and into Alaska during the breeding season, and in the lower Mississippi Valley in the winter.

Pacific Flyway biologist L. J. Goldman had much of his experience in wildlife survey work on expeditions into Mexico and the Southwest with his older brother, E. A. Goldman, a pioneer biologist in the Biological Survey. Although he participated in some of the early breeding ground survey work in western Canada, his major contributions were on the Mexican wintering grounds for Pacific Flyway waterfowl.

Robert H. (Bob) Smith replaced Charles Gillham in 1942 to become the first "second generation" flyway biologist. Shortly after World War II, three other personnel changes occurred. In 1946 Art Hawkins joined Bob

Smith in the Mississippi Flyway and Allen G. (Al) Smith joined me in the Central Flyway. C. E. (Ed) Addy replaced Peters in the Atlantic Flyway in 1947 when Harold became the Southeastern Dove Study coordinator. For a brief period, until he retired, Stanley Jewett replaced L. J. Goldman in the Pacific Flyway. In 1948 Bob Smith left the Mississippi flyway to become Pacific Flyway Biologist and G. Hortin Jensen was added to the flyway group by way of a duck-banding assignment in Canada. That same year, a section of Waterfowl Management Investigations in the Division of Wildlife Research was established in Washington and Cecil S. Williams, its chief, became our boss. Harold Peters and I are the surviving members of the original foursome.

Fortunately for my career as Central Flyway biologist, I was born in the Southwest where the migrations of ducks and geese were familiar and much loved sights and sounds of my boyhood. By ten I was observing them at close range on trips with my father, who had watched and hunted them as a boy and young man at Reelfoot Lake, Tennessee.

During the four summers of my undergraduate years, 1925-28, my Model T Ford and I visited many of the good waterfowl areas in this flyway, including those in the United States as well as some in the prairie provinces of Canada. En route I picked fruit, worked in the harvest fields, collected rocks and mineral specimens for sale later, had jobs at several national park hotels, and did other work to pay all of my expenses. In the summer of 1928, I taught field ornithology at the Rocky Mountain Biological Station, at Gothic, Colorado. Except when I was working at the hotels, my room was the great outdoors and the board of my own doing. One of my best skills acquired during those trips was repairing flat tires. Fortunately, the roadside fences had many songbirds then, and many a repair was made to the spirited songs of the western meadowlarks perched nearby.

During graduate school at Cornell University I also worked as laboratory assistant to Professor Arthur Allen. Before receiving my PhD in ornithology there in 1932, I took time off in 1930 to serve as assistant ornithologist on an expedition to southern Africa for the Philadelphia Academy of Natural Sciences. During 1932-33 my research was continued on a fellowship from the National Research Council. In 1933 I became staff ornithologist for the Michigan Department of Conservation, a job vacated by Dr. Miles D. Pirnie when he moved to Kellogg Sanctuary and Michigan State University. However, a regional position in the Division of Wildlife Refuges of the USBS lured me back to the Southwest in 1936. While there, I worked with J. Clark Salyer and Neil Hotchkiss on a reconnaissance and planning survey of the Gulf Coast marshes from the Mississippi River Delta to Port Isabel, Texas. I also scouted for new refuge sites in Oklahoma, Kansas, Colorado, Utah, New Mexico, and Arizona, and recommended for purchase the Aransas, Laguna Atascosa, Santa Ana, and other areas in Texas.

Late in 1936 I was offered the Central Flyway biologist position. Because of the continuing disastrous drought on the breeding grounds in the prairie provinces of Canada, it was decided that I should concentrate on annual summer field studies there to obtain as much comparative information as possible on the productivity of areas, habitat conditions, population numbers and distribution, brood counts, mortality factors, and other needed data. After reports on these studies were submitted from Denver, I was to proceed to Brownsville, Texas, and survey wintering waterfowl in that area and southward, including the coastal waters of eastern Mexico.

I learned that flyway biologists worked independently; in fact, we seldom saw each other. We received broad instructions by memorandum from Washington, such as "go up there and find out what you can." No detailed instructions on methods or techniques were issued, so it was up to us to plan our own methods and coverage within the limits of our budgets. Once I recommended to Fred Lincoln that the four flyway biologists have a standardized system for describing water and marsh areas, counting ducks and broods, making food studies, and so on. He replied that, since all of us had different training and abilities, he preferred to let each of us do the surveys as we thought best. Our reports reflected this freedom and divergence in approaches.

As the new Central Flyway biologist, I reported to the Denver Wildlife Research Laboratory in the spring of 1937, received a Pontiac sedan, was assigned an office, and headed for Canada early in May. In Edmonton I met my partner for the summer surveys, U.S. Game Management Agent Bob Bach. I obtained sectional maps of all the areas we planned to visit, including those covering Peace River and Lake Athabaska as well as others for British Columbia, Alberta, and Saskatchewan. In Edmonton, Alberta, we met with provincial wildlife officials and the Royal Canadian Mounted Police personnel most familiar with the waterfowl areas to be visited, and talked to bush pilots who flew from Edmonton to more northern areas. We

This photo shows R. S. Bach scouting the bulrush islands of Stobart Lake in Saskatchewan in 1937. Note: 8' folding boat. USFWS photo by G. B. Saunders.

also discussed our mission with Dr. William Rowan and other biologists at the University of Alberta, and with Tom Main and associates of the recently organized Ducks Unlimited. As we progressed in our survey we contacted local duck hunters and ornithologists at every opportunity. Before leaving Denver I had discussed with Ed Kalmbach the areas in Alberta where he and his team had done extensive fieldwork on crow-waterfowl relationships.

During the previous summer Bach had assisted another U.S. game management agent, Webb Ransom, in scouting duck-breeding areas in Alberta and Saskatchewan, so by revisiting these areas we were able to make comparisons in duck numbers and habitat conditions between 1936 and 1937.

Returning to Edmonton, I met Charley Gillham, Mississippi Flyway biologist, and together we entrained to Fort McMurray where a float plane flew us to Fort Chipewyan on Lake Athabaska. Charley knew an Indian guide there who took us in his freight canoe to a series of fine duck lakes. We spent a week in this area estimating duck numbers,

counting broods, and assessing the habitat and duck food conditions. Our budget permitted us to make a charter flight to survey some of the lakes between Lake Athabaska and Edmonton, where I rejoined Bach, while Gillham departed for the Mackenzie Delta and Alaska. We continued our survey on foot, by car, rail, plane, and canoe. I also had an eight-foot boat made of marine plywood that folded into a compact, flat parcel for use on float plane surveys. It could be unfolded quickly and used to go ashore, or for other short-range uses. Our small outboard motor could be used on it and on the canoe.

Except when we were near a large city, we camped out at lakes and marshes, either in the open or in a small balloon cloth tent. This allowed us to make field studies early and late each day, saving a great deal of time, extra mileage, and travel over unpaved roads. When driving we recorded the speedometer reading and pertinent notes about the marsh and its waterfowl at each water area. Similar records were kept and compared in subsequent years. We photographed many sites of special interest.

In 1938 I returned to Canada alone but received the assistance of interested Canadians in several localities, notably O. C. Furniss, a teacher and ornithologist in Prince Albert, Saskatchewan. I revisited most of the areas of the previous summer and reported on comparative conditions by letters to Fred Lincoln. The drought conditions noted in 1937 had further intensified.

I met an old-timer living in Swift Current, Saskatchewan, who had a fine old mounted specimen of a male passenger pigeon. He claimed to know a place near Swan River, Manitoba, where passenger pigeons were living. I visited the area but could find only large, healthy mourning doves; I was told by homesteaders there that they, too, had mistaken them for passenger pigeons.

Again in 1939 my budget could not afford a paid assistant, but Tom Morrison, a friend, volunteered to go at no cost to the government. Our survey took us as far north in Alberta as Lac la Biche. Conditions and duck numbers on areas revisited were compared with those of previous years. We also covered southern Saskatchewan eastward to Regina where I conferred with Fred Bard, curator of the Provincial Museum. Accepting an invitation from Ducks Unlimited, I flew with their officials on a survey of duck-breeding areas between Prince Albert and Lake Athabaska, including Lake Claire.

Late in August 1939, as in August 1938, I received a wire from Washington directing me to terminate my studies in Canada and proceed immediately to Brownsville, Texas, to investigate the white-winged dove situation. That was my last summer with waterfowl in Canada, sorry to say. Whitewings became a major part of my work from then on, since I served as project leader of the new investigation.

The whitewing dove is an important game bird in the Lower Rio Grande Valley of Texas and in Arizona, Mexico, and parts of Central and South America. As I had made several earlier trips to Mexico and knew some Spanish, Fred Lincoln decided to change my spring-summer assignment from Canada to the whitewing breeding grounds in southern Texas and adjacent parts of northeastern Mexico.

Beginning in 1939 and continuing until 1946, studies were conducted there to learn the biology of these doves to determine why the Texas population had decreased so much, and to identify what management methods would help to increase their numbers. The decrease was found to be due chiefly to the clearing of so much nesting cover and to excessive shooting seasons. The results of these studies were given in my reports dated 1940 and 1950, and much of the information was included in the book *Whitewings,* edited by Cottam and Trefethen, published in 1968.

Surveys, chiefly of mammals in Mexico by members of the Biological Survey, had been conducted between 1892 and 1906 by E. W. Nelson and E. A. Goldman. Although no specific studies of waterfowl were made, observations on them were recorded for several important wintering areas, notably at Lake Chapala and at the Lerma marshes, near Toluca. Transportation was by wagon, horseback, boat, and railroad.

In 1926 E. A. Goldman returned to Mexico for a general survey, including some of the waterfowl wintering grounds. He returned again in 1934-1935 and 1935-1936 accompanied by his brother, L. J. During the winter of 1936-1937, Flyway Biologists Gillham and L. J. Goldman, accompanied by Dr. Logan Bennett, Luther C. Goldman, and Game Management Agent Frank Colcord, visited several wintering grounds in central and western Mexico, while I worked the Lower Rio Grande Valley of Texas and northeastern Mexico.

By 1937 we knew that many thousands of northern ducks migrated south of the United States for the winter. Some, especially bluewings, went as far as northern South America, but there were no estimates of their numbers because of inadequate studies south of the border.

I spent the winters of 1937 and 1938 studying waterfowl populations, their numbers, distribution, habitats, and foods in the Rio

Grande delta and adjacent coastal areas of northeastern Mexico. My headquarters were transferred to Brownsville, Texas, in the autumn of 1939, as it was the logical base for the field surveys.

It became obvious to me that a specially equipped vehicle would be needed to travel coastal trails in northeastern Mexico to reach Laguna Madre and other lagoons to study waterfowl and their habitat. Using a vehicle specially equipped with hand winch and tractor wheels and tires, I visited accessible areas along the northeastern coast of Mexico during the winters of 1938-1940. Later a power winch was standard equipment. The only way to get accurate information on numbers of waterfowl present would be by low-level aerial reconnaissance.

In January 1938, I learned from a brief aerial survey by chartered plane that there were several hundred-thousand pintails, redheads, and lesser scaup on Laguna Madre, Tamaulipas, and even more ducks on the extensive lagoons and marshes of the Tampico delta. Obviously, there were more northern waterfowl wintering in Latin America than had been guessed. It was also obvious that the only means of observing and estimating their numbers there would be by low-level aerial surveys.

I made additional exploratory flights by charter plane the following three winters, including a round trip from Brownsville to Tabasco and one to Yucatan. While my coverage was very limited by lack of funds, it proved that these coastal lagoons and marshes were important wintering areas for migratory ducks and had several million or more of these birds during winter and migration.

In January and February of 1947, USFWS pilot-biologist Dave Spencer and I made the first midwinter waterfowl survey of Mexico and Central America. We intended to continue into northern South America, but our plans were cancelled by the State Department due to civil strife in Venezuela. Spencer and I also flew the survey of Mexico in January 1948.

The principal objectives of our ground surveys included the study of waterfowl numbers and distribution, their habitats, especially the available foods, and also the food preferences and use by the various species of these birds. We collected more than 1,200 specimens of food and cover plants in Tamaulipas and northern Veracruz and other localities in Mexico; these were identified later by USBS and USFWS botanists and other authorities.

To learn the foods the waterfowl were eat-

Beginning the first aerial waterfowl survey in Mexico, January 1947. George B. Saunders (left) and David L. Spencer shared the pilot and observer duties. USFWS photo by Luther Goldman.

ing, I obtained hundreds of gizzards and almost as many gullet contents from hunters' birds, mostly in Gulf coastal areas. The gizzards were largely from birds shot by market hunters, but the gullet specimens were chiefly from ducks shot by sportsmen who did not want the visceral cavities of their birds opened. All of these hunters were cooperative and interested in knowing what the waterfowl were eating. The only birds we shot were in localities where no hunters were present, or where we needed evidence as to whether a local food was being eaten. Occasionally, in remote places, we bartered cigarettes in exchange for food samples or duck bands from native hunters. In all, James Kerwin, USFWS biologist at Patuxent Wildlife Research Center, identified the items in 784 gizzards, and I identified the contents of 776 gullets. It required many contacts over a period of several years to obtain that many specimens, as duck hunters were very few in Mexico in contrast to the many in the United States. Neil Hotchkiss and Fran Uhler were very helpful in identifying the food items.

There are many beautiful places in Mexico where large numbers of northern ducks winter or stop during migration. One of the loveliest lakes in Mexico is Patzcuaro, nestled in a scenic mountain basin, about 150 miles west of Mexico City as a duck flies. It is not far from the famous volcano, Paricutin, that sprouted in an Indian's cornfield in 1943 and soon grew to adult size. One of the unique features of Lake Patzcuaro is its Tarascan Indian duck hunters who, long before firearms were invented, were using "throwing spears" to bag waterfowl. These hunters used a combination of cane spear (*tiraflecha* or *fisga*) tipped with a three-pronged iron head and launched with an *atlatl* type of "throwing stick," which gave much greater leverage and distance to the throw.

Usually the Tarascans hunted the marshy margins of the lake in one or two dugout canoes in each chosen place or bay. At the time of ceremonial hunts, many dugouts, each with crews of two or more Indians, took part. The canoes formed a curved line and quietly approached a raft or flock of ducks or coots. In recent years most of the crews had one or two old muzzle-loading shotguns in each dugout, and the first salvo was from them. Usually the cripples were taken with the spears, as the hunters were very accurate with them. Most of the birds bagged were coots, but a few of the less wary ducks, chiefly ruddies and teals, were obtained. It was easy to visualize the ancient scene when there were no guns, the waterfowl were more numerous and less wary, and the Indians had only their *tiraflechas* as hunting weapons.

Every year for their religious celebration of the Day of the Dead, Tarascans stage these special hunts. The birds obtained are cooked and placed on the graves with other food. Anything left after a day or two is used by family members.

During our survey there in January 1949, we saw from eight to fourteen dugouts daily hunting coots and ducks, some using only spears. The largest day's total of the fourteen canoes was about 250 coots and fifteen ducks.

This was the principal and possibly the only lake in Mexico where for two centuries the local Indians hunted waterfowl regularly.

My exploration of these wintering grounds resumed fully after World War II, and lasted until 1952; in 1948-1951 it was extended inland to include part of the interior highlands and several areas along the Pacific Coast previously scouted by L. J. Goldman.

My final ground survey in Mexico was during the winter of 1959-60, when selected areas along both coasts and in the interior highlands were visited briefly. My companions on that trip were Ralph Andrews, USFWS biologist, and V. Aguilar Ibarra, biologist for the Mexican Department of Game.

The chief objective was to obtain information regarding habitat conditions for comparison with earlier findings and for our manuscript on migratory waterfowl in Mexico. The latter, co-authored with my wife, Dorothy, who assisted me on ground surveys from 1948-1952, summarized information

At Lake Patzcuaro in Mexico, where this picture was taken in 1935, the Tarascan Indians bagged ducks and coots by throwing spears called fisgas. USFWS photo by E. A. Goldman.

obtained by USFWS personnel in Mexico from the 1930s through 1964. She was a scientific collaborator for USFWS, unsalaried, and had a PhD in biology. Additionally, she was fluent in Spanish and had years of experience in Latin America. On our surveys she prepared plant specimens and blood slides, took field notes, and was camp cook. In localities where I could examine ducks that hunters had bagged, she made blood smears while I obtained food samples from gizzards and gullets.

ments in Mexico, I served as head of the U.S. Fish and Wildlife Service-State Department Mission to Guatemala that made a fish and wildlife survey of that country in 1946 and 1947.

In all, I was Central Flyway biologist for sixteen years, from 1936 to 1952. During that period I was in Canada three summers, in the Lower Rio Grande Valley of Texas seven summers, and in Texas and Mexico parts of fifteen winters, chiefly on the Gulf Coast.

Although I traveled mostly by truck and plane, I got there by whatever transportation was available, including skiff, canoe, cruiser, horseback, and train (including freight trains). Once, accompanied by Dr. Charles Plummer, an entomologist, I had a round-trip train ride

from Veracruz, Mexico, to the Guatemalan border, via the Isthmus of Tehuantepec, on a flatcar, "camping" beside my tied-down truck, cooking on a tiny one-hole charcoal stove, and sleeping in tied-down bags to keep from rolling off the flatcar on rough stretches. Shipping the truck by rail was necessary as no adequate road to Guatemala existed in 1942, and we rode with it to be sure that it was not stripped at night while the train was stopped at sidings. We were three days en route each way. At each train stop, and there were many, we were an unexpected sideshow for the villagers, from whom we obtained much useful information on wildlife.

Our freight train arrived in Tapachula, Chiapas, within a few miles of the Mexico-Guatemala frontier, about midnight, February 28, 1942. The last thing we remembered before falling asleep was the loud, bumpy switching of flatcars and our being shunted off on a dark siding. Imagine our amazement upon awakening at daylight to see we were parked beside the main railway station, with several hundred Indians and other Mexicans for an audience. So our rising and dressing for the new day was witnessed by the largest and most interested crowd of the entire trip. From Tapachula we drove east across the border and began our field survey in Guatemala and El Salvador.

Another of the many well-remembered incidents in Mexico came at the end of an exciting but tiring day exploring coastal lagoons in southern Chiapas. Dr. Plummer and I checked in at the small hotel in the nearest town and stretched out on our beds, so tired that we decided on a brief rest before cleaning up and going to dinner. It was pleasantly cool with the paddle fan on and the breeze streaming in the open windows.

We had hardly relaxed before Charlie jumped out of bed shouting, "Great Scot, look at that pot of gold!" He slid a chair beneath the ceiling fan and looked with amazement at the large glass bowl beneath the small light bulb under the fan. That bowl was filled with insects that had been attracted to the light and dry-cured in the bowl beneath. To a professional entomologist skilled in the identification of insects, that lamp bowl was literally a pot of gold. In no time we, who had been so exhausted, had the bowl down on the table and a spare sheet spread for sorting the loot.

Needless to say, Charlie spent the next day sorting and packaging his specimens, while I returned for further study of the coastal lagoons. Subsequently, back in Mexico City, he wrote that more than one-hundred species were in that bowl; five were new records for Chiapas, one or two new to Mexico, and at least one subspecies was new to science. Although Charlie was a USDA specialist on insects injurious to citrus, with years of experience in Mexico, he was also interested in birds, especially waterfowl, and was a fine field companion.

Fascinating and useful observations and discoveries were recorded at other lakes, lagoons, and marshes. Many of the most interesting and rewarding experiences of my life came during these field surveys, and many of the friendliest and most helpful persons I have known were met there on the flyways. Judging from my own career, I believe that wildlife biologists are among the happiest people to be found, especially if they have a wife who is also a biologist and shares their adventures in the field.

Luther J. Goldman, shown here in 1940, was the first flyway biologist for the Pacific Flyway. Photo by L. C. Goldman.

Portraits of Goldman and Gillham

Henry M. Reeves

Luther J. Goldman

Luther J. Goldman, brother of Major Edward A. Goldman, was among the pioneer Biological Survey biologists who worked on early waterfowl investigations, both in Canada and Mexico, as well as the western United States. His unpublished reports filed in the Smithsonian Institution Archives show that he conducted field investigations in North Dakota in 1931, western Canada during 1932-43, and in Mexico during 1934-37 and 1941.

Goldman first entered Canada on June 6, 1932, to undertake waterfowl investigations. His field report of June 14, 1932, describes

A laguna near San Martin Texmelucan, Puebla, Mexico, in 1903. This type of lagoon once dotted the area, but most have disappeared because the water that fed them has been diverted for agriculture. Photo by E. A. Goldman.

his entry and first impressions of drought conditions in Canada: "Continuing to Regina I passed through a region showing lack of spring rains. In some sections where the ground was plowed and planted, the loose dirt and seed had blown away and reseeding was necessary. Between Weyburn and Regina were sections where the gravelled highway was covered with black dirt."

Ironically, it was raining at the time and Goldman commented that travel was difficult due to the black "adobe" (a reflection of his southwestern heritage) dust which had lodged on the highway. On arriving in Regina he learned that all dirt roads over the greater part of Saskatchewan were reported closed to travel. Evidently this and later rains improved water conditions in some portions of Canada that Goldman visited that summer. But other areas he visited were drought stricken.

Goldman's letter of June 15, 1932, to Paul Redington, then chief of the USBS (in those days field biologists often corresponded directly with the chief), reported his views of Canadians, and future work plans:

> These Canadians are fine fellows, and I have never been shown greater assistance and courtesy. The contacts I have made are most important particularly in the initial stage of gaining an understanding of the situation. Along with this I need to be turned loose to go and come as I please, at least part of the time.

> Unless there are reasons of which I have no knowledge, it seems to me I can do a greater service for the Survey by continuing my studies in the Prairie Provinces and in North Dakota. Not even the Canadians know much about the region far North. With continued cultivation of contacts it may be that sometime I might get on with some Canadian Government outfit and have opportunity to travel by plane into the vast, practically unexplored regions far north where waterfowl are presumed to nest in vast numbers. Personally, I doubt this is a fact. This of course is just an idea, worth carrying out if opportunity presented. Next winter if possible I should like to get down into Mexico. We seem to know little more about Mexico than the far North.

The last comment is interesting in view of the extensive travels of Luther J.'s brother, Edward A., in Mexico during the turn of the century. Very likely, Luther J. was thinking of the current situation in Mexico.

Goldman requested permission to extend his Canadian studies an additional month and this was granted. He noted on July 26, 1932, to Paul Redington: "I have received letter of authority and other mail at this point. The per diem authorized will, I believe, on an average cover subsistence. There are times when $5 in Canada would fall considerably short. But at others the expense is very reasonable."

In the same letter he reported upon waterfowl conditions observed in western Saskatchewan and southern Alberta:

While conducting a waterfowl survey in Jalisco, Mexico, in 1937, Luther J. Goldman encountered rainy weather and bad roads, a combination all too common in the early years of waterfowl surveys. USFWS photo by L. J. Goldman.

Wetmore uses his traveling laboratory for badly needed shade during his duck sickness work in Utah in 1916. Photo courtesy of Smithsonian Institution.

It is my experience that it is not the large lakes that the ducks frequent to a large extent during the nesting season, but the prairie sloughs and potholes of the glacial hills. A cross section of country recording findings on all sloughs encountered will I believe give a better idea of the picture as a whole than concentration on large lakes. Close study of all lakes in the vicinity of a large lake would be good, but there is scarcely time for much of such work. My investigations to date and such as I will pick up on my way out will give a fair idea of conditions on the open prairies or cleared bush country . . . I am very glad to have this additional time here. The first month, owing to the need to reconcile several angles, it was impossible to carry out very systematic work. Also at that time few of the young ducks were in evidence. The females were on the nests and the drakes represented much of the number seen. The hatch is undoubtedly good and the young birds are reaching maturity with small losses. The sloughs where waterfowl is found present a different appearance. Due to heavy rain the vegetation in the fields adjacent to the sloughs is very rank over much of the territory. This has protected the nests from the swarming crows, and may be largely responsible for the large families. So much of the information is guess work that at this late date there is little we can depend on. Meanwhile I believe it a good idea to watch the ducks very closely and take no chances. There is an angle no one knows anything about. That is the nesting grounds farther north. There is a big job finding the facts in the matter. The Canadian officials know nothing about it.

Goldman's statements may seem contradictory insofar as water conditions and duck production are concerned. Experience has shown, however, that water conditions and duck numbers across the expanse of western Canada typically vary by locality. Seldom, if ever, are conditions uniformly excellent or poor across the breeding grounds. Goldman's observations point out the difficulties in coming to an overall assessment of conditions and duck production over the expanse of the prairies, and it was not until years later when scientifically designed aerial surveys were begun was such an appraisal possible.

Goldman's July 26th communication went on to provide information about the economics in using aircraft in Canada:

Mr. Etter has written you relative to a plane trip, for next year. The plane would be mainly of use in reaching desirable locations. Thereafter the investigations would have to be done by canoe. The price made him by the . . . Airways, Inc. of $6,000.00 for a 30 day trip is out of all reason. I am not saying it is not right enough from their standpoint, but it is too much. I have in a small way looked into the matter. I met a Major Bell at Manitoba who has spent many years in the north . . . He told me that he had connections with companies whereby he believed a price of $30 per hr. actual flying time could be had, with a minimum price of $50.00 per day up to a point where gas cost no more than $.50 per gal. That if he knew in time, that during the winter preceding a trip gas could be sent in and cached where needed. I think on a properly run trip an hour's flying per day is as much as an investigator would need. With a $50 minimum the trip could then be done for $1,500.00 instead of $6,000.00. Mr. Clark tells me that he knows of good companies who make a similar arrangement with $90.00 per day minimum. If an American Army plane could be had, the cost could be reduced to wages of a pilot and operating expenses. I presume that under present conditions a plane trip could not be managed at any price. However we are not going to know everything about waterfowl nesting conditions until something is done in the north. I believe a lot of ducks do nest north.

Goldman's desire to visit the vast area north of the prairies by plane was satisfied quickly. On July 1, 1932, he sent the following wire to Washington:

TRIP BY PLANE FROM EMMALAKE OVER UNSETTLED FORESTED AREA NORTH TO ISLE A LA CROSSE STOP WATER ABUNDANT WEATHER CLEAR COULD OBSERVE WATERFOWL ON SURFACE OF LAKES FEW DUCKS SEEN STOP RESIDENTS REPORT DUCKS PROGRESSIVELY DECREASING STOP OBSERVATION ON AREAS EXAMINED INDICATE FEW DUCKS NESTING ON SLOUGHS WITHIN THE FORESTED AREA AND LARGE PERCENTAGE OF LAKES UNSUITABLE STOP IN CLEARED AREA CONTIGUOUS TO THE PRAIRIES FULLY SEVENTY FIVE PERCENT OF THE SLOUGHS DRY STOP LARGE PERCENTAGE OF THE SLOUGHS OF PRAIRIE PROVINCES PROBABLY PERMANENTLY DRY.

Goldman's letter to Redington, written the following day, provided additional details of what may have been the first use of aircraft to assess waterfowl conditions and populations in Canada, at least by a USBS biologist:

> Have just returned from the trip by plane north over the uninhabited bush and muskeg and lake country. The trip was made with Mr. Etter and Ted White of the American Game Association. The plane was chartered by the Saskatchewan Game Branch and as cost of operating is high —$70 per hour actual flying time, our trip was very limited. We had two days on the trip spending much of the time at landing points. Plane was equipped with pontoon landing gear as there are not landing places in that country. We visited lakes north to the Churchill district which is tributary to Hudson Bay. On our return we stopped at Prince Albert National Park, picked up the superintendent, Major Woods, and covered a part of that region. Lakes visited were in part Smooth Stone, Sled, Isle A La Crosse and Waskesiu and Emma Lakes. From the air we looked down on multitudes of lakes, potholes and sloughs and streams. Landing was also made at Dore Lake. We had a good look at the Beaver River which flows into Churchill waters and should be good nesting ground. The waters are now in flood and may have drowned out nesting birds. Weather was clear and with good glasses I could at 2,000 feet altitude readily see waterfowl.

On the same date in a personal letter to Redington, exclaimed Goldman, "Skiing down a steep mountain side is the sport of kings, but flying over that magnificent picture beyond the edge of the bush country is a fit diversion for the gods."

It seems evident that the airplane was then viewed primarily as a means of going to remote areas where grounded studies would be undertaken. No thought had yet been given to flying transects at low altitudes to count waterfowl, but the use of aircraft in waterfowl management had begun.

Goldman returned to western Canada in 1933 through 1935, and an undated and unedited handwritten report of 1936 or later graphically described the major waterfowl habitats found in Canada. His description of the key prairie and parklands zones of western Canada follows:

Treeless Prairie (Transition Zone)

This area is situated immediately north of the International Boundary in Alberta and Saskatchewan. It extends north to Red Deer in Alberta and Saskatoon in Saskatchewan, and from the Rocky Mountains in Alberta to Regina in Saskatchewan. The length east and west is about 400 miles. The extreme width about 230 miles. The area is approximately 100,000 square miles.

The general topography of the region is prairie, varying in contour from flat to abruptly rolling and with many groups of low rounded hills, the debris of glacial moraines. An outstanding physical feature of this region is the great terminal moraine of the last glacial period which extends across the provinces south of Medicine Hat and Moose Jaw.

Precipitation varies from 15 inches up. Much of this is in the form of summer rain. June is normally a wet month.

Natural vegetation is buffalo and grama grass and a variety of land and aquatic plants. There is practically no natural timber.

The region contains several lakes and great numbers of sloughs and potholes. The sloughs are mainly supported by local run off of snow and rain water. The best of these are usually in the abruptly rolling prairies and glacial moraines.

Much of the area due to arid nature, topography and subsoil condition was probably never important slough country.

Since pioneer times the region has been greatly modified by settlement. Much of the prairie sod has been plowed up and planted to grain. With settlement followed drainage and lowering of the water table and heavy grazing of the sloughs. From about 1921 followed a generally dry cycle. In late 1929 a severe drought began. By 1931 with the exception of the best lakes and scattering of sloughs, the nesting ground had disappeared. In succeeding years up to 1935 possibly 10 percent of the sloughs, particularly along the northern half were in some years partially restored. With lowered water table, moderate accumulations in the sloughs no longer resting on ground water, quickly disappear. During several years this block of country has been practically out of the picture as nesting ground. This is the so called "drought stricken area" credited with losses among nesting ducks.

Poplar Savanna (Transition Zone)

This life zone is situated north and east of the treeless prairie in Alberta, Saskatchewan and Manitoba.

The northern limit in Alberta is Lesser Slave Lake, in Saskatchewan, Prince Albert. In Manitoba the southern part of Lake Winnipegosis.

The area in the three provinces is approximately 130,000 square miles.

The general topography of this area is prairie varying in contour from flat to abruptly rolling and with many groups of glacial hills. Soil condition is generally favorable to the production of abundant plant foods including aquatic species.

Precipitation is greater than on the open prairies. The region contains a number of large lakes and multitudes of sloughs and potholes where contour, drainage, subsoil and ground water conditions are favorable. These sloughs are largely the result of local precipitation.

In pioneer times this region was partially timbered with small poplar, aspen and willows. Wild rose and saskatoon are common. It is now much modified by settlement. Much of the timber has been cleared and the lands planted to grain.

Settlement has resulted in much drainage, the water table has lowered and many lakes have receded.

During the drought the southern borders of this zone were affected. The drying of sloughs appears to have been gradual, with no evidence of direct losses among nesting ducks. Although modified by settlement and unproductive in part, this block of country is one of the best nesting units on the continent.

Modesty and the appreciation for the efforts of others were evident traits of the Goldman brothers. Apparently a number of Canadian officials wrote to the USBS in 1932 complimenting it on the work performed by Goldman. L. J. characteristically explained: "Any success I may have had in Canada, in many contacts with officials and others is due to the fine courtesy . . . I encountered throughout my work. An American official who could not get along with these people would be poor stuff."

Charlie Gillham, the first Mississippi Flyway Biologist, appropriately attired for waterfowl survey work in the Arctic. USFWS photo by J. Lynch.

Charles E. Gillham

Charlie Gillham, the first Mississippi Flyway Biologist, spent "several eternities" in the Arctic. Waterfowl survey assignments took him to broad areas of northwestern Canada during 1935-1940 and later into Alaska. Impressed by the raw character and vicissitudes of the Canadian Subarctic and Arctic, he combined an easy and unaffected writing style into colorful and interesting field reports. Excerpts from his 1937 report titled *Trip to the Delta of the Mackenzie River, N.W.T.* richly describe his experience in conducting waterfowl investigations in the far North:

> A field trip in almost any part of the United States is not hard to reckon with for the most of us. We can drive to the job in our cars, or go with our pack outfits, or in our boats, and need give but little consideration as to where we will be stopping the next night. Provisions can be had, communication with our superiors for advice is easy, and almost anything that we need can be procured without any great difficulty.
>
> Such is the absolute reverse in the Far North. Transportation is the most difficult

problem unless unlimited funds are available. Even small trading posts and villages are often several days apart, and frequently real hardship must be encountered in reaching them. Pests, mosquitoes and black flies, are one of the greatest reducers of the human morale that has ever been encountered. Poor and inadequate food is another. Lack of news of the outside world and possible need of medical attention is also a boogey man always hiding behind one's back. Well equipped costly expeditions do not have this trouble. However, the limited funds, and the hiring of conveniences as one goes make field work very difficult in the North.

Preparing to search for the then unknown breeding grounds of the Ross' goose, Gillham elaborated:

For any of these trips to be undertaken, much detailed work must be done previous to the going. It is not a lark in any sense of the word and represents hours of planning and thought. In the early part of April, 20 degrees below zero weather will be encountered. Hard Arctic winds will confine one to a very small snow house, or board shack during this time. Caribou skin clothing must be made and paid for. Foods will need be flown in, and they are very limited and poor at the best. The Morse code should be learned, and a sending and receiving set taken along, for one is out of contact with all the world. Natives must be hired, they have no conception of money or proper wages. Gifts must be produced — it all runs into a lot of money and preplanning.

After such a trip one is out of touch with things. It is hard to settle down and get one's work done. The world has revolved and one is out of step with things. It takes months to get back on a firm equilibrium again. For days in a row the sun never sets and sleep is interrupted and not restful. The monotonous fish diet and poorly balanced meals reduce one's vitality. The millions of mosquitoes — forever pestering — and the wondering if all is well on the outside, seems to take something out of one that is hard to restore. Such are the things one need experience if the Ross' goose is to be located. It is anything but a pleasure jaunt and should not be confused with large well equipped expeditions that have all the comforts of home with them.

Gillham repeatedly referred to mosquitoes, one of several insect scourges of the North which affect whites and natives alike during the brief summer period. After but three summers in the Arctic, he wrote, "several eternities have seemingly been spent in an isolated mosquito infested wilderness."

He repeatedly described the problems of transport over vast and nearly inaccessible areas.

Working in the barren and coast areas, transportation is still a more difficult problem. Boats must be resorted to entirely, unless a plane is available. It is impossible to get any place overland. Many of the lakes to be visited are inland from any navigable waterways.

Any boat drawing more than three feet of water is very difficult to manage in the Deltas and on the Arctic Coast. Even a boat of this size must have a canoe aboard for side trips into more shallow areas. Fuel for boats is also a great problem.

Gillham lived among Eskimos and Indians over broad areas of the Arctic and was in a unique position to observe their taking of wildlife for subsistence purposes. He stated:

One still hears considerable of the damage done by the Eskimo and Indian on account of their egg gathering activities. Several white trappers at Aklavik were bitter in their accusations of the Eskimos for this practice. After spending two summers with the Eskimos, the writer does not attach a great amount of importance to these charges. Natives do use a few wildfowl eggs. However, the population is so small that it is hardly the gigantic thing as represented by many would-be conservation groups. The Police are steadily discouraging the practice, and with the Indian tribes have accomplished a great amount of good. The traders have done their part, in developing the north and making it possible for natives to be able to trade at many places, and buy food stuffs, rather than feed off the country.

Practically all Eskimos bunch up in the summer months and visit. Their congregating points are seldom in a good location for egg gathering, then too, the trader is handy and has many things more toothsome. Many villages of Eskimos are formed to hunt whales, and fish, and this occupation prevents much time being spent in hunting eggs.

Waterfowl are killed at odd times for food, but it is not the young, or nesting females that are chosen. When fall migration comes on, it is impossible to legally kill birds, as the open season comes after the freeze-up. Also when fall birds are on wing, all hands are working feverishly to get up a supply of fish to freeze and be used for dog feed.

Field reports of USBS and USFWS biologists assigned to waterfowl investigations in Canada are replete with praise for the many Canadians with whom they worked or associated. In addition to his association with Indians and Eskimos, Gillham worked with Royal Canadian Mounted Police, government officials, trappers, traders, missionaries, doctors, and representatives of that ubiquitous corporation, the Hudson's Bay Company (often simply referred to as "the Bay"). A great deal of understanding and tact was obviously necessary in such situations. Gillham's appreciation and praise for the diverse peoples of the far North is best described in his own words:

> There is no lack of cooperation by the residents and officials. They are always more than willing to help out in any way that they can. In fact, their interest and spirit is such, that often one wonders would the reverse be true if they were working in our country. One thing has been always kept in mind by the writer, and should be strictly remembered by all investigators who are the guests of the Canadian Government. Remember that we are their guests, and are there by their courtesy. Over-officialness, and over-inquisitiveness are two cardinal sins that will never be forgotten by the Northern Canadians. They are a pioneer people and are over friendly to those who are likewise. There is no place in the North for the man who cannot look after himself. He must shoulder his burdens and make himself as little an imposition on the various communities that he visits as he can. People in the North all have duties to perform, and none are engaged in the enterprise of guiding. When they help you, it is not for the monetary considerations involved, but because they are a fine friendly people and anxious to be of assistance to you.

Elsewhere, Gillham asserted, "Canadians are truly the most hospitable people in the world."

One of Gillham's goals was to find the breeding ground of the Ross' goose, the diminutive white goose that wintered in the Central Valley of California. The populations at that time evidently numbered only a few thousand birds and considerable concern existed about the status of the species. During the spring migration, Ross' geese stopped near Fort Chipewyan for a few days and then

Newly hatched goslings.

departed northeasterly for their breeding grounds. Gillham wrote the lack of fear of man was perhaps the chief cause of their scarcity. He wrote: "Often the hunter could attract a wide flying flock of birds by waving his hat at them and shouting. For this ungoose-like characteristic they were called silly galoots, and today go almost entirely by the name of Galoot by the native population."

Gillham discussed and corresponded widely with people in the Arctic about the possible locations of the Ross' goose nesting ground. His several attempts to locate the site were interrupted by poor flying weather and other mishaps. It fell to Angus Gavin of "the Bay" to find the Perry River nesting grounds, thereby earning himself a niche in the annals of North American ornithology. Gavin later joined Ducks Unlimited (Canada).

Those interested in the conditions in the Canadian Arctic during the mid-to-late 1930s will enjoy Gillham's *Raw North,* published in 1947. This earthy but highly readable book was obviously written by one who understood and loved the Far North and its inhabitants.

Charlie Gillham attaches a leg band to a gosling, assisted by an Eskimo named Raymond. USFWS photo by J. Lynch.

Voyages of the Flapjack

John J. Lynch

"You seem to be a middlin'-fair botanist, John. Perhaps you should come north with me this summer."

"Glad to, Charlie, if you think I could be of help."

"If I didn't think you could help, I wouldn't have asked."

Gillham's voice had a certain gruffness, but there was a twinkle in his eyes that took the sting out of that. I certainly wanted to go north with this fabulous character, Charlie Gillham. I was very pleasantly surprised with the fact that he asked me to go. Charlie didn't invite many people to go along with him on these trips.

I had met Charlie on the Gulf Coast, where I was working for the Branch of Research in what was then the Bureau of Biological Survey (USBS). My winter sched-

ule and his were such that we had frequent opportunities to work together. It was certainly an education to be in the field with a competent outdoorsman like Charlie.

Once the decision to go north had been agreed upon, there was a long period of preparation. This I could appreciate. I had spent a bit of time in the outdoors myself, and knew the value of being ready for whatever might occur.

We assembled our gear, clothing, and eiderdown sleeping bags. Uncle Sam didn't supply his troops' photographic equipment in those days, so we packed our own Leica cameras. We bought, out of our personal funds, bulk black-and-white film, Agfa Superpan Supreme, and cartridges that we were able to load in a changing bag. I might mention that the changing bag was the cause of much amused comment later that summer; whenever one of us had to load film, with both hands stuck in that bag for several minutes, the rest of his body would be surrounded by blood-thirsty mosquitos. One coudn't really do much during that time but grin and bear it (and the grin, as we consoled one another, was optional).

Charlie had taken a liking to some of our southern goodies, and so insisted that we bring along a fifty-pound sack of white hominy grits. He felt this would be a fine thing to introduce into the Far North, and it also made fine camp groceries.

I finally got all my gear together and met Charlie at what he called his "hog ranch" at Edwardsville, Illinois. At about that time Charlie was walking around and around a box which had just arrived. We both opened it, finding in it a large bundle of canvas, some two-by-fours, machine bolts with wing-nuts, and a bunch of metal ribs. I asked Charlie, "What in heaven's name is that?" Charlie replied, "After many years of research, this is the kind of boat we need for this summer's work." I said, "Charlie, I'm very anxious to see how this thing operates," so we got out the direction book and put the cotton-pickin' thing together.

It was really quite a rig. The two-by-fours, when all bolted together, extended a distance of about twenty feet from bow to stern, and the ribs were placed in at right angles to this keelson (I guess you'd call it). Then the canvas was snugged in over the whole thing, which up to that time had looked like the skeleton of a fish but now was fleshed out with waterproofed skin. An inflatable sponson ran around the gunwales of this strange-looking watercraft. Then there was a cover that could be laced in place over the top of the entire boat and its load. It had two openings such as one might find in a kayak and some of the other Eskimo types of boats, complete with drawstrings.

After having assembled this thing, we hauled it down to a creek near Charlie's hog ranch, and I noted that at least it did stay afloat. Charlie said, "Tentatively, we can give this vessel a name now that it has officially been launched. It shall henceforth be known as the *Flapjack*." I said, "Dr. Gillham, *Flapjack* it is." May I remark for the benefit of naval architects of the future that this thing appeared to have the buoyancy characteristics of a piece of newspaper that is gently allowed to float on the surface of the water. Any wave that might strike the *Flapjack* would not break over the obstruction. Its movement merely ran right through it. Strangely enough the idea seemed to work. The craft was really quite seaworthy. I can speak as an authority on this subject, for I cut my eye teeth on a catboat on the cold North Atlantic Ocean, and I knew something about boat-handling in rough water.

So we dried the *Flapjack* out, put it carefully back in its box along with the rest of our gear, and shipped the whole works by rail to Seattle, then by steamer to Seward. Charlie and I took the train to Seattle, and rode the steamer along with our gear to Seward. Then we boarded the old Narrow Gauge Railroad to Fairbanks, stopping to chase stray moose off the tracks. When we arrived at Fairbanks, folks there were giving serious consideration to installing sidewalks (although they were not quite ready for such foolishness, back in 1940).

We finally pried loose from Fairbanks via a stage route up to a settlement called Circle City. The latter was a small village on the banks of the Yukon, located almost on the Arctic Circle, hence the name. There we reassembled the *Flapjack* and got it out on the turbulent Yukon River, and the thing *still* floated. After many fond farewells and sad shaking of heads among Charlie's friends —and Charlie seemed to know everybody in that country — we headed down the Yukon, having ourselves a wonderful time. We stopped here and there in the braiding channels to study nesting geese and other wildlife, until finally we got to the settlement known as Fort Yukon. That's where the boisterous Porcupine River meets the Yukon.

Charlie's friends, naturally, were gathered at the beach there at Fort Yukon, and they offered a great deal of comment (not much of it complimentary), on the *Flapjack*. One guy said, "Charlie, I have seen many things float down this river, but never in all my born days have I ever seen anything like that. What is it?"

Charlie, with his usual aplomb, answered, "That is the *Flapjack*, the very latest thing in flotation for all purposes." I will say this, there was method in this madness, because the *Flapjack* had by then already passed many tests in shoal rapids, backwaters, and deep eddies. At the termination of all that use, it could be knocked down, rolled up in a little package and thrown into an airplane, such as an old bush Fairchild or some other relic, and flown to the next place.

So after having made amenities there at Fort Yukon, where I met some very wonderful people, we started up the Porcupine. It is quite a river, and we had no business trying to go upstream against the torrent of water that poured down from its source in the Yukon Territories. But we went anyway.

Very fortunately, we ran across a trader who was pushing a barge load of trading goods up to the village of Old Crow. And after a brief conversation and a cup or two of the "juice of the grape" we arranged to ship aboard as deck hands. We folded up the *Flapjack* — and loaded it on the barge. So long as the barge was under way during the day, Charlie and I were now free to watch the country go by. The barge was pushed by a Kermath-powered motorboat. When it would tie up for the night, Charlie and I would scour the nearby country, having had a good rest during the day. It was a very convenient arrangement.

At long last we came to the village of Old Crow. This is located in the Yukon Territories at the point where the Old Crow River flows into the Porcupine. Of course, we immediately got in touch with the local Royal Canadian Mounted Police (RCMP). This RCMP man was Corporal Bayne. Like so many of the mounties, Corporal Bayne was a good bird observer, and made Charlie and me very welcome. He arranged things so we could spend our first ten days in the Yukon Territory in the local "slammer." Let me hasten to explain, both Charlie and I have always been models of rectitude. Certainly we were not given to the bending of any laws. It so happens that this jailhouse at

Old Crow had just been erected and was really the best building in town. In fact, Corporal Bayne admitted in a moment of weakness that he had given serious thought to moving into the place himself. He said, "My God, this edifice has wall-to-wall floors — made of straw but, nevertheless, quite comfortable."

We spent the next two weeks probing into the fabulous wetlands of the Old Crow Flats. We found all sorts of interesting things, such as nesting canvasbacks, with the guidance of Corporal Bayne.

At long last, a bush plane flew in from Aklavik, so we rolled up the *Flapjack*, put it aboard along with the rest of our gear, and headed over the Richardson Range into the village of Aklavik in the Mackenzie Delta — the "Mississippi of the North."

Another period of meeting folks and making amenities. This "amenities" bit may sound a bit ridiculous, but one did not travel in that country all by oneself. And one did not, as long as he was with Charlie Gillham, go into another man's territory without first stopping and meeting the local fellow to tell him who he was, what he was doing, and generally be as nice a guy as he knew how.

I also learned that while these folks in the Far North were always friendly and happy to see a new face and have a new voice enter into the local conversations, they sized a man up very quickly. It seemed as though they placed a man into one of two categories. First, there was the casual visitor, to whom they were always very gracious; but that's as far as it went. Then there was another category, but not many people made this higher grade. Yet Charlie Gillham certainly did, with everybody he met all over the Far North. Charlie was invited to go on trips where no one else could "buy in," for a very simple reason. These folks didn't rent out their services as guides back in those days. When they asked someone to come along on a trip, they did so for two reasons: one, they liked the guy; and two, they had enough confidence in him to believe, should some accident intervene, he could take over and get them both back to safety.

In any event, after all the amenities had been attended to, we unrolled the *Flapjack* again and down the MacKenzie we went, stopping here, there and the next place. I might mention we went into that country at a time when the bush planes couldn't have done us much good on the Arctic Coast. They could get us into Aklavik on wheels, but north of there they could not land because there was still too much floe ice to land an airplane on skis. And of course, wheel landings were out of the question.

After many vicissitudes, we finally got down to the Arctic Coast where the snow geese nest on the outermost islands of the MacKenzie Delta.

The *Flapjack* was proving to be a remarkable vessel. The more I saw of that strange contraption, the more respect I had for it. It was utterly incredible. On board this contrivance of two-by-fours, metal ribs, and water-proofed canvas, we carried all of the equipment we needed for an entire summer's work. This included tents, sleeping bags, food, and most importantly, fuel.

Being on the river delta, we were fortunate enough to have firewood brought by the mighty McKenzie River down from the timbered lands into the treeless tundra country. The firewood was always damp, to be sure, but it burned. We also had all of our camera equipment and first-aid supplies.

We had to do some improvising, however. It was very difficult to keep glassware of any sort intact in a limber watercraft that flexed with every passing wave.

Part of my job was collecting invertebrates and the stomach contents of various animals. Instead of carefully pickling these in glass containers with formalin, I found that an old automobile innertube worked just fine. I cut a V-shaped hole in this innertube that could be sealed with a piece of adhesive tape. I also had a can of formalin a water solution of formaldehyde gas. My specimens were first soaked in the metal can of formalin, allowed to drain, then popped into the innertube. Then I sealed the hole with the tape to pre-

vent the escape of the preserving gas.

We also had two or three (or maybe seven or eight) containers made of genuine glass. These containers were filled with a fluid far more precious than formalin. Chemically known as ethanol, it was 190-proof alcohol. This ethanol was originally designed to preserve any specimens we might collect. But for some reason or other, it seemed to have a very high rate of evaporation, especially when we stopped to visit with some of Charlie's friends in the thirsty Far North.

Anyway, we finally made it on out to the tip end of the McKenzie Delta, past country where sandhill cranes were nesting. We could see where the snow geese had waited for the ice to go out of the Beaufort Sea, during which time they gouged out great holes in the beds of equisetum (horsetail) along the channels of the MacKenzie. Finally, almost within sight of Kendall Island, we came upon the islands where the snow geese were nesting.

After some scouting, we located an island high enough to pitch a tent and make camp. It wasn't really very high, and, as we found out later, it wasn't quite high enough.

Once we had camp set up, then came the business of doing our routine studies of nest success among the snow geese. We also checked the nest success of the brant, which were mostly the black subspecies that nested in that country (although we did collect some specimens of the Atlantic brant that far west). Our observations were not by any means confined to waterfowl. As a matter of fact, the whole plant and animal kingdom in that fascinating land won our interest. I struggled with my plant press trying to collect specimens of various types of vegetation. As for specimens of animal life, if they were big enough to eat, we ate them. Along those lines, I recall rather vividly when we ran a bit short of groceries. We feared, during one period of really bad weather, that we might have to shoot nonbreeding birds for food.

We had tried to launch our boat from the tip end of one of the islands, only to get caught in a storm and tossed back to shore, ripping the bottom out of *Flapjack*. Things got a bit "hairy." For four days and nights we made sure there were two of our party, which included Charlie, myself, and an Eskimo boy, awake and walking around. We were only inches above thawing permafrost, sleeping in eiderdowns. We don't know what might have happened to us had we slept overlong in that all-pervading chill, but we saw what happened to nesting snow geese under such circumstances. They tried to keep their eggs warm in that thawing permafrost and dared not leave their nests to feed. Many saw fit to stay with the eggs and died. However, we put those victims to good use.

Our party didn't have to shoot birds after all. We merely picked the dead females off the nests and ate them, and had the half-incubated eggs for dessert. It sounds a bit primitive, but the Romans have a saying that covers situations of that nature: "Hunger is the finest of flavoring." The Arctic can be a grim country. I had suspected this right along, but when one finds himself face to face with this fact, it is a bit shattering.

Before we completed our work on the actual nesting grounds of the snow geese, Charlie learned that once the young hatched and were able to leave the nests they then moved back into the inner islands of the delta. So we broke camp and went back into the inner islands in hopes of catching a bunch of these birds and banding them, thereby enabling us to track down their wintering grounds. (No one was sure at that time whether they wintered along the Pacific Coast or went down to the Gulf Coast.)

We had aboard the incredible *Flapjack* quite a bunch of fishnet that could be used for many purposes — and was. It could be employed as a barrier or a drive fence to catch flightless young and their parents, who were undergoing wing moult and could not fly.

Our first drives were not very productive.

1980-81 Mallards *by Richard W. Plasschaert*

This tent was home to Charlie Gillham and John J. Lynch on their 1940 waterfowl survey in the MacKenzie Delta of Canada's Northwest Territories. USFWS photo by J. Lynch.

We soon found that the place where we were trying to catch these geese enabled the birds to make fools of us. They were going down one channel and not coming out the far end of it. After a little scouting, we found that they were crossing overland and coming out the mouth of another channel. So we took our fishnet and made a new barrier and a catching chamber on either end. We then came very close to catching almost four-thousand of these geese in one big drive, but actually only got about forty-five. Our Eskimo boy, Raymond, happened to be in the wrong position at the key moment, and that blew that operation. Unfortunately, we had staked as much gasoline as we dared expend on that operation, and so had to quit banding.

We had two outboards, by the way. One was a five horsepower for the heavy work, such as going up the McKenzie to Aklavik to get back home. We also had a half-horse "eggbeater" for routine missions, and we fed gasoline into that little outboard almost with an ink dropper. We learned about the conservation of petroleum very early in the game. Remember, all the gas that we would have burned that summer was aboard the *Flapjack* when it left Aklavik.

Well, that pretty well wraps up our experiences on the MacKenzie Delta. Of course, I could branch out in many other directions, but eventually we got back into Aklavik.

There we rolled up the *Flapjack* again, and a bush plane picked us up. We had hopes of getting over to Coppermine, but those plans fell through. So we made our way south via Great Slave and Port Radium down to Fort Chipewyan and spent ten very wonderful days on the Athabasca Delta. We tried some banding there, without a great deal of success. Then we headed towards Edmonton for a little bit of respite from those mosquitos and to enjoy such a thing as a square meal and a sleep between sheets. It was quite an experience.

That summer taught me many, many things. But foremost among them was the high esteem that the folks of the Far North had for a flyway biologist by the name of Charles E. Gillham.

It seemed then that everybody in the Far North knew Charlie, and he knew them. He was accepted, but because he was liberal with his money, because he didn't have much. He was accepted not because of this or that or the next thing — but because he loved that country just as so many of them did. I still remember vividly some of the people we met in the Far North during those years. There were some folks there who had more academic degrees than you could count. Yet, they decided they would rather spend their lives in the North where the action was, where things were real. Charlie was cut out of that same bolt of cloth, and was welcome among those folks, regardless of their background.

Charlie wrote a book in 1947, published by A.S. Bond and Company, in New York. In that book, Frank DuFresne, who was an old veteran of the Far North and especially Alaska himself, mentioned that there was actually three Charlie Gillhams.

The first Charlie was pretty much the one I described. As Frank put it, four days after he had left the last railhead, given time to grow a decent stubble on his ruddy face, Charlie could match any of the old-timers of the Far North. The second Charlie was a man who, given a shave and a clean shirt, was a country squire, a gracious man with a lovely family and a fine farm in Illinois. Yet there was still another Charlie, the one familiar to those who attended the wildlife meetings. He liked to hunt and fish, and was a crack shot with a rifle and shotgun. He was a crusader and a conservationist. He knew whereof he spoke because he had covered North America, and I do mean covered it, from the Far North to Central America.

To some he may have appeared to have been a rather crusty individual with the hide of a snapping turtle. Yet there was a part of him not generally known; he had the soul of a poet. He had written another book, a book entirely of Eskimo fairy tales.

Charlie could not abide sham. He was tolerant, almost to a fault. But the one thing that would rouse his ire was for some character to speak as though he knew "all the answers" when he obviously didn't even have a very good grasp of the questions.

Charlie was not the first biologist, by any means. It is to be hoped he will not be the last of his special kind. He blazed many trails through regions, north and south, trails that are now relatively easy going for today's flyway biologist.

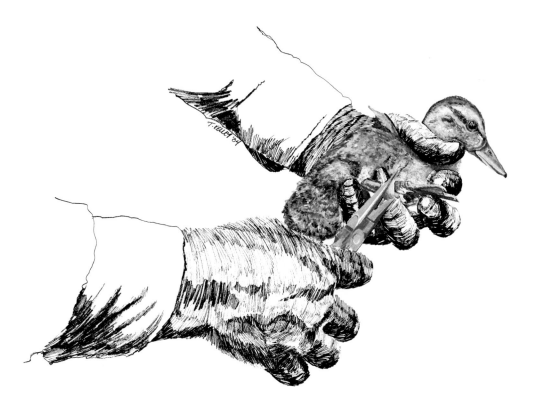

© H. A. Hochbaum

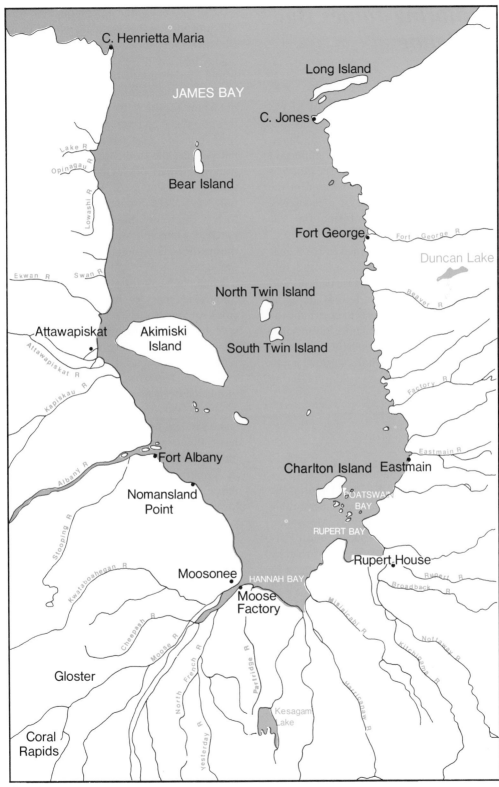

James Bay

Exploring James Bay by Canoe

Robert H. Smith

The annual status report of the USFWS for 1943-44 tersely stated: "Investigations were made on the marshes bordering James Bay. Although believed to be an important breeding ground for Canada geese, little was known of the waterfowl population of the region. During the course of a six weeks' study much valuable information was obtained."

I was the biologist assigned to the James Bay investigations, spending June and July of 1943 along the south and east coasts, and from June 19 to October 1, 1944 along the west coast. My mission was to determine the nature and function of the James Bay marshes with respect to waterfowl and their total contribution to the continental waterfowl population. Here is the log of my field work during the two seasons.

1943 Trip

I arrived at Moose Factory, Ontario, the evening of June 2, 1943, after a memorable train ride from Cochrane to Moosonee, Ontario, and thence by canoe to Moose Factory. Fortunately, I had been forewarned by Dominion Wildlife Officer Dr. Harrison F. Lewis and had provided myself with a lunch for the 186-mile, 12-hour journey. I was also fortunate in selecting June 2 as the date on which to travel, as the next train, leaving Cochrane on June 9, did not arrive at Moosonee until June 11!

Since I had made no advance arrangements some delay was experienced in obtaining a guide, canoe, and motor. But with the help of W. J. Cobb, manager of the Moose Factory post, I finally obtained the services of George Carey, a Metis, his twenty-three-foot freight canoe and outboard motor. The

weather also conspired against me, so it was not until June 14 that we finally set out from Moose Factory on the morning tide.

Our first camp was made at Ship Sands Island at the mouth of the Moose River. Here, I had the unique experience of bailing out a tent, for the water and bug-proof contraption that I had purchased especially for the trip leaked nearly as rapidly as the rain fell outside; the floor, which was the only waterproof part of the tent, prevented the water from seeping out. Consequently, the only way to keep our duffle partially dry was to bail constantly during the night. Fortunately, the tent underwent a metamorphosis during the soaking and leaked no more after that date.

I had planned to spend only a day on the Ship Sands marshes, but a fresh northwest gale kept us marooned on the island until the seventeenth, when we made a short run east along the south coast to Partridge Creeks, remaining there until the noon tide the following day. From this camp the pack ice was visible a mile or more out to sea.

Shortly after leaving Partridge Creeks, a sudden storm forced us to put in at Nattabiska Point, where we stayed until shortly after midnight, breaking camp at two o'clock in the morning to take advantage of the early morning tide. We attempted to run to the lower end of Hannah Bay but were left stranded on the mud flats during the ebb. Travel was resumed on the flood tide in the afternoon. We made camp at the mouth of West River (Kesagami), where we remained until the afternoon of the twenty-second, part of our stay being enforced due to high winds. In fact, during a heavy gale on the morning of the twenty-second, a ten- or twelve-foot tide — at least six feet higher than normal — flooded our camp and food cache.

On the evening of June 22 we left West River to make a short run up the Harricanaw River, investigating the concentration of Canada geese around the lower islands the following day. Late in the evening of the next day we again broke camp and headed for the

Misisikabie River on the east side of Hannah Bay, but falling tides forced us in Piscapecassy Creek, a few miles short of our goal. Here again we were delayed by adverse winds and were not able to get away until the morning of June 26, making a short run to Plover Shoals.

It seemed as though bad luck dogged our wake as we were wind-bound on Plover Shoals for five days. During that time we ran out of fresh water. As our camp was situated only slightly above normal high tides, we watched the water come in each night with some apprehension, resulting in little sleep for all because the flood during that period came in during the wee hours of the morning. The wind at last moderated the night of June 30, so we broke camp at midnight, poled our outfit across the numerous reefs and were in the clear by daylight. That day we ran as far as Point Comfort by laying up at Mosakonan Point during the ebb. From Point Comfort I covered the upper end of Cabbage Willows Bay marshes. On July 3 we ran to Ruperts House, Quebec, as we were running short of supplies.

Through the cooperation of the Hudson Bay Company personnel at Ruperts House, I was able to purchase my requirements on Sunday. The next day, however, the wind was too high to travel. We did not get away until July 6, running that day to Boatswain Bay. We left there late in the evening of July 7 and ran to an island off the mouth of the Jackfish River, where we camped. The following day we broke camp early and arrived at the Hudson Bay post on the Eastmain River, where I received word that the company's motor vessel *Fort Charles* would arrive at Factory River the following day.

Since I had planned to return to Moose Factory on this vessel, we set out on July 9 and ran all the way to Factory River, meeting the *Fort Charles* there that evening. Upon learning that the vessel was en route to Fort George and would return to Moose by way of Factory River, I left my outfit and guide at the latter post and went to Fort George on the *Fort Charles*. This unexpected bit of fortune enabled me to obtain an idea of the coastal habitat and attendant bird life along the northeast coast, as the channel follows the inside passage among the islands all the way.

We arrived at Fort George on July 10, running through pack ice part of the way, and left again on July 14, picking up my outfit at Factory River the following morning. We then ran to Charleton Island, where we rode out a heavy gale in the lee of the island on the sixteenth. This delay allowed me to make a short reconnaissance of the area. The next morning we made the crossing to Moosonee where, even though the wind had abated, the water was still so rough that some of the crew became seasick.

On July 19 I again ran down the Moose River as far as Ship Sands Island to get a series of marsh plants for identification, returning to Moose Factory the following day.

I left Moosonee three days later on the weekly train and was pleasantly surprised at the rapid progress made to Cochrane, the trip back consuming only ten hours.

From the above itinerary one would naturally suppose that a considerable amount of time was lost due to inability to travel. Such was not the case, however, as practically all of the time we were wind-bound was profitably spent in the marshes, resulting in more intensive studies carried on in fewer areas. We were able to cover about four square miles of marsh from each camp of over one day. We covered much less area at other spots where we stayed one day or less. The ideal system would be to travel on the still days and spend the windy days in the marsh, which would not only simplify navigation but keep the flies and mosquitoes blown clear. Unfortunately, this plan seldom worked out in practice.

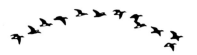

1944 Trip

I arrived at Moosonee, Ontario, the evening of June 14 on the semiweekly train from Cochrane, Ontario, and made the crossing to Moose Factory by canoe. As evidence that James Bay was rapidly becoming exposed to the influence of civilization, I wish to submit that there were now twice as many trains running to Moosonee as in 1943 and instead of being required to fast during the trip as heretofore, the equipment now included a "club car" where one could appease the pangs of hunger. The engineer, however, had not lost his delicate touch; I still marvel at his ability to jerk the train harder from a standing start than I had thought possible.

Upon arrival at Moose Factory, I learned that George Carey, my guide in 1943, was not particularly anxious to make the trip because he was unfamiliar with the coast beyond Fort Albany and loath to start with only one outboard motor, his spare being broken. Rather than start on a trip of several months with a man who was not particularly willing to go, I decided to engage natives who were at home on the entire west coast. Consequently, with the help of R. M. Duncan, manager of the Moose Factory post, I made arrangements with two Cree Indians from Attawapiskat to make the trip, John as steersman and Joseph as bowman. Duncan furnished a twenty-foot freight canoe and the extra equipment needed. Because no outboard motor was available, we rigged the canoe with a mast and a sail, the end product resembling a Chinese junk.

The next few days were used in assembling and packing the gear and supplies. On June 19 we left Moose Factory on the evening tide, paddling to the mouth of the Moose River before making camp in the marsh. In the meantime I had acquired a passenger for Attawapiskat, an Indian boy of six, Joseph's grandson. I was undoubtedly lucky to get away without an entire Indian family, complete with women, kids, and dogs.

The next day we poled the outfit out of the river mouth and sailed up the coast about twenty miles. But because we couldn't find a creek to get in, the tide left us stranded on the mud flats about a mile offshore from a place the Indians call Shiagoakaw. Rather than sleep in the canoe, we packed our duffle through the mud to a beach ridge for the night. On June 21 we lugged our stuff back across the flats to the canoe. We got away after noon on the rising tide and sailed to a long point called Pasquache, about twenty miles distant. Traveling as we were by paddle and sail, it was necessary to take advantage of fair winds. Consequently, I could not spend as much time at some marshes as I would have liked. There were, however, certain advantages. When wind-bound, we had the opportunity to cover the marshes intensively, and get a more detailed view of the terrain and attendant bird life. I would not, however, recommend this mode of travel, as too many days were lost due to headwinds. In some stretches it became a real struggle to make any progress against tide rips, heavy seas, and adverse currents.

At Pasquache we were held up by a north wind and couldn't leave until the afternoon of June 23, when we paddled and sailed about twenty-five miles to Cockispenny Point (Kakagesheminuk), where there is relatively deep water right up to the beach ridge and the bush is but a few yards back. The following day we sailed to a small creek about a mile south of the Nawahbiskow River and camped in a good duck marsh. We left this camp the following morning at daylight, paddled to Kapiskowakuk, waited for the next flood tide, then sailed with a fair wind to the mouth of the Albany River, paddling up to the post at Fort Albany the next morning.

I stayed at Fort Albany until June 28; W. J. Anderson, manager of the Hudson Bay Company post provided accommodations in his residence. Here I obtained over 100 goose bands from the Indians as well as much valuable information from Mr. Anderson.

Soon after we left Fort Albany, a headwind sprang up that blew so hard we had to pole the canoe downstream to make any headway. Finally we reached the shelter of a small island where we made camp in a driving rain. The next day we got away on the early morning tide and paddled to the mouth of the river, waited on the evening tide and then sailed up the coast to Chickney Creek (Cheganuk), about ten miles from the mouth of the Albany, staying at this camp one day. The following day, July 1, was a memorable one as far as travel was concerned; we sailed the forty miles to the Kapiskaw River, staying well offshore for both tides. We could see Akimiski Island from the mouth of the Kapiskaw.

Shortly after we left Kapiskaw on July 2 our luck went sour. We had to paddle, pole, and drag the canoe to the mouth of the Nowashi River, a distance of about fifteen miles. The next day was a repetition of the trip to Nowashi, as we had to fight our way to the Hudson Bay Company post about eight miles up the Attawapiskat River.

I stayed at the Attawapiskat post two days, replenishing supplies and collecting goose bands from the Indians. Messrs. Dunn and Houston very kindly provided accommodations for me in the already-crowded manager's residence. At Attawapiskat I lost my passenger, for which I was thankful.

We left the Attawapiskat post the afternoon of July 6, sailing with the aid of a very strong fair wind to a small creek about two miles south of the Ekwan River. At times I thought John would drive the canoe under the heavy swells. But, being a "coaster," he was a good seaman who seemed to sense just how hard he could drive the little craft without danger of foundering.

We camped just below the Ekwan River until July 8 when we made a short run to Ekwan Point (Nealkan). At this point the coastal marshes change perceptibly, there being a series of high beach ridges most of the way to the Cape. Canoe travel beyond Ekwan Point became more difficult as ground swells were usually present and the inshore waters generally rough.

On July 9 we sailed around Ekwan Point, passing through a school of white whales that were surfacing and spouting in the shallow water, to a small creek called Cheganogohish about fifteen miles up the coast. Adverse winds held us at Cheganogohish for two days, after which we sailed to the mouth of Swan River (Wapahee seepe). We moved again on July 12 to the Neatalkan River, which proved to be nothing more than a small creek, and the next day we set sail for Kishkimon; but when the wind went north on us, we were forced to camp about four miles south of our destination. The next day the Indians sailed the canoe to Kishkimon while I walked up the coast through the marsh.

We were forced to stay at Kishkimon two days, finally getting away at daylight on July 17. We paddled to a sand reef in a pea-soup fog, waiting there for the next tide. In the late afternoon we sailed to Natanow, continuing on to the Lawashi River the next morning. While at Lawashi, the weather turned exceedingly foul, with north winds, line squalls, and almost continuous rain. To cap the matter, abnormally high tides flooded our camp three times. It was, therefore, with considerable relief that we finally left on July 22. Our good fortune was short-lived, however, for we barely reached the Opinagaw River when another siege of bad weather caught us, forcing us to camp there four days and flooding our camp once more. On July 27 the weather moderated so we paddled to the Hudson Bay post at Lake River, the last habitation on the west coast of James Bay, approximately 250 miles from Moose Factory.

We remained at Lake River for three days, replenishing supplies and collecting bird bands from the Indians encamped there. As this post had not received any supplies since the summer before, we were not able to obtain much, but the manager was good enough to furnish some food stuffs from his own mess.

We left the Lake River post on July 30, paddling to a barrier beach called Kapisquarkuk about five miles up the coast. Headwinds held us on this beach until the afternoon of August 1, when we made another six miles to Esquawakow Creek. At the latter place, the character of the coast changes from marsh and muskeg to tundra, the spruce and tamarack are only about three feet high and very scattered, and the vegetation is typically arctic.

On August 3 we paddled up the coast about twelve miles in a dead calm to a place which I named Bulldog Creek in honor of the abundance and vivacity of the flies there; it offered a good example of what life must be like in a beehive. Adverse winds held us at Bulldog Creek until August 7 when we sailed to a point called Estiguanowakaw — skull beach — because of a number of skeletons found there some years ago.

Our luck, which had been bad, became worse, so that we were not able to move again until August 15, when we paddled up the coast to a shallow bay the Indians call Kawashahowewenepaykowuk but which I called Loon Bay for simplicity. From this camp I was able to explore the tundra lake region. We moved again on August 18, paddling to a shoal about four miles up the coast where we were forced to put in again due to the heavy ground swell and breakers on the beach. We tried again on August 19 but only made a few miles more, and as we came through the surf the canoe nearly foundered, wetting our equipment. We were forced to stay at this camp which I called Eider Creek until August 21, when we paddled the last remaining miles to Cape Henrietta Maria —sixty-four days and 300 miles from Moose Factory, the last 100 miles being tough ones.

I had planned on spending a number of days on the Cape, but on the morning of August 22 we saw two vessels pass far out to sea en route to the Weenusk Post 250 miles beyond on Hudson Bay. As I had arranged to go back to Moose from Lake River on one of these vessels on its return trip, it was necessary to return as soon as possible to Lake River in order to make connections; consequently, I had only two and one-half days on the Cape.

We left the Cape at daylight on August 24 and for the next two and one-half days battled our way down the coast to Lake River against headwinds, paddling and poling all the way. When we arrived at Lake River we learned that the vessel would not stop at Lake River on its way out, but there was to be one more trip. There was nothing to do but wait, which I did for twenty days, expecting the boat in from day to day. All of this time was not lost, however, as I was camped in the marsh at the mouth of Lake River. I obtained a thorough coverage of the marsh within walking distance, and had an opportunity to observe early fall waterfowl movements on the coast. If it had been possible to have radio contact with the vessels or the dispatching office at Moosonee, this mix-up in plans could have been avoided.

On September 16 we loaded our outfit aboard the Hudson Bay motor schooner *Joy H* and started out for Moose. This little forty-five foot schooner was manned by a crew of three half-breeds and, besides myself and my two Indian guides, carried as passengers two Indian families complete with dogs, two unattached Indians, and a Catholic priest from Attawapiskat. It was a rough passage to Attawapiskat — too rough to prepare food. Most of the passengers were more interested in losing what they had already eaten, however, than in taking on anything more. The situation was further complicated by the fact that the only running water on the vessel was that which came aboard in heavy seas; consequently the rail saw double duty, often the fore and aft portions of the passengers being draped over the rail simultaneously. This scene was accompanied by the howling of the dogs, the bawling of the babies, and weeping of the women.

We arrived at Attawapiskat the evening of September 17, discharged most of our passengers but took on six more Indian families bound for Akimiski Island, a Catholic priest, and several other Indians bound for Moose. We left again on September 19, making a relatively smooth passage to Akimiski and on to Fort Albany in the night.

We left Fort Albany on the morning of

A moment of relaxation during a survey. Pilot Bob Smith strings up a flyrod on Artillery Lake Narrows, Northwest Territories. USFWS photo by J. Lynch.

September 21, then anchored in the river mouth all day and attempted the run to Moose River at night. In the meantime, however, a gale had come up out of the north, and in the storm we ran past the mouth of the Moose. At daylight we found ourselves almost in Hannah Bay. Since we only had two hours of fuel left, we anchored off the reefs at Big Stone Point to ride out the gale. We got along fairly well until one of our anchors broke; we nearly drifted on the rocks before the other anchor hit soft bottom and held. Finally the wind moderated and we ran into Moose the night of September 23. As far as I was concerned it was joyful indeed to disembark from the *Joy H.*

I left Moose Factory again on September 28, running down the Moose River to its mouth to obtain data on the food habits of the blue geese, returning to Moose Factory the next evening. After assembling and re-packing my gear I left Moose Factory for the outside on October 2, thus ending our two summers' study of the James Bay marshes.

James Bay, a Wild Inland Sea

For those unfamiliar with this great inland sea, here are some additional facts about it.

Although extending far inland, James Bay is actually an arm of the Arctic Sea, a 300-mile southward protuberance of Hudson Bay between latitudes 51 and 55 degrees north. Separating James Bay from Hudson Bay are Cape Jones and Cape Henrietta Maria on the northeast and northwest, respectively. The bay is about 130 miles wide, covering an area about the size of Lake Huron. It lies directly north of Toronto, Ontario, and Miami, Florida, at approximately the same latitude as Lake Winnipeg. Bordering it on the east is the Province of Quebec and on the west is Ontario. Islands of the Bay are in the Northwest Territories.

In addition to being an important breeding ground for certain species of waterfowl,

James Bay occupies a strategic position in the waterfowl flyway pattern of North America, being literally the spout of the Hudson Bay funnel. Migrating fowl coming out of both the eastern and western arctic regions strike the coast of Hudson Bay, turn southward and pour through the James Bay constriction, concentrating along both coasts and particularly at its southern end. From this point, some go down the Atlantic Flyway following the St. Lawrence or the Great Lakes, while others trend more to the west, following the Mississippi Flyway to south-central United States and the Gulf coast.

Geologically, the flat, monotonous south coast is underlain by nearly horizontal Devonian limestones, while the east coast is broken by outcrops of pre-Cambrian granites, gneisses, shists, and later instrusions of trap rock which give this coast its irregular shoreline, numerous islands, and rough topography.

Most of the bay is shallow, especially on the west and south coasts where, during low tides, barren boulder-strewn mud flats are exposed for distances of up to five miles out to sea. Its water is saline except near the mouths of the larger rivers where it becomes fresh to brackish, depending upon the amount of fresh water being discharged. Wave action over the shoal mud flat areas and runoff from the rivers keep the water perpetually turbid. The deeper waters of the east coast are relatively clear and quite saline, supporting growths of kelp and eel grass *(Zostera marina)*.

Along the south and east coasts the daily tide range varies from four to six feet; but under exceptional conditions, such as moon tides coincident with strong on-shore winds, this may be increased to ten or twelve feet, flooding all of the marsh lands and causing considerable destruction to bird life when occurring during the nesting season. It is from such occasional floodings, spring freshets on the tributary streams, and precipitation that water levels in marshes and the interior ponds are maintained.

On the south coast the marshes begin at the limit of normal high tide and extend shoreward for an average width of one mile. They are typical tidal marshes being dissected by numerous channels and creeks and dotted with small ponds. Superficially, they resemble the middle Atlantic marshes of the United States, but on James Bay the predominant vegetation is sedge (Carex) rather than grass (Spartina). At their upper limits the marshes grade gradually into a narrow zone of low willow growth which, in turn, merges imperceptibly with the black spruce-tamarack muskeg of the interior. In places, stranded beaches grown over in willows separate the marsh into several different zones, with the interior marshes being more peaty than those fronting the bay.

The west coast resembles the south coast except that its marshes are wider and its mud flats, during low tides, broader. Along the entire west coast there are few places where deep water comes close to shore. Between the Moose and Albany rivers are several points where the spruce forest approaches the water's edge. Below Nomansland Point most of the marshes occur as pockets between points, but between Nomansland and Ekwan Points the marsh is continuous. At Ekwan Point the marshes change perceptibly and, except for areas immediately adjacent to river mouths, there is a frontal beach ridge most of the way to the tundra. In fact, the marshes occur in strips between a series of beach ridges. About ten miles above Lake River the tundra begins and continues to Cape Henrietta Maria. In this stretch, the shoreline slopes so steeply that, even at low tide, the surf breaks along the outer beach.

The human population around James Bay in 1944 was about thirty-thousand, all natives with the exception of a few post managers, missionaries, traders, prospectors, and government officials. Of the natives, practically all were Cree Indians. A few Eskimos (Huskys) inhabited the east coast. During the summer months practically the entire native population concentrated around the few trading posts, dispersing to trapping grounds with the approach of winter. Hunting and

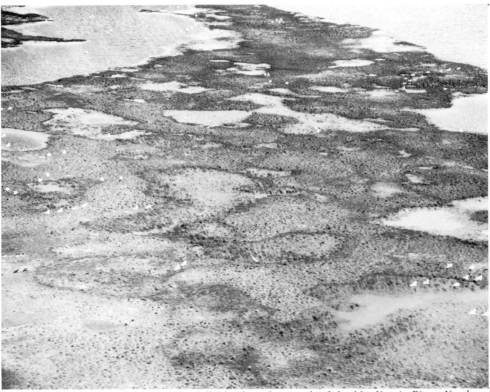

A snow goose nesting colony near Kendall Island, at the mouth of the MacKenzie River, Northwest Territories. USFWS photo by R. H. Smith.

trapping were still the principal activities of these people, just as they were during the early history of the settlement of James Bay.

It was a revelation to me to find a spot in North America, settled since 1663, where in 1944 furs were still traded for powder and shot. The natives still lived in tepees, slept in braided, rabbit-skin robes, referred to Americans as long knives — and lived much as they had for the past two hundred years. Since the fur harvest was the most important event of the year, the exchange of furs for goods was serious business. Each fur was traded individually for its worth in goods and the process often took days. The same philosophy prevailed regarding aluminum bands removed from geese that had been shot. I got them one at a time for tobacco or a cigarette, each with its own story of the place and the hunt. In short, the country was still as underdeveloped as it was when Radisson and Grosseliers first came overland from the St.

Lawrence 280 years ago and established a post.

More than thirty years after my 1944 trip, a huge development is rapidly changing the picture along the east coast of James Bay. The James Bay hydroelectric power project is designed to produce enough electricity to meet the needs of eastern Canada with enough left over to sell great amounts to northeastern United States. It involves damming and diverting some of the wild rivers entering James Bay on the Quebec side. It means connecting the area with roads to the "civilized" part of Canada, a great influx of people and money, and a total disruption of the lifestyle of the natives. Their hunting and fishing grounds will be altered or destroyed. Some of the villages will have to be relocated. The native people, of course, will be paid off in white man's currency, but in the process a great tradition and heritage will be lost forever.

But for a moment, let's return to the way it was in the early 1940s. It was, and still is, generally recognized that Indians kill migratory fowl both spring and fall. In places, the spring kill exceeds the take in the fall. This is probably a necessity in a country where other game is scarce or lacking, and is part of the Indian economy. If it were not for the waterfowl the Indians would be in a bad way, indeed.

Along the east coast practically all of the hunting was done by natives because the area was too remote to attract outside hunters. Moreover, except at a few places, there were no concentrations of fowl such as occur on the south and west coast. The heavy kill was on Canada geese, except at the south end of Hannah Bay (Cabbage Willows) where blue geese took the brunt of the shooting. My estimates of the kill based on reports from Hudson Bay post managers totaled about forty-five hundred Canada and one-thousand blue geese for the east coast. Probably at least as many ducks as geese were killed —mainly black ducks and pintails.

My estimate for the annual kill of Canada geese along the west coast of James Bay and south coast of Hudson Bay to Fort Severn was seven-thousand, 95 percent of which were taken in the spring. During the spring migration the geese arrive on their breeding grounds April 15-25. In fact the Cree designation for April is nisku pesim — goose moon. At that time the country is still locked with ice and snow, and it is then that the big kill is made, for the birds decoy readily to crudely made decoys. In April and until May 15, most Indians were scattered through the muskeg country trapping muskrats. Those fortunate enough to have their trapping grounds on or near good goose territory made big kills, in some cases up to one-hundred, while others located in poor goose habitat took few or none. The average kill of blue geese along the west coast spring and fall was about 52,000.

To benefit waterfowl using the west coast of the Bay, Akimiski Island Bird Sanctuary was established in 1940. This included the eastern two-thirds of the island and adjoining waters for a distance of five miles. Twin Islands, directly east of Akimiski was set aside as a sanctuary in 1939. The entire west coast has been organized into beaver preserves, and big-game restoration programs are contemplated to restore stocks of deer, moose, and caribou which have been almost eliminated throughout this region. The assumption was that anything done to decrease dependence on waterfowl as a stable source of food would lessen pressure on the waterfowl resource of the bay.

In recent years, sport hunting by white hunters has become increasingly significant, both as a source of income for the natives who provide guide services, and to others because of the number of birds taken.

1936-37 Canada geese *by Richard E. Bishop*

Surveying the Atlantic Flyway

Harold S. Peters

The Atlantic Flyway covers a tremendous area of eastern North America, from the Canadian Arctic down through Labrador, Quebec, the Maritime Provinces, Newfoundland, seventeen eastern states, and the larger West Indies Islands. On February 1, 1937, I received the awesome assignment of surveying for the U.S. Bureau of Biological Survey (USBS) the breeding, resting, and wintering grounds of waterfowl and other migratory birds within this huge flyway.

Raised in Columbus, Ohio, I attended schools there, including over six years at Ohio State University. There I received degrees of B.S. and M.S. and did additional graduate study before starting field investigations of insects in Ohio, New York, Virginia, Texas, and in Florida where I studied fire ant control.

My first extensive travel was in the summer of 1930 as an assistant to Dr. Paul Bartsch, curator of molluscs of the National Museum, during his expedition to the southern Bahama Islands and Cuba. Most of our time was spent on uninhabited islands reached by our chartered ship — a small tug based in Miami. I was sent by the Bureau of Entomology, where I had worked for several years studying mosquitoes and other insects affecting man and animals. We collected many birds for the National Museum, and I studied their parasites. Dr. Bartsch's three student assistants secured bushels of tree snails at each landfall. He even named one after me: *Cerion petersi*!

My summer of 1935 was devoted to fire ant control experiments on the large hunting preserves near Thomasville, Georgia, and Tallahassee, Florida, for the Bureau of Entomology and Cooperative Quail Study. Herbert Stoddard, the widely recognized authority on the bobwhite, induced me to transfer

Two biologists with similar missions. Harold Peters, the first Atlantic Flyway Biologist, (left) with Harrison F. Lewis, the Canadian Migratory Bird Officer for the eastern provinces at Green Island, near Kegaska, in July 1938. Courtesty of Smithsonian Institution.

into the USBS and to establish a cooperative wildlife research unit at Alabama Polytechnic Institute that fall.

Meanwhile, the Biological Survey was beginning its waterfowl program by hiring four biologists — one for each of the major flyways of North America. Before this, game agents Hotchkiss and Brackett had gone to eastern Canada in the summer of 1935, followed by agents Boswell and Atkinson in 1936.

My first trip to the Maritime Provinces, following my appointment as Atlantic Flyway biologist in February 1937, was with Ernest Atkinson. His company gave me the benefit of information obtained by game agents during the previous two summers. We traveled from May 19 to June 17 in New Brunswick, Nova Scotia, and Newfoundland.

At the invitation of the well-known Arctic explorer Donald B. MacMillan, I joined his Arctic expedition as a member of the scientific staff. We would help twenty-four boys, sent by their parents, see the north country on the famous American fishing schooner *Gertrude L. Thebaud* of Gloucester, Massachusetts. The boat was chartered for the trip by Commander MacMillan. We sailed from Gloucester on June 24, 1937, covering 5,500 miles of ocean and bays and inlets along the Labrador and Baffinland coasts. The Biological Survey assigned me to this expedition to secure information on the breeding areas and concentration spots of migratory waterfowl and other birds. I obtained this information from Eskimos, Indians, missionaries, and Hudson's Bay employees at each port-of-call during our ten-week trip. I planned a side-trip by canoe and on foot from the head of Frobisher Bay, Baffinland, to investigate reports of goose and duck nesting areas around unexplored marshes and interior lakes. However, because of low tides our ship grounded on the rocks of Frobisher Bay, so the trip to the interior had to be cancelled. We were advised to sail no further north than the Arctic Circle. I gathered many notes from our contacts in Labrador and Baffinland, and began to realize the necessity of aircraft to survey the vast and little-known interior — especially the tremendous Ungava Peninsula. Snow and blue geese, Canada geese, black ducks, and other species of ducks were reported to nest in marshes at the heads of numerous bays and inlets and along the interior rivers. It was apparent that this part of the flyway contributed many game birds to both Canada and the United States.

As a result of our trip, MacMillan, a rear admiral in our Navy in World War II, was later asked to help revise and update coastal charts during the war. He subsequently named a peninsula on the southern shore of Frobisher Bay, Baffinland, after me. "Peter's Point" is near the rocks that grounded our ship!

Since woodcock were important game birds in my flyway, I made an intensive fall survey of their status that year throughout the northeast. I also took notes on the species on my subsequent annual trips to the northern parts of the flyway, as well as on their wintering grounds in the southeast states and Louisiana. The winter months of 1937 and 1938 also included my first intensive studies of wintering waterfowl in the central and southern Atlantic coastal marshes and wildlife refuges.

Thus, during my first years as Atlantic Flyway biologist, I began a program of "living with the ducks" to secure information to help our government, Canada, and Newfoundland manage hunting regulations under the Migratory Bird Treaty Act. This necessitated nearly continuous field explorations to locate the important nesting, feeding, and wintering grounds of the important migratory game birds. Repeated visits and censuses helped determine trends in their populations. All this was undertaken without an assistant, a secretary, or office except in my home. But whenever I traveled there was plenty of enthusiasm and fine cooperation from officials, biologists, wardens, and interested individuals to offset the limits of my meager budget!

Since my flyway included the Washington area, with the Biological Survey offices and the Patuxent Research Center, I was able to benefit from close and frequent contact with my boss, Fred Lincoln. Fred never directed the flyway men; he simply asked us to use our judgment about the best way to cover our huge assigned areas in order to secure needed information and submit narrative reports and essential information from time to time. Consequently, I began a series of reports in 1937 that were usually submitted at the end of each trip or season, with copies to Ottawa. Occasional conferences of flyway biologists and other waterfowl investigators and officials enabled each of us to keep informed about the continental picture. This influenced hunting regulations and plans for establishing sanctuaries and refuges in the more important areas of North America.

I made annual, summer trips into much of

eastern Canada and Newfoundland, and soon developed a number of reliable cooperators — interested naturalists and officials. These were contacted regularly, by visits and by mail. Many accompanied me on field surveys and often provided boats, cars, guides, and sometimes even planes, to facilitate examination of areas and census of birds. In New Brunswick, American Consul Johnson and Colonel H. H. Ritchie, chief game warden, were most helpful. In Nova Scotia, Federal Migratory Bird Officer Robie W. Tufts was a most helpful and pleasant field companion. His knowledge was based on many years of residence in the area. On Prince Edward Island, Spurgeon Jenkins, a special constable of the mounted police, was an energetic assistant. Migratory Bird Officer Harrison F. Lewis, who later became chief of Canadian Wildlife Service, always offered valuable guidance. In subsequent summers, I traveled with Lewis by small boat along the north shore of the Gulf of St. Lawrence, to Anticosti Island, around James Bay, and to Akimiski Island. Two-thirds of this large island was set aside as Canada's largest wildlife sanctuary as a result of our exploration. On that trip we documented important waterfowl concentrations along the eastern shore of James Bay.

My second year in the flyway was a busy and productive one. In January, I was asked to investigate pollution by several paper mills in coastal areas of South Carolina. For four consecutive years, I covered coastal South Carolina on the annual waterfowl inventory by Coast Guard plane. I visited duck-wintering areas from Ohio and Pennsylvania to Maryland and south to Florida. I visited the most important areas and wildlife refuges once or twice each year for comparable estimates of population and migration.

My headquarters' move to Charleston, South Carolina, in March proved favorable for my coastal activities. The staff of the Charleston Museum — Milby Burton, Burnham Chamberlain, and Bob Lunz — were very helpful. This was also the home of Alex Sprunt, naturalist-author-lecturer for the National Audubon Society.

I've always been a firm believer in the importance of bird banding, and I was able to band many thousands of birds both before and during my years with the Biological Survey. I received important and helpful information from the Bird Banding Laboratory at Laurel, Maryland, both from the staff and through my examination of return records, so I visited the lab often. Also, I contacted many banders during my travels, assisting them by answering questions, demonstrating techniques, and introducing state and federal personnel to game bird banding. At Pymatuning Lake in March and April 1938, I assisted Ohio, Pennsylvania, and USBS biologists and wardens in a waterfowl project. Waterfowl and mourning doves were banded in increasing numbers throughout the central and southeastern states from 1938 into the 1950s to obtain information for their management.

My 1938 field work in the Maritimes, Quebec, Ontario, Gulf of St. Lawrence, and Newfoundland ran from April 18 to September 10. I revisited major areas and surveyed new ones after exploration by car, canoe, or plane. After my assignment to the Atlantic Flyway, I traveled on every road in New Brunswick, Nova Scotia, Prince Edward Island, Ontario, and Quebec. This was necessary in order to secure firsthand information since there was no record of the location of the better waterfowl areas. When I realized a plane would have saved much time, I started taking flying lessons and frequently begged rides when planes were available in local areas.

Mourning doves were of increasing importance to the southeastern states, so I helped in banding projects in Alabama, South Carolina, and on refuges. I worked in waterfowl concentration areas and our refuges during fall and winter months. My fieldwork in 1938 totalled 270 days away from my Charleston headquarters, including forty thousand miles of travel by car, boat, plane, train, and on foot. During that time, I wrote approximately 550 official letters (without a secretary) to keep up with my cooperators, observers, officials, and headquarters.

In my third year, 1939, I started waterfowl inventories in many of the Atlantic coastal states and refuges. A rather short trip to the Northeast and Maritime Provinces, from April 24 to June 4, provided data to compare with previous years' records. My big trip began July 3, when I went to Montreal upon invitation of the Canadian government to join their eastern Arctic patrol on the icebreaker *RMS Nascopie*. I was one of the half-dozen scientists gathered to help collect information and select a location for a much-needed scientific laboratory for Canadian research on the North. The ship passed through the Gulf of St. Lawrence, up the coast of Labrador, into Hudson Bay to Churchill, then back to Baffinland and northward to Ellesmere Island — one about eight hundred miles from the North Pole and as far north as ships could travel. We had stops at twenty-two outposts of the mounted police, the Hudson Bay Company, and missions. This ship carried supplies to each post for the following year and brought out products of the country, as well as exchanges of personnel and a very few paying passengers. Thus, our time at each stop was necessarily limited and always involved a rush of activity and even some confusion. In spite of this, I managed to talk with officials and some natives about the status of migratory game birds and other species. Limited time did not permit any exploration. In fact, I had to stick rather close to avoid being left behind for a whole year when the captain blew the whistle to up-anchor! I prepared a detailed report for Washington and Ottawa on the Biological Survey's first Arctic expedition.

In all, we cruised through part of the Northwest Passage, back to Bylot Island, southward past Baffinland, and down the coast of Labrador, to return on September 25 after covering 10,600 miles.

When England and Germany declared war during our homeward stretch, the captain opened sealed orders given him before the voyage. They told us we must keep radio silence, blackout the ship, and watch for any enemy. Anxious moments occurred when we heard distant firing along the mid-Labrador coast. It proved to be several ships shooting harpoons at whales!

Our rugged ship pushed through ice floes and into little-known waters, but we felt safe with the experienced captain and crew. Nevertheless the *Nascopie* hit rocks in the Hudson Strait in 1947 on a similar patrol, and eventually sank without loss of life.

Fall and winter visits to waterfowl refuges in states of the central and south Atlantic again enabled me to "keep up with the ducks." I passed the examination for private pilot in small planes in March 1939, and began occasionally renting a Cub-type plane to fly over refuges or marshes in short flying range, but lack of allotments kept this to a discouraging minimum. I had to await an opportune time to acquire a plane for my area.

I was busy in January and February 1940, conducting surveys of coastal South Carolina, doing dove studies in North Carolina, and making flights over southern Florida in a Coast Guard plane to assess numbers of waterfowl, eagles, great white herons, roseate spoonbills, and other large birds. I then returned to Patuxent Refuge to study returns from banded waterfowl. The annual Canadian studies ran from May 21 to July 10 and involved visits to the more important waterfowl and woodcock areas. In August I spent another week in North Carolina banding doves and conducting nesting studies with state biologists.

Upon invitation from the Canadian Wildlife Service, I joined Dr. H. F. Lewis on a six-week survey of waterfowl in marshes and hunting areas around James Bay and parts of Quebec and Ontario, beginning on September 8. Together we traveled in a rather small motorboat with three Indians as crew and guides. I was pleased to see so much of this shallow bay's shoreline and marshes. On one occasion we encountered a group of United States hunters with too many birds in their bag, so Dr. Lewis prosecuted them. I always had a good working relationship with Harrison Lewis and enjoyed discussing mutual problems with him at meetings whenever our paths crossed in either of our two countries.

Following my early visits to Newfoundland, the USBS entered into an agreement that I would make a complete study of the bird life there. My supervisors agreed to assign Thomas D. Burleigh to accompany me on future Newfoundland trips to assist in taxonomic and distributional records. Tom was an energetic field collector with many years of experience. I made twelve trips to Newfoundland, usually with Tom, to collect material for a book. Newfoundland contracted with famed artist-writer-birder Roger Tory Peterson to paint thirty-two color plates and draw forty text illustrations for the book. I wrote *Birds of Newfoundland* with Tom's assistance, and it was eventually published by Riverside Press in August 1951.

My 1942 investigations were somewhat restricted by World War II, so I traveled to and from Canada by train, and depended upon cooperators for local travel.

Again, in 1943, due to war travel restrictions, I had to make special arrangements with ration boards in both the United States and Canada. I was able to do a better survey job in 1943 than in the previous year when I had stored the car and traveled by common carrier or begged rides from cooperators. I spent nearly four months that year in Canada and Newfoundland, beginning April 19. By October, I was conducting mourning dove investigations in the southeastern states, cooperating with state game biologists and college students.

Once Burleigh and I made a trip to Funk Island, off the northeast coast of Newfoundland, where we found bones of the great auk, extinct in the world since 1844. Another time, during one Newfoundland trip in a warden's boat along the south coast, we obtained permission to go over to the free-French islands of St. Pierre and Miquelon. There we had an opportunity to see parts of the little-known islands, finding their bird life similar to that of Newfoundland's. These islands have very little traffic with North America, being tied

closely to France and European ports. Fog and dangerous tidal waters hampered our visit, but officials welcomed us and showed us around by car. A list of the thirty-five species of birds we recorded was published in the *Canadian Field-Naturalist*, September-October 1951.

Ducks Unlimited had asked me on several occasions about possibilities for duck refuges in eastern Canada, so at my invitation, Tom Main and Ray Benson flew to visit some possiblilites with me in 1945. We decided the huge Tantramar marshes on the border of New Brunswick and Nova Scotia presented the best possibility. I recommended Bruce Wright to them, from his teaching post in Frederickton, so they employed him for preliminary work that summer and in the following year. Interested sportsmen gave financial support to this expansion of their Canadian program.

Our pleas for planes to assist flyway waterfowl surveys finally resulted in official permission for the Biological Survey to acquire ten World War II surplus airplanes. I was directed to select eight of these first ten planes, so I chose five of the grasshopper observation-type plane, the L-5 with 185 horsepower single engine, from surplus stock at Camden Airport, South Carolina. I also selected a Grumman Goose and two Norseman planes from the Bush Field depot at Augusta, Georgia. After final arrangements, I picked up the five L-5 planes and flew them individually from Camden to a small airfield at Charleston in December 1945. The following month I was authorized to hire Bill North as pilot-mechanic to recondition and certify these planes for our use. Thus began the fleet of USFWS planes.

Much of my time in the first three months of 1946 was involved in the details of establishing our airplane fleet. I secured a block of 700-series license numbers for our planes, and made arrangements to secure needed supplies to overhaul the L-5 fleet. Soon we began to use them locally. In April I flew the first licensed L-5 from my Charleston headquarters to Winona, Minnesota, to be used by pilot-biologist Ed Wellein. An unfortunate accident in May with two of our planes on the beach of Cape Romain Refuge caused Bill North to suffer a broken leg. This slowed our reconditioning, but in July another L-5 was licensed and given to Roy Ferguson to fly to Minnesota for his survey work. Gradually we increased local use of our planes, and the Service was in the aerial census and survey business!

The first field conference of flyway biologists and other waterfowl biologists was held at Brigham, Utah, October 26 to November 7, 1946. I attended by train.

On January 19, 1946, the oldest museum in continuous operation in North America — the Charleston Museum — elected me honorary associate in zoology. I was proud of this recognition of the almost continuous collaboration and mutual assistance that began in 1937 and continued until I moved to Atlanta in 1949.

I was gradually forced to give up flyway investigations. My time was limited due to additional assignments and a broadening of programs to include mourning dove investigations in conjunction with the Southeastern Association of Fish and Game Commissioners, and work with woodcock, waterfowl, and other game species. Ed Addy was assigned to my old position of Atlantic Flyway biologist. I then worked more closely with the regional office in Atlanta until, in 1949, I was transferred to that office and was given secretarial assistance as well as larger quarters. This presented an opportunity for closer contact and cooperation with biologists, game agents, and officials.

As a summary of my northern work, I prepared a report, *Ten Years as a Flyway Biologist*, 1937-1947. This tabulates my travels and together with earlier trip reports constitutes a permanent record of my investigations as the first Atlantic Flyway biologist. One table presents the number of days that I spent in the various provinces and other areas; approximately three years of the ten were spent outside of the United States.

I conducted the first waterfowl inventory of the West Indies from December 1947 to January 1948, using Navy planes from Roosevelt Roads Naval Operating Base, Puerto Rico. We flew at low altitudes over the Virgin Islands, Puerto Rico, the Dominican Republic, Haiti, Great Inagua Island, and Cuba, observing approximately 92,650 ducks and coots. In mid-February 1948, a cooperative study of migratory birds was initiated in Cuba by Fred Lincoln, Tom Burleigh, and Allen Duvall with several Cuban ornithologists. My second inventory of the West Indies was January 2 to February 4, 1949, again by Navy planes from Puerto Rico. For three weeks after completing this inventory, I worked in Cuba with Fred Lincoln, Allen Duvall, and Dr. Abelardo Moreno, who represented Cuba, on the newly formed Cuban-American Ornithological Commission. We hoped to conduct studies and negotiations that could result in a migratory bird treaty between Cuba and our country. We were able to visit the areas that I found to hold the most ducks, utilizing ground and boat travel.

I made the third waterfowl inventory of the West Indies from January 3 to 19, 1950. Planes from our Puerto Rico base and Dominican Air Force took me over the coastal areas and interior lakes and marshes of the same countries of the first survey, whereas the previous year's flights included all of the Bahama Islands and Jamaica. I made a fourth aerial waterfowl inventory from January 28 to February 6, 1951, a bit later than usual because of an accident to a USFWS plane that was assigned to cover the West Indies. In subsequent years, some of these countries were covered by USFWS planes and pilots. Due to the coups by Batista and then Castro, all negotiations for a migratory bird treaty with Cuba had to be cancelled. Let's hope that the treaty may some day be finalized.

Waterfowl studies occupied most of my time for the years 1937 to 1947, but gradually I became involved in mourning dove investigations, especially when the Southeast Association of Game and Fish Commissioners decided upon a cooperative study of this important game bird. Eventually this study was extended to include the entire United States, under my supervision.

I retired on January 31, 1958, after thirty years of government service. My years as Atlantic Flyway biologist were strenuous, and at times hazardous, but they were always interesting and enjoyable. They were hard on my family, and it does seem unfair that extended field studies so often take one away for many months of the year. But we flyway investigators were fortunate in living in those early years when we searched for ways to get into remote areas and discovered methods of summarizing and comparing results from year to year. Our work was necessary for development of proper management for an important natural resource — our waterfowl and other migratory game birds!

1983-84 Pintails *by Phil V. Scholer*

The Canadian Team

Victor E. F. Solman

General History

During the negotiations that led to the signing of the Migratory Birds Convention in 1916, considerations was given in Canada to the creation of an Advisory Board on Wildlife Protection. Such a board was recommended by the Minister of the Interior and approved by the Governor-in-Council in December 1916.

One of the first assignments of the board (an interdepartmental committee) was to prepare regulations for implementation of the Migratory Birds Convention Act, which came into force in August 1917, so that Canada could carry out its responsibilities under the 1916 convention. The first Migratory Birds Regulations came into force in April 1918. Those regulations established hunting seasons. An amendment approved two years later set bag limits. From then on, regulations were amended as needed to meet changing conditions.

The work leading to the act and subsequent regulatios was centered in the National Parks Branch, Department of Interior, under J. B. Harkin, the commissioner. In 1918 a competition was advertised for an officer to head up the administration of the Migratory Birds Convention Act and perform other duties.

Hoyes Lloyd was appointed to the position. He reported for duty as Supervisor of Wildlife Protection in December 1918. As his responsibilities increased, three migratory bird officers were appointed to assist him: Robie W. Tufts in 1919, for the Maritime Provinces; Harrison Lewis, for Ontario and Quebec; and James Munro, for Western Canada. These, then, were the original foursome in Canada.

The western responsibility was later split between J. Dewey Soper in the Prairie Provinces and James Munro in British Columbia.

Harrison Lewis succeeded Lloyd as Superintendant of Wildlife Protection in 1944, becoming the first chief of the Canadian Wildlife Service (initially the Dominion Wildlife Service) when that unit was renamed in 1947.

Unfortunately, little in the way of details of these men's lives and work has been recorded, so the following accounts will be more limited than would be desirable.

James Alexander Munro

James Munro was born at Kildonan, Manitoba, in November, 1884. His father came to Canada from Scotland in 1857, followed by his mother in 1865. The family moved to Toronto in 1898.

Munro went to work for the Corticelli Silk Company, continuing his employment there for ten years. During this time he began a life-long hobby of collecting birds and their eggs. He also began to publish articles on birds in newspapers and periodicals.

In 1911, Munro and his wife moved to Okanagan Landing, British Columbia, where he became an orchardist. There Munro continued with his collecting of birds, other animals, and plants. Some of these collected specimens he sold to museums, other institutions, and private collectors. Munro became a member of the American Ornithologists Union in 1913, later becoming a fellow.

After Hoyes Lloyd assumed responsibility for administering the Migratory Birds Convention Act, it soon became clear he would need assistance. Jim Munro was appointed to provide clerical and enforcement assistance for western Canada in 1920. In 1934 the western responsibility was split between J. Dewey Soper, who took charge of the prairie provinces, and Munro, who was then assigned to British Columbia. Munro retired from his post in 1949 and died in 1958. His son, Dave, followed in his footsteps and served as Chief (later called Director) of the Canadian Wildlife Service.

Munro published many reports on water-fowl and other birds. His concept for preservation of waterfowl on part of the delta of the Kootenay River near Creston, British Columbia, was carried out after his death in 1961. The 17,000-acre Creston Valley Wildlife Management Area — his brainchild — was dedicated in 1968.

Robie Wilfred Tufts

Robie W. Tufts was born in Wolfville, Nova Scotia, in 1894. As a small child he was introduced to the out-of-doors by his mother, who taught him to recognize wildflowers. His older brother's interest in birds spilled over to Robie.

Tufts attended Acadia University, where his father was professor of history and economics. But his training did not include biology because it was not then on the curriculum. That is hardly surprising: biological or wildlife conservation positions were virtually non-existent in those days. Robie left the university for the business world, where he was employed in a bank and in a broker's office. He later conducted his own business as a securities dealer.

But Tufts continued his interest in birds, becoming the Chief Federal Migratory Birds Officer for the Maritime Provinces in November, 1919. His initial staff included five paid officers plus several honorary (unpaid) officers who enforced the Migratory Birds Convention Act and its attendant regulations until that duty was taken over by the Royal Canadian Mounted Police in 1932.

Robie Tufts retired from the service of the federal government in May, 1947, and lived in Wolfville, Nova Scotia, until his death in 1982. He published many papers and several books on ornithology.

In 1975 Robie Tufts published a series of stories from his career entitled, *Looking Back, Recollections of a Migratory Bird Officer.* One of the tales was entitled "Henry's Tea-Pot." It concerned the caretaker, Henry McLaughlin, for a newly established

At the southern end of James Bay in 1940, Harold Peters and Harrison F. Lewis encountered this hunting camp. The white hunters had over-limits, so were fined ... "to the delight of the Indians, who were surpised to see that laws also affected white men." Photo courtesy of the Smithsonian Institution.

bird sanctuary at Grand Manan, New Brunswick. As Tufts wrote:

> The sanctuary, an area surrounding a marshy-bouldered lake, is located about a mile from Grand Harbour where Henry lived. During the period from late summer until freeze-up it was necessary for him to spend much time on patrol in the immediate vicinity of the sanctuary. When overtaken at such times by inclement weather he required shelter and in due course he was given authority to erect a small cabin on the shore of the lake for his physical comfort. To save on expenses Henry provided all the labour but after the structure was completed it was necessary to have a stove and other ordinary camp equipment for his further well-being. To acquire such he was authorized to submit monthly expense accounts. These he sent directly to me and after certifying them as being justified and correct they were forwarded to Ottawa.
>
> Henry was a frugal soul and honest by nature to the ninth degree. This became abundantly apparent month by month as his expense accounts were checked. I recall having to remind him that certain small items of expense, postage for instance, were legitimate charges. After the cabin was finished and a stove installed, his monthly accounts rarely exceeded two dollars.
>
> One time when I was with him patrolling the sanctuary we were overtaken by a cold rainstorm and the shelter the cabin afforded was greatly appreciated. He lighted a fire in the little stove and moments later I suggested a cup of tea, but he informed me that

he was not equipped to serve such a luxury. I told him to buy himself a tea-pot and a pound of tea at the first opportunity and to charge it on his next statement. In due course his account for that month was received and officially certified by me as being correct. I recall that it totalled less than two dollars, and among the items listed was "one tea-pot, 25 cents."

> Some months later I again visited Grand Manan and called upon Mr. McLaughlin at his home. While I was there he produced some correspondence he had had with the Treasury Department in Ottawa. It concerned his purchase of the tea-pot. It was brief and to the point. They asked him to explain why he had bought a tea-pot, not why he had charged them with one, but simply "Why did you buy a tea-pot?"
>
> Henry said he had wished at the time that I had been there to help with his reply, adding, "But since you weren't I did the best I could. I kept a copy of my letter to show you. Here it is. I hope I did all right." After I read his reply, while trying to subdue a smile, I asked him if he had had any further word from Ottawa and he said he hadn't. He then asked me, "Did I do all right?" "You couldn't have done better," I replied, and he seemed quite relieved.
>
> This is what he told them, and knowing Henry, impertinence was farthest from his mind as he penned these lines: "Dear Sir: In reply to your letter I beg to say that I bought the tea-pot to make tea in. Hoping this is all right, I am — Your obedient servant, Henry McLaughlin."

J. Dewey Soper

Dewey Soper was invited to contribute to his recollections about his early days for this book. Then eighty-five years old, he didn't feel up to it. But he did forward the following letter to Art Hawkins, dated December 21, 1978:

> I joined the Canadian Wildlife Service in the late summer of 1934. I had been busy for two years investigating the bison and other wildlife in Wood Buffalo Park for the N.W.T. Administration. When this was finished, Ottawa immediately transferred me to the CWS where I opened a new office in Winnipeg. Hoyes Lloyd was then director of the wildlife service. I was always interested in wildlife and prior to Wood Buffalo Park had spent many years in the Canadian eastern arctic for the National Museum in Ottawa and the NWT administration (1923-1931). I was not the first wildlife officer. Lloyd, Lewis, Munro, and Robie Tufts of Nova Scotia were all ahead of me there while I worked in the Arctic. I had my headquarters in Winnipeg for fourteen years. I was then sent to Edmonton in 1948 to open a new office. Ottawa then relieved me of Manitoba and Saskatchewan, but I retained Alberta and became the chief federal officer for that province and the Northwest Territories and Yukon.
>
> My venture in finally discovering the nesting grounds of blue goose in the summer of 1929 in Baffin Island was only for that purpose, and gaining life history information all new at that time was a wonderful expedition for me — total happiness, despite hardships and with the companionship of two grand Eskimo men that I shall never forget.

Dewy Soper was born in 1893 near Guelph, Ontario. Most of his early education was obtained in rural schools near Guelph and Rockwood. He attended Alberta College and the University of Alberta from 1921 to 1923. Beginning in his teens, he studied birds and mammals and made collections.

In 1923 Soper joined the staff of the National Museum of Canada as a naturalist on an Arctic expedition that visited Baffin, Beechey, Devon, and Ellesmere Islands and Greenland. He led a National Museum expedition to Baffin Island in 1924, 1925, and 1926. In 1927 he surveyed mammals and birds along the international boundary from the Rocky Mountains to Manitoba.

Dewey Soper served the Northwest Territories and Yukon branch of the Department of the Interior while carrying out investigations in southern Baffin Island from 1928 to 1931. In 1929 he discovered the breeding ground of blue geese near Bowman Bay, on the Foxe Basin side of southern Baffin Island.

From 1932 to 1934 he made wildlife investigations in Wood Buffalo National Park.

In 1934, Dewey Soper became Chief Federal Migratory Birds Officer for the provinces of Manitoba, Saskatchewan, and Alberta, with headquarters in Winnipeg.

His assignment in 1942 was to conduct formal investigations with special reference to waterfowl, on water areas in the prairie provinces built under the Prairie Farm Rehabilitation Act. According to his report:

> "The projected program worked out very satisfactorily. In continuing the regular waterfowl survey and other duties, total motor car traveling for the field seasons was slightly in excess of 8,000 miles. Considerably additional traveling was done by means of railroad, small paddling canoe, and freighter canoe with outboard motor. Extra cautions were exercised in respect to conservation of tires and gasoline; otherwise motor car travel would have been considerably more extensive resulting in greater accomplishments through this faster and incomparably more efficient means of conveyance. I customarily established a camp and remained from one to several days. This is indisputably the most practical means of securing the information required. In several instances a modification of this plan was adopted when given areas required only one day's attention and a hotel could be reached at night in the direction of the project to be covered on the following day. Under normal conditions the average daily time spent on field work amounted to about twelve hours, but his was sometimes extended to fourteen or fifteen hours."

In 1948 his responsibilities were changed to include Alberta and the Northwest Territories, with headquarters in Edmonton. He retired from Federal Government Service in 1951, living in Edmonton until his death in 1982.

Harrison Flint Lewis

Harrison F. Lewis was born on December 15, 1893 at Sag Harbor, Long Island, New York State. His father, a native of Yarmouth, Nova Scotia, was rector of the local church, and his mother was a daughter of a previous rector. Dr. Lewis was the eldest of seven children. At an early age he developed a deep interest in birds, stimulated when he was three years old, he said, by the gift of a subscription to the magazine *Birds* from his grandfather. In addition to his interest in birds, Dr. Lewis as a boy fished, dug clams, caught crabs, picked wild berries, and was exposed to much natural history. He early developed a liking for, and familiarity with, water and acquired his first sailboat at age fourteen. When he was fifteen he spent a summer at Yarmouth in his father's boyhood home and came under the influence of a school principal with an interest in natural history. Already familiar with much of the natural history there, he moved back to Yarmouth in 1911 with his family. In 1912, he began subscribing to ornithological journals beginning with *The Auk* and *Bird Lore*. His interest in ornithology was heightened by meetings with ornithologists of note. He was elected an associate member of the American Ornithologists' Union in the autumn of 1912. While he was a student at Nova Scotia Provincial Normal College, he reported the first evening grosbeak record for Nova Scotia.

His first publication was a note about the grosbeaks in *Bird Lore* in 1913. After a couple of years of school teaching in Nova Scotia, he entered Acadia University as a sophomore in the fall of 1914. He graduated with a B.A. degree in 1917. His education was interrupted by service in the First World War. After the war he worked as a civilian auditor in the Department of Militia and Defense at Quebec City.

While at Quebec City, he used the library facilities of Laval University to build up his knowledge in ornithology while continuing his field observation of birds in the Quebec area. He familiarized himself in a relatively short time with developments in ornithology in North America from 1876 to 1911, as represented in the published work in that library. That was a turning point in his career. Without that background knowledge of ornithology he would not likely have qualified for the position he entered in the federal government service.

Lewis accepted the position of Chief Migratory Bird Officer for Ontario and Quebec on November 1, 1920. In 1921 his headquarters were changed from Quebec to Ottawa. His position was in the Dominion Parks Branch of the Department of the Interior. Lewis served throughout the provinces of Ontario and Quebec from 1920 until 1944. His knowledge of boating was helpful in his long boat-patrols of the north shore of the gulf of the St. Lawrence River.

Among his important work, he developed a system of migratory-bird sanctuaries along the north shore of the Gulf of St. Lawrence and in James Bay which have maintained bird populations that would otherwise have declined. During his career he travelled widely to meet and address the public, carry out enforcement of the migratory birds regulations and conduct scientific research and gather information for management of bird populations. He played a very active role in the annual revision of the regulation under which migratory birds were hunted throughout the area. That required a broad knowledge of the whole area (one-fourth of Canada), its bird populations, and the timing of their movements.

Lewis spent a year at the University of Toronto in 1925-26 to secure his Master's degree. He then registered at Cornell University as a graduate student in 1926, working under the A. A. Allen. He attended Cornell during the academic year 1928-1929 and received his PhD degree in 1929 while on leave, without pay, from his government duties.

In 1944, Lewis assumed the position of Superintendent of Wildlife Protection for Canada — the head of the agency he had joined in 1920. As human knowledge (and population) increased, the work of the agency was supplemented by wildlife research and management at the request of other government agencies. The WPC's task was also to provide cooperation with provincial and territorial governments. By 1947 the agency became known as the Wildlife Service. At first it was called Dominion Wildlife Service, but as the term Dominion fell into disrepute it was soon changed to Canadian Wildlife Service. Lewis was the first Chief of the Canadian Wildlife Service. At its beginning on November 1, 1947, it was a small unit. It is now the well-known national agency working in the wildlife field throughout Canada. It is known throughout the world for its involvement in multi-national wildlife programs. Lewis headed the service through its formative period from 1947 to 1952. On April 1, 1952, he left the public service of Canada.

Lewis' international work was exemplified by long membership in the International Association of Game, Fish and Conservation commissioners, by his presidency of it in 1949-1950, and by his involvement in several of its committees for many years. His initiative in new developments was illustrated by the creation, at his urging, of a National Research Council Associate Committee on Wildlife Research of which he was the first chairman in 1947. The work of that committee did much to stimulate an expansion of wildlife research in Canadian universities.

Throughout his long career Dr. Lewis published reports and articles on his work; they cover the period from 1913 to 1973, and deal with a wide range of subjects, from new species records, losses of birds at lighthouses, to recommendations for bird hazards to aircraft.

His life-long interest in ornithology led him from an associate membership in the American Ornithologists' Union to fellow and council member of that organization. He served also on local and regional naturalists' organizations and was sometimes editor of *The Canadian Field-Naturalist* and *Sportsmen's Province*. At his death he was a charter member and former president of both the Nova Scotia Bird Society and the Nova Scotia Resources Council.

From 1952 until his death on January 16, 1974, he lived in West Middle Sable and later Sable River, Nova Scotia. Those communities are near where he spent some of his youth. After his retirement from the government service, he made studies, under contract, for provincial and federal government agencies. For his last eight years he was a valued member of the Associate Committee on Bird Hazards to Aircraft of the National Research Council of Canada. As a contractor working on behalf of the Committee he personally examined more than forty airports, mainly in Eastern Canada, provided detailed information on the bird problems, and made recommendations for changes to reduce them. Many recommendations were put into effect to increase flight safety.

While in charge of the Wildlife Service and afterward, Lewis had a strong influence on the biologists with whom he came in contact. He was always well-informed and precise, and was an excellent writer and editor. Many of us, including the author, learned a great deal about research methods, research reporting, and the use of the English language under his kind but firm instruction. The ideas he left behind and the habits he helped many of us to form will ensure that for a long time he will be in our minds as a great leader, encourager, and example.

In his high uncompromising standards, complete honesty and capacity for thorough conscientious work, he had few equals in this or any other time and place.

© R. Plasschaert

©L. Kouba

Exploring the Hinterlands

The late 1940s and early 1950s were auspicious years for the budding science of waterfowl management. The soldiers returned home with a strong desire to make up for lost time in the recreations they had missed. Improved transportation and a recently acquired familiarity with firearms encouraged many who had not hunted waterfowl before to take up the sport.

In response to this new level of pressure, wildlife departments on the state and federal level built up depleted staffs as quickly as possible. New sources of funds permitted expansions so that initially the few wildlife schools in existence were hard pressed to supply trained people fast enough to fill the job openings. Soon more colleges offered wildlife programs, and many veterans used the GI Bill aid to study at these schools.

The years spent in armed service were useful to many of these students, especially those who used their familiarity with aircraft to help study and manage waterfowl. What was most needed was a group of trained biologists who could also fly, and they soon appeared.

Their work was anything but easy. Working from airplanes that had been declared surplus by the military, they flew over the most remote territory in North America —much of it unmapped — to observe waterfowl and learn where they nested. While fatal crashes were fortunately rare, these pioneer pilot-biologists sometimes were forced to land in remote and insect-infested bush country, occasionally being obliged to make repairs under adverse conditions.

The duties of these men took them from the tundra to the tropics. The work was almost always arduous and occasionally even life-threatening.

The stories told in this chapter reflect the spirit of the time, a heady period that was supercharged with anticipation and hope. Almost everything these early fieldmen did or saw was a discovery, and their zest for meeting challenges knew no bounds. Many of today's management techniques stem from this productive period.

Here, for the first time, these men tell their stories in their own words.

Pre-Statehood Alaska

James G. King

The enforcement agents and biologists of the USFWS in Alaska who piloted small planes in pursuit of their duties have made an exciting and productive contribution to the annals of flying. Their pioneering use of the small airplane as a tool and observation platform brought a new dimension to the ability of wildlife workers to operate in both populous and remote areas. These individuals, displaying an almost religious zeal in their attempt to stem the forces threatening Alaska's wildlife, recognized the value of aircraft and developed techniques for their use.

Confronted with overwhelming evidence, the administration of the USFWS supported a flying program, at least sporadically. In spite of ups and downs, the USFWS still maintains leadership in the use of light planes for wildlife work. The benefits have been enormous. As the quality of equipment continues to improve, there is a great potential for wildlife pilots to pioneer ever-more-valuable wildlife management techniques.

In 1925 game and fur populations in Alaska were low. A part of the horde attracted by the gold rushes at the turn of the century had learned to live in the Alaskan bush. They had fanned out everywhere in their search for gold, trapping and living largely off wild meat. Moose and caribou became scarce, and Alfred Hulse Brooks, writing in 1918, thought beaver and marten were doomed to extinction. Game meat was regularly served and sold in restaurants, roadhouses, and markets. There was no regard for age, sex, or species of animals killed. Huge dog teams roamed the interior all winter, often fueled with moose and other game meat. Hunters and trappers regularly used strychnine and other poisons to kill wolves, foxes, and any other meat eaters that came around, including birds and bears. Beaver were shot and

their dams or lodges wrecked to force them to show themselves. Alaskans were paid bounties to collect a host of creatures, including wolves, eagles, and Dolly Varden trout.

Pioneering biologists such as Olaus Murie and Alfred Bailey of the Bureau of Biological survey (USBS), forerunner of the USFWS, documented this carnage in the early 1920s. As a result, Congress passed the Alaska Game Law in 1925. Conservation regulations were adopted quickly and a much-needed warden staff was hired beginning in 1926.

Sam O. White became the first full-time game warden in northern Alaska. White was reared in the back woods of Maine and later gained substantial experience as a packer and guide for the U.S. Geological Survey in Alaska and elsewhere. He brought a wealth of bush lore to his job as federal warden. Provided with a pickup, a dog team, and a poling boat with "kicker," White began to attack wasteful and illegal practices in a quarter-million square miles of northern Alaska inhabited by the small but completely undisciplined population of pioneers. Obviously, most of his time was spent traveling, leaving little for contacting violators. He became weary of catering to what he termed "a team of free-thinking dogs."

In roadless Alaska, the light airplane did for isolated residents what the Model T Ford did for the farmers of the western plains, and more. Noel Wien was the acknowledged pioneer of commercial aviation in northern Alaska. Though a few pilots predated his arrival in Fairbanks with an airplane in 1924, it was Wien who proved an airplane could be relied upon for service. Wien delivered the goods, making trips in hours that formerly took days or weeks or that were impossible. He was the first to fly regular commercial trips during the harsh Alaskan winter. Noel Wien and his brothers developed skis, oil quick drains, motor covers, wing covers, firepots, and light camping equipment necessary for man to live and keep his airplane going in isolated areas in spite of 60-degree-below-zero temperatures. Wien also perfected

Alaska Wildlife Agents conferring in the Fairbanks office in 1939 (left to right): Sam O. White, pioneer aviator; Jack Benson, agent; Frank Dufresne, agent, popular book author, and later a Regional USFWS Director; Clarence J. Rhode, agent, pilot and later Regional USFWS Director; Jack O'Conner, agent, later Regional Director; Gerald Collins, agent pilot; Frank Glazer, pioneer trapper and first animal control specialist in Alaska, who specialized in protection of domestic reindeer herds from wolves. USFWS photo.

techniques of visual navigation in an area without detailed maps, radio communication, resident facilities, or a developed surface transportation network. He and his brothers founded Wien Alaska Airlines, an organization that still serves most of Alaska.

A good game warden has to be an opportunist, so it wasn't long before the activities of the Wiens caught Sam White's attention. In 1929 the Wien brothers taught him to fly. He bought a small open-cockpit Swallow, a biplane registered as NC422. At first he reported being somewhat disappointed because he could not spot as much as he had hoped from his airplane (a reaction common to all observers when they first take to the air). But after a while he got the hang of it. In 1930 Sam apprehended the first poacher ever arrested by a flying game warden anywhere in America. Sam White soon became known as "the flying game warden" overmuch of northern Alaska. People inclined to flaunt game laws learned that isolation no longer guaranteed safety, a startling revelation for the independent residents of the north.

Though effective in the field, "aviation," as it was sometimes termed, created an administrative monster. The "flying warden" was in continual hot water for flying his own plane during working hours, for using government time and equipment to service his own plane, and even for using government gas in a personal plane. It mattered not that he had revolutionized game law enforcement in a huge area or that wildlife populations were benefiting.

In 1936, $30,000 became available for new transportation equipment. White, who was still subsidizing the organization by use of his own plane, made a strong campaign to buy three SRJR Stinsons, available then for $7,500 new. The money, however, was spent on four "scout boats" that were sent to Fort Yukon, Marshal, McGrath, and Dillingham. These boats proved useless and were surplused the following year. Strong feelings evidently developed over this incident, because White sold his troublesome airplane in

1937, perhaps in protest. He continued to fly patrols in government-leased aircraft.

The Fourteenth Annual Report of the Alaska Game Commission (1937-1938) states:

> Airplane travel is becoming more and more important and necessary in enforcement of the game laws in Alaska. This type of travel was utilized during the past year by engaging passage whenever practicable on regularly scheduled flights, by chartering planes with commercial pilots and by chartering one plane which was flown by an Alaskan Wildlife Agent who is a licensed pilot. The last method proved to be by far the most economical and effective.

The value of aviation for wildlife work was finally getting some recognition. That report also shows 25,000 miles of patrol by air and only 1,161 by dog team.

Clarence Rhode was hired in 1936. After duty in Juneau and Cordova, he was assigned to Fairbanks with White. In 1939 they made a joint patrol with Canadian mounties, using Alaskan aircraft along the international boundary. They discovered a host of violations and made a number of arrests. This mission was reported in the press, attracting wide attention.

At long last the USFWS got into the airplane business in a serious way, and by 1940-1941 the game commission report shows three government planes and three pilot agents. This report also shows that Sam White was not among these flyers. He had entered commercial flying. In later years he described the frustrations of his ten-year battle to prove that wildlife conservation in northern Alaska depended on airplanes flown by agents.

Old-timers reminiscing about Sam White remember his scrupulous honesty. Yet Sam was accused of unethical behavior when he used his own little Swallow to advance the cause of conservation, admittedly often on government time and sometimes using government gasoline.

After leaving the Service, Sam White flew bush planes for Wien Airlines until his seventieth birthday in 1962. It was another govern-

ment regulation that forced his retirement: commercial pilot's licenses had to be surrendered at age seventy. He flew his own plane, a World War II vintage Stinson L5, for several more years. A few days after he sold it, fire destroyed the plane. "Died of a broken heart," White said.

Sam White flew the bush for some forty years. His name is on all lists of pioneer Alaskan pilots. Parts of his story have been printed in the *Alaskan Sportsman* magazine and in Harmon Helmerick's book, *Last of the Bush Pilots*. His hand-made wood stove and other gear he carried in the Swallow are on display in the Pioneers Museum at Fairbanks. His field diaries are preserved in the archives of the library of the University of Alaska.

Sam White remained always a strong spokesman for wildlife conservation. Even today, game wardens in interior Alaska are highly aware of the respect that rural people have for the beliefs of that man.

Clarence Rhode absorbed much of White's enthusiasm for flying. On furlough during World War II, Rhodes flew for a commercial airline in the interior. After the war he returned to become supervisor of a newly created USFWS Aircraft Division in Anchorage. He selected the sites at Lake Hood and Juneau for the construction of maintenance facilities and acquired a fleet of surplus military planes.

Theron Smith was hired as aircraft supervisor when Rhode moved to Juneau as regional director in 1948. "Smitty" was the consummate Alaskan pilot. He spent his youth during the Depression in the Mata-

Flyways Biologist Bob Smith refuels a Grumman Goose during a 1951 stop at Yellowknife, Northwest Territories. USFWS photo by Rex Gary Schmidt.

nuska Valley, where he doctored and flew rejected airplanes the way many other American boys doctor rejected automobiles. During World War II the Air Force made him a captain, and he accumulated a long record of bombing missions over Germany. Returning to Alaska as a surplused pilot, Smitty teamed up with a surplused single-engine Stinson Gullwing and established an air charter service out of Bethel on the Yukon Delta.

Rhode's philosophy was that "the airplane is to our people what the horse is to the cowboy." He expected field workers in Alaska to fly just as workers elsewhere are expected to drive. However, no stigma attended those who could not. It was Theron Smith who made this philosophy a practical reality. Personnel were expected to get a private license on their own and then could fly government planes when accompanied by an authorized USFWS pilot. When they had 100 hours of experience, limited flight authority was granted under the supervision of a more experienced pilot. Even those employees with military flying experience were expected to follow the same procedure. The tricks of the trade developed by Noel Wien, Sam White, and those who followed them were passed on verbally from pilot to pilot. Smitty watched everyone like a mother hen.

The Aircraft Division operated as an aircraft pool. Several varieties of planes were available on all configurations of landing gear. A pilot could make arrangements for the equipment most suitable to his needs and might use several different types as the seasons changed.

Standard models and military surplus planes were modified somewhat in the Lake Hood shop to accommodate the special needs of wildlife pilots operating in the bush. The men at the shop did a noble job in anticipating needs and problems, and a high level of rapport developed between pilots and mechanics. Engine failures were virtually eliminated as a factor in the wildlife operation.

Jerry Lawhorn was, and still is, the consummate wildlife airplane mechanic. Prior to working for the USFWS, he spent some years with a private aviation firm in Anchorage. He was frequently dispatched to resurrect small airplanes that had succumbed to the forces of gravity in remote locations but were thought to be repairable. This required camping at the scene, often in severe winter conditions, and innovating sufficient repairs to get the machine back to civilization. Lawhorn's father was a long time USFWS agent in the western states, a fact that perhaps accounts for his interest in the Service and his desire to join Smith's staff at Lake Hood.

A variety of engine modifications developed at Lake Hood allowed operation in the coldest weather. Landing gear was modified and strengthened for off-airport use. Special recording, communication, and photographic aids were installed and perfected. And a variety of gadgetry was built to aid the servicing of airplanes at remote locations in extreme weather.

Two aircrafts were completely rebuilt by the division, an amphibian Grumman and a DeHaviland Beaver. Among other innovations, these planes have long-range fuel tanks and specially modified windows to improve visibility. The Beaver, appropriately named *Anseriforme* by waterfowl biologists, has extended the ability and improved the economy of long-range surveys over land. The Grumman, dubbed the *Aleutian Goose* has enabled such surveys to be extended to the resorts of birds and marine mammals far out at sea.

Concurrent with evolving flight needs, the Rhodes-Smith team developed the best radio network in Alaska, working largely with surplus military equipment. Before statehood there were some 150 USFWS radio stations all over Alaska in offices, airplanes, cars, boats, field camps, and government residences. USFWS pilots at that time did not normally file flight plans with the Federal Aviation Administration, but reported each landing and takeoff on the Service network. Radio logs were maintained at all ground stations and on vessels. Smith usually knew where his airplanes were and what they were doing. Pilots experiencing difficulties could always contact someone and usually Smith directly. He offered advice on faltering engines, failing landing gear, cold weather problems, or anything else that happened in the air or on the ground, and he monitored the situation until a safe landing was accomplished at the home base. In occasional situations where a plane could not proceed without repairs, it was often Smith who showed up to solve the problem.

Pilots taking aircraft from Anchorage for extended trips were usually briefed by Smith before departure. He always wanted to know what was to be done. He provided a wealth of information on field conditions, weather conditions, the peculiarities of the airplane, and anything else of relevance. When pilots were delayed during the week and elected to depart on Saturday or Sunday, Smith was usually present. He tracked planes in the air continuously, especially if the weather was poor. Often pilots arriving in Anchorage after working hours were waved to a tie-down spot by Smith, who had remained alone at the facility until the last plane was in.

In the twenty-five years that Smith ran the Aircraft Division, there were some nineteen accidents causing serious aircraft damage, but only four resulted in deaths or serious personal injury. Of these, two were twin-engine Grummans flown by experienced, professional pilots. Only one fatal accident involved a Smith-trained pilot, a peculiar incident where a landing Cessna collided with a canoe, killing one occupant of the canoe.

Unfortunately, Clarence Rhode was one of the fatalities. When he went down in a Grumman Goose in 1958 he became the subject of one of the most extensive air searches in history. The plane was finally found by hikers in 1979, high in the Brooks Range. Evidently all on board had died on impact.

After retirement Theron Smith wrote:

> The 1950s were the "Gung Ho" years; Clarence was a builder and a driver; he surely did want to see a lot of country, and the fishery folk were moving from Seattle to Alaska. We were operating over 35 aircraft prior to Statehood; averaging 17 after 1960. Hours during my time totalled about 150,000 for about 17,000,000 miles. We hauled thousands of tons of freight into the backwoods; flew patrols almost around the clock in the summer; and tried to convince the commercial fishermen that we would catch them in any kind of weather, at any time of day, in any kind of water. We were reasonably successful.
>
> Our agent and biologist pilots had varied backgrounds; some already had lots of flying time; some we trained from scratch. We taught them all to fly the bush — flying to know where they were, to stay out of the clouds, to have gear to survive in the wilder-

ness; to fly with a tender touch to the bitter end in a fiasco; and to sacrifice the machine to save their necks. Some were better than others, but I'm proud of them all. We never had a man wandering around lost, except for one, we never had a man lose control of his airship.

Statehood for Alaska and the nearly simultaneous loss of Clarence Rhode in the wilderness brought changes to the Aircraft Division. Those changes were the result of a reduced operation, but Smith's attitude toward his pilots never wavered.

The pilot agents learned to monitor the activities of people by reading their tracks in the snow. This required the ability to identify suspicious activity from the air and then to pick safe landing spots in the wilderness so apprehensions could be made. Agents had to be prepared to land at any location used by airborn hunters, including high lakes, ridge tops, sand bars, glacial rivers, beaches, and so on. Agents had to be prepared to snow-shoe long distances, camp overnight, and heat up their airships after letting them stand in subzero temperatures. A successful flying warden had to master landings on skis, floats, and tires.

Flying wardens stopped violations along the Canadian boundary, such as importation of Canadian wolves to receive the Alaskan bounty. Aircraft were also suited to monitoring the activities of salmon fishermen and enforcing closed fishing periods and closed areas. Even the nocturnal "creek robber" could never be sure that first light of day would not find an airplane hovering above his illicit operation.

Respect for the USFWS and its conservation programs was an important side effect of the surveillance by the agents. No other pilots traveled so widely or monitored activities on the ground so closely. USFWS pilots delivered letters and messages, provided supplies to those in need, took the sick to medical help, reported emergencies, and saved lives. The result was that at the time of statehood, the "flying game wardens" were not regarded as an outside and unwelcome force inflicted on the country by an unres-

ponsive bureaucracy in Washington, but rather as an element of local society that provided a useful service.

Biologist pilots joined the wardens after World War II. Their efforts provided the first major baseline information on the ability of Alaskan habitats to carry game resources. This work became extremely important when the number of people living in Alaska soared after World War II. Biologist-pilots were assigned a wide variety of tasks involving big-game populations, pelagic species, migratory birds, prey-predator relationships, habitat mapping, and location of banding sites.

Innumerable publications and reports document these aircraft-assisted projects.

That the USFWS flying agents and biologists were successful in their conservation efforts is attested by the fact that big game and fur bearers were more abundant than anyone could remember by the time Alaska became a state. The beaver and marten that Alfred Hulse Books had thought on the verge of extinction in 1918 were again an important item in the economy of hundreds of rural trappers. Moose were everywhere. Of the animals, only the muskox and the sea otter were below peak numbers. Salmon, though badly depleted by poaching in the name of patriotic food production during Word War II, were showing signs of recovery. The flyers didn't do it all, of course, but the boaters and dog drivers would have frequently been helpless without them.

Some dozens of USFWS employees participated in the events described here, and it is unfortunate that the story of each can not be told. Each contributed individually to the success of the whole operation. Dedication and determination enabled these people to survive and do a good job in the roughest terrain and the harshest climate in North America.

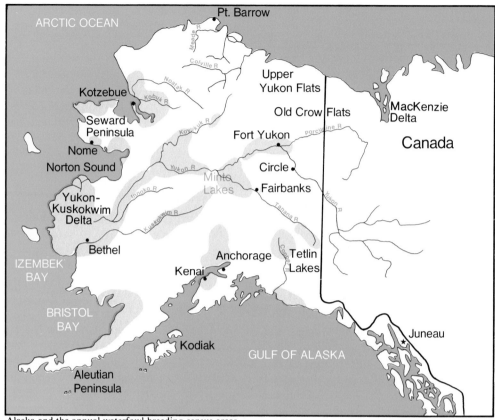

Alaska and the annual waterfowl breeding census areas.

From Tundra to Tropics

Robert H. Smith

In the spring of 1942 I made my debut as a second-generation flyway biologist. Charlie Gillham, one of the original four of that group, had retired as the Mississippi Flyway biologist, and it was my good fortune to replace him. I was sent packing off to the prairie provinces of Canada with Fred Lincoln's explicit instruction to "go up there and find out what you can about the duck population."

I was not altogether a greenhorn in the duck business, having had more than six years of experience as a waterfowl biologist in the swamps of Arkansas, the coastal marshes of Louisiana, and, finally, as a member of the Washington staff in the refuge division, where I had the opportunity to see and inspect the waterfowl habitat on wildlife refuges throughout the country.

These experiences were all good background but, when faced with the magnitude of the task assigned me, the problems seemed almost insurmountable. The settled parts of the prairie provinces, a vast area of prairies and parklands with some rough roads, would be hard enough to cover. But what about the bush country, the subarctic forests, and the tundra, an area larger than the eastern United States? These hinterlands had no roads, roads, so travel was limited to what could be done by canoe or boat in summer, dog teams in winter, or aircraft in any season when weather permitted. And how was I to cope with the physical, cultural, and linguistic barriers of Latin America where I was to conduct winter Surveys? In confronting these problems, I had many exciting moments, some of which are recounted in this article.

Western Canada

By the early 1940s, there was some fragmentary knowledge of waterfowl on the great deltas of the North. The edge of the Saskatchewan Delta could be reached by car or train; the MacKenzie Delta had been visited by Charley Gillham and John Lynch; and in the early 1900s, Edward Preble had penetrated the Athabaska Delta. But these choice waterfowl areas, spectacular and productive as they are, were mere pinpoints in a great, unknown region spattered with innumerable lakes and ponds. When the parklands and prairies dried up, or ducks were scarce for other reasons, most people explained the dearth by pointing vaguely to the north and saying, "They all went up there someplace."

My first summer on the prairies in 1942 produced no breathtaking discoveries or definitive conclusions on the current waterfowl populations. I was literally afoot. Ducks Unlimited "keymen" and members of the various provincial game departments provided what transportation they could to the various waterfowl areas. Otherwise, I traveled from here to there by train, carefully noting the ducks I could see from the coach window. Having had no previous data for comparison, I based my conclusions about the duck situation that year on an opinion poll of the local authorities such as numerous game guardians and Ducks Unlimited "keymen," plus my own meager observations.

Perhaps the most important event that first summer on the prairie was my visit to the Delta Waterfowl Research Station and the Delta marshes at the foot of Lake Manitoba. There, Al Hochbaum, the director of the station, took me canoeing through the marsh waterways by day. Later, we would sit in the long prairie twilight, slap mosquitos, and talk about ducks. Al was directing research that showed that ducks were territorial. A pair selected a territory and the drake defended it against all others of like species. He awaited the hen at some particular spot such as a section of creek bank, a muskrat house, or a mat of tules, while she selected her nest site, laid a clutch of eggs, and began incubation. Thus, the drake occupying an exposed spot would be readily visible at all hours of the day, indicating that the hen was on a nest or somewhere else nearby.

Bob Smith's camp on the Hudson Bay lowlands, west of James Bay in 1944. USFWS photo by R. H. Smith.

We suddenly realized that the waiting drake provided a sound method of counting nesting ducks. But how could we accomplish this? Surely it would be feasible to census a small marsh or individual potholes in this way. But applying this principle to the vast area of prairies and parklands — to say nothing of the bush country in the far north -would be another story.

I was convinced that aerial surveys were the ultimate means of censusing waterfowl after my first attempt at this from a Good-year blimp in 1940. That flight was part of a midwinter waterfowl survey conducted annually by the USFWS. I was assigned to cover the lower Potomac marshes below Washington, D.C. Although the blimp cruised a bit too high for ideal waterfowl observation, it demonstrated how looking down on duck concentrations was vastly superior to ground observations. Later, as a flyway biologist, I had participated in other aerial midwinter inventories, covering the coastal marshes of Louisiana, east Texas, and the barrier islands along the Mississippi

coast in Coast Guard and Navy amphibious aircraft. In fact, John Ball, then a lieutenant in the U.S. Navy and later chief pilot of the USFWS, took John Lynch and me on a memorable flight over the Louisiana coastal marshes in a contraption called a "Grumman Duck." Despite the weird appearance of this plane, I was more convinced than ever that aircraft would prove to be the answer to my problems in Canada.

Then began a long period of agitation to convince the USFWS of the desirability of obtaining an aircraft to census waterfowl on the breeding grounds. In the meantime, I learned to fly, or more correctly I should say that I got a license, for the learning process never ceases. At first the powers provided nothing but sympathy, but in 1946 they relented and I became the proud custodian of a Stinson L-5, a surplus Air Force reconnaissance plane. The Stinson proved to be an ideal tool for work on the prairies and parklands though it lacked the range and seaplane capabilities for safe use in the north.

In 1946, Art Hawkins joined our group,

working with me along the Mississippi Flyway and in Canada. Art was as enthusiastic as I about the possibilities of obtaining counts of breeding waterfowl by the "lone-drake system," as we called it. We worked together with the aircraft around Delta, Manitoba, and in the nearby pothole region. We concluded that censusing a breeding population of waterfowl from low-flying aircraft was possible. The ducks were visible as lone drakes or pairs and could be counted and identified as to sex and species.

Our next step was to apply this new technique on a broader scale. We found that circling individual marshes, lakes, and potholes was too time-consuming. Time was important because after the hens are well into incubation, the drakes leave their territories to gather in moulting areas. Then evidence of nesting disappears. Sampling appeared to be the answer, so we began flying cross-country transects, counting the ducks on a strip one-eighth mile on each side of the aircraft — the distance at which we could reliably identify ducks. It gave us a count on a square mile basis. To avoid bias, our transects were straight lines, and if a pothole or a portion thereof was outside of our line, we didn't count it, tallying only those ducks within our strip. This technique involved a lot of experimental flying which was refined as we progressed. We had some difficulty in convincing our bosses and even some of our co-workers that this was a feasible way to count ducks, but this method, with refinements, is still being used today.

One special assignment should be mentioned. The search for the nesting grounds of the whooping crane had already begun before I became involved, but on a low key. Fred Bard, then assistant director of the Saskatchewan Historical Museum at Regina, acted as the coordinator for the Canadian effort, investigating reported sightings and doing some actual aerial searching with the help of the U.S. Air Force out of Edmonton.

In 1945 arrangements were made with the Air Force by the Washington office of the USFWS for me to make some flights out of Edmonton to cover areas of recent sightings. That summer I left Cooking Lake in a Stinson L-1 with a Lieutenant Quick piloting. We covered the muskeg between the Pembina and Athabaska rivers in Alberta but saw no cranes.

In 1946 I used a Stinson L-5 to cover the same area as well as the Peace River district with Olin S. Pettingill III. We discovered a hundred trumpeter swans, but again saw no cranes.

In 1947 I met Bob Allen of the National Audubon Society at Flotten Lake, Saskatchewan, where he was camped with his family. We made a gas cache there and from that base covered northern Saskatchewan and northern Alberta with a Grumman Widgeon. We then went north as far as Great Slave Lake, giving everything in between thorough coverage.

In 1948, again with Bob Allen and Widgeon, we covered much of the same area as in 1947 but extended our search to the Arctic Coast, covering the entire coastline and adjacent tundra from Point Barrow, Alaska, to Bathurst Inlet, Northwest Territories, from our base out of Aklavik. In both 1947 and 1948 the primary emphasis was on the whooping crane, but waterfowl transects were run as well.

In the years following 1948, primary emphasis shifted to waterfowl surveys but we always had a weather eye out for the whooping crane. I flew the same areas year after year, but it was not until 1952 that I finally saw the first whooper. I was flying southwest of Yellowknife on the north side of Great Slave Lake — between Providence and the north arm — with Ev Sutton and a young Canadian Wildlife Service summer employee whose name I don't remember. The whooper was standing on the margin of a small pond under some open-grown spruce. It moved a short distance as I took several passes over it at about 100 feet. We thought there must be a nest but were unable to spot one.

The following day Ev and I returned. After about thirty minutes of searching, we found the whooper within 100 yards of its original location. We then began a systematic search of the surrounding marshes and muskegs. In about an hour, and possibly five miles from where we saw the first crane, we found another. I made a low pass so that Ev could take a photo with my camera. I was so close and so low that I couldn't see the crane over Ev's shoulder but did see two juvenile cranes about the size of brown leghorn chickens. They ran out from the vicinity of the adult and into the marsh grass.

In the ensuing years I looked over these areas numerous times without ever seeing another crane, but other pilots flying out of Yellowknife and Hay River reported seeing whooping cranes in this area from time to time.

In 1954, while at Yellowknife with Gus Swanson and Ev Sutton, a shock strut on the Grumman Goose went flat. Because there was no compressed air at Yellowknife, I left Ev and Gus there and flew to Edmonton to get the strut tightened and blown up. Returning the next day, my route passed west of Fort Smith. About twenty miles out, I saw a whooper flying directly above me at about three-thousand feet. I made a mental note to search the area at the first opportunity. Before I could do this, however, the cranes were found nesting near the location of my sighting of the lone crane by Don Landells and a forester flying from a fire near Hay River to Fort Smith. The rest of the crane story is history.

From this point on, I devoted each summer to the northern waterfowl surveys. First, it was necessary to map the survey areas so that the transect data on waterfowl could be applied to specific ecological units on a square-mile basis to come up with a meaningful figure for comparison from year to year. This proved to be quite a task, for in those early days accurate maps were available only along established routes of travel, such as along the MacKenzie River. Otherwise, an aerial chart consisted of a sheet of paper with a few dotted lines for where the larger rivers and lakes were thought to be; but for that, the charts were blanks with a few unreassuring notes such as "unsurveyed," with all elevations given followed by a plus or minus sign. minus sign.

Those first years of flying in the arctic were memorable. The country was pretty much as it always had been, for "progress" had not yet caught up with it. Settlements were few and far apart, established by the fur trade except for the mining communities at Yellowknife and Great Bear Lake and oil fields at Norman Wells. They were all supplied by ships or barge, via navigable waterways. In the Northwest Territories, there were not more than twenty of these centers of culture, all on the MacKenzie or its tributaries or scattered along the Arctic Coast. All travel and freight followed these water routes from one place to another — even airplanes, for that was where the people were. This pattern of settlement, with resulting lines of transport, left the great bulk of the country uninhabited and unexplored, penetrated by only a few native hunters, white trappers, and prospectors from the fringes.

This was the country we had to find out about. What was the density of nesting waterfowl in that vast region? What species were there and what habitats did they prefer? Was this the mythical place where they found sanctuary when the prairies dried up?

This was a country of awesome beauty, of mind-boggling vastness. It was a pristine wilderness, without a mark of man except for the occasional rock cairns placed on ridge tops by wandering Eskimos. We could fly for hours on a constant heading and watch the land roll away under our wings: muskeg, covered with sparse subarctic forest, or tundra arctic prairies extending to the far horizons. Water was everywhere, with lakes of all sizes and shapes feeding networks of creeks that wound their way to the master streams. To some, I suppose, such vistas would constitute unrelieved monotony, desolate and forbidding. To us, sailing along on our magic carpet 100 feet over the terrain, it was fascinating. At our altitude, we could see and identify not only the waterfowl on our strip but shorebirds and the larger passerine birds spooked out by our passage. Moose barged out of the willows along the streams and, on rare occasions, a small group of woodland caribou would be found standing knee-deep in a shallow lake trying to get away from the flies. Black bears shuffled out of our path or sat to watch us pass, and family groups of wolves were a common sight. Red, cross, and black foxes loped for cover as we sailed along, and now and then a wolverine would skulk into a thicket.

As we approached the barren lands, trees became few and dwarfed and then disappeared altogether, with the arctic prairies rolling away to the horizon. Here, pairs of whistling swans set up their territories, and along the coastal strip old squaw ducks, king eiders, and arctic and red-throated loons became common. Barren-ground grizzly bears were often encountered, some running off in fright, others offering to do battle. In the area between Coppermine and Bathurst Inlet south to the Thelon River, we found immense herds of barren-ground caribou working their way to the coast with occasional wolves hanging around the edges, looking for stragglers. The caribou were following their age-old migration routes in loose herds of from a few-thousand individuals to small bands of ten to twenty. In the vicinity of Bathurst Inlet or the Thelon River, musk oxen frequently galloped away out of our path to form a ring of defense around the calves. This pristine world, untouched and unspoiled, must have looked exactly the same to us as it did to Samuel Hearne when he made his historic trip from York Factory on Hudson Bay to Coppermine in 1772.

After each survey flight, we would put into one of the small settlements along the coast or the MacKenzie where gas had been cached during the previous year. Typically, each settlement had a Hudson Bay store, a church, a detachment of mounties, and a summer gathering of a few Eskimo or Indian families. Often being the first plane in for the year, we would bring the mail and we were always welcome. Upon our arrival at the beach fronting the post, we would be met by the entire population. Everybody, including babes in arms, lined up in a reception line. Protocol dictated that every hand be shaken once. Even the babies proffered a pudgy hand. Whereupon, to the accompaniment of howling sled dogs, we retired to the house of the Hudson Bay factor, followed by the entire population. Those who couldn't crowd into the living quarters filled the kitchen and entry-way, listening intently to every word spoken even though little, if anything, we said was understood. What they did understand, though, was laughter, for Eskimos are naturally happy people; so when we laughed, everybody laughed, for this was a festive event — the first plane of the year.

Eskimos along the Arctic Coast at that time were little affected by "progress." They wore beautifully sewn skin clothing, caribou parkas trimmed with wolf or wolverine, caribou britches, and sealskin mukluks. The older women had tattoos on their faces. They lived as they always had, fishing for arctic char when they ran in the rivers and hunting caribou and seals in season. White foxes were trapped in the winter to trade at the Hudson Bay store for what was needed of civilized goods. Most of the men had rifles, but the bow was still in use, made of spliced musk ox horns and backed with braided sinew.

Most of the arctic villages and those along the MacKenzie River and its tributaries had outposts of mounties who kept the peace and administered welfare programs, issuing rations to the needy. There were three towns in the northwest, however, that by comparison with the outposts were veritable metropolises — Fort Smith, Yellowknife, and Aklavik.

Fort Smith was on the southern border of the Northwest Territories, the gateway to the north, where all the goods shipped by water had to be portaged around the rapids of the Slave River and loaded on a different fleet of barges bound for points down the MacKenzie. This was the headquarters for the Hudson Bay Company transport system. They operated the MacKenzie Hotel for the boat crews and any itinerant wayfarers. Fort Smith was also the seat of government for the Northwest Territories and the headquarters of Wood Buffalo National Park.

Yellowknife was a gold mining community. There were two large mines and several smaller ones in the vicinity. There were actually two towns — the "old town" at the waterfront on an arm of Great Slave Lake and the "new town" up on the hill. There were hotels, pubs, stores, and a hospital. On paydays for the miners, the pubs were well patronized and occasionally rowdy.

Aklavik was situated near the western side of the great delta, on the Peel Channel of the MacKenzie. It could be said that all roads led to Aklavik, since there was only one, the mighty MacKenzie. It was the end of the line and the hub of the Arctic. Several hundred souls called it home. Here was a headquarters of the Royal Canadian Mounted Police, two churches with adjoining mission schools, a hospital, several government offices, a hotel, a restaurant, and a couple of stores besides the Hudson Bay Company. It was a great center for the harvest of muskrats. In spring at breakup there was feverish hunting and trapping activity for the feisty little critters. Since it never got dark, a good hunter could take over one hundred muskrats daily. It was also the port of call for the "Banks-landers" coming in with their schooners from the high Arctic, loaded with winter's catch of white foxes. It was one of the few places in the north where Eskimos and Indians rubbed shoulders, Aklavik being on the boundary of their common grounds.

Aklavik was also our headquarters for extended periods each summer. It was right on the extensive waterfowl breeding grounds of the delta, near the Old Crow Flats in the Yukon, and close to the coastal barrens running east to the Anderson River delta. We were often weatherbound in Aklavik, as it was wide open to the arctic storms howling out of the north. But it was better to be stormbound here than fighting out the weather on some unnamed lake on the barrens.

Air navigation at the beginning of our aerial explorations and surveys was a prob-lem, requiring large amounts of faith and hope. Once away from the mapped areas of the MacKenzie and around Great Slave Lake, we relied on two things: time and bearing. Our bearing was established by the magnetic compass, with constantly changing variations ranging between 0 and 50 degrees, depending upon our position. Moreover, being relatively near the magnetic pole, our compass needle would sometimes swing wildly in an arc up to 90 degrees. The only solution was to obtain a mean value as the needle swung from one extreme to the other. We would then set the directional gyro on the mean reading of our compass since the gyro would not swing. Although it had to be reset every few minutes, it at least pointed a straight course to steer on. We estimated wind-velocity and direction to calculate ground speed. Our position at any given time was computed by time and bearing. Thus, when my observer would shout over the roar of the engines "where the hell are we?" I could mark a point on a chart innocent of any detail and say calmly, "I think maybe we are probably about here."

This is not to say that I didn't sweat it out on occasion. In those early years our Widgeon was not noted for its long-range capabilities. It was necessary to get there and back in our allotted time or run out of gas. Later, I flew a Grumman Goose, a bigger, tougher, and more versatile craft. I installed enough extra gas tanks in the old bird to stay airborne eight hours, which took the pressure off and extended our range. We never got really lost — confused maybe, but we always got where we were headed and, most importantly, we got back!

Weather station reports were then hard to come by. Since we couldn't fly waterfowl surveys in poor visibility or in excessive winds, we sat out periods of bad weather. But since the starting point and the end of the survey might be several hundred miles apart, we were often caught somewhere in between. With experience, we learned to make our own forecast and, having butted our heads against innumerable frontal systems, we could recognize by cloud formations what we were likely to encounter enroute. Consequently, most of the really bad weather-related experiences had happened during our early years. Later on, we got smarter.

Bob Allen and I burned our fingers in a brush with the weather in 1948. We had left Coppermine on the Arctic Coast, heading for Yellowknife with the Widgeon. Flying in marginal weather, we got as far as Great Bear Lake, but that was the end of the line. Visibility was zero. We managed to sneak into a protected cove on a little island near the head of Hunter Bay on the northeast side of the lake. With wheels extended to protect the hull, we secured the aircraft against a sloping slab of granite with lines from the nose and wingtips tied to scrubby spruce trees. We were protected from all quarters except the northeast. Since the wind was westerly, we thought we were snug and safe. Our grub was running low, too, and after a delicious supper of oatmeal, we retired to our sacks spread out on the deck of the aircraft.

Lulled to slumber by the sound of the surf on the rocks outside our harbor, I was awakened in the darkness by the slap of waves against the hull. We piled out to see what was going on. The wind had gone northeast and was freshening by the minute. Seas were surging into our cove. We couldn't move the aircraft without causing damage. If we slacked off the lines, the plane would weathercock into the wind, putting its tail section into the rocks.

Our only recourse was to snug up the lines as tightly as possible, so we cinched them tight enough to play a tune. This eliminated horizontal movement, but the plane still surged up and down. To keep the keel from banging on the slab of granite, we wedged a section of spruce trunk under the bow. That left the hull banging up and down on the wheels. To try and dampen the impact, we stood in the water pushing on the wings to offset every wave. It was a long night.

In the morning the wind abated somewhat, but the swells continued until late in the afternoon of the third day. In the meantime, we lived on oatmeal and lake trout we caught by casting from the rocks of our harbor. When it calmed down enough to move the aircraft, about eight o'clock on the evening of the third day, we pulled out and flew to Sawmill Bay where the Canadian Air Force maintained a small outpost. The landing gear, fortunately, had withstood the pounding, and the hull was intact. Our only damage

Pack ice on the Arctic Ocean was another hazard. Ev Sutton and I had gone to Holman Island, a small Hudson Bay outpost on the coast of Victoria Island, en route to make a Survey of Banksland. As we crossed Coronation Gulf, small pans of pack ice began to appear and, upon arrival at Holman, there was too much ice in the inlet at the site of the post to get in. However, we landed offshore and taxied into a small bay adjacent through a narrow inlet that was ice-free. The people from the post brought us a couple of drums of gas by boat, and we wobblepumped the gas into our tanks. We had no sooner accomplished this than the wind shifted and brought the ice into our bay, completely filling it up. As soon as we saw what was happening, we beached the Goose tail to shore, and got a couple of long oars from the boat. By standing on the wings and fending off the icepans as they pushed in, we managed to hold the ice off the bow of the aircraft.

At low tide the ice would ground itself on the shelving shoreline, but during high water the ice would push toward the shore again, and we would have to fend it off. We could rest a few hours during low water. I would crawl into my sleeping bag and spread out on the beach, but the snow buntings would keep me awake by hopping back and forth on my sleeping bag. Sutton elected to sleep in the airplane, but he fared no better than I did because the snow buntings hopped all over the airplane, making a great din on the metal top. This went on for two days and two nights until the wind shifted and the ice drifted out. Needless to say, we were glad to get out of there, complete our surveys on

Banks, and return to Coppermine for hot food and a bed to sleep in.

We had our share of mechanical problems, too, for "Murphy's Law" works in the Arctic as well as elsewhere. When problems occur deep in the wilderness, far from any repair facilities, you have to make do as best you can with whatever materials are available. Thus, we found that spruce gum makes as satisfactory a seal on a leaking wing float or a loose rivet on the hull as on a seam of a birch-bark canoe.

Fortunately, our more serious problems occurred where at least some mechanical help was available. We replaced a cracked cylinder on the Widgeon at the Yellowknife airport amid a cloud of bulldog flies, and once we changed an engine on the Goose on the river at Aklavik. The engine change proved to be quite an operation. Just getting a new engine there was problem enough, but with the ingenuity of Mike Zubko, local expert on all matters pertaining to aircraft, we accomplished the task, though in the process we dropped enough wrenches in the river to stock a mechanic's tool kit. Our work was well supervised, however, for the river bank was lined with Eskimos watching intently and offering unsolicited advice and comments. One young fellow, a Bankslander, was particularly interested, and I asked him how it was on Banks Island. "Good," he said, "no mosquitos — not hot like here." At the time the temperature was about 36 degrees with a wind blowing fresh off the pack ice on the Beaufort Sea. It made me wonder what a cold spell on Banks would be like.

Those wonderful, free and not-so-easy days in the north are gone now. With the advent of the Dewline, the country began to open up, followed by increased oil and mineral exploration, road development, and the establishment of sport fishing camps on some of the lakes. The arrival of an aircraft in a once-remote Arctic village was no longer an event. Now you can go "down north" as a tourist in a jet aircraft and find posh accommodations. During my last few summers in the Arctic I saw not one wolf or grizzly bear,

and it was evident that the time had come for me to depart also. I had seen the country at its best and had no desire to go back.

In all, I spent twenty-six summers on the Canadian waterfowl breeding grounds: three in the prairies and parklands, two on the coast of James Bay, one in the eastern Arctic, and the remaining twenty in the western Arctic — the Northwest Territories and Yukon. In the process I flew well over a half-million miles over country seldom if ever seen by white men — much of it unmapped at the time.

Many hardy souls participated in these Arctic Surveys, sharing the workload and adding immeasurably to our accomplishments. In naming them I hope I have not forgotten anyone: Bob Allen of the National Audubon Society; Bud Safranek of Winona, Minnesota; U.S. Game Management Agents Chuck Lawrence, Ev Sutton, Tom Garrat, Joe Matlock, and Jim Johnson; biologists John Lynch, Ed Wellein, Jake Chamberlain and Hortin Jensen. In addition, many others rode along on parts of the surveys to see this vast waterfowl area, among whom were Dr. Clarence Cottam, assistant director of the USFWS; Dr. Gus Swanson of Cornell University; John Biggs, director of the Washington Game and Fish Department; Bill Leitch, chief biologist of Ducks Unlimited; and Canadian Wildlife Service Biologists; Vic Solman, Tom Barry, Ian McEwan, Ron MacKay, and Dave Monroe. I hope all of these people enjoyed the experience as much as I did.

When it came time for me to turn in my suit, Hortin Jensen, by then a veteran of the north, took over in my place. I was happy to leave the operation in good hands.

Mexico

I first became involved in the winter waterfowl surveys in Mexico in 1948. George Saunders had become ill while conducting a survey in Mexico that year, so I was selected to return in his place, little knowing that I had inherited an annual responsibility.

Having been recently checked out in the Widgeon, I shared the piloting chores with Dave Spencer. We made the circuit down the east Gulf Coast from Brownsville, Texas, to Chetumal on the British Honduras border, then across to Tapachula and back up the west coast through Baja, California. We didn't find any more ducks than George and Dave had on their previous survey, but we did find great numbers of black brant on Scammon Lagoon, an area famous as the wintering grounds of gray whales.

The following January, Floyd Thompson, then game management agent in Salt Lake City, joined me in Brownsville as an observer to make the same run, except that we would cover the coastal swamps and marshes of Guatemala as well as those in Mexico. We were plagued by misfortune from the beginning. My port engine gave up after Corpus Cristi, forcing me to limp into Brownsville on one. It took a week to replace the engine. We finally started out on our adventure, but about ten minutes out of Brownsville an explosion shook the cabin and great clouds of smoke and showers of sparks poured out of the instrument panel. Back we went, posthaste. I flipped off the master switch, and the sparks abated. But as we approached the field, I switched it on again briefly to advise the tower of our predicament, and that started the fireworks all over again. Needless to say, we didn't fiddle around with the landing pattern but came straight in. Another week passed before we were ready to try again.

Later, we were cruising up the west coast of Guatemala when a buzzard went through the left prop and caved in the engine nacelle. He went through without touching a blade,

which took good timing considering that the prop was turning about 2,000 rpm. Had the buzzard hit the blade, we would have been knocked out of the air. As it turned out, the only damage to the aircraft was cosmetic and the crew got by with nothing worse than a few seconds of stark terror. I think by that time Floyd was beginning to have doubts about the infallibility of aircraft for waterfowl surveys.

The rest of the survey went off without incident until we got back to the border at Calexico, California. At our first refueling on United States soil, our tanks were loaded with water.

About this time, we began to get pressure from Mexican officials to include one of their own observers on our flights. The Widgeon with extra fuel didn't have the capacity to accommodate an extra person, so in 1959 we borrowed a twin-engine Beechcraft from the Alaska Game Commission. Clarence Rhode ferried it down to Klamath Falls, Oregon, my headquarters at the time, and John Ball and I took it on down to Brownsville, where we expected to meet our Mexican observer. We finally tracked him down in Tampico, where he made one flight with us, observing that "we flew very close to the soil." He then left for Mexico City, saying that he would meet us at Acapulco on the way back up the west coast. When we arrived in Acapulco on the appointed date, there was no observer, and as we were unable to get through to Mexico City by telephone, we flew there and ran him to ground. But he had had enough of "flying close to the soil," so we returned to Acapulco and continued our survey, having at least fulfilled our part of the bargain.

In 1951 I was relieved of the onus of conducting the entire Mexican survey and was responsible only for the west coast and the interior. Another aircraft was used to survey the east coast so that a simultaneous sweep could be made. Later on, a third aircraft was assigned to the interior so that I could concentrate on the west coast entirely. That same year I was assigned the Grumman Goose, much more suitable for our surveys than the

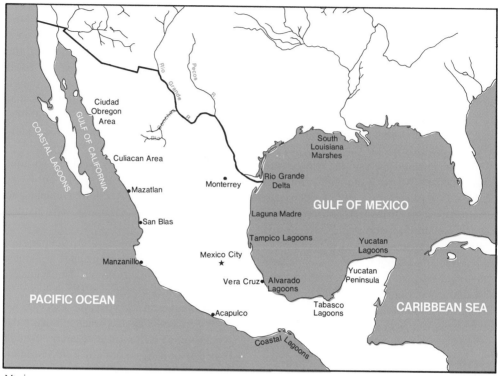

Mexico

Widgeon or the Beechcraft. While we were mostly land-based in Mexico, it was reassuring to be in an amphibian when flying back and forth across the Gulf of California.

The Goose could accommodate extra passengers, a fortunate capability. The USFWS was then being criticized by hunting groups unhappy with restrictive regulations for deliberately concealing the true numbers of waterfowl wintering in Mexico. Consequently, the USFWS organized a number of "show me" trips in connection with our annual winter survey to allow an observer of the duck hunters' choosing to see that we were actually finding and making a reasonable estimate of duck populations present. Fortunately for us, Starker Leopold was designated by the California Duck Hunters Association to represent them. Starker proved to be an unbiased and keen observer. He made two trips with me, after which a representative of the Pacific Flyway Council made the yearly pilgrimages and did the counting on one side of the aircraft.

Also about this time, the Mexican military was becoming suspicious of our annual survey, thinking it unlikely that we were just counting ducks. Consequently, their observers also accompanied our flights for the next several years.

The early years in Mexico were a far cry from conditions as they exist today. Fortunately, Pan American made available to us the refueling and maintenance facilities of its Mexican subsidiary, Compañia Mexicana de Aviacion. However, these facilities were present only in those places served by the company, usually larger cities. In the hinterland, airports were small, runways were covered with dirt or sod, and there was no gas. Before landing at such places, we would first spook the burros, cows, and goats off the field and, once down, we would head for town to arrange for gas to be hauled out to the field in drums. If we were lucky, this would be accomplished the next day, when we would gas the aircraft by wobblepump or bucket brigade. Because of the distance between gas stops and necessity of conducting surveys between these remote towns, we were forced to use these little fields frequently. With the coming of the tourist boom, facilities improved, at least in the tourist-oriented places, and it became less difficult to service the aircraft.

The coastal marshes and lagoons were spectacular wetlands. On the coastal plains of Sonora and Sinaloa between Guaymas and Culiacan, there were numerous irrigation developments and, through a series of ditches, waste water was dumped into coastal flats and sumps. These waters and adjoining mud flats, though not pleasing to the eye, combined with nearby grain fields to create an attractive environment for pintails and other puddle ducks. Beyond Culiacan and south to the Guatemala border, there were vast marshes and swamps, pristine and untouched, altered only by slow geologic processes. There were black-water lagoons bordered by mangroves, marshlands partitioned by open-water ponds, and a labyrinth of sluggish waterways where crocodiles lurked and native fishermen, in dugout canoes, plied their nets and tended their weirs.

Amid this setting was bird life almost unbelievable in numbers and kinds, a milling mass surging out of our flight path. We flew over shorebirds by the thousands, from tiny peeps to curlews and willets, droves of ibis, herons, cormorants, anhingas, jacanas, gallinules, coots, pelicans, and, now and then, a limpkin. Mixed in with all of these were the ducks, sometimes divers packed tight in rafts, or puddlers concentrated on mud flats. Mixed with the wintering ducks from the north were flocks of black-bellied and fulvous treeducks, and scattered individuals or pairs of the pato real, ancestor of our domestic muscovy. This was indeed an avian paradise, but the sheer numbers and variety of birds made our task difficult, for we had to tally ducks by numbers and species.

All of the birds were by no means beneath us, flushing out as we passed by. The stratum of air at our survey altitude, from 100 to 150 feet, also hosted a distinctive bird population that soared, flapped, or sailed about in our path. Innumerable buzzards, man-o-war birds, wood ibis, and flocks of green and red parrots had to be avoided to avert disaster. Wood ibis were not a problem unless we flew under them, whereupon they would panic and dive. It is a startling sight to see a wood ibis as big as a turkey plunging down within inches of the nose of the aircraft. On one occasion, an ibis passed between our port wingfloat and the fuselage. Man-o-war birds never caused any problems but acted as if they might, making erratic maneuvers as we approached. Fortunately, they always got out of the way. Buzzards were usually easily avoided if they were seen in time, and after my collision with one in Guatemala, I was a litle bit tender about them.

Buzzards were so numerous, it seemed as though I was constantly maneuvering around them. To do this, I needed room and so did they. One time, however, both parties misjudged. We had just completed our survey of the Marismas Nacional and had started our climb out en route to Mazatlan when a buzzard appeared dead ahead and close. Every maneuver I made, the buzzard duplicated; we were perfectly synchronized. It was probably no longer than five seconds from the first sighting until the buzzard came crashing through the windshield. Shattered glass was everywhere, and one large chunk hit me on the side of the face. Fortunately, I had a long-billed cap and sunglasses; otherwise my eyes would have been filled with shattered bits of glass. We left the buzzard wedged in the windshield and proceeded to Mazatlan, hoping the windshield wouldn't cave in completely. Seldom has a wildlife biologist had the opportunity to observe the forward end of a turkey buzzard so completely. I can still see that naked red head dangling in front of my face all the way back to Mazatlan.

On another trip, Hortin Jensen, Don Smith of the Utah Fish and Game Department, and I had just made a long run, completing our survey of the marshes and lagoons on the delta of the Rio Culiacan, the

NC 702 heads for Mexico over a duck concentration near the mouth of the Rio Grande River during the winter waterfowl survey of 1951. USFWS photo courtesy of J. Ball.

nearby Ensenada del Pabellon, and were headed for Mazatlan when the weather began to deteriorate. The ceiling progressively lowered, and finally there wasn't any room between the clouds and the long Pacific swells. I had made a mental note of a deep water lagoon back up the coast that could be used for an emergency landing. We turned around and headed back, landing on the lagoon just before dark. We taxied up to a small fishing village and threw out the anchor. The entire population turned out to greet us, yelling and screaming. Nothing like this had ever happened before. There couldn't have been more excitement if we had been men from Mars. We were promptly ferried to shore in dugout canoes. There were no public facilities in the village whatsoever except one large palapa, a thatch-covered open-air pavillion with tables and chairs where beer and soft drinks were served.

Hoping to find some food, we went in, followed by the crowd. We arranged with the proprietor to boil up some shrimp, which was all he had to offer. There were three rough-looking characters standing at the bar as we came in. They seemed friendly at first, but the more beer they gulped down the more hostile they became. Sensing that trouble was likely, the crowd began to disperse and finally slipped away entirely except for one man who had promised to paddle us back to the airplane. When the shrimp finally arrived, we ate a few, but the situation worsened and we left, walking back down to the beach. It was pitch dark by then. As I leaned over to take my shoes off to wade out to the dugout, somebody bashed my head. When I came to, I was in the airplane. Hearing the waves slap against the hull, I couldn't figure out what we were doing in the water.

Hortin brought me up to date. When I stooped over to take off my shoes, he had heard a dull thud and saw me lying on the sand, out cold. Hortin had fought the ruffians off singlehanded. He had a black eye to show for it. We took turns keeping watch over the aircraft that night, expecting an ambush. At daylight, we pulled up the anchor and took off for Culiacan to refuel before going on to Mazatlan. I guess we must have looked a bit disheveled. My neck was so stiff and sore I couldn't turn it, and Hortin's beautiful black eye had turned a deep purple. I am quite sure that had Hortin not been there to fight off the banditos, I would never have made it off that beach. I later heard that our assailants were not from that village but from Durango and that the ringleader was later killed in a fight.

The daily routine of a duck counter sometimes involved a lot more than counting ducks.

Back's Great Fish River

Walter J. Breckenridge

My work as preparator, curator, and finally director of the Bell Museum of Natural History at the University of Minnesota has not been limited in scope to investigations of waterfowl. Nevertheless, a number of my activities have involved waterfowl studies. For example, part of my museum public-education work included making 16-mm motion pictures. Some of my work was later incorporated into short educational films distributed by the audio-visual program of the University of Minnesota. One of these, "Duck Hunters' Dilemma," briefly covered some of the work of banding and other field studies carried on by various waterfowl specialists, particularly those at the Delta Waterfowl Research Station at Delta, Manitoba. Some projects covered by these films included captive rearing of ducks and trumpeter swans at the research station and netting flightless adult and young ducks for banding and fluoroscope studies for lead-shot ingestion at Whitewater Lake in Manitoba.

Later two brothers, Bob and Jim Wilkie, Minneapolis industrialists, became interested in arctic wildlife studies. They generously subsidized several northern expeditions, one of which centered along the Back River in northern Keewatin Territory in arctic Canada during July and early August 1953.

Few areas remain in North America for which at least distributional notes on the breeding bird life present are not available. The interior of Northern Keewatin, Canadian Northwest Territories, is such a practically virgin area. The area we visited comprises the lower portion of the Back River below Garry and Macdougall lakes. This region lies just south of the Arctic Circle and between 97 degrees and 99 degrees west longitude, roughly six-hundred miles northwest of Churchill, Manitoba.

Preble, writing early in the century, summarized early explorers' notes on bird distributions along the west coast of Hudson Bay and in the District of Mackenzie very well. C. H. D. Clarke, in his report on the Thelon Game Sanctuary, continued the work up to 1937 and extended the coverage eastward from MacKenzie and northward from Manitoba. These reports have extensive bibliographies. Since then, Peter Scott, cooperating with Harold Hanson and Paul Queneau, reported on the life of the Perry River region, 150 miles to the northwest of the lower Back River. Saville has published on the birds of Chesterfield Inlet 300 miles to the southeast, and Manning has added data on the region to the south between Reindeer Lake and Baker Lake.

During the first week in July 1953, after a week of impatient waiting at Churchill, we learned that the ice was beginning to break up in the District of Keewatin, north of Baker Lake. Finally on the morning of July 12, expedition leader Breckenridge led off for points north in the USFWS' amphibious plane with pilot Ed Wellein and observer Wes Newcomb. Following closely were the rugged Norseman plane of Arctic Wings piloted by Charlie Weber and another Norseman of the Royal Canadian Air Forces. We took off from Laning Lake, heading for Back's Great Fish River. As we flew north, we crossed over ice-covered Kaminuriak Lake, little guessing that this would be the scene of a near-disaster on our return trip. Ice still covered most of Baker Lake, but the western end was open. Here we landed and taxied up to the Hudson Bay post to refuel and to spend the night.

Baker Lake is a tiny, disjointed sort of settlement that sprawls for a mile along the shore of a narrow inlet at the mouth of the Thelon River. In 1953 it boasted an excellent two-way radio station, Anglican and Roman Catholic missions, Department of Transport representatives, and one of the few airstrips north of Churchill. A few Eskimo families made up the rest of the village. It is the trading center for the Eskimos of the Thelon

Coastal tundra in an area lying between the MacKenzie and Anderson Rivers in the Northwest Territories in Canada. USFWS photo.

River and from the vast barren country to the north, including the lower Back River.

After Captain George Back's Arctic Land Expedition of 1834, when he explored the river from its source to the Arctic Ocean, it became known as Back's Great Fish River. Maps now refer to it simply as the Back River. This last name is fitting in another sense since it is as remote as any large river entirely within the Barren Grounds of Northern Canada.

Its source is the height of land northeast of the Great Slave Lake. From here the Back River flows eastward through 530 miles of rock-studded barren lands roughly paralleling the Arctic Circle. Not a single tree grows along its entire course. Three enormous lakes are located midlength of the River — Lake Pelly, Lake Garry, and Lake Macdougall. Over eighty cascades, rapids, and waterfalls interrupt its turbulent and often tortuous passage as it descends to the Arctic Ocean.

After three weeks spent among the abundant wildlife around Churchill, we were not prepared for the extreme barrenness of this part of the Arctic tundra, though we had read enough to realize that the rugged interior of Keewatin would not be as rich in bird and mammal life as the coastal areas and the Thelon Wildlife Sanctuary two-hundred miles to the southwest. Our best efforts in three-and-a half weeks identified only thirty species of birds, fourteen of which were represented by only five individuals or less.

The terrain surrounding the base camp was rugged and rocky for the most part, with occasional boggy meadows interspersed, few of which exceeded two or three thousand acres. Bold outcroppings of metamorphosed rocks rose to as much as 450 feet above the river. Extensive sloping boulder fields of frost-shattered rocks and some talus slopes occupied much of the area between the bedrock outcroppings. Many small clear lakes,

©W. Breckenridge

bordered here and there by narrow spongy peat meadows, filled the depressions. Drainage slopes were often carpeted by dense, hummocky mats of sphagnum moss, sedges, cottongrass, Arctic labrador tea, dwarf birch, and bearberry.

Following are our observations on the three species of waterfowl recorded during our three-weeks stay on the Back River.

We only recorded five Canada geese, probably the lesser or tundra Canada goose, seen flying along the Back River near camp on July 15. A few primary feathers found along the shore of the bay near camp and at other points have been identified as of this species. Since they must have been shed before our survey, at least some of these geese must have been present in this area, possibly the year previous.

A single white goose was seen July 18 flying down the river near camp and veering off toward the south. Presumably it was of the lesser snow goose species, although it could have been a Ross' goose.

The only duck positively identified in the area visited was the old squaw. Flocks of up to twenty-three birds, mostly males, were seen on several lakes within five miles of camp. A few small groups were made up of females only. We saw no evidence of nesting. Males showing white feathers in the head, indicating the beginning of moult, were seen as early as July 14. All birds appeared capable of flight until August 2, when two females were collected, one of which had shed the primaries and the other was just shedding them. We saw no evidence of a flightless condition in the males. Four specimens were taken.

No birds whatsoever would be called abundant in this deserted place, but families of Lapland longspurs were scattered regularly over the tundra about camp, while a few American pipits lived in the scattered boulder fields. Here and there, the contrasting black and white of a male snow bunting made it conspicuous, while the grey females and young, no doubt, often escaped notice.

Two of us were flown to Lake Macdougall, some fifty miles south as the crow flies, for an eighty-five mile return trip by small boat. En route we got good aerial previews of the really awesome stretches of wild white water we would soon be navigating. We recalled Captain Back's names — "Escape Rapids" and "Whirlpool Rapids" — with some trepidation as we thought of our flimsy canvas boat lashed to the pontoons.

Double-checking the outline of the lake below us as beyond question that of Lake Macdougall, we glided down onto a choppy bay that reflected ominous storm clouds. After launching our tiny craft and taking aboard the equipment, we watched the plane disappear into the eastern sky. Our little three-horsepower "put-put" purred along reassuringly as we started out, although the clouds, now breaking and now thickening again, left us wondering what sort of weather the fates were whipping up for us.

The next day's travel set the pattern of our navigation for the trip. Although it was exhaustingly strenuous, we did make fair progress and had no accidents. With a sturdier boat and conditions where our lives did not so completely depend on our equipment, we would have attempted shooting more of the rapids than we did.

Further downstream, a golden plover on a meadowy shore invited investigation. The concerned retreat of the obviously nesting bird led me past a tiny tundra pond where a strange two-syllabled wailing call suddenly diverted my attention to a black-throated Arctic loon sitting on a nest.

Late in the afternoon of our third day, when we climbed a rocky hill to lay out our course through some especially boisterous whitewater ahead, we spotted two objects that looked like tents perched high above the roughest part of the rapids far downstream. We had been fooled by huge boulders looking like tents or houses before, but binoculars proved these were really tents. We hurried expectantly through the mile of tracking between us and the village. Our previous information was that no white men had ventured on these waters in the last hundred years, so we would certainly surprise the inhabitants of the village.

We approached with much doubt as to our reception, but if they were astonished by our arrival they were most successful in concealing it. Some slight excitement was evinced by the two women and the five children, but the two men simply left their work, which appeared to have been cleaning fish for drying, and walked slowly to meet us. We smiled and waved our open hands to assure them of our friendly intentions and were received with smiles in return.

We were at once amazed by the simplicity of their living. Obviously their major, and as far as we could determine their only, food was fish (no evidence of waterfowl). They used the Eskimo fish spear, with wooden shaft, to acquire fish.

Some of our party were to experience the hazards of traveling in this remote land. For Jim and Bob Wilkie and Dr. Lou Larson, the expedition came to a storybook climax. They took off to fly back to Churchill on July 28. Bob here gives a firsthand account of the experience:

> An hour out of Baker Lake at 12:30 A.M., still 300 miles north of Churchill, Charlie Weber, our tundra pilot, pointed below us to Kaminuriak Lake, sixty miles long. The plane, droning its way over this monotonous stretch of water, soon had us all dozing, when suddenly we awakened to the sickening sound of the motor sputtering to a stop! Flames shot out of the engine cowling. Charlie pulled on the fire extinguisher and the flames were quenched, but the cabin filled with black smoke, and oil

splashed over the windshield, completely blacking out our vision. Charlie kept his eyes glued to the altimeter reading set at Baker Lake to judge his landing height. Then he leveled the plane out, blindly hoping we were still over the lake. We mushed hard into the water in a tail-down position; then, bouncing clear of the water, we struck what we later found was the last projecting rock tip of a long reef. A few feet further out from the reef and we would have been safe.

The blow doubled up the right pontoon at a 90-degree angle. A pontoon strut stabbed through the cabin between Jim's legs, providentially ending up in a packsack. The plane slithered and skidded in the water and slowed to a stop. Everyone scrambled up on the motor cowling. No one seemed badly hurt, and our minor bruises and bumps seemed insignificant under these circumstances. With the tail settling steadily in the water it appeared certain that the plane would eventually sink, we hauled out our air mattresses and blew them up. Charlie got out an old Mae West, but this would be almost useless in the icy 34-degree water. We were more than half a mile off shore and realized there was no chance whatsoever of swimming that distance. Evidently our time had not come, however, for the ship finally reached an equilibrium and a slight wind and possibly a current in the lake started it drifting at a rate of about two miles per hour.

Unluckily, we drifted considerably off shore of several reefs, although it appeared with each that we might approach near enough to attempt swimming. Soon the tail settled to an almost vertical position, and the wing surfaces made a fair sail. We debated the possibility of going ashore on our air mattresses, but since there were only three floats for five people (young Mrs. Weber had come along for the thrill!) we didn't think all of us could make it. Our decision was to stick with the ship. For eight miserable hours we sat on the wings, ready to jump at any minute if the plane should slide into the water. Finally, some distance out from what seemed to be the last reef, sounding indicated that we had a good chance of grounding. A few minutes later the tail and one pontoon scraped on the bottom in ten feet of water, and we came to a halt — but still we were a quarter-mile from shore.

Charlie seemed to thaw out first and started looking the plane over for materials to build a raft. The only tools we had, since there was no salvage equipment on the plane, were a couple of light hand axes and a Boy Scout knife with a screwdriver blade. One axe went overboard, but we managed to hang onto the second and with it chopped out one of the gas tanks. We removed the wooden plane doors and took off all the metal parts. Using our tent ropes, we lashed the door frames under the 50-gallon tank in order to stabilize it. One man, we found, could float on the tank in a prone position. After lashing on the doors, it supported two of us.

Then we got the idea of lashing our air mattresses around the outside edge of the tank. This made a very stable raft. In some rubberized sacks we placed sleeping bags and some canned food. These were blown up like paper sacks and tied to the raft. The rest of our equipment was under water down in the tail of the plane, and we were afraid to try to salvage any more. By this time, a strong wind was blowing, and we decided it was now or never.

Gingerly, each of us crawled onto the raft and found a place on top of the tank. We paid ourselves out on the anchor rope, and when we found that we were still afloat, we let go and allowed the wind and waves to take us in their arms. For awhile, it looked as though we would miss the long point and float out into the main part of the lake. It wasn't until we were within a hundred yards of shore that we were sure we would gain the tip of the reef. Icy waves were breaking over the raft, but after thirteen hours afloat we were now so jubilant that such incidentals no longer disturbed us.

Our jubilance, however, gradually calmed down and disappeared during the next three miserable days spent trying to get something to eat, fighting mosquitoes, and hoping for a plane to pass over. The meagre amount of food we had salvaged consisted of twelve tins of canned meat, twenty packets of dehydrated soup, and some chocolate. Anticipating that we might be marooned for as much as twelve days, we rationed ourselves to one can of meat and two packets of soup per day. We tried to sleep as much as possible to conserve our strength; the rest of the time we spent gathering heather for signal fires and for cooking. Jim and Charlie constructed a slingshot, using rubber from the Mae West and wood from a specimen box. They were successful in getting a few ptarmigan and some small birds. These helped thicken the soup immeasurably. None of the arctic berries were ripe. Although there was a plentiful supply of mushrooms, we were afraid to try them. So we got along as best we could on our soup and canned meat, supplemented with a small supply of pilot biscuits that had floated ashore.

All of the specimens in the plane were lost, but on the second day we discovered a large shiny aluminum specimen box lying on the shore. This made a perfect mirror if we should have a chance to "shine" a rescue plane. On the third day, while making fish hooks out of the keys from the meat tins, we heard a faint drone and spotted a tiny plane passing south several miles to the west of us. Charlie and I grabbed the aluminum box and cover and started flashing the plane, while Jim and Lou started up the signal fires. Only a few flashes of the reflectors were needed to alert the pilot, and he swung around and glided to a stop in the bay in front of us. And a couple hours later, we landed in Churchill.

The losses from this plane crash included about fifty prepared bird and mammal skins, a number of preserved fish specimens, about three thousand feet of exposed 16mm movie film, and numerous rolls of 35mm slides. The numbers of specimens lost may not seem great, but considering the scarcity of wildlife in the area and the difficulties of collection, those small numbers took on greater importance.

The remaining four members of our party, not knowing of the loss of the plane, made no attempt to replace the lost materials but concentrated on getting additional, rare and hard-to-collect specimens we had not previously encountered. Our collection of five hundred botanical specimens, fortunately, was not sent back on the ill-fated plane and so were saved.

Regarding the scarcity of waterfowl, it is pertinent to point out that Back passed the location of our base camp on July 26, 1834, and camped a few miles below. In describing this camp, he stated, "It was opposite to a solitary bank that formed the western entrance to a small river apparently a favorite resort for geese, which, having frequented it in numberless flocks during the moulting season had left thousands of the finest quills strewn on the sand. Carts might have been laden with them."

Back gave no clue to the species of these geese, but Anderson, another early explorer of the area, mentioned repeatedly the abundance of Canada geese. Anderson's party crossed Macdougall Lake and encamped at Sinclair Falls on July 25. (We camped there July 29.) His notes for that day mentioned that they "killed 13 male Canada geese." On

July 28, while still above the mouth of the Montresor River (covered by us by plane on July 14 and again on July 28), Anderson reported that "immense numbers of Canada Geese were seen — 20 killed."

Considering the changes in waterfowl populations throughout North America during the last century, it would not be suprising to find the birds breeding in this region reduced in numbers, but we hardly anticipated the total absence of any evidence of either ducks or geese breeding in this area in 1953. Perhaps the particular local breeding population from this area was decimated or even completely eliminated by hunting during the past seventy-five years, leaving little or no breeding stock whose ancestral nesting grounds was the Lower Back River. Another explanation for this puzzling lack of waterfowl in 1953 might be that this was a year with a particularly late break up of the ice. Pilots who flew us into the Back River from Churchill stated that the spring weather turned out to be unusually late that year.

The following explanation for the lack of birds during late seasons was suggested originally by Arthur Hawkins and Ed Wellein, USFWS biologists working on Arctic waterfowl problems. Species of geese and ducks normally adapted to Arctic nesting move northward along the west coast of Hudson Bay as rapidly as possible in spring. But when they encounter frozen, uninviting conditions, as they might have in 1953, they tend to follow the southeast-northwest isotherms toward the northwest, where the ice disappears earlier. Thus these birds would nest farther to the north and west when the breeding urge finally made nesting imperative, rather than moving directly north into this Back River area.

Whether or not these theories apply to the barren situation we found in the Back River area in 1953 depends entirely on whether or not that year's spring break up could correctly be considered unusually late. Back described in graphic terms how huge masses of ice from Lake Macdougall temporarily blocked the Back River at Rock Rapids on

July 24, the year that geese occurred abundantly on the river. Yet we saw no ice on Lake Macdougall or at Rock Rapids on July 28 and 29, indicating that the 1953 spring break up could not have been later than it was in 1834. However, river temperatures recorded at our base camp dropped suddenly from 46 fahrenheit degrees on July 18 to 43 degrees on July 19, and some ice was seen on the bank above camp on July 21. This suggested some major mass of ice entered the Back on this date or earlier, which might have been the same phenomenon mentioned by Back.

A study of the monthly weather maps issued by the Meteorological Division of the Canadian Department of Transport shows that during 1953, the central Keewatin region had tempertues during April of 10 degrees fahrenheit above the long-term average; May, 3 degrees fahrenheit above average; June, 2 degrees above average; July, 1 degree below average; and August, 2 degrees above average.

Since the Back River area has no reporting weather station, the above data are interpolated from Baker Lake and Cambridge Bay reports. Still, these data do not seem to support the supposition that 1953 was an unusually late season in the Back River area. These fragmentary bits of evidence, then, suggest that our report on waterfowl breeding must be fairly typical, and that, as far as temperatures are concerned, only occasional seasons might be expected to be more favorable.

One further possible explanation of waterfowl scarcity would be that a major shift had taken place in the breeding grounds of these geese. If this occurred, weather or food conditions must be the cause, since human interference in this area has been negligible in the past one hundred years. There is some precedent for supposing that such a shift away from a large area as a breeding grounds could occur. Preble did not mention finding in 1902 blue and snow geese around Eskimo Point where Soper reported they were nesting in 1944 and where there were still large numbers breeding in 1953. Furthermore, Soper's report of the unexplained shift of the migrating blue and snow geese in spring from their Grant's Lake, Manitoba, resting area suggests that geese are capable of making major changes in what might be considered "permanent" ancestral flight lanes.

Yet another reason for our failure to find breeding geese in 1953 was that we simply missed the lakes where they bred that year. But if they retained their habit of moving down onto the river, as both Back and Anderson found them doing at about the same time as our visit, we should have encountered them somewhere on the 130 miles we covered along Back's Great Fish River.

The wooded delta of the MacKenzie River, north of Aklavik, Northwest Territories. USFWS photo by A. Brazda.

The Bush

Arthur R. Brazda

Between the prairie-parklands and the tundra lies a tremendously important piece of waterfowl real estate commonly known as "the bush." In more refined wildlife habitat circles, however, it is technically known as the boreal forest.

For many years this intermediate zone, comprising approximately 400,000 to 500,000 square miles in Alberta, Saskatchewan, Manitoba, and Ontario, was not given proper recognition as waterfowl habitat. Prairie survey crews scoffed at the data and the efforts of personnel operating in the bush, often suggesting that the area was second-rate. Granted, there were neither power nor section lines to guide northern survey crews, and at times the weather made operations somewhat difficult and hazardous. However, after a change in viewpoint and adjustments

in investigative procedures, it soon became apparent that "herein lies the mother lode."

The bush, with its relatively stable habitat, accommodates many displaced prairie waterfowl during drought periods, waterfowl which later replenish the breeding stock for the prairies. True, this less-fertile northern habitat will never produce the abundance of waterfowl evident after two or three successive wet years on the prairies. But one thing seems certain: the bush waterfowl habitat will remain long after most of the waterfowl areas on the prairies are producing tumbleweeds or wheat.

Early investigators or waterfowl biologists involved in the study of this transition zone include many stalwart and foresighted individuals. Among them are E.B. "Jake" Chamberlain, Ed Wellein, Hortin Jensen, Fred Glover, Joe Perroux, and Al Smith, to name but a few. I entered the scene in 1962, sharing the pilot/observer duties with flyway biologist Ross Hanson that summer. For the next four years, agent Gust Nun participated as observer, followed by agent Bob Slattery for three years, agent Dick Gimby for five years, biologist Lonnie Schroeder for one year, flyway biologist Bruce Conant for two years, and flyway biologist Jim Goldsberry for the past three years as pilot observer.

Ours was the last survey crew to use the old twin-engine Grumman Goose amphibian as a survey aircraft. The "iron monster," as it was sometimes affectionately called, had been built for the U.S. Navy in 1942 and was twenty-three years old when it was replaced in 1965 by the DeHavilland Speedster, better known in the North as the *Beaver*. This relatively new aircraft, thirteen years old when USFWS acquired it from the U.S. Air Force, is still in service. It has proved to be a rugged, dependable machine on surveys and an excellent freighter when we developed a northern remote-area, preseason duck banding program. Actually, the *Beaver* will haul anything you can get into it or on it, taking off from practically any airstrip or water area, for it was built with the North in mind. It has one unredeeming or questionable quality, however, and that is its inability to develop much forward speed, regardless of engine power settings, rarely exceeding 100 miles per hour. It is the only airplane that I know of that a tailwind will not help, thus the name "Speedster."

The *Beaver* was replaced as the primary survey aircraft by the Cessna 206, which is a good survey aircraft but an extremely poor water performer on amphibious floats. The purchase of the floats was one of those cases where purchasing through the bid system caused the Service to come out second best. One Cessna 185 and one Cessna 206 are presently in use in the North, but the intent is to replace the 206 in the near future since the 185 appears to handle our overall survey needs adequately. Although the 185 is no freighter, it has excellent land and water operational qualities.

Shortly after becoming project leader for these northern surveys, I realized that this vast region was far more important to the continental waterfowl resource than had previously been determined. Stratum boundaries were redrawn to better fit habitat types and geographical distribution, coverage was increased by adding more survey lines to the important waterfowl areas, and more appropriate annual survey starting dates were set. For several years, one crew flew the northern portions of three provinces: Manitoba, Ontario, and Saskatchewan. However, with the addition of more survey lines, primarily in Manitoba and Saskatchewan, Ontario was assigned to another crew. As the waterfowl habitat and breeding population index in Ontario appeared to be relatively low and stable, the Ontario survey was dropped in the early 1970s until additional qualified personnel and equipment were available. At present the survey team which covers the prairie-parklands of Alberta also includes a small sample of the Alberta bush. Another crew covers 224,000 square miles of northern Manitoba and Saskatchewan.

In the more than twenty years that I have flown in the North (including Alaska as well as the Canadian areas), inclement weather and the general lack of reliable weather reporting stations caused more anxious moments than all other operational facets combined. Northern Saskatchewan, Manitoba, and Ontario are near enough to the Arctic and to Hudson Bay that they frequently receive weather conditions unfit for flying. In the early 1960s, there were few weather stations in this area to warn pilots of changing conditions. One regular weather station was located at Prince Albert, Saskatchewan; a distance north — approximately 450 miles — there was another at Uranium City. Our survey was serviced by another weather station at Lynn Lake, Manitoba, on the east and at Fort McMurray, Alberta, 400 miles to the west. It was not unusual to land three or four times between Lynn Lake and McMurray to wait out a thunderstorm or squall-line activity. One occasion, this wait turned into a stay of two or three days, during which time the Canadian Air Rescue and other flight service agencies would become alarmed at our failure to return.

In recent years, partial weather stations have been activated in Saskatchewan at Cree Lake, Buffalo Narrows, Meadow Lake, and Colins Bay on Wollaston Lake, and these stations have been most helpful. In northern Manitoba, relatively new stations at Gillham and Norway House provide assistance, as do the new stations at Big Trout Lake and Fort Severn in northern Ontario. Northern Ontario has separate weather problems. Some of the foulest flying weather in the North can develop just west of James Bay, including the Attawapiskat-Albany River area, north to Winisk and Fort Severn, and south to Lake Nipigon. The North is beautiful, but it can also be unpredictable and unforgiving.

Many changes have occurred in the North over the past twenty years, mostly of negative value to wildlife. Roads are being built into remote regions, mainly to service the developing mining industry. Massive hydroelectric projects have been built on several of the major drainage systems in northern Manitoba, and on the east side of James Bay. There is a continual search for sites in northern Saskatchewan. In most cases, these huge impoundments have destroyed an abundance of established waterfowl habitat, while creating very little new habitat. Crews exploring for oil and other minerals seem to be everywhere, making one wonder what the future holds for wildlife. Our fuel caches no longer can be depended upon to be intact when needed. Operational costs and cost of living have soared. In the early 1960s, hotel or motel accommodations ranged from $10 to $20 a day; these same accommodations now are $25 to $50 a day. Aviation fuel was once $.55 a gallon instead of the present $1.75, and aircraft maintenance costs, which were once $8 to $12 per hour, are now $25 to $35 per hour.

With respect to aircraft operations, one thing hasn't changed — the willingness of maintenance shops and personnel, and northern Canadians in general — to help visitors out of difficult situations. One hopes this admirable northern trait will never change. Three operators that have been especially helpful to our operation in the bush are Athabaska Airways and NorCanAir in Saskatchewan, and LambAir in Thompson, Manitoba. LambAir also operates out of The Pas, Manitoba.

The duties of the flyway biologist are as many-faceted in Canada as they are elsewhere in the continent. Surveys of waterfowl breeding pair and production have top priority, but preseason banding activities rate a close second. Sometimes we receive additional assignments. For several years, late-June "show-me" tours were offered, involving personnel from the flyway councils, the national wildlife agencies, Ducks Unlimited, plus sportswriters and occasionally members of the U.S. Congress. In addition, there have been searches for the whooping crane to check out reported observations of the "great white bird" on other than the traditional breeding grounds. So far these have been unproductive.

One special assignment deserves comment here. The Central Flyway Technical Committee, after several years of discussion and planning, determined that there was a need to delineate the high Arctic breeding range of the Tall Grass Prairie Canada goose, *Branta canadensis parvipes*. I was asked to accomplish the exploratory phase of this project along with Ernie Kuyt, a biologist with the CWS and Charles Schroeder, a waterfowl biologist with the North Dakota Game and Fish Department.

Chuck Schroeder and I departed Saskatoon, Saskatchewan, on July 7, 1971, in the *Beaver*. En route to Yellowknife, we stopped in Fort Smith, Northwest Territories, where Ernie Kuyt got aboard. Three days later we were still in Yellowknife, grounded because of the lack of visibility due to smoke from huge forest fires in Alaska. Northern stations such as Inuvik, Coppermine, and Cambridge Bay, our first destination, were also having smoke problems, so discretion overruled valor. Adding to the interest of the expedition was the fact that only one weather reporting station, Contwoyto Lake, existed in the six hundred miles between Yellowknife and Cambridge Bay.

Our first stop out of Yellowknife was Bathurst Inlet, where we replenished our fuel supply from a previously established cache. Before taking on fuel, we stopped at Arctic Lodge. We learned that an old waterfowler, Al Hochbaum, was vacationing there. But Al was scrambling around the rocky cliffs looking for peregrine falcons and similar birds, so we missed him.

Cambridge Bay was the next stop. We were informed that our most important fuel cache, supposed to be at the CWS cabin at the mouth of the Perry River, was not there. The Perry River, on Queen Maud Sound, was to be the center of our operation, so until the fuel was delivered, we were stymied.

For the next few days we covered all the area that we could out of Cambridge Bay, including much of Victoria Island, Jenny Lind Island, Kent Peninsula, Fitzgerald Island, Melbourne Island, and Collinson Peninsula, to name a few. On one of these flights we encountered one of the most severe lightning storms I have ever witnessed. We were flying low along the edge of a squall-line back to Cambridge Bay when suddenly the barometric pressure "dropped out of the bottom" and bolts of lightning struck the ground, causing spurts of smoke in a wide area below the aircraft. This encourages one to hurriedly review his life.

Eventually Northland Aviation delivered our fuel to the Perry River location, and we operated from there for the next several days, encountering daily snow squalls and sometimes gale-force winds. During one storm we nearly lost our aircraft to the elements. We were using full fifty-five gallon drums as tie-down anchors. However, on this particular occasion, the high-tide point and 50 MPH winds arrived simultaneously, so the fuel drums began to float. Only Schroeder's and my herculean efforts saved the day. The thought of losing the aircraft was unpleasant, to say the least, since it was our only contact with other folks, as the radio in the camp was out. That, plus the possiblity of having to fill out the reams of government accident-report forms, provided the incentive to draw on undiscovered reserves of strength.

Along with the data being obtained for the Canada geese, we recorded all information for snow, Ross', and white-fronted geese, swans, sandhill cranes, muskox, caribou, and other forms of Arctic wildlife we encountered. Only the second observation of a blond muskox was recorded near the Ellis River on one of our flights. Another casual observation was that of a large, handsome bull muskox which had tentatively trapped himself on an island directly across part of the river from camp. Possibly knowing that love was close at hand and it was "that time of the year," he had circled the perimeter of that island constantly for several days. Finally, unable to restrain his ardor any longer, he left the island.

After completing our work out of the Perry River camp in the third week in August, we departed for our Bay Chimo gas cache on the north end of Bathurst Inlet. En route to Bay Chimo we encountered heavy fog, forcing us to land on the Kognluk River to wait for a few hours. Unknowingly, we landed in an area where the Eskimos had made a large caribou kill earlier in the spring. As we taxied up to the beach, a large grey wolf, which had been picking on the carcasses, trotted away. We then realized that the entire large slope leading to the water's edge was covered with caribou skeletons and that the kill, including many cows with unborn young, had been substantial.

The return trip from Bay Chimo to Yellowknife was without problems, and the reports of our findings were prepared by Schroeder and Kuyt.

In 1972 flyway biologist Ross Hanson accompanied Schroeder and Kuyt into the Queen Maud Sound region. Shortly thereafter, the first phase of the Tall Grass Prairie Canada goose delineation project was completed.

When professional people finally began to realize the importance of the bush in respect to the overall waterfowl programs, it was also apparent that we knew little about the disposition of the waterfowl in this area. Several banding programs were planned, the first of which was an attempt to drive-band diving ducks at Gordon Lake, Alberta, in 1963. This operation was a complete success, and in two efforts 12,103 ducks were banded, of which approximately 11,800 were lesser scaup, ring-necks, goldeneye, and buffleheads. Gordon Lake is approximately thirty miles southeast of Fort McMurray, Alberta. It was accessible only by air, which meant that boats, outboard motors, and all other equipment came in by USFWS aircraft.

Lake Athabaska Delta, Fort Chipewyan, Alberta, and Mills Lake, near Fort Providence, Northwest Territories, were the next projects in an expanding bush banding program, and both proved to be successful in respect to banding mallards and pintails. Past unsuccessful banding operations near Lake Athabaska made the banding of approxi-mately six thousand ducks, primarily mallards and pintails, in two years especially gratifying. The Canadian Wildlife Service took over this operation in 1975, while Mills Lake is still being worked by Fish and Wildlife Service personnel.

The Grassy River, near Thompson, Manitoba, was the next successful area to be developed in 1975. Since that time, approximately ten thousand ducks, mostly mallards, have been banded there. One of the remarkable developments on the Grassy River has been that between 90 and 95 percent of all the mallards banded have been the young of the year. We are presently banding in other areas, such as Pinehouse Lake and Cumberland House, Saskatchewan, and we are hoping to get into other remote areas. The problem is (and will be) money, specialized equipment and qualified personnel. Much of the success in our northern programs has been due to the

fine cooperation we've enjoyed from the provincial governments involved, the Canadian Wildlife Service, Ducks Unlimited, and several dedicated sportsmen.

One such sportsman was Orville Erickson of Prince Albert. Orville was president of the Prince Albert Chapter of the Saskatchewan Wildlife Federation when I first knew him, then provincial president of the same organization, and finally holder of the top job for the entire Canadian Wildlife Federation. He was tireless in his efforts to promote quality wildlife programs and was always willing to assist us in overcoming operational difficulties. His untimely death on August 21, 1975, at the age of fifty, was a great personal loss, as well as a loss to wildlife resource programs. Another good waterfowler from Prince Albert was Gordon Lund. Gordon's father developed Lund's Wildlife Exhibit in Prince Albert, and Gordon, too, was very active in the Saskatchewan Wildlife Federation. George Hart, a bush pilot and owner of a small air charter service at Fort Chipewyan, Alberta, was another who helped make our work in Canada easier. George was killed while making a mercy flight to Fort Smith in January 1969.

I have tried to indicate how the North has been changing over the past twenty years; to establish the importance of the huge area to the continental waterfowl program; to show some of the newly developed programs that will help make us more knowledgeable about waterfowl in this region; and to establish the fact that we now have some surfaced runways and some navigational aids. One final statement of fact: I would not have been involved in any of this if Ross Hanson and I had not escaped from the Flin Flon Hotel in Flin Flon, Manitoba, when it burned to the ground at 4:14 AM on June 9, 1962.

East of Hudson Bay

Charles D. Evans

The crippled black and orange Grumman Widgeon labored against a thirty-knot headwind toward our destination — a large rock-rimmed lake in the tundra of northern Quebec. The port engine on our amphibious aircraft had emitted a series of loud popping noises a few minutes earlier, and its oil pressure had fallen alarmingly. Port Harrison, the closest settlement, was 150 miles to the west, too far to nurse the heavily loaded plane on one engine.

The large lake near our course offered the obvious solution to our immediate problem, so I elected to land while we still had some use of the bad engine. Even though the wind was kicking up large whitecaps at the downwind end of the lake, a narrow bay there was too inviting to pass up. It would provide a sheltered harbor to inspect and, I hoped, to repair the damaged engine.

I leveled off over the choppy seas, settled to the surface, and was bounced roughly back into the air, finally coming clumsily to rest on the lake — not one of my best landings, but good enough under the circumstances. Only then did Jake's downeast twang come through over the noise of the engines, "For a moment theah, I thought we'd bought the fahm!"

What had brought Everett "Jake" Chamberlain, waterfowl project leader of the Delaware Department of Fish and Game, and me, Atlantic Flyway biologist for the USFWS to "Widgeon Lake" was a cooperative migratory bird management program between the USFWS, the Canadian Wildlife Service, and the fish and wildlife departments of a number of states and Canadian provinces.

My introduction to the Ungava Peninsula was the culmination of a series of attempts by Walter F. Crissey, C.E. Addy, Fred Glover, Ross Hanson, Alvin Noltemeier, and me to develop a systematic spring waterfowl survey in Quebec, Labrador, and eastern Ontario that would provide information on the annual status of birds in time to be useful in setting hunting regulations for the next fall. These attempts had been fraught with frustration by the relatively short range of the aircraft with respect to the size of the survey area and the distances between refueling points, by frequently late spring break up, and by the highly varied migration and nesting patterns of the waterfowl species of that region. These factors, particularly late break up and behavior of the birds, presented practically insurmountable difficulties to completion of a survey before the end of June in a "late" year.

Our surveys were normally flown along east-west tracks, at an altitude of about 150 feet above the terrain, and at an airspeed of 110 miles per hour. The width of our survey strip was 220 yards on either side of the aircraft. Within this strip we tried to record numbers of all ducks and geese by species and group size. We estimated the width of this survey strip "by eye," as there were no such reference points as the friendly hydro-power poles of the Canadian prairies with which to compare distances.

In settled southern portions of the survey area, fuel could be purchased commercially, and all-weather airstrips permitted landings without worry about whether ice would be off the lakes. We also purchased fuel by prior arrangement from the Royal Canadian Air Force at Bagotville, Quebec, and Goose Bay, Labrador. Farther north, we were forced to rely on purchases through prior arrangement from companies that flew in fuel for their own use.

We also had fuel shipped in barrels from Montreal to Great Whale River, Port Harrison, and Fort Chimo on Hudson Bay Company ships a year or more in advance of our surveys. Ships would not reach northern Quebec and Labrador until late summer and fall when the routes became free from ice. The Hudson Bay Company looked after our fuel until we used it, sometimes several years later.

Flights to the east coast of Hudson Bay from central Quebec were too hazardous during the spring of a late year when lakes and streams remained frozen, because weather forecasting and communications were uncertain, and aircraft had limited ranges. In summer, when open water was available for landing, we worried less about weather. We carried ample camp gear and often landed on convenient lakes or streams along the route to camp and wait out the weather.

In 1956, the year before our forced landing on Widgeon Lake, spring was exceptionally late. When U.S. Game Management Agent Al Noltemeier and I began our survey in southern Ontario and Quebec in early May, most lakes there were free from ice and ducks appeared to be nesting. By May 18, however, when we had completed our transects in the southern lowlands, most lakes and streams in the interior uplands west to James Bay were still ice-covered, and ducks were few. The Royal Canadian Air Force fighter base at Bagotville, Quebec, provided a sheltered hangar and a warm welcome while we waited in the greening southern Quebec lowlands for spring to arrive in the north country.

Finally, by early June, after we had made three attempts to survey northward, we decided to proceed as far as we could, even though conditions were still far from ideal and much snow and ice remained in the uplands of Quebec and Labrador. Even south of James Bay on May 24, when we encountered unexpected bad weather too far from our starting point to return, we droned on for an hour before finding enough open water for a landing.

We were able to complete only about two-thirds of our planned surveys that year. Most discouraging from a long-range standpoint was the difficulty of interpreting our data on species whose life cycles and behavior patterns in the region were so little known. Our flights of May and June, 1956, were the last attempts to conduct spring waterfowl surveys in that region.

The total impossibility of completing the spring survey that year enabled us to return home by mid-June — in time to have the aircraft inspected and serviced and to make final arrangements for the summer Canada goose nesting-ground survey. Experiences in the Mississippi Flyway had highlighted questions about the distribution of the summer nesting grounds of Canada geese that wintered in the Mississippi and Atlantic flyways. Wintering ground goose banding and subsequent returns from Indian and Inuit hunters along James and Hudson Bays suggested that most birds that wintered in the Mississippi and Central Flyways were raised in that area.

No such program had been carried out for birds wintering in the Atlantic Flyway, although large numbers of Canada geese were known to nest on the Ungava Peninsula. More information on the numbers and distribution of these birds on the nesting grounds was needed to delineate populations managed in fall and winter on the Atlantic and Mississippi Flyways.

Canada geese nest late and remain as families through their first year. This provided an extended period when families with flightless young could be counted on the nesting grounds, usually with assurance that they had indeed nested locally.

Our exploratory survey provided the data we needed to refine the sampling pattern for future surveys, based on expected densities of geese and optimum allocation of survey effort. Survey tracks were also re-oriented with respect to the "grain of the country." That is, lines were run perpendicular to major drainage patterns and slopes of land. The 1956 Survey also provided a rough estimate of the number of Canada geese nesting in the survey area.

Jake Chamberlain passed up goose banding in 1957 to join me as observer on the summer survey. Jake's long experience as a waterfowl biologist and pilot, as well as his constant good nature, were great assets on such an extended survey.

We began our runs south of James Bay on July 1. By July 4, we arrived at Moose Factory, Ontario, where we created quite a sensation with the Widgeon. We had anchored

This abandoned mining camp provided welcome shelter from foul weather encountered by the 1957 survey team somewhere east of Hudson Bay. USFWS photo by C. D. Evans.

in the river opposite the village, but when we checked the plane in the evening, it seemed to be taking on water. Rather than risk sinking I decided to taxi up to the barge loading ramp and into the hospital yard. Unfortunately, the crowds that gathered on the ramp to watch the funny-looking boat didn't understand that we had wheels and intended to taxi up onto the land. When Jake opened the bow hatch to stand up and try to explain, he only added to the fascination. I finally decided they all looked spry enough and started up the ramp, with Jake gesticulating wildly in the bow to shoo the crowd out of the path of the aircraft. It worked; the people all scattered, and we became guests of the hospital staff.

Although we found no further evidence of hull leaks, the left engine had developed a disquieting overtone during warmup — nothing that could be identified or that could even be considered significant. At the Knob Lake airport several days later, I rotated the propeller by hand, as usual, to listen and feel for irregularities. A loud grinding noise in the left engine assured us that we would soon get to the root of the problem. The left engine starter

would not disengage from the engine and was full of oil. Although this could have accounted for all sorts of odd noises, we made a thorough inspection of the engines and found no further problems.

After six days of waiting, a new starter arrived and we were on our way again by July 18 — but still with a disquieting overtone in the left engine. Two days later, when we had landed at "Widgeon Lake," made the aircraft fast to shore, and removed the engine cowling, the problem became apparent. The head of the number two cylinder had separated cleanly from the cylinder body. The break showed evidence of having been cracked for some time. It had apparently let enough gas escape during engine runup to cause the noise that had been bothering me. Although the question was answered, it was apparent that we would be at "Widgeon Lake" for a long while.

That evening, I made radio contact with Great Whale River to have someone assist us with repairs. We then set up camp and went to bed. A few hours later, I became restless and got up to disassemble the damaged cylinder. Just as the job was done and I had all the pieces laid out, a PBY "Canso," alerted to our plight, showed over the horizon. Larry Roluf, "King of the Cansos," swung the big amphibian over our camp, made several circuits of our harbor, and came in for a graceful landing.

Based on existing information, much of it gained through a reconnaissance survey conducted by Carl Eklund and Leon Cool in consultation with Dr. Aelred Geis at the Patuxent Wildlife Research Center, we laid out exploratory survey tracks covering known Canada goose habitat. We oriented east-west survey lines along each degree plus ten minutes of latitude. The ten minutes were added so that no lines would fall on the margins of the Canadian charts that we used for navigation. Our survey techniques were the same as those used in the spring, except that only Canada goose observations were recorded.

Al Noltemeier and I began our survey in mid-July south of James Bay. By then, the waters were ice-free, all our flight lines and fuel caches were accessible, and water landings would be possible throughout the area.

We began flying a survey pattern over some of the most spectacular country in North America. Much of it is granite bedrock with a relatively thin cover of vegetation. Habitats range from the muskeg-tundra south of James Bay to the boreal spruce forest of the interior, and from mixed forest and tundra to the barren lands of the Far North. Moose, caribou, and black bears were common along our survey tracks.

Innumerable clear rivers and streams, supporting eastern brook trout, Arctic char, and Atlantic salmon, flowed westward into James and Hudson Bays, and eastward into Ungava Bay and the Atlantic Ocean. Seldom were we out of sight of deep, clear, rockbound lakes. The quality of these waters was spectacular — the clearest I have ever seen.

The people there are among the most helpful and friendly in the world. Hudson Bay Company managers, Department of Transport communicators, and the Air Force personnel at remote stations all welcomed strangers. Most cordial were the fifteen meteorological observers at Nichicoun who had not seen a new face for more than three months.

The Inuit families that clustered around some of the settlements added interest and color. Soapstone carvers at Port Harrison are among the finest, and some have since received international recognition. Their handmade tents, perfectly designed without special tools, were a stunning backdrop for the activities of the people.

Our opportunities to enjoy these communities were few, as we had undertaken a survey that would require 120 hours of flying. An almost equal amount of time was spent arranging for fuel, working on the aircraft, establishing communications for flight planning, and trying to decipher the weather. The latter was nearly futile because of the east-west direction of our flights. Communication networks were set up to service north-south flights along the coasts of James and Hudson Bays out of Winnipeg. North-south flights in the interior were serviced out of Montreal. Even when accurate, the weather reported for the Hudson Bay region had usually passed before word of it could pass through numerous channels to stations in the interior. As a result, we usually flew when the weather looked good and stopped whenever it turned bad.

That summer we had good weather, few aircraft problems, and were able to complete the survey in about three weeks without major incident. At Payne Bay we joined Louis Lemieux, of the Canadian Wildlife Service, and Jake Chamberlain. They had been attempting to band locally reared Canada geese without much success. That evening, after a dinner of Arctic char in their tent and a few rounds of vodka, Jimmie Ford, Hudson Bay Company manager, offered to sell us a barrel of gasoline for $75. This bargain, at less than $1.40 per U.S. gallon, was too good to pass up at Payne Bay, where the going rate was $2.50 per gallon, even in 1956. This enabled us to range for three hours over excellent Canada goose habitat north and east of the

Jake Chamberlain checking the HF radio antenna amidst a cloud of mosquitoes on "Widgeon" Lake in Quebec during the trouble-packed survey of 1957. USFWS photo by C. D. Evans.

settlement of Payne Bay. We found geese for Louis and Jake, and gathered data for our own use that we could not otherwise have collected — thanks to that bottle of vodka. Government finance officers seldom appreciate the value of this type of barter, by which we obtained a variety of services that ranged from mechanical help to car rentals from people who would not accept cash.

Thanks to my restlessness, we were ready to stuff cylinder parts, engine overhaul manuals, sleeping bag, camera, and clothes into a sack for a quick departure. Jake stayed behind to look after N744, while I ordered replacement parts. I could stay in contact with him.

Our wait for parts was sixteen days, time enough for me to become acquainted with Great Whale and its residents while gathering raft materials, fuel, and other items needed for the repair job ahead. I also haunted the communications station, where Fred Woodrow, his wife, Isabell, and Fred's assistant, Joe McIsaac, worked to keep all the signals straight.

The parts finally arrived, thanks to Lauren-

tian Air Service at Ottawa. The staff had spent a weekend shepherding parts through customs. Without the Royal Canadian Air Force we still would have been licked. The cylinder and valves arrived in separate boxes, and the job of assembling these parts required the hangar's largest wrench, abundant coathanger wire, and the strength of five aviation mechanics. Jake and I could not possibly have done it alone.

The following day, Larry Roluf picked me up on a run north and deposited me with all our gear at "Widgeon Lake." Jake and I then constructed a raft to serve as a work platform, since we had no way to get the aircraft ashore. We slung mosquito netting under the engine to keep dropped tools and parts from plunging into twelve feet of icy water. Then we set to work.

The cylinder went on easily enough over the undamaged piston, piston rings, and connecting rod, but we couldn't get adequate valve clearance. We learned later that the factory had shipped us parts for a different series engine. Part numbers and engine serial numbers don't help much when a supplier has something else on his mind. At any rate, we were able to get enough valve clearance to run the engine safely. After applying a hack saw to some propeller mechanisms that had been thrown out of adjustment by rough running on the last flight, and taking a few more wire stitches in our cracked windshield, we were ready to go.

N744 was in no shape to continue the surveys, so we set course for home, after a short stop at Great Whale River to have a licensed mechanic look over our handiwork.

After that experience, we took a critical look at N744 to see how it might be modified to provide a better chance of completing surveys. But a decision was finally made to sell the aircraft, effectively putting us out of business in Quebec and Labrador. The stratified Canada goose survey is yet to be completed.

Mulling over that summer's events, I was moved by idle curiosity to do something I'd never done before; I read my job description. Much to my surprise, it turned out that some imaginative personnel officer had seemed to foresee our trials and tribulations. Nothing had happened to me that could give reason to protest, "but that's not in a flyway biologist's job description!"

Foreign Service for a Game Management Agent

Leon D. Cool

During the drought years of the 1930s when duck populations were precariously low, several enforcement officers of the U.S. Biological survey (USBS) were assigned to duck investigations in Canada. After World War II, the Biological survey became the USFWS, and enforcement was officially broadened into a Management and Enforcement Division, with duties split between management and enforcement. I was a game management agent with flying experience, and as a result, was quickly inducted into the Service's air arm. Here is an account of some of my experiences as the first agent-pilot for the USFWS to engage in surveys outside the United States.

Early in January 1948, I received word from the Washington office that, upon completion of the waterfowl inventory in the Chesapeake Bay area, I would receive travel orders to Panama to make a waterfowl reconnaissance in Central America and northern South America. To save time, I used my own plane for the remainder of the survey so that I could fly as many hours as necessary and make a more accurate count than I could with a Navy PBY.

When I arrived at the Washington office on January 9 I was informed the travel orders would be ready by the time I got the necessary shots (three in each arm), vaccinations, and visas. By the time this was completed and the travel orders had been cleared, it was January 26. I left Washington the next day and arrived in Panama that evening.

The following day I went to Albrook Field to make arrangements with the Air Force for survey flights in military aircraft. I found that, due to political situations, some countries would be difficult to enter or fly over and others were off-limits entirely. Clearance approval for a direct flight took a minimum of three days, usually longer. Clearance for low flights was almost impossible to obtain, and high flying is hardly compatible with duck counting. Some of the flights were dual purpose, and most of the pilots enjoyed a diversion from daily routine by making low-level passes to give me a chance to get a closer look at the birds here and there.

We made one flight to drop supplies to the Corps of Engineers surveying in the mountains between Panama and the Columbian border. The jungle was so dense in this area that it was necessary for the ground crew to release a colored smoke signal so our pilot could find them. He also dropped a two-way radio to provide communication with the plane. When the parachute failed to open, the radio bounced off some large rocks; I was sure it was destroyed. On the return flight, we surveyed the northern coastal area for waterfowl.

Clearance finally came through for Nicaragua and Guatemala, again involving a dual purpose flight with an inspection team. At the first stop, Managua, the airport was swarming with soldiers brandishing machine guns. The problem seemed to be two B-24 bombers parked nearby. We were instructed to take a direct route to town and give a wide berth to the bombers. Later that evening we heard two U.S. pilots had come in with the planes the evening before. One pilot was on sick leave from a GI hospital in Texas. He joined our party and returned to Panama with us. The other pilot was an ex-GI. I never knew what happened to him. Somoza seized the two bombers. In Managua that night, the story being circulated was that the pilots were to meet here with Venezuelan guerillas who intended to use the B-24s to bomb Caracas. Things were exciting in Managua, to say the least, with everyone watching over his shoulder and staying away from dark alleys.

Due to confusion it was impossible to make a waterfowl survey flight at that time. However, on the return trip I was able to cover the area around Managua en route to Guatemala city via the Pacific coast.

The marketplaces of these Central American cities were very different from a supermarket in the States. Part of these markets were under a shed roof, but the rest were out in the open. This is where all food items changed hands. Clothing, hardware, and other supplies could be purchased in small shops and stores. Before light in the morning, two-wheeled ox carts made their way to market. Burros were also common, some with loads so heavy that both packs had to be removed at the same time to keep the burro from falling over. Women with large bundles balanced on their heads accompanied men leading cattle to market to be butchered. There was no such thing as aged beef. On reaching the marketplace, the beef was butchered and hung up. One cow I saw butchered contained an unborn calf. The calf was skinned and hung beside the cow. There were no steaks, chops, roasts, or hamburger. When the customers indicated how much meat they wanted, it was chopped off with an axe. Most of the fruits and vegetables were fine quality — avocados as large as your fist for two cents each.

Before noon the market would be sold out, and all the shops and stores then locked their doors for siesta time. The streets were deserted, and there was no more activity until late afternoon — except for the buzzards that came down to scavenge a meal from the meat shed.

I conferred with a number of people in Guatamala who claimed there were many waterfowl present in late October, November, and December, but after Christmas they saw no large flocks. The servicemen at the air base in Guatamala had good duck hunting in November and December. However, we saw fairly large numbers of wintering waterfowl in the coastal marshes.

After another stop at Managua, we returned to Panama, where some local flights were made. Then clearance came for a flight to Cali, Columbia. This was another dual-purpose flight with some officers from Albrook Field. In Columbia we encountered more political turmoil, but fortunately for us, the fighting was some distance from Cali.

In 1948 the only highways were located near the towns and cities. The Air Force sergeant stationed at Cali had a jeep that enabled us to travel out about twenty miles from the city. All the wetlands had plenty of ducks and provided excellent shooting. The ducks shot at that time of year were native to the area, but in December the sergeant had shot some blue-winged teal. He said that the teal disappeared after Christmas. I guessed that this marked the start of their migration northward.

As in Guatemala and Nicaragua, some of the hotels in Columbia were quite modern and run on the American plan. Each meal began with a huge platter of very nice fruit. The meat was usually tough, but generally the meals were good. "Chicken" dishes were sometimes actually iguana, but it was just as good.

On the return trip to Panama, a stop had been scheduled at Medellin and a flight over part of the Magdalena River was planned; but due to low ceilings with rain and fog, it was not possible. I made uneventful flights from Albrook Field and with the Navy from Coco Sola, some in smaller aircraft which were more suitable for survey observations.

After conferring with many people in this area, some who had been there many years, I concluded that a large number of waterfowl wintered throughout the area. However, at the time of our survey many had started their migration north. Most of the waterfowl harvested locally were killed by servicemen and civilians from the States. By contrast, today there is some commercial hunting scattered through the tropical regions.

One person who provided helpful information was Dr. Herbert C. Clark of the Gorgas Institute in Panama. A resident of Panama for many years, he was a member of the La Jague hunt club (eight members), located about thirty-five miles east of Balboa near Corral Falsa. The club kept records for sixteen years, from 1928 to 1943. They killed 826 waterfowl in their best year (1929) and 217 in their poorest year (1934). From 1928

to 1932 they hunted twelve months of the year; but after 1932, due to the decline in native species, they did not hunt from June until Christmas.

Even though I had the necessary visas, it was impossible to make any flights in Costa Rica, El Salvador, Honduras, or Venezuela. All these countries were off-limits to the military at that time, and the USFWS was then obliged to depend upon the military because we did not have our own equipment.

I returned to Washington on February 20, three weeks after my departure. I was happy to have made the trip but somewhat frustrated by the many limitations imposed on me that prevented my getting more information about waterfowl.

The feasibility of conducting a waterfowl survey of northeastern Canada as far north as Hudson Strait was discussed at a conference held in Washington early in March 1949. The Service's game management branch had acquired a wheeled Fairchild aircraft donated by a friend. (At that time all USFWS aircraft were hand-me-downs no longer needed by the military.) The first step was to install floats shipped from Alaska to Baltimore.

In late March the plane was ready for a test hop. The first flight was to Pea Island Refuge to pick up a load of sick geese for delivery to the Patuxent research station for study. The plane's performance left much to be desired, so it was necessary to replace the engine and propeller before the CAA (now FAA) approved it. Finally all was ready, and I arrived at Fredericton, New Brunswick, the evening of May 24.

From our base at Fredericton, I surveyed areas in New Brunswick, Prince Edward Island, Nova Scotia, and some of the St. Lawrence River in Quebec. Eight days out of twenty-five were lost to weather and an engine oil leak, but it was still possible to average about five-hundred air miles a day for the remaining seventeen days.

The ice was going out of the lakes to the north, and the time was drawing near to head for Ungava, so I flew the plane to a repair

An Eskimo family separating eider duck feathers from the down on Wakeham Bay, Ungava, in 1949. USFWS photo by L. Cool.

and maintenance base at Lac á la Tortue for a one-hundred-hour check before leaving. Returning to Fredericton, I was joined by Carl Eklund, who was to accompany me in the northern trip. On June 28, we were on our way, stopping at Seven Islands, Quebec. There two weeks earlier I had met with the manager and some of the pilots of the Northern Wings Company. I had marked their gas caches on my air charts and received their okay to use what we needed and to pay later. Northern Wings was serving the survey crews running a line for a railroad to Knob Lake, where a large deposit of iron ore had been found. At that time the crew was only as far north as Ashuanipi Lake, a distance of about two-hundred miles. One of the pilots who had flown over much of the north country said that there was very little wildlife in Ungava. I found out later that something had wiped out the caribou many years earlier, but there were plenty of ptarmigan, waterfowl, and fish.

After a one-night stop at Seven Islands, we were on our way. After a wave at the survey crew en route, a stop at Ashuanipi Lake for lunch, and a raid on a gas cache, we arrived at Knob Lake in good time. Knob Lake was a surprise after three-hundred miles of nothing but bush and water. Equipment had been brought in with float planes and assembled there. A small airstrip had been built to allow larger aircraft to bring in mining equipment. There was a cook shack, bunk house, and test holes everywhere. The engineer in charge said that they already had 110 million tons of ore blocked out. We stayed the night and then flew to Crystal One.

At that time the U.S. Air Force was maintaining the airstrip at Crystal One, a wartime base six or seven miles up the Koksoak River from the small native settlement of Fort Chimo. Fort Chimo was the summer meeting place for Indian and Eskimo people. Eskimos didn't travel south of the fort, and Indians didn't go north. Only very recently had the two groups intermarried.

Navigation was a problem throughout this area. Mineral deposits or some other phenomenon caused major compass deviations all the way to Hudson Strait. At times the compass would roll 40 or 50 degrees in both directions. We hoped that it was on course when we set the gyro. There was also 36 to 44 degrees of westerly variation to consider. Blank places on the charts marked the unsurveyed areas. Few lakes were named, and the shape of the lakes shown didn't necessarily match the chart. Fortunately, major rivers usually ran in the direction indicated on the map.

We arrived at Crystal One on June 30. The next day we made a reconnaissance flight, stopping overnight on an unnamed lake. When returning to Crystal One the next day, we encountered gale-force winds, but fortunately the riverbanks were high, and we found a sheltered place to land. Rain and fog moved in soon after we landed, grounding us for several days.

While waiting for a break in the weather we traveled by boat to Fort Chimo. The tundra "grapevine" had preceeded us, so all the natives knew about our mission. A man in his seventies volunteered (for a small fee) to take us to a place on the False River where the nesting geese were as "thick as the mosquitos." His old boat was about thirty-feet long, with a one-cylinder engine that must have been the first one built. The boat had a short mast for a sail. For a barrel of gas, five gallons of oil, and fifteen dollars a day, his proposition sounded like a bargain.

He met us at Crystal One early the next morning. We loaded sleeping bags and a week's supply of food aboard and sailed on the ebb tide. At Fort Chimo, his four grown sons loaded a kayak on deck and then, with grins on their faces, came aboard. I wondered out loud how long the food would last, but the old man passed off the query with a wave of the hand and a grin. He could speak English but his sons could not. I asked why he hadn't taught them. "Because," he said, "it would only get them in trouble." His father had been Scottish and his mother Eskimo. After spending the first seven years of his life in Scotland, his family had returned to Fort

This skipper and boat took Leon Cool and Carl Eklund to a Canada goose nesting grounds near the mouth of the Koksoak River on Ungava Bay. USFWS photo by L. Cool.

Chimo.

With the ebb tide, we made good time to Ungava Bay. East of the river mouth, the skipper eased up to the rocky shore, landed, and tied the boat. One son launched the kayak and went seal hunting, while the rest of us fished. Before long we heard shots, and soon the kayak appeared out of the fog. A

feast of seal meat and fish followed. At one of our stops for a seal hunt the old man told us that the caribou had disappeared from the area many years before. Now the Eskimos depended on seals, fish, and white whales, when they could harpoon one. He recalled that when he was young caribou were so abundant that they captured them much like

Plains Indians took buffalo, by running them over cliffs. Later, when flying over Ungava we say old caribou trails worn deep in the tundra, but nowhere did we see caribou or tracks.

We cruised eastward for a while, with more stops for the seal hunters. When I asked the skipper if we could get to False River, he had one of the deck hands climb the mast for a look around. He decided that we had passed the river, so we turned around and headed west. The next landmark we recognized was the Koksoak River, so we headed for the Crystal One. We never did find False River, with all its geese, but at least the Eskimo village had meat. When we flew over False River later we saw nesting geese, but with all the rocks and shoal water, it would have been impossible to land. I suspect that the old-timer knew that all along.

We had to buck the tide all the way to Crystal One, but finally arrived on the evening of July 8. Word had come from Goose Bay that the gas we ordered would be dropped at Payne Lake the next day, weather permitting. So we loaded up and headed for Payne Lake, arriving late that evening. By morning the rain and fog had returned, and the temperature was near freezing. It was light nearly twenty-four hours a day, so we had plenty of time to hike around. Mosquitos and black flies hung about us in clouds. Unless there was a good breeze blowing, it was necessary to wear a head net. We had the best bug repellent the Air Force issued. The bugs did not land to bite us; they just flew in our eyes, nose, and ears. It was two days before the weather cleared enough for the plane to bring gas. We spent the time well, collecting birds and making up skins for the Smithsonian. We collected some specimens at all our stops.

Late the evening of July 11 a C-82 (the "flying boxcar") arrived and dropped six drums of gas and ten gallons of oil. The pilot and crew were on target, so we only had to roll the barrels about 150 yards through the muskeg. Some barrels were dented but none broke open.

The next morning, after leaving a note indicating our destination and time of return, we took off for Payne Bay. By the time we reached it the wind was blowing a gale and it was too rough to land on the bay. We decided to land in a lake about five miles north and walk to the Hudson Bay post. We were made welcome by the Hudson Bay factor, Tom Crawford, who lived there with his family. They had not seen a white man for over a year. We spent two days there waiting for a break in the weather, then continued to Diana Bay, where another fog bank engulfed us.

That post was called Baffin Island Trading Company. This time we were welcomed by Bill Davidson, who was in charge. It had been more than a year since he had had a visitor. The fog lifted the next day. After the tide came in enough to float the plane we were off to Wakeham Bay. There was no trading post there, only a priest and a few Eskimos. The day before we arrived two boys had cornered a polar bear with their kayaks and killed it. We had a change of diet — bear steak. When the tide went out the plane was a half-mile from the water.

The next day on high tide we took off for Payne Lake. About forty miles out we ran into a storm with fifty-knot head winds, forcing us to land on a small lake. Our gas supply was inadequate to make Payne Lake with ground speed cut in half by the wind. The storm lasted for two days and nights. There had been no provisions available at Wakeham Bay because the supply boat had not returned since the previous summer. We were short of rations, but there were plenty of ptarmigan and lake trout to be captured, so there was no danger of our going hungry. When the storm ended we made it to Payne Lake with the hand of the gas gauge bumping empty.

We made other flights from Payne Lake until our gas supply ran out. We flew west over the Kagaluk and Pavungnituk Rivers, south over the Leaf River, and north to Klotz Lake. Of all the lakes and rivers where we landed, only two places showed evidence that anyone had ever been there. At Payne and Klotz lake we found stone rings where Eskimos had camped year after year. All of the Eskimo tents were round or oval in shape. Rocks were used to hold the walls down. Around the campsites were very old bones and some antlers from caribou, but nothing recent. At Payne Lake we found the very old skeleton of a kayak, with the scraps of rotted seal skin, rawhide bindings, and parts of a long abandoned dog sled. Apparently no one had been there for many years.

On July 27, we loaded the gear and parachutes and stacked the empty gas barrels on the beach. We returned to Crystal One. We made more flights from there, including an interesting one eastward over the False, Whale, and George Rivers. Almost everywhere we went we saw family groups of geese. A time or two we managed to drive some into a gill net, carried for survival purposes, and band them. We never needed the net to catch fish. Everywhere we stopped, five casts produced five strikes. For example, at Payne Lake four casts produced three lake trout over twenty inches, and the fourth strike broke the middle section of a good bamboo fly rod. Luckily I had taken two

along (The April 1980, issue of *Field and Stream* carries an article on fishing the Payne River from a commercial camp there.) There is also a hunting and fishing camp on the George River. Incidentally, the caribou are back in numbers throughout that area.

On August 2, we loaded the plane with camping gear, bird skins for the Smithsonian, and some rations from the commissary and headed southeast for Indian House Lake, where the Canadian government manned a weather station.

At the station, we were welcomed and told — again — that there had been no outsiders visiting for some time. There were ptarmigan with broods of young feeding in the yard around the buildings, and the fellows told us about shooting some caribou and a black bear in the area recently.

About twenty minutes before reaching Indian House Lake, we saw the first caribou of the trip. We stayed overnight at the weather station, then flew to Goose Bay to square up for the gas drop at Payne Lake. We remained there two days because of bad weather before returning to Washington, D.C.

Eastern Canada

C. Edward Addy

Surveys of wintering populations were begun by the U.S. Bureau of Biological Survey (USBS) on a coordinated basis in the early 1930s with military aircraft often used for this purpose along the Atlantic and Gulf Coasts. Up until 1947, Harold Peters was the Bureau's waterfowl biologist responsible for surveys in eastern Canada and winter surveys along the Atlantic Coast. His summer surveys were done on the ground, primarily in the Maritime Provinces, including Newfoundland. Some years he was able to visit the St. Lawrence River estuary, the coast of Labrador, and the Arctic Islands. Tom Burleigh joined Peters in observations of the birds in Newfoundland, finally leading to a book on that subject.

Prior to the 1950s, several explorers, collectors, biologists, and other specialists gathered wildlife information on the Ungava Peninsula (Quebec and Labrador), the St. Lawrence River estuary, the Arctic Islands, and the shorelines and islands of Hudson and James Bays. Some of those who, in addition to Peters, made significant contributions to our knowledge of waterfowl populations and habitats of eastern Canada were Harrison F. Lewis, W. E. C. Todd, O. J. Murie, G. M. Sutton, O. Hewitt, R. Smith, H. Connolly, O. Austin, F. Harper, and H. Manning. Most early investigators traveled the shorelines and the rivers, since overland travel was arduous and frustrating, especially in summer when black flies and mosquitos were unbelievably abundant. During the 1940s and 1950s many geological parties penetrated the interior of Quebec and Labrador in search of commercial deposits of minerals.

Surveys of waterfowl breeding populations got under way in the Maritime Provinces in 1948 when Canadian biologist George Boyer and I commenced ground surveys. We hired aircraft for limited experimental transect and shoreline coverage. I was fortunate to be teamed up with Boyer, a most interesting, pragmatic, and innovative person with whom to work. In addition to the aerial surveys, I began to organize summer ground-production surveys and brood-banding projects. Also at that time, Ira Gabrielson and Bruce Wright investigated mid-summer Canada goose and black duck status by airplane in the Fort Chimo area of northern Quebec. In 1948, most states in the Atlantic Flyway were participating in periodic surveys, bag checks, and, to a limited extent, banding.

The need for detailed duck and goose breeding and production data for the Atlantic Flyway necessitated the development of surveys, not only for the northeast states and the Maritime Provinces, but also for the fascinating and largely unknown country north to Hudson Straits and the eastern Arctic Islands. Our principal concern at the time was the vast, unmapped Ungava Peninsula. A very few towns or settlements were located in the interior, with an additional number of small Indian and Eskimo villages along the coasts of Labrador, Ungava Bay, Hudson Bay, and James Bay. The larger communities usually had a Hudson Bay post and a mission church. The natives survived on fishing, hunting, and trapping. However, following the appearance of large numbers of white men prior to and during World War II, disease wiped out some native communities. Unfortunately, many of the natives living near the wartime airbases in the Far North became dependent on the white man for sustenance and survival.

William Sweet of Attleboro, Massachusetts, donated a single-engine Fairchild aircraft to the USFWS for conducting surveys in eastern Canada. The plane, equipped with pontoons, took off for eastern Canada loaded with camping and survival gear (dried food, guns, and fishing tackle) in May 1949. Game management agent Leon Cool was pilot, and I was the observer. This was the beginning of several eventful years of flying waterfowl surveys in the wilderness of the north.

Two waterfowl explorers at camp south of Goose Bay in eastern Canada in 1950: Leon Cool (left) and C. E. Addy. USFWS photo by L. Cool.

The first stop was Fredericton, New Brunswick, where we flew experimental transects on the broad St. John River estuary, the mixed forest region to the south, and the extensive conifer and muskeg region to the north. The estuary, from just north of Fredericton south nearly to the City of St. John, encompassed the Northeastern Wildlife Station's waterfowl study area. The area contained several thousand nesting black ducks, ring-necked ducks, teal, and a scattering of other species. This estuary was obviously one of the important nesting areas for the northeast. It demonstrated what later surveys confirmed: duck production is generally very low but widespread throughout the Precambrian Shield region of the northeast, while pockets of more concentrated production occur in areas of neutral to alkaline waters. In contrast to these pockets, the extensive acid muskeg country to the north revealed less than one duck per square mile of transect.

In the extensive Sheffield marsh just down river from Fredericton, twelve to fifteen

moose fed on lilypads and other vegetation in the shallows. Leaving Fredericton, we flew shorelines and overland transects throughout New Brunswick, Nova Scotia, Prince Edward Island, and the tidal shore and coastal ponds north to Gaspé. Here again, the rocky-shored, dark-stained waters of Lake Rosignol and the hundreds of other such lakes and muskegs produced only a few broods of mergansers, loons, and black ducks. Only in tidal marshes and freshwater alkaline marshes did we find exceptional numbers of black duck broods, pairs, and moulting adults. The best producers of black ducks were the tidal marshes of Prince Edward Island, the tidal and fresh marshes at the head of the Bay of Fundy, the Annapolis River marshes, the tidal areas of Yarmouth, and the Canso area of Cape Breton.

It was interesting to see about two hundred nesting pintails on the Midgic Marshes, a rare sight in the northeast. These extensive — and at one time tidal — marshes were diked by the French nearly two hundred years ago in order to grow grain and fresh hay. The original dikes were built by hand labor. Prince Edward Island has very deep productive soils, reportedly of marine origin, which .produce excellent grain, other field crops, and above-average duck crops. At one time Prince Edward Island produced enough Hungarian partridge to support an eight bird daily bag limit.

After flying over the marshes and shorelines of Prince Edward Island, we tied up at the dock in Charlottown Harbor. Lobster fishermen had just arrived with their catches, so we quickly purchased (at twenty-five cents a pound) four one-to-two pound lobsters, borrowed a large kettle from a ship's cook, and cooked the lobster right on the wharf. Ignoring the onlookers, we sat on the dock and ate them. To my comment that they probably were sick of eating lobster, the fishermen said, no, they just couldn't afford them. I felt a bit subdued.

The next week we flew several hundred miles of overland low-level transects and tidal shorelines of northern New Brunswick, the Gaspé, and Anticosti Island. Almost half that time was spent on Anticosti, immobilized by fog and rain. Fog often keeps travel by small aircraft at a standstill for days at a time in Maritime Canada. The south shore of Anticosti Island had several thousand black ducks and eiders in scattered groups. To the east in some sizeable fresh marshes, we saw several black duck broods. We also recorded a few broods of red-throated loons, red-breasted mergansers, and Canada geese. Lake Wickenden, the largest lake on Anticosti, was largely devoid of vegetation, its waters probably quite alkaline. In some places, the bottom was almost paved with fossil trilobites, and in the forests white-tailed deer were extremely abundant. They provided considerable food for the people at Port Menier. We often encountered the remains of winter-starved deer.

Before returning to Fredericton, we flew the north shore of the Gulf of St. Lawrence, recording large numbers of eiders and flocks of black ducks, and up the St. Lawrence

River, covering the Seal Islands, Lake St. John, and Lake St. Peter. At Fredericton I joined George Boyer by car to conduct ground surveys and brood banding (with traps and Labrador retrievers) during the rest of the summer in the Maritimes.

In 1950, Cool and I continued aerial breeding and production surveys of the Maritime Provinces and Anticosti Island, and investigated southern Labrador. During this period two things happened to the plane that made us wonder whether the summer's project was jinxed. When taxiing for takeoff on a lake in southern New Brunswick where we camped one night, a loud knock developed in the engine. We weren't sure of the cause but suspected a broken bearing or broken piston rod. We decided to try to get to Fredericton and took off, following water courses at about two-thousand feet in case the motor quit. Fortunately, the motor didn't break apart in front of us, and we made it to Fredericton. There we tied up on a muddy river bank as close to the airport as possible. For the next ten days we stood in mud and water six-inches deep disassembling and reassembling the engine. We had to send for parts and frequently ran to the airport mechanic for advice. The problem was a broken piston rod. Thanks largely to the ingenuity and resourcefulness of agent Cool, we got the engine back together and running smoothly again.

Our next difficulty also demonstrated that Cool lived up to his name. We had finished surveying Prince Edward Island and had tied up at a wharf in Charlottown Harbor one evening. Our next day's objective was to survey the north shore of New Brunswick, the south shore of Gaspé, and the Island of Anticosti. However, when we arrived at our plane we found it tipping at an alarming angle, with one pontoon practically submerged. Wave action during the night on the ebb tide had caused a sharp submerged object to puncture the pontoon. We decided it would be better to repair the damage at Port Menier a few hundred miles to the north. There we could land in the shallow tidal waters of Ellis Bay,

Boulder-filled lakes and rocky shorelines are poor places to park a plane, but sometimes they were better than any other available harbor. USFWS photo by C. D. Evans.

Our next objective was the unknown interior of southern Labrador east of Goose Bay. Our rough maps suggested the presence of an extensive marsh along the Eagle River. Bruce Wright had speculated this might be a big production area for black ducks. However, our flight revealed a flock of only about two hundred moulting blacks on open water and put pulp logs under the pontoons, and work on the damaged pontoon when the tide was out. We taxied out from Charlottown and gradually picked up speed. By making a long run while partially raising the damaged pontoon, we got enough water to escape from the pontoon to allow us to get into the air.

Fortunately, the tide was in at Port Menier so we were able to land and place pulp logs under the pontoons. Within a few hours the tide receded, leaving the plane high and dry. We had the pontoon patched in a day, and we took off on the next high tide to run shorelines and overland transects on Anticosti. That night, fog and rain forced us to land at the eastern end of the island.
a few broods on the marshy periphery of the

lakes. Why there were no broods out on the open water soon became apparent. From the air we spotted a place that looked like a possible fishing spot, and since it was about time to eat we landed nearby. We walked out on the rocky bar between the lakes and cast our treble-hooked daredevils. The water erupted. In the next hour or so we had beached about fifteen brook trout averaging at least three pounds. In addition, we landed about the same number of northern pike, some of which exceeded three feet in length. In fact, so voracious were the pike that some would follow our returning lures to the water's edge. Their mouths were easily large enough to swallow ducklings. Perhaps there were pike in these waters large enough to be capable of taking teal adults. Obviously, no brood of ducks could survive for long on the open waters of these lakes. Even among the lily pads in the shallows there were pike large enough to take black ducks up to a week old. These fish in Labrador were apparently subjected to very little fishing pressure and would attack any object moving through the

218

water.

Our destination was the air base at Goose Bay. We had decided to present those beautiful fish to the commanding officer, whom Cool had previously met in Washington. So, removing the caps from the pontoons, we laid the fish in the compartments, resealed the caps, and took off heavily loaded for Goose Bay. With the fish as an offering, we were given red-carpet treatment — a room in the bunk house, a visit to the officer's club, and an invitation to join in a big fish breakfast.

We later participated on a Navy reconnaissance flight to Baffin Island, at which time we had a wonderful look at the spectacular coast of Labrador and, on foot, the tundra in the vicinity of Frobisher Bay. At Frobisher it was a thrill to see snow buntings, longspurs, and pipits on their nesting grounds. From the air, the scouring effect of glaciation along the coast of Labrador was most interesting. We got a close look from the plane at a couple of glaciers on southern Baffin Island.

Before leaving Goose Bay we flew a thousand miles of low-level overland transects and shorelines of southern Labrador and the Hamilton River inlet. A scattering of black ducks and broods appeared on tidal marshes of the Hamilton River but rarely on the rocky lakes and acid wetlands of the interior. We saw several woodland caribou in this area. Caribou are widely scattered in eastern Canada in summer.

We left Goose Bay late one afternoon for Mingan, on the north shore of the Gulf of St. Lawrence. However, we ran into a violent storm with strong headwinds. We were blown off course, our gas was low, and we decided to land for the night to wait for better weather. Weather kept us grounded the next day but cleared so we could take off on the following day.

Apparently the Mingan radio signal was not broadcasting. We figured that if we kept heading south we would arrive before long at some recognizable spot on the shore of the Gulf of St. Lawrence. Unfortunately, the shore was shrouded in a heavy blanket of fog. Since we didn't know our location, the radio signal coming from Seven Islands to the west could have been beyond our range. Both gas gauges were nearly empty as we headed west. When we approached Seven Islands the gas gauges read empty. We had no time to fool around. Dropping to the edge of the fog bank, we discovered it had lifted about fifty feet off the land. We slipped under it and slid right up to the fueling dock. Fifty-six gallons of gas went into our sixty-gallon fuel tanks.

By 1952, the USFWS had obtained a Grumman Widgeon for summer surveys in eastern Canada. Prior to leaving for Canada, we assembled maps and plotted several thousand miles of systematic transects on them. The interior of northern Quebec and Labrador were largely blank. We would have to use a compass when crossing extensive blank areas, even though we knew our magnetic compasses were highly unreliable. However, if we got lost and managed to keep the plane on an east-west course, we might, with enough gas, make it to the Atlantic Ocean or Hudson Bay. That winter, 1951-1952, we arranged to have drums of gasoline placed at several Hudson Bay posts located at strategic points. Walt Crissey was assigned as pilot-observer in charge, and I served as observer.

During May and early June we flew the transects and tidal shorelines in the Maritime Provinces and along the St. Lawrence River in southern Quebec. We were surprised at the large number of black duck broods out in early May. Heading into the interior of Quebec and Labrador, we initiated the first extensive and systematic aerial transects of this largely unknown portion of the waterfowl breeding range. Our fueling points were scattered, but a considerable part of southern Quebec and southern Labrador could be covered from centrally located Knob Lake, about three-hundred miles north of the St. Lawrence River on the Quebec-Labrador border.

Previously, only float planes had serviced the area, but now there was a gravel strip where DC3s landed with cement, reinforcing rods, parts of bulldozers, lumber, furniture, food, and other items needed to establish the town of Shefferville, construct a railroad, and commence extraction of iron ore. In 1952 preparations for the new town were just getting under way, and the principal base of operations was at the airstrip. We landed at about 3 P.M., were welcomed by those at the field, and assigned quarters in the bunkhouse. We had expected to tent-camp as usual and cook our own meals. We were offered apologies for the lack of a regular meal but were given an impromptu meal of filet mignon. It was the best meal of the whole trip. Such hospitality was the rule throughout the north country.

At Knob Lake we picked up several pieces of ore that we were told contained about 85 percent iron. Mountains of this ore extended over several square miles in the vicinity of Knob Lake. Since air transport was the main source of supply in the beginning, we were impressed by the fantastic cost of the project. It was impressive to see plane after plane loaded with freight landing on this crude and obscure airstrip, day and night, in almost any weather. It was a tribute to human courage and ingenuity.

From Knob Lake we ran several transects west, south to the height of land, and east to headwaters of the Hamilton River. Occasionally a pair of black ducks would be seen, rarely a pair of Canada geese, and more often red-breasted mergansers. Blacks seemed to be more common in the vicinity of Knob Lake and to the east. We wondered whether, with the establishment of Schefferville, domestic sewage pollution would increase the fertility of some of the drainages and thereby improve conditions for some kinds of wildlife. In 1952 most of the lakes and streams around Knob Lake were devoid of vegetation and marsh habitat.

Leaving Knob Lake, we headed north to Fort Chimo across unknown rocky and almost treeless country, following nearly blank maps. Fort Chimo was an abandoned World War II airbase (Crystal One) located at the south end of Ungava Bay near the mouth of the Koksoak River. Hundreds of rusty drums of gas lined the paved airstrip. Unfortunately, over the years, the drums of gas had accumulated considerable water from condensation.

At Chimo in summer we were in the land of nearly perpetual daylight. It was interesting to cross the Koksoak in a boat at midnight without needing a light. We had to watch the tide there, because tide fluctuations in the Ungava area are comparable to those of the Bay of Fundy. On the ebb tide the current is extremely swift. We were told that the Koksoak, Whale, Payne, and other rivers of Ungava Bay have large runs of Atlantic salmon and Arctic char. The char reputedly reach a larger size than the salmon. Unfortunately, we didn't have a chance to check this out.

We flew several overland transects, rivers, and the south shoreline of Ungava Bay. Here we encountered thousands of flying black ducks and Canada geese on or near the tidal shorelines and marshes, but very few in the interior south of Ungava Bay. Most black ducks were in flocks, and we only saw one brood near the south end of Ungava Bay. We continued flying shorelines and overland transects, covering much of the eastern part of the Ungava Peninsula up to Payne Lake. Here, by July 1, newly hatched Canada goose broods were common and widespread on the hundreds of lakes, ponds, and streams that laced this extensive, flat tundra area.

In the north country, to remove the condensation, gas from drums must be filtered through felt or chamois leather as it goes into the plane. At Chimo a tank trunk serviced the transient aircraft. The operator insisted that the truck had filtered the gas three times. Therefore, accepting his advice, we took on a load of gas without using our funnel filter. A Canso destined for Montreal had just gassed up, so we figured the fuel was all right. Our next destination was Port Harrison, three-hundred miles across the peninsula to the west on the shore of Hudson Bay. We taxied to the runway, got in position for take-off,

Canada geese nest in this muskeg bog located south of the Pas, Manitoba. Bogs of this type occupy hundreds of square miles of the "bush" country. USFWS photo by Rex Gary Schmidt.

and started to rev up. One engine quit and the other faltered. We must have drained six gallons of water out of one tank and three out of the other before gasoline began to show on the pavement. We taxied back to the hanger and replaced the gas, making sure it was properly filtered. We also contemplated the rocky, rough terrain where we would have crashed had we actually taken off.

The route to Port Harrison was uncertain because the maps were blank for central and southern Ungava. However, the valley of the Leif River was roughly depicted. We could use it as a reference point, then follow a gyro compass setting across the rocky barrens of the central peninsula and descend the Innuksuak River valley into Port Harrison. Looking at this bleak and forbidding terrain gave me a deeper appreciation of the early explorers who crossed this land on foot many years ago. Not only was the terrain difficult to traverse, but during the summer mosquitoes and blackflies assumed unbelievable numbers, especially when the wind was calm. When camping in some places we had to cook under netting or we would accumulate

a quarter-inch of mosquitoes and black flies on top of our morning eggs.

At Port Harrison we had to land on the bay and taxi upstream, dodging submerged rocks, to the small beach near the Hudson Bay post. The bank at the water's edge was of such loose gravel that the small wheels on the Widgeon could not function properly for getting the plane on shore. However, with a heavy rope and the help of about thirty strong Eskimos pulling while Crissey revved the engines, we finally got the plane up the bank and turned around.

From Port Harrison we flew transects over the rolling tundra and muskeg of western Ungava Peninsula north to Cape Smith. On the return we followed the bay shoreline to Port Harrison. We saw impressive numbers of Canada geese, flying groups and broods throughout the tundra and along the river and tidal shorelines. This area, as well as the eastern part of Ungava, was obviously important for Canada goose production. Black ducks were limited to a few small flocks along the shore.

Our next destination was Great Whale River on the east coast of James Bay. En route, we flew the shoreline of Hudson Bay and the lowlands and shoreline of James Bay. While we saw some Canada geese and black ducks along the shore, their numbers were disappointing. On the overland transects we recorded fewer than one black duck per square mile. After a day of unprofitable overland transects we changed course for Moosonee, following the lower parts of rivers and the shoreline of James Bay. While we saw several hundred black ducks in flocks along the shorelines, we did not encounter the thousands we expected. A few broods of geese were observed, but the principal goose production area was obviously to the north in Ungava.

After Moosonee, we spent several days flying east-west transects across eastern Ontario and western Quebec. In a number of areas, particularly where alkaline ponds and marshes occurred, as in southern Ontario, we recorded fair numbers of duck broods and a few Canada geese. We saw only a few waterfowl in the rocky lake and acid bog areas that make up a major portion of the habitats in Quebec and northern Ontario.

In 1952 a comprehensive aerial survey was made for the first time of the Maritime Provinces (excluding Newfoundland), Quebec, Labrador, and eastern Ontario. Results showed small numbers of Canada goose broods in the eastern James Bay lowlands and the east coast of Hudson Bay, but the main concentrations were on the Ungava Peninsula and habitats associated with the south shore of Ungava Bay. Elsewhere, Canada geese were found to be very thinly distributed. Black ducks were also thinly scattered throughout much of the Precambrian Shield area, with concentrations often associated with alkaline waters and tidal habitats. Many thousands of blacks occurred in flocks; primarily on the tidal shorelines from Nova Scotia to Ungava Bay. Red-breasted mergansers seemed to be the most common duck on the rocky ponds and lakes of the interior. Limited numbers of nesting ringnecks, teal, wigeons, mallards, and pintails were mostly restricted to the Maritimes, the St. Lawrence River valley, and eastern Ontario.

While the data collected and the operational difficulties experienced left some doubt as to whether annual aerial breeding and production surveys for eastern Canada and the northeastern states would be practical, these surveys were continued experimentally until 1968. Several USWFS biologists and game management agents participated in these surveys, with crews changing personnel almost every year. The coverage was modified or expanded as better maps were developed and techniques were refined.

The surveys in eastern Canada were eventually discontinued for several reasons. The poor visibility of birds, wide variation in percent observed, and highly variable distribution of the black duck made the aerial transect method unsuitable for determining annual population status and production. In addition, it was impossible to check aerial data against ground observations. Weather conditions also were so variable from year to year and the area so large that it was impossible for one plane to cover the area adequately on a consistent chronological basis from year to year. Finally, while the principal Canada goose production areas could be surveyed reasonably well, the annual production survey proved not as necessary with geese as it was with the ducks, so a goose survey was recommended to be conducted no more than every five years.

Taking the flyway representative job in 1953 phased me out of the summer surveys in Canada. However, to locate potential northern banding sites, Fred Glover and I took off in the Widgeon in early September 1954, to fly parts of the Maritime Provinces, Newfoundland, Labrador, Quebec including the Ungava and Hudson Bay shores (eastern shore), the Belchers, James Bay islands and shorelines, and most of eastern and southern Ontario. Here again we found no major duck concentration areas in the thousands of square miles of rocky lake and muskeg country of Newfoundland, Labrador, and central Quebec. Most of the ducks we sighted were along shorelines in the Maritimes; the valley of the St. Lawrence River including the Gulf, southeastern Ontario, Lake St. John and Lake Abitibi areas of Quebec; the shorelines of James, Hudson, and Ungava Bays; and the tidal areas of Newfoundland.

It was interesting to see changes from the previous flights in 1952. A complete set of highly detailed maps was now available. We could easily follow our route from lake to lake or point to point. Startling progress had been made in the development of the iron ore field at Schefferville, with a 300-mile-long railroad in operation. The town of Schefferville now had a population of about 2,500. Additional houses and dormitories were being constructed and a tremendous dining facility had been completed. Most of the workers ate there. We were impressed by the fact that in the middle of Labrador, three hundred miles north of the St. Lawrence River, delicious baked Alaskas were served to almost 2,000 people.

We then flew on to Chimo, from which we surveyed much of the tundra and shoreline of Ungava Bay and the surrounding vicinity. In our 1952 survey we had noticed extensive iron ore deposits south and west of Ungava Bay. Now there were jeep tracks visible in the reindeer moss, indicating the probable presence of geological survey crews.

On our run up to the north end of Labrador and back to Chimo we were forced down by bad weather. The lake hastily chosen for our landing was not very satisfactory for anchoring a Widgeon and lacked decent campsites. We picked a cove, set up a sparse camp, and then spent a few hours trying to anchor the plane to the rocky bottom. Meanwhile the storm gathered force as the temperature dropped. When we were sure the anchors would hold, we crawled into our sleeping bags for the night. The howling wind was driving wet snow and sleet.

We weren't in our sleeping bags half an hour when we heard the crunch of metal on rock and realized the plane was loose. We dashed out in our underwear. I pushed the plane away from the rocks while Fred reset the anchors. It took about forty-five minutes.

We were soaked and nearly frozen. We saved the plane but didn't get much sleep that night.

In contrast to the earlier summer survey, there were relatively few Canada geese on the Ungava tundra, although small flocks of black ducks and geese could still be found along the tidal shorelines. It was not, however, until we headed south from Port Harrison along the west shore of Hudson Bay that we encountered large numbers of waterfowl. The east shore of James Bay, in particular, was a spectacular sight, with hundreds of thousands of large Canada geese, tens of thousands of small Canada geese (Richardson's), snow and blue geese, and brant. Mixed in with this early fall concentration of migrants were thousands of black ducks and a scattering of other species.

Leaving James Bay, we headed south to sweep lakes and marshes from Lake Abitibi to Kapuskasing and the Port Arthur area. While we found several potentially good banding sites, there were many attractive areas that were almost devoid of ducks. Later, when reviewing the data, it was obvious that from the air we were seeing only a small fraction of the birds actually present. Many ducks were found to use areas intermittently during days or nights. So if we recorded fifty ducks, the area might have held several hundred and would have represented a good banding site. One principal concentration of ducks was in the extensive marshes of Lake St. Peter.

During the years following our reconnaissance surveys, several banding stations were established under the sponsorship of certain individual states, Ducks Unlimited, the USFWS, the Canadian Wildlife Service, and some provinces. The Baie Johan Beetz station was responsible for banding many black ducks and other species. Several thousand Canada geese were banded on Akimiski Island in James Bay. Crews also went to Ungava for a fairly successful attempt at Canada goose banding. Other crews tried duck banding at Nain, Labrador, without success. Crews equipped with small planes and trapping equipment worked the interior of southern Quebec with limited success.

From these endeavors there developed a permanent annual banding program for eastern Canada that covered the principal duck species. However, there is enough flexibility built into the program to allow shifts in emphasis to brant, certain duck species, or even Canada geese when necessary.

This concludes my efforts concerning surveys in eastern Canada.

The thatched-roof dwellings of Mexico and Central America present quite a contrast to the igloos and caribou skin enclosures of the far north. Both were part of the beat for Refuge Biologist David L. Spencer. USFWS photo by D. L. Spencer.

Beyond the 48

David L. Spencer

In 1946, I left big game work with the Wyoming Fish and Game Department to become pilot-biologist for the Everglades National Wildlife Refuge. The Everglades were then managed by Dan Beard, who became the first park superintendent when the reserve was taken over by the National Park Service in 1947.

My first assignment with the USFWS was to fly with George Saunders on the Mexican-Central American winter waterfowl surveys. Thereafter, I was to spend the better part of two years on flyway work from Canada to Mexico, with only brief fall and spring sojourns at a home station in the Everglades.

The Navy surplus plane we were assigned for the Mexican surveys was a Grumman Widgeon twin-engine amphibian, numbered N-701. It was sent to a shop in Birmingham, Alabama, for a pre-service overhaul. This was our second such craft; its sister ship was demolished while landing on Lake Mead on its maiden flight.

John Ball went with me to pick up the machine and check me out. I recall careening from side to side down the runway, suddenly aware that the characteristics of the craft were new to this Navy pilot's experience. By then, John, too, sensed something amiss and brought us to a halt before we were airborne — making it possible for me to be able to write this story. It seems the rudder was rigged backward.

After much further delay — more repairs at Albuquerque and the Naval air station in Corpus Christi — George and I did survey both coasts of Mexico and Central America down to Panama, spending some six weeks at it. George had studied Mexican waterfowl for years and knew where to look. He was also concerned at the time (1947) with the USFWS-State Department mission to Guatemala. We, therefore, spent considerable time in Guatemala, flying over much of the country to learn the nature of its wildlife habitat.

It was a country of great contrasts, ranging from jungle marshes at sea level to high mountain plateaus that severely taxed the altitude capabilities of our little flying boat. The Peten country of northeast Guatemala was particularly fascinating. In December of 1945, I had accompanied Starker Leopold on gamebird survey work on the Mexican fringes of this vast jungle lowland and knew it from the ground. From the air, we occasionally noted Mayan ruins looming up above the forest and wondered how much more evidence of ancient cultures was concealed by the tropical forest.

Fuel supplies along the Mexican-Central American coastal route were generally near enough to allow adequate survey flight time over the intervening marshes. One interval longer than usual extended from Guatemala City to the Isthmus of Tehuantepec in Mexico. On one trip, George Saunders and I in our Widgeon came out of the Guatemalan highlands and were comfortably proceeding northward along the west coastal marshes. Some time after the point of no return, we realized that in the lee of the Sierra Madre we had encountered an intense easterly wind flow. As the resulting turbulence tossed the plane about, we progressively lost interest in counting ducks, until finally our only objective was setting foot back on the ground.

After speculating about splashing into a coastal lagoon, we thought better of it. At last, we arrived at Ciudad Ixtepec, where a single runway was aligned in the venturi of the isthmus that, at that moment, seemed to be the route of all the air in the Gulf of Mexico passing through to the Pacific. The tower advised us that the wind speed was seventy-five knots. After taking three unsuccessful shots at the runway, we made it down and were immediately flanked by jeeps keeping pace at each wing tip. Ropes were soon fastened to our wing floats and the jeeps dragged us off the runway to shelter.

Later, in the local cantina, pilots of the Mexican Air Force assured us, "Ah, Señor, there is no danger." Their viewpoint has sustained me many times since. The remark, however, may not have been entirely true, for we noted the remains of their aircraft — a number of P-47s — scattered about the airport. We learned that the isthmus wind could last for months and considered ourselves fortunate to depart the next morning in a near-calm of fifty-five knots.

Shortly thereafter, passing huge flocks of pintails in the Los Mochis farming country, we crossed to Baja California. Here we knew that brant should be found wintering in the coastal lagoons. Sure enough, there they were. We also knew of the gray whales but were still greatly excited to find them with their calves in the clear waters of Scammon's Lagoon.

As George and I made our way around the coast of Mexico, we also wanted to evaluate the extent of market hunting for waterfowl. We visited many Mexican markets along our route, finding waterfowl available in small numbers and with no particular pattern as to species. I can still recall, however, the shock of seeing great blue herons and roseate spoonbills hanging by the bill, stark naked.

George and I again surveyed Mexico in 1948, going as far as Guatemala and covering both coasts. George wired our report to Washington when we arrived back in Brownsville, Texas. We hadn't counted as many ducks as anticipated (it was probably too

Few serious accidents have occurred in all the miles of flying airplanes on waterfowl surveys. This Grumman Widgeon, left, in a banana plantation in Costa Rica, is one of the unfortunate exceptions. Fortunately, both occupants suffered only minor injuries. USFWS photo by John Ball.

early), and were dispatched to try it again. This time Bob Smith and I went, and we picked up more birds in the Mexican highlands.

The Mexican marshes seem endless — an ever-changing scene, always interesting but sometimes exhausting. The survey went well until we got to Mazatlan, where Bob and I came down with severe cases of flight fatigue. For R&R, we elected to go marlin fishing. We chartered a boat and enjoyed a great day, capturing three of these fish. Enthusiastically, I later recalled with seemingly gross exaggeration, "Why, they were nine-feet long!" But as I searched for photos to accompany this story, I found Bob standing

by one of our fish. Indeed, it *was* nine-feet long! The boat skipper hustled the fish to market, where they undoubtedly netted him considerably more than he made from our charter fee.

The summers of 1947 and 1948 I spent on the Canadian surveys, working out of Delta, Manitoba, and covering the prairies of Manitoba, Saskatchewan, and Alberta. The Canadian work in those years — in fact, most waterfowl survey work — involved two objectives: counting waterfowl and developing technology for more reliable surveys. We tried many ideas. Some things worked; others didn't.

We spent much time working out of Delta,

Flight of redheads over a freshwater marsh adjacent to Laguna Madre, Tamaulipas, Mexico. USFWS photo by G. B. Saunders.

with Al Hochbaum, Lyle Sowls, and others at the Delta Waterfowl Research Station. Delta Marsh, its ducks, and the adjacent pothole country served as a laboratory where we sought to develop correlations between the numbers of birds seen from the air and those spotted from canoes or cars. Many of the aerial transects in southern Manitoba were flown from our base at Delta.

We felt sure that a voice record of the transects counts would be vastly more efficient than written tabulations. A recorder was the obvious answer. But recorders, in those days, were complex and expensive. The model we selected was a wire recorder — fragile, temperamental, and costing $600. To

protect it, we constructed a case lined with foam rubber, a precaution that caught fire on its first extended flight, filling the cabin with smoke and necessitating an emergency landing. Art Hawkins, who was my observer on this flight, reminded me recently that as smoke filled the cockpit, my Navy training surfaced as I calmly gave the order to "stand by with fire extinguisher." Luckily, the wartime emergency landing field at Neepawa, Manitoba, loomed dead ahead, and we landed without a dent. Bob Smith also tried out the wire recorder. On one flight of four hours he carefully recorded his observations of habitat and ducks. He played back his recording when he returned to home base, but nothing came out. The entire trip record was a blank. Bob, in exasperation, issued a few choice cuss words. They played back loud and clear. In retrospect, the recorder wasn't one of our great successes. Total failures on these flights sent us back to the record written on a knee pad. Today a few dollars can buy what we would have considered a miraculous device that produces simple, foolproof taped recordings.

By 1947, it had been determined that vast areas of the waterfowl breeding grounds of the north could be covered rapidly by aircraft. Ducks could be counted along a quarter-mile strip from the air from a low flight altitude with some assurance of accuracy. It was evident that we would gain improved reliability if we developed valid sampling methods, as well as giving us an assessment of the proportion of the actual population of waterfowl that could be seen from the air. Through the guidance of Cecil Williams, our surveys of the period were aimed at recording the status of the birds as well as experimenting with survey methods.

The quarter-mile flight line transects could be chopped up into any appropriate segments of plots, with records kept in terms of ducks per mile. Since only a small percentage of the breeding grounds could be covered, we needed a form of sampling, and, in addition, statistical examination to determine its validity. Something on the order of a sample plot system with accompanying analysis, as used in forest mensuration, seemed appropriate, and we generally proceeded in that fashion. The business of random plot selection was further complicated by the necessity of flying from place to place in search of aircraft fuel and other support. Surely the predetermined travel segments over wetlands could not be wasted.

As with any sampling technique, many questions arose: how to select sample plots, how many plots were necessary, what sample size would be adequate, what were the various sources and magnitudes of error, and how could these things be quickly analyzed in the field. Biometricians were seldom to be found in those days; they seemed more concerned with fruit flies than with ducks. When the biologist sought the statistician's stamp of approval for a sampling scheme, the latter was dismayed by the inherent variance of the wildlife universe, the unpredictable mobility of the subject, and the imprecise, even crude, enumeration systems. It was some years before peace was made between biologists and biometricians.

Meanwhile, we made do as best we could with crude, elementary sampling texts that we could read and put into practice with primitive calculators. The usual manual office machines were too cumbersome for our packsack logistics. We tried various abacus-type devices, but generally wound up doing calculations in longhand on big columnar pads. What we wouldn't have given for a modern, rapid-fire pocket calculator!

In the spring of 1948, Floyd Thompson and I blanketed southern Saskatchewan with point-to-point transects as well as other random transects. To reduce sampling error, we stratified the samples on the basis of areas with comparable breeding populations. The stratification on the basis of waterfowl numbers later proved unworkable because of excessive annual variance and was replaced with a zoning system based on soils and morphological features. Floyd and I almost bit off more than we could chew that June. We found ourselves taking off at daybreak, flying all day, then working far into the night on calculations of the results in the attempt to survey over 120,000 square miles with 1,600 square miles of sample transects.

The nesting environment of the Canadian prairies was known to be highly variable from year to year. Major fluctuations in waterfowl production resulted from changeable early summer water conditions and the number and extent of viable potholes on the glaciated topography. We expected that a measurement of water areas could be correlated with waterfowl production, and that might give a forecast of anticipated production for the year. We tried a number of indices to measure this water variation. One

Palm trees and mangrove thickets border many of the lagoons where ducks of several species spend their winter. USFWS photo by D. L. Spencer.

prospect was the field record of potholes in a sample area by vertical photography — a rapid do-it-yourself job with standard field equipment — that could be repeated annually.

Gus Swanson and I made some tentative tries at pothole-monitoring photography and then, with Art Hawkins, we selected a 100-square-mile section of the Minnedosa pothole country in Manitoba, conveniently sectioned into square miles by the public land survey system. We used a Stinson L-5, one of our standard military-surplus survey planes, as a photographic vehicle. One of our ornithological associates, Bill Carrick, was a Canadian commercial photographer. He agreed to operate the camera and lent an air of professionalism to the project. We used a temperamental hand-held, military-surplus 4″ by 5″, K-20 camera. At about 11,000 feet, we calculated that it would cover about one square mile. The project proceeded without incident except that we had neglected to consider that the temperature at 11,000 feet is not the same as it is on the prairie. Having coaxed the L-5 to this altitude, we were reluctant to return for jackets and nearly froze before we covered the final square mile. The flight yielded a usable photo-mosaic that we laboriously put together like a jigsaw puzzle and pasted on a sheet of cloth.

After the aerial counts of breeding populations, it came time to set aside the flying machine and to take up hip boots, to stop counting ducks and to start banding them. This was great fun, but I came to know what Johnny Lynch meant when he said that it was time to go north and "combat the savage Ruddy duck." The banding work generally went without incident, although I do recall Frank Bellrose getting a fingertip nipped off in the propellor of an airboat. Some of the prairie sloughs were deep, and the capture of birds inclined to excessive under-water activity required drift fences set in deep water. One hot, dry, very windy day, we had been at this all morning, often securing netting in several feet of water. When we came out of the water we would dry instantly in the wind, and the evaporation cooling was a real shock. After a couple hours of this I was shivering uncontrollably. Seeking a hot drink, I grabbed a handful of tea and dumped it into a can of boiling water. Turning to a local visitor, I asked, "Care for some tea?" "Naw," he replied, "I seen you make it."

In 1948 Art Hawkins and I were assigned to take our banding gear from Delta to Lower Souris (now J. Clark Salyer) National Wildlife Refuge in North Dakota to help the refuge staff catch some ducks and geese. One banding drive was particularly noteworthy. We set out long leads made of heavy nets hung on steel fenceposts, extending the leads far out into the muddy-bottomed pool. After several hours of that, we built a large catch pen and were ready for the drive. We took row boats to the upper end of the pool and launched them. Between us and the trap were hundreds, if not thousands, of birds. As we slowly pushed them toward the trap we noted that some of the birds were slipping around the ends of our three-boat driver line. A bed of tules concealed what was happening until, with great expectations, we rushed to the trap. In it was one willet! All the ducks, coots, grebes, and geese had leaked through our drive line. Later, we made some good catches in a drift net across one of the channels with traps on either side, so the initial failure was turned into some measure of success, and we learned a lot.

In the fall of 1948 I moved to the Kenai National Moose Range in Alaska. The next summer, in western Alaska, i again participated in flyway work. We set up transects in the breeding ground of the Yukon-Kuskokwim delta, flying point-to-point transects as well as U-shaped random transects of seven square miles. As with most flyway work, when the aerial surveys were done, we switched to boat and foot travel for banding operations. Charlie Gillham had preceded me on waterfowl work in the Yukon-Kuskokwim delta, leaving his mark on the region as well as some equipment in George Sheppard's trading post at Mountain Village. I intended to use the boat that he had stored there, but it proved to be a canvas device with wire ribs, somewhat resembling a beach umbrella. As a further detriment, mice had been at work on it since Charlie left. This was the famous *Flapjack* described by John Lynch elsewhere in this volume.

Charlie Gillham also knew some promising places to band: the coastal goose-nesting region between Hooper Bay and Nelson Island. We were mindful of Charlie's directional guide to the coast. Charlie told us that. when disoriented in the hundreds of miles of the Kashunuk Slough as it made its way through the flats to the Bering Sea, we should drop a stick in the water to see which way it floated.

Raphael Kuponak, a local Eskimo, and I

set off for the nesting ground on the lower Kashunuk in a rented river boat and seven-horsepower Mercury motor. Our minimal equipment and crew of two limited our strategy to the simple process of running geese down on foot, one by one. There were many geese, and we captured several hundred this way. We had trouble finding fresh water in the stormy, tide-swept coastal lowland. One day a deaf and dumb Eskimo came up the Kashunuk towing a dead walrus. He stopped with us for tea. We were able to communicate our need, whereupon he led us to a freshwater pond not far from camp.

The region was concentrated nesting habitat for much of the continental populations of black brant, cackling geese, and emperor geese. Band returns were, therefore, of considerable interest. This was the country of some of the great annual bird drives, a centuries-old practice to obtain large quantities of flightless geese for food. In subsequent years it was possible to enlist the help of real local professionals in the goose-capturing business.

I worked some with Ed Chatelain and Sig Olsen, Jr. (Ed is deceased, and Sig is now chief wildlife biologist for the U.S. Forest Service in Alaska.) Our instructions tended to be rather flexible: "Go out and band up some birds." We were pretty well-fixed for aircraft, but not for the rest of it. I once landed at Chevak, where we stored a boat and motor, to find only part of the motor still there (a sixteen-horsepower Johnson). Upon inquiry of one of the local Eskimos, I was advised that the rest of it was at Owl Village, some thirty miles away. Sure enough, there it was in a deserted trapper's shack. We finally got it all together and running again. On another occasion, we sent Dave Hooper into the Innoko River country to band birds with a parting shot, "Oh, by the way, there's no boat. You'll have to get someone to build you one." He did indeed get a local man to make him a green lumber skiff and had a reasonably successful trip.

After 1948, I spent the next twenty-eight years working on the National Wildlife Ref-uge System in Alaska. As with much work in the USFWS, one is never far away from flyway-biologist-type assignments. Some of our Alaskan refuges are major waterfowl breeding and migration areas, and others have strong components of waterfowl habitat. There were continual population estimates to make, plus other waterfowl studies necessary for a variety of reasons. One of my last assignments before I retired in 1976 was goose banding on the Arctic Coast in the Cape Halkett area, a mission related somewhat to the search for breeding grounds of the tule goose. (After years of scouring the vast north country for the tule goose nesting grounds, birds banded on the wintering grounds were found a year ago near Anchorage, breeding on Cook Inlet marshes.)

Over many years, Tremblay, King, Hansen, Lensink, and others had brought great efficiency to Alaskan waterfowl banding. The operation was entirely supported and conducted by aircraft. It involved six men, three aircraft, rubber boats, nylon nets, aluminum posts, and a higher mobile net corral. The main logistic support, a Grumman Goose amphibian built thirty-two years previously, was older than half the crew. The geese were arrayed in groups of several hundred out in the big tundra lakes. The capture procedure went like clockwork, and actually the hardest part of the mission was endless hours of banding geese, white-fronts, Canadas, brant, and snows.

It has been exciting work, and it has been gratifying to engage in a field with an optimistic future. One is often reminded of the durability of our waterfowl friends. We keep a little float plane on Hood Lake in Anchorage, perhaps the most heavily used lake of its size in the world. The place is alive with birds, as hundreds of ducklings begin life in the midst of intense float plane traffic. You have to shoo them off the floats to get airborne. With any help at all, these birds will be with us for a long time into the future.

1961-62 Mallards *by Edward A. Morris*

6

Assessing Pothole Nesting Success

As important as the airplane was to the new science of waterfowl management, it could not do it all. There was still ample need for trained biologists who could conduct intensive ground studies, particularly biologists who had the zeal and stamina needed to slog through miles of soft-bottomed potholes in heavy hip boots.

Not until intensive ground studies were conducted could managers understand the carrying capacity of various types of habitat for various species of ducks. Eventually, airplanes were used to conduct censuses of nesting ducks. But before the information gathered from the air could be evaluated, it had to be carefully related to data from ground censuses. Through direct ground-air comparisons, corrective factors were devised that compensated for the fact that air observers missed some birds visible to ground crews.

Ground studies have been conducted on the Canadian prairies for over half a century. Three project leaders who initiated these post-war studies tell about their experiences in the following chapter. One of them began developing duck study techniques in Minnesota while working for the Civilian Conservation Corps.

Ground-Air Coordination

Charles D. Evans

The prairies and parklands of the central plains are the nesting grounds of a large share of the ducks sought by North American wildfowlers. Extensive continental glaciation created many depressions that fill with water. These are commonly termed "potholes." Depending on rainfall and other factors, these potholes may be rimmed with small trees in a matrix of prairie (parklands) or may exist in a predominantly grassland community (prairie). Emergent vegetation often grows at the margins or entirely across these potholes, providing cover in which ducks can nest and raise their young.

These habitats were already familiar to me in 1953 when I undertook the job of flyway biologist for the Mississippi Flyway for the USFWS. I had spent the spring of 1948 at the Delta Waterfowl Research Station at the south end of Lake Manitoba as graduate student assistant to Lyle Sowls. Lyle, a PhD candidate in wildlife management at the University of Wisconsin, was working on the nesting ecology of the pintail. I spent that summer becoming familiar with the country and the behavior of ducks.

The following season, I made detailed independent studies of duck nesting and brood use of pothole habitats near Minnedosa, some seventy miles to the west. I followed this with three years of intensive study for the USFWS on the relationship of ducks to the various types of ponds and associated upland habitats near Waubay, South Dakota. This project was designed to provide a basis for predicting effects of wetland drainage on waterfowl and to help develop means of ameliorating effects of drainage programs. Two or three of us biologists made these studies on foot, usually with the aid of a Labrador retriever, observing behavior and making counts of all adult ducks and young throughout the season. We recorded the types of ponds and other habitats used by the ducks for nesting and raising broods. We determined home ranges of adults by marking them for individual recognition after capturing them with cannon nets. We marked broods for individual recognition by means of dyes injected into eggs before the young had hatched. This gave us an ideal education in the way these birds made a living from the time spring arrived until their autumn departure.

When I took on the duties of Mississippi Flyway biologist, knowing I would be responsible for gathering information on duck nesting conditions in southern Manitoba and southeastern Saskatchewan, I was surprised to discover that my equipment did not include an aircraft. My dog, George, and I eventually grew another layer of calluses from our efforts to gain a ground-level view of much of the best duck nesting habitat in Manitoba and from helping in banding work on the Delta Marsh.

Then John Lynch, who had been serving as a flyway biologist in Saskatchewan for several years, arrived at Delta late that summer in his mouse-ridden, cattle-chewed Piper Super Cub. When he offered to show me what it all looked like from "topside," I was more than ready to exchange my boots and paddles for wings! The nesting season was over but my extended introductory tour with John was an exhilarating educational experience. He knew the country from topside and on the ground and had developed a colorful lecture to go with each leg of the trip. John also shared with me his wealth of experience in the aircraft.

I was particularly grateful for the flight demonstrations and lectures. My previous experience had been in heavier military aircraft — quite different from the Super Cub assigned to me for surveys the following spring. It seemed to me a fragile, spindly contraption that was certain to cartwheel down the runway like a tumbleweed in the slightest gust.

My first spring aerial survey gave me one of my most intensive flying experiences.

Pilot John Lynch stands beside one of the faithful Super Cub airplanes used by the FWS for making water-fowl investigations.

Game Management Agent Wes Newcomb and I normally began our surveys in the quiet of dawn, because by late morning winds usually picked up to twenty knots, our upper limit for surveys. On this particular day, by the time we arrived back at the airport winds of twenty-five to thirty knots were picking up dust from the plowed fields. I believed we had no room for error as I taxied the little plane. After that, each time I approached the airport that spring I made a careful mental rehearsal of the entire trip, from the end of the runway to the shelter of the hangar. I now know a Super Cub can be taxied in much stronger winds.

The aerial Survey technique in use at that time consisted of a series of designated routes (transects) established at various intervals, but always running east and west along the usually recognizable section lines which divided the prairie country into one-mile squares. We made our flights at roughly 150 feet above the terrain. Early surveys were run at a ground speed of about seventy. Later surveys with faster aircraft were run at higher speeds. The width of the strip varied from 220 yards on either side of the aircraft during the spring survey to 110 yards on each side during the summer brood surveys. We recorded our observations for individual transect segments, each eighteen miles long.

By the time Nolan Perret, Dominion wildlife officer, joined me for the July survey, the Super Cub had become for me like a pair of well-worn pants you jump into in the morning. Nolan, however, found it a tight fit. Considerably taller than six feet, he was badly doubled over in the back seat with his knees nearly wrapped about my ears. In spite of his hardy spirit, he still complains about what I did to his back twenty-six years ago.

Although Nolan's background had been in fisheries, he brought an objective and quantitative approach to our surveys. After he had made three runs — two summers and one spring — he retired from the air and began ground studies of feeding habits of juvenile ducks near my old Minnedosa study area. Even though not part of the survey crew, he remained in frequent contact with me and was a stimulus for ideas. U.S. Game Management Agent Jerry Pospichal, who was assigned leadership of the ground surveys, also had a lively interest in both ground and air work. Jerry lent enthusiastic support to attempts to study the aerial survey technique.

One of the major problems in aerial surveys has been to establish a relationship between the estimates of numbers of animals made by the air crew to the number of animals actually present. While this problem has not been completely solved, progress has been made. When I began my assignment as flyway biologist, we were beginning our attempts to establish this relationship.

At that time we attempted to establish "ground truth" by using the linear ground survey areas that Bill Kiel, a graduate student from the University of Wisconsin, had established in southern Manitoba in 1949. These study areas consisted of strips extending 220 yards on both sides of main roads. They were surveyed intensively on the ground and concurrently from the air. My first assignment as flyway biologist in the summer of 1953 was with Arthur Hawkins, then Mississippi Flyway representative, conducting these ground "beat-outs."

Data from these two survey methods, when compared, provided an index by species of relative observability of birds. Using the two methods, a higher density of birds was usually recorded by ground crews than by air crews. Air crews, however, did not readily accept this data, feeling that their abilities or methods were somehow being challenged. Legitimate questions can still be raised about the relative merits of a high degree of precision on a small area compared to a lesser precision over a larger area.

Although experience shows the assumption that ground counts are "ground truth" is only partially valid, the ground-air comparison technique was continued with some modifications. It has provided a useful means of "calibrating" air crews in different habitats under various conditions.

Although little time was available, we were able to squeeze in a few experiments that helped to satisfy our curiosity regarding pos-

sible reasons for the large differences in results between the two methods. Many birds are screened from aerial observation by vegetation, yet this did not seem to account for all the difference. As a first effort, Jerry Pospichal and I climbed into the Super Cub and ran a survey over an area where there were many ponds and many ducks. We did not seek quantitative data, merely an insight into the problem.

Standard equipment in our aircraft was a dictaphone, on which each observer could record his observations with his own microphone. At the same time, each observer could, by means of a device on the dictaphone that fed into each of our earphones, hear what was being recorded. Both observers could record and both could hear what the other was recording. In this experiment, we both observed the same strip, but took turns recording observations. When I recorded, Jerry would watch the strip, listen to my recording, and make a note of birds I missed that he could see. During the next run, he recorded and I listened.

We weren't surprised that each of us missed birds that the other noted. The big surprise, however, was the fact that birds missed were often in plain view, sometimes immediately adjacent to birds we had seen and recorded. John Lynch once had a discussion with an opthalmologist who outlined the limitations of the human eye in scanning a field of view. This seemed to be the problem we encountered in this experiment. We surmised that our eyes were physically unable to adequately scan the large number of ponds.

A later experiment included a ground crew in an attempt to learn more about the distribution and behavior of the birds missed by the air crew as well as to provide a measure of the percentage of birds missed. While the aircraft circled at a distance — just close enough to watch the ground crew — the latter selected a pond they felt certain would contain ducks. This they identified for us by laying out on the ground a panel of brightly colored cloth pointing out the pond, far enough away so that the ducks would remain

Edward G. Wellein "glasses" a water area for ducks while Arthur S. Hawkins records the sightings during a 1951 survey in Manitoba. USFWS photo by Gary Schmidt.

undisturbed. We would then make an aerial survey run on the pond at normal transect height and speed, recording ducks we observed, while the ground crew watched and recorded those that flushed from the pond. The ground crew then went in to make a complete count of the remaining birds. Although we certainly introduced a number of biases by this technique, we confirmed what we had already suspected. Many of the ducks we missed observing from the air were in the open and easily visible, but usually were not moving. This was a time-consuming and expensive technique, and hard work for the ground crew. The twenty or so ponds we were able to cover in this fashion probably provided as much understanding as the method can deliver.

To assess quantitatively how problems of scanning a strip 220 yards wide might affect the survey data, we established a series of short aerial study strips, along which Jerry and I alternated counts on strips 110 yards and 220 yards wide. We divided these strips of different width between us systematically so that each recorded an equal amount of each strip width under similar conditions of light and wind direction. The results were not totally unexpected. We recorded a higher density of birds on the narrow strips (97.5 birds per square mile) than on the wide strips (72.2 birds per square mile), suggesting that the narrow strips could be surveyed with greater efficiency. We made the tentative assumption, based on logic, that the visibility bias we had sought to assess was also greater on this wide strip than on the narrow. Analysis of these limited data also suggested that the lower variability on the narrow strip provided data with statistical precision similar to that from the wider strip, even though the area surveyed was only half as large.

Other assignments and time constraints intervened, so we were unable to carry out

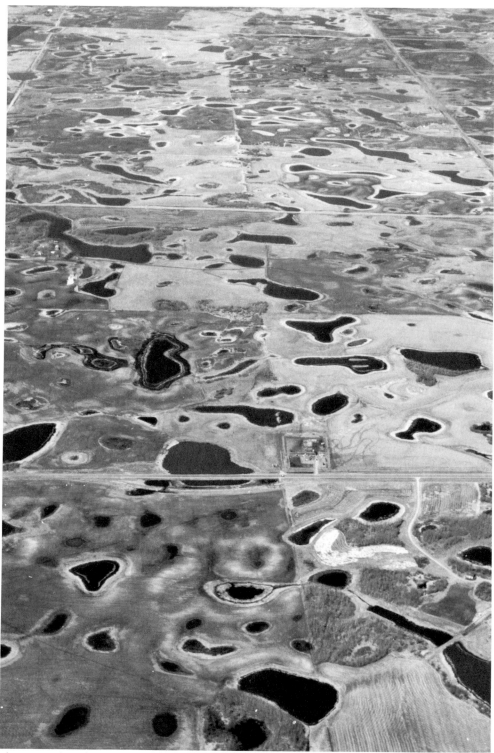

The Rosneath study area in the Minnedosa pothole region of Manitoba exemplifies prime duck nesting habitat. USFWS photo by C. D. Evans.

further experiments. By the time I returned to the prairies after two years of surveying in Quebec and Labrador, techniques had become standardized on the basis of ground-air comparison transects.

Surveys in the northern "bush" also included the difficulties of estimating strip width and the need for careful navigation. Deteriorating weather and dwindling fuel sometimes diverted attention, adding the "terror factor" to other visibility biases. Viewed in this context, prairie surveys seemed sufficiently precise and adequate, at least for regulatory purposes.

My later experiences in Alaska, however, have resurrected some of the questions we sought to answer on the prairies. Data from aerial surveys in Alaska have been put to a wide range of uses that include evaluation of habitats under threat of inundation by proposed hydroelectric impounds, evaluation of lands being considered for special management systems, and counts of marine birds. It has sometimes been possible to modify techniques to suit special conditions. For the most part, however, the existing data must be used.

My experiences on the prairies, both afoot and in the air, particularly the few hours I spent on our informal experiments, have helped me develop an appreciation for the potential uses of aerial data, and the possibilities for adapting them to other needs. I've also learned about the limitations of aerial data.

Whenever it seems as though we're getting pretty good at it, I remember our first experiment and Jerry's incredulous outburst: "Didn't you see those five mallard drakes in the middle of the pothole?"

Pothole Hopping in Old 724

Leon D. Cool

I left Washington on May 6, 1948, flying an Army surplus Stinson L-5, numbered 724. After a stop at Delta, Manitoba, to confer with Bob Smith, Art Hawkins, and Al Hochbaum, I proceeded on to Lethbridge to meet other members of the Alberta survey team. Roy Anderson, a college student employed by the Canadian Wildlife Service, was to fly with me as observer. We eventually had many memorable days together, covering a lot of air miles and having an adventure or two.

The air charts were spread out with the transects marked on them. We had to fly at 150 feet over the prairie to see how many ducks were nesting there. Starting in southern Alberta, we worked our way north. By the time we reached Calgary, "old 724" needed some time off because the generator was no longer "jenning." After some phone calls, the local mechanic found a rebuilt model and got us back in the air.

Except for the normal windy days, the weather was kind to us, and we covered many miles in a short time. At first our survey routes took us over open prairie, never far from the grain elevators on the horizon that marked small towns. As we approached Edmonton, we noted a sharp change from prairie to bush country.

On May 29, we left Edmonton on a flight to Peace River via Lac La Biche, Athabaska, Lesser Slave, and Utikuma Lakes. We were checking the shoreline and islands of Utikuma Lake when a large flock of ducks flared up in front of us, scattering in all directions. One splattered on the left strut and, as we found later, one lodged in the engine cowl. Soon the cylinder head and oil temperatures were reading in the red. With Peace River still about ninety miles away, we decided to make a landing along the lakeshore while we still had power rather than dropping into the spruce trees later with a dead engine. Luck was with us, and we landed safely. The L-5, which had been designed for rugged field operations, came through with flying colors, but the wheels sank in the wet marsh and there we sat.

We took a long hike, finally finding higher ground, but wondered how we could get the plane there through knee-deep water. We spent the rest of the day cutting brush to put under the wheels, managing to move the plane only about two hundred yards. At that rate it would take most of the summer and all of the gas to reach a possible takeoff place. That evening we sat around the fire speculating on how soon they would start looking for us. We had not filed a firm flight plan, but had told the fellows at the hangar in Edmonton that we would be back in three or four days.

The next morning, still in our sleeping bags fighting mosquitoes and black flies, we heard something splashing through the marsh. Coming in our direction was an Indian on a small pinto pony. He had seen the plane and had come to see who was there. He told us his name was John Grayknife. He was on his way to meet some Indian families headed for Peace River to try and find work on nearby farms. Each family, he told us, had a team of horses. I asked if he could have them come by the lake and give us a hand. He said he would try. About two hours later they arrived at camp with two teams and wagons loaded with women, children, and everything they needed for the summer.

While waiting for the Indians to arrive, Roy and I had cut four spruce poles about thirty feet long and six inches at the butt end. We lashed the poles in pairs to put under the landing gear so the wheels would not sink in the marsh. Then, with a team of horses hitched to each skid, the plane was moved about two and a half miles around the shoreline. In places where the water was knee-deep, the teams were stopped and a big powwow took place, with much laughing and gesticulating. We could not understand the language, but I am sure they were thinking it would be a good joke to leave the plane in the deepest place. Roy and I laughed along with them. Eventually, we made it to the place where we planned to build the runway.

We removed some down timber with the horses, lashed the four skid poles together, and dragged them back and forth many times to smooth out a makeshift runway. After considerable work by everyone, we paid the Indians, loaded our gear back in the plane, headed down the S-turn runway, and took off. From the air we could see no obvious trails or roads. The Indians had just come out of the bush. Where they came from or where they went is still a mystery to us. Even today this remains a desolate area.

Later in the summer we were flying a transect east of Calgary, when without warning the engine quit. Directly ahead was a pothole. There was only time to make a ninety-degree turn to the right, pull on the flaps, and haul back on the stick before we bounded to a stop. We sat there in the silence for a minute or two. Then Roy tapped me on the shoulder and said, "I think you just ran over a prairie dog." After Utikuma, it wouldn't have surprised me if Roy had taken off across the prairie for good. Fortunately, he was made of stern stuff. These incidents made me appreciate good observers like Roy. The emergency landing was forced by an air lock. With the air lock gone, the engine started. We taxied to smoother terrain and took off.

While having a 100-hour check on old 724 in Edmonton, a bush pilot I knew invited me to fly with him to Hay River and down the Mackenzie to Mills Lake. This gave me an opportunity to see some more of the Far North.

On another flight to Saskatoon, I met J. Dewey Soper and Angus Gavin, two men who had spent considerable time in the Arctic and made important discoveries about waterfowl. Mr. Soper, an employee of the Canadian Wildlife Service, traveled by boat and dog team before aircraft transportation was available. He discovered the nesting grounds of the blue goose of Baffin Island. He presented me with an autographed book he wrote about the trip. Angus Gavin, while a Hudson Bay factor at Perry River, found the first nest of the Ross goose in 1938. Hearing these men talk was a rich experience.

The banding crew assembled during the first week in July. Promising banding sites were checked by air. Later, we moved in with nets, air boats, canoes, and all the gear necessary to get the job done. Many ducks and geese were banded in Alberta and Saskatchewan. That year when we were about ready to leave, "old 724" started acting up again, losing cylinder compression. We had to send for a new engine. In the absence of a mechanic, I had to install it before heading homeward.

Duck Nesting Studies

Jerome H. Stoudt

I became a duck counter even before transferring to the USFWS. In May 1933, shortly before completing requirements for my master's degree, I became technical foreman at a Civilian Conservation Corps (CCC) camp. Jobs were so scarce in those depression years that taking a job seemed more important than completing my education.

That November I was assigned to a timber survey crew. We lived in a tent for ten months, cruising timber on the La Croix and Temperance River ranger districts. It was very cold that winter (52 degrees below one day), and the snow was from four to five feet deep. A short-lived thaw in February formed a crust on the snow. Many deer died from starvation or were killed by timber wolves, who ran over the crusted snow while the deer broke through.

In 1935 I became a Forest Service wildlife technician, assigned to the La Croix Ranger District. There I developed a rather crude method of censusing waterfowl production by canoe. In 1936 I moved to Ely to take over wildlife work on three ranger districts, and in July of that year I was transferred to Cass Lake, Minnesota, to serve on the forest supervisor's staff in charge of wildlife management for the Chippewa National Forest.

It was there that I developed a system for inventorying duck production. A good CCC enrollee and I paddled a canoe or walked around the shorelines of 10 percent of all lakes, streams, and rivers on the Chippewa National Forest. Later we eliminated a num-

Jerome Stoudt, FWS Biologist, checks a mallard nest on Redvers Study Area in Saskatchewan. USFWS photo by Rex Gary Schmidt.

ber of census areas that had little vegetative cover and thereby reduced the number to ten lakes and one river flowage. Except for a period during World War II, this census was conducted annually for nearly twenty years. At this same time I developed a system of ageing broods by dividing them into three classes. With the brood census method and data obtained from it, I was able to complete my master's thesis and degree at the University of Minnesota.

In the summer and fall of 1940 we conducted a food study on mallards. Twelve mallards were collected from each of two study areas every two weeks from August 15 to freeze-up. The most interesting result of this study was the complete changeover in food habits between the pre and posthunting season. Prior to the season, the food consisted of over 90 percent wild rice; but as soon as hunting began, the wild rice beds were "burned out" by gunning pressure, after which the food taken consisted mainly of pondweeds and other foods low in nutritive value. We planned to continue this study the following spring, but discontinuance of CCC funds terminated the wildlife programs in 1941. I was then transferred to the Superior National Forest and became a district forest ranger.

In 1942 I joined the USFWS as refuge manager at Horicon, Wisconsin. After a year at Horicon, I was transferred to the Necedah Refuge in south-central Wisconsin, and later to the Sand Lake Refuge in South Dakota. During my first fall at Sand Lake, there were only about 200 blue and snow geese on the entire refuge. Later this flock built up to a population of close to 200,000! Activities of the USFWS were sharply curtailed during the war, but immediately afterward there was renewed interest in waterfowl. I was assigned to the Upper Mississippi Refuge as biologist to study the effect on wildlife of draw-downs of dams.

During this period, the Upper Mississippi Conservation Committee was formed. I served as chairman of the Technical Committee one year and then as chairman of the overall committee. The states represented were Minnesota, Wisconsin, Iowa, Illinois, and Missouri.

In November 1949, I moved to Aberdeen. I worked in the two Dakotas on breeding-ground surveys and on migration and hunter-kill surveys south to Oklahoma. I also continued the Chippewa National Forest duck census in Minnesota.

Game management agents Harry Jensen and Everett Sutton assisted me with breeding ground transects in those years. I couldn't have had better help. Harry was on old-timer and the senior agent. Everett had just been hired after the war. We used .22 automatic pistols to flush ducks from ponds where visibility was poor from the road. One day Everett fired a shot that accidentally killed a drake mallard as it rose from the pond — on the wing, mind you. When this happened, Harry turned around to him with a stern, angry look and said, "Everett, damn you, the next time do what I tell you, and aim *at* them; then you won't hit one!" For a second or two, he had Everett worried.

In 1952 I was sent to Saskatchewan where I was assigned to set up a duck study area. Cecil Williams, USFWS survey chief, helped me lay out the area after we got some suggestions from Bernie Gollop and Alex Dzubin, Canadian Wildlife Service biologists. We settled on the Redvers area in southeastern Saskatchewan. Finding a place to stay turned out to be a problem. The hotel at Redvers had burned down, and the hotel at Manor had no running water. After considerable pleading I talked the hotel manager at Carlyle into renting me a room for three months. There were no showers or bathtubs in the hotel then, so I had to drive to Bowbells, North Dakota, to take a bath on weekends!

The high count on the Redvers Study Area of 120 pairs per square mile in 1952 and 1953 has never since been equaled, although the number of water areas and the total acreage of water have several times been greater. Consequently, I believe that duck populations in southeastern Saskatchewan and southwestern Manitoba are presently well-below the carrying capacity of the habitat.

In addition to duck census and reproductive surveys, we obtained valuable information on habitat, land use, and predation. We also did considerable banding. One year we banded over eight hundred ducklings, mostly mallards, with the help of dogs. I was the first biologist to extensively use dogs for duck banding. The dogs, two black Labradors, were also very helpful in locating duck nests and flushing broods from cover on brood counts. In fact, in my reports I raved so much about my dogs that Dr. Joe Linduska, chief of the Branch of Research, once said, "Jerry, you better not teach that dog, Dinah, how to write reports, or I will hire her and fire you."

The early years at Redvers were no picnic when heavy rainfalls occurred. In May 1955 the town of Redvers was isolated from all vehicular traffic. One day a caterpillar tractor pulled us through a half-mile of gumbo. When we got out of the mud the wheels on the car wouldn't turn, and we had to be pulled another half-mile to free them. Many times to get to the north leg of our study area we had to go north from Carlyle, through the Moose mountains, then east to Wawota and Fairlight, and back south to Redvers. Now the entire road through the study area is blacktopped.

Mammal and bird populations fluctuated quite a bit in the twenty-three years I covered the study area at Redvers. High populations of snowshoe hares occurred the first two or three years, but never approached those numbers afterward. Foxes, quite rare in 1952, increased at a rapid rate until recent years, when they were abundant over the entire area. There were no raccoons in 1952, but they were common by the late 1960s. Crows almost disappeared during the drought of 1959-1963 and never did reach the high populations present prior to 1959. Except for highways, land use has changed only slightly.

Water conditions also varied. The water dried up in 1959; no natural ponds were left on the study area, and only ten dugouts and stock dams contained water. Conditions were a bit better in 1962, but very bad again in 1963. In 1961 I prepared a canvasback study outline and spent two weeks in May looking for enough canvasback habitat to work on. I finally choose one near Minnedosa, north of Brandon, Manitoba. There I studied the habitat requirements and population dynamics of the canvasback. We also established roadside transects to inventory all species of waterfowl. We had data collected previously by Hawkins, Kiel, Dzubin,

Bernard Gollop, Canadian Wildlife Service Biologist, records waterfowl data during the 1951 survey. USFWS photo by Rex Gary Schmidt.

Olsen, and others for comparative purposes. We continued two breeding pair censuses and one brood census on the Redvers area, adding the Lousana, Alberta, study area after Al Smith retired in 1968.

The Minnedosa study yielded valuable information. Canvasback pairs and broods were found to utilize ponds over one acre in size most extensively, while nesting hens preferred the seclusion of ponds one acre or less. Cattails and bulrushes were favorite nesting sites. Parasitism by the redhead was very prevalent, and nest destruction by raccoons proved very severe. My suspicion that hen canvasbacks tended to nest in the same pond year after year was later confirmed in tagging studies by Dr. David Trauger and Jerry Serie. Other data on land use, clutch size, nesting success, flooding, and mortality were equally revealing.

When I took over the Alberta study area, I was struck forcefully by the fact that in Manitoba and eastern Saskatchewan there was about one duck for every three or four ponds, while in western Saskatchewan and eastern Alberta there were about three or four ducks per pond. This was in early May when many of the latecomers, such as blue-wings, had not yet arrived in numbers. Our records showed that, over the years, blue-wings increased to comparative abundance while mallards declined.

Recently Dr. Trauger, then assistant director of the Northern Prairie Migratory Bird Research Station at Jamestown, North Dakota, and I collaborated on a paper given at the 43rd North American Wildlife and Natural Resources Conference. By statistically analyzing ground study data, we concluded that the present duck population has more habitat than required, despite drainage, agricultural practices, pond filling, and so forth. This finding suggests that unless enough breeders are allowed to return each year to utilize the existing habitat, acquiring more habitat will not bring about an increase in duck production.

Most of my memories of Central Flyway Council meetings are of the debates I had with other biologists, especially with those from the state game departments. They often wanted to relax hunting regulations when I didn't think we had enough ducks to justify relaxation. I also argued against increasing the harvest when it looked as if we were entering a drought period. Additionally, I fought the notion that the next year's duck production could be predicted from the number of ponds present in the current year. Trauger determined from our data that the number of ponds one year has no relationship to the number of ducks produced the next year.

In addition to my work on the breeding grounds, I made several trips to Mexico. From 1958 to 1962, I served as an aerial observer for the midwinter survey along the Gulf Coastal area of Mexico. I was impressed by how few duck hunters we saw along the coast and the lagunas of eastern Mexico.

As part of the canvasback study, during the falls of 1951 to 1959, I flew with Ed Wellein in a survey of all major stopping places of canvasbacks in the Central and Mississippi flyways after the birds left Canada but before they reached the wintering areas.

In 1973 I decided to retire. It was getting a little tougher all the time to walk around those brushy ponds and wade through knee-deep water to find canvasback nests in bulrushes and cattails, especially on hot July days. While retirement is fine, I miss the work in Canada, all the good people who worked with me, and the friendly people of Canada.

Duck Studies in Alberta

Allen G. Smith

My first association with the USFWS came in 1946. After accepting a position as biologist with the state of North Carolina, I was informed of an opening as a flyway biologist with the Service. I applied for that position, was accepted, and thereupon reported to the Chicago office (where the central office was located at that time) en route to duty at the Denver Research Station and my new work under Dr. George B. Saunders. This was in mid-November of 1946, immediately following one of the worst blizzards Denver ever experienced.

Here began the most thorough and impressive period of orientation that I have ever undergone. George was one of the best instructors I have had the opportunity of working with. Intellectually brilliant, morally impeccable, personally charming, and a joy to be with, he instilled in me a feeling of what it should mean to be an employee of the United States government. That was a period when government employees were dedicated people with little thought for themselves and the hardships they might encounter along the way.

In the beginning, my Canadian assignment was in Alberta and the eastern wedge of British Columbia. In those days, my surveys were wholly confined to ground transects in all roaded areas of the provinces. Accompa-

After the nesting season, the ground and air survey crews combined forces to trap and band samples of the waterfowl produced in the area. One such crew (from left to right): William G. Leitch, Ducks Unlimited; Dennis Weisser, Alberta Game Branch; Douglas Williams; son of Cecil S. Williams, who supervised many waterfowl investigations; Fred Sharp, Ducks Unlimited; G. Hortin Jensen, FWS; and Allen G. Smith. FWS. USFWS photo by Rex Gary Schmidt.

nied by one biologist from the Canadian Wildlife Service and one from the Alberta Game Branch, I conducted two complete ground surveys of breeding pairs, one in May and one in June, to pick up both early and late nesting waterfowl. In the early years, a large crew would gather in July and August, travelling from place to place in the province where duck production warranted setting up traps for banding. Our crews were composed of U.S. and Canadian federal employees and provincial and state men. The banding, while hard and dirty work, was not without its compensations. From the beginning, the Ducks Unlimited men were of great assistance, not only in offering manpower but also in furnishing equipment and guiding us to places that we probably would not have found on our own.

In my first few years on the prairies and parklands, we did a great deal of experimenting with survey methods. The first aerial surveys in Alberta were begun by Leon Cool in 1947. Hortin Jensen continued this work, flying transects along railroads and highways in the summer of 1948. From then on, we flew a series of planned routes, following certain positions from west to east and back again at fixed intervals across the waterfowl producing areas. Once we worked out the aerial techniques, the ground transects were phased out. Breeding pair surveys were flown in May, production surveys in July. We continued ground studies, though not for the purpose of determining duck numbers over large areas.

Four ground study areas were established in the prairie provinces to learn about the breeding ecology of the waterfowl produced in prairie habitat, transitional areas, and parklands. We discovered almost at once that acre for acre, duck populations were higher in the parklands than in the grasslands, but that nest and duckling predation were also heavier. American, Canadian, and provincial biologists manned the study areas, beginning work the first of May and continuing it without a break until sometime in August.

Separate banding crews were eventually set up, beginning work around the first of July and continuing either into August, or on into the fall months, if bait-banding stations were established.

I spent the winters of 1946 through 1949 in southern Texas, headquartered at Brownsville, studying the ecology of the Laguna Madre and coastal Texas to the Louisiana border. This included making several aerial surveys of the Louisiana marshes, to and including the Grand Chenier, with John Lynch and Bob Smith. In early January, I flew with Dave Spencer and George Saunders while taking the winter inventory of waterfowl in south Texas and the northeastern Mexican coast. I flew as observer for many years with Hortin Jensen in Alberta during the breeding pair and production surveys in May and July. At the same time, I was supervising four individual ground study areas, one in Louisiana, another in Vermilion, a third in the Brooks-Medicine Hat area, and a fourth in Strathmore. The last two were manned by Ducks Unlimited personnel, Vermilion by Canadian wildlife biologists, and the Louisiana area by USFWS and Alberta game branch personnel.

For two winters in the early 1950s, I conducted a study of hunter memory at a field checking station at the Tule Lake National Wildlife Refuge. This was one of four such tests conducted across the United States to evaluate the accuracy of hunting success reports from hunters.

My career as flyway biologist was personally rewarding. I learned about Canada and Canadians, and came to love them. This, above all things, has been one of the most important results of my years as a flyway biologist. Secondly, I literally fell in love with my job. That was easy to do in the years when Dr. Clarence Cottam and Cecil Williams were at the helm.

Manitoba's Duck Factory

William H. Kiel, Jr.

Borrowing a bit of public relations lingo from Ducks Unlimited, we might describe this 4,000-square-mile district in southwestern Manitoba as a duck factory. In the late 1940s through the mid-1950s, it produced over one million ducks annually for the fall flight — and its production is only slightly less today. Fertile soils of glacial till, gently rolling terrain in aspen parkland, and 100,000 rather deep potholes make this district one of the most stable high-duck-production regions in the pothole country.

I was introduced to the Minnedosa district in July 1948 by Art Hawkins. He, Lyle Sowls of the Delta Waterfowl Research Station, and Gus Cooch of the Canadian Wildlife Service had conducted waterfowl surveys in the area in 1947 and in the spring of 1948. That summer, as a graduate student at the University of Wisconsin under Joe Hickey and Bob McCabe, I was to gain experience at Delta. Cleaning duck pens at the hatchery wasn't a new experience, since I was reared near a poultry farm and had participated in that chore. But banding ducks on the Delta marsh with Hawkins and Cooch was new, as was portaging the canoe loaded with several sacks of grain across broad mud flats when the water was low.

As a duck hunter raised in Texas, I was familiar with waterfowl in winter plumage; but seeing ducks in dull eclipse plumage was different. I didn't voluntarily identify ducks at a distance for awhile! My confidence was somewhat restored one evening when Al Hochbaum of the Delta Waterfowl Research Station was showing some of us the country along the edge of the marsh. Al and others were identifying ducks at great distances, and I was properly impressed. At one point, we were alerted to a flock of pintails in a field at considerable distance. Then the road curved in that direction and the pintails turned out

This excellent duck production area being examined by Gerry Pospichal, Art Hawkins, and Bill Kiel in 1951 no longer exists, having been drained in 1982. USFWS photo by Rex Gary Schmidt.

to be rocks! I felt better.

In the Minnedosa district in 1949, Hawkins and I laid out twelve ground transects over fifty square miles along passable roads, selected a sample of 120 pothole intensive study areas, and established eight quarter-section blocks for surveys. These studies continued through 1954, followed by less intensive surveys in later years. We documented changes in the density and species composition of the waterfowl breeding population, habitat differences caused by drainage and woodland clearing, and trends in nesting success.

We observed several trends in habitat and waterfowl population changes over the thirty-year period. Habitat has been lost to drainage, which has eliminated over 15 percent of the deeper potholes since 1949 and adversely affected many more. Woodland clearing has markedly reduced wooded acreage, and farmers with new four-wheel-drive tractors

and thirty-two foot discs don't leave much nesting cover for upland nesters around pothole margins. The increasing use of herbicides and fertilizers undoubtedly affects pothole ecosystems. Rainbow trout are a relatively new crop of some deeper potholes. Stocked as fingerlings in the spring, they are harvested as pan-size trout in the fall.

Predators are more effective at finding nests in the limited upland cover, and raccoons are having a field day preying on overwater nesters such as redheads, canvasbacks, and coots. Coons weren't present in the district in the 1949-1954 period but increased markedly in the late 1950s. Severe winters and high fur prices may eventually reduce their numbers, but until that time, raccoons will seriously affect duck production.

The future will show whether removing the aspen groves and draining the potholes served the best long-range interests of agriculture. This district now enjoys high-yield, stable production of wheat, oats, and barley. Crop failures are practically unknown. Yet it seems possible that the many wetlands and windbreaking aspen groves help insure stable crop production. One thing is sure: the pothole drainage will create a permanent drought for ducks.

Waterfowl production has changed too. Though somewhat below the level of the 1949-1954 period, the district still produces about one million ducks. The major decline has been in mallards, pintails, and wigeons, ducks that mostly nest early. Early nesters apparently are adversely affected by limited nesting cover and high predation rates. Late upland nesters use current-season vegetation growth to a greater extent and so are faring better. Redheads and canvasbacks have suffered a drop in nesting success from over 70 percent in 1949-1954 to less than 50 percent in the 1970s, and in some years 25 or 30 percent.

Even the tenacious coots have experienced increased nest predation and recently have nested more than before in the fringes or points of the cattail and bulrush that extend into deeper water. This is apparently an attempt to escape raccoons. For coots, this is not surprising; they also have the ability to "predict droughts" and avoid nesting in potholes that will go dry later in the summer.

For overwater nesting ducks, the loss of production because of increased nest predation may be greater than the number of birds harvested by hunting.

In the late 1940s and early 1950s, the USFWS established aerial transects to sample the major duck breeding grounds. We on the ground contended that the visibility of ducks from an aircraft must vary with changes in water levels, aquatic vegetation density, time of day, and species and density of ducks. We found such variations when comparing roadside counts to intensive beat-outs of the same potholes. The aerial approach was necessary to sample the broad range of breeding ducks, of course, but the results could be significantly altered by changes in the visibility rate. More recently,

correction factors for changing visibility rates are being applied to aerial data, but I wonder whether the correction factors can be evaluated on a statistical basis.

Walt Crissey was flying a Seabee for the USFWS, and we made some comparisons of air and ground duck counts on the Minnedosa transects. Since the frequent dogleg turns in our ground transects were not designed for optimum aerial transects, I felt less than airworthy on some flights. The Seabee was not an ideal aircraft for this work. One day at Delta, Walt and coworkers had loaded the Seabee with gear and prepared to fly to a conference in Alberta. The Seabee had a peculiar high-pitched whining sound, and that day it was really wound up. While several of us watched from the dock, Walt tried to get the Seabee airborne from the rather calm waters of a Delta bay. But to no avail. In three tries it failed to get off the water, so the load was repacked to produce a better balance. The other pilots on the dock thought it was the funniest show they had seen in a long time. On the next try, the Seabee finally cleared the water and staggered off over the phragmites in cootlike flight.

I now work in south Texas in the land of prickly pear, mesquite, and hundreds of thousands of wintering waterfowl on Laguna Madre and freshwater rangeland ponds. Some questions come to mind as I reflect on waterfowl management today. I wonder what's happened to the federal game management agents who used to work in waterfowl management on survey and banding crews? I thought their combination of management and enforcement work was productive and efficient. I'm afraid most of them are now stuck in customs offices checking for spotted cat hides or in related assignments far removed from waterfowl management.

And what about Ducks Unlimited (DU)? I understand they are outstandingly successful in raising funds from sportsmen and other sources. But are they successful in producing ducks? Is there some way the pothole habitat that produces most of the ducks can be pre-

The ground and air teams compare notes at a coffee break during the May waterfowl survey along a Saskatchewan transect. USFWS photo by H. Brown.

served? In the United States, we rightly or wrongly subsidize landowners to produce or not to produce agricultural crops. Why not pay them to produce ducks? Even Canadian farmers worried about crop depredation by grain-feeding ducks might not mind producing diving ducks for a profit. Some DU projects such as the Maryland Duck Factory near Erickson, Manitoba, seem to be principally staging areas for ducks. We might not need new staging areas if production in the highly fertile potholes is not maintained.

Should there be more emphasis on duck production on the waterfowl production areas and refuges purchased by the USFWS in the northern states? If good production means controlling nest predators and providing dense nesting cover, so be it. These wetlands benefit many species of wildlife, and nobody can reasonably say that nature is in balance in these islands of habitat that concentrate predators and duck nests. Let those who oppose wildlife management —

the protectionist and preservationist organizations — finance their own system of refuges for their own purposes. Lands purchased with duck-stamp dollars should be used to produce waterfowl as the primary objective.

Back to Manitoba, where a farmer near Erickson once watched me wading in a pothole with clipboard and binoculars. It was a hot, windy, dusty day, and the farmer was caked with dirt from driving his tractor downwind in the blowing dust. What I was doing must have looked like fun to him. After exchanging pleasantries, he asked, "But what do you do for a living?" I look back on my years in Manitoba and conclude I might have worked smarter, but not harder. I have fond memories of the northern prairies and parklands, and of Canadian friends, who used to greet me upon my arrival in the spring with, "Well old chap, what's new in the Excited States?"

Harry Tollas

7

Tools of the Trade

"Tools" is perhaps the wrong term to describe such a diverse bag of techniques and studies as wing collections, taxonomy, wing identification, duck trapping, and computerized analyses of populations. But that word will have to do as a way of referring to the many techniques, sciences, and tricks that constitute the "how-to" of studying waterfowl populations.

Waterfowl, after all, are very difficult to study. They live in remote places, move around frequently (sometimes covering great distances), and mingle so that different age groups and species are found together at different times. Until recently, there were few answers to some of the most basic questions managers asked about ducks and geese.

This chapter tells how many of the answers were developed, often involving cooperation between scientists with very different specialties.

Some examples. Sometimes it is necessary to sort through the skins of dead birds in museums to determine just what birds live where. Data used to be unreliable, so that people like Walt Crissey had to combine a little voodoo with hard data in their calculators to find the most reliable information. It was the job of people like Sam Carney to gather much of the information that was fed to the calculators, but first they had to devise sampling techniques for aging and sexing birds and for determining the take by hunters. Techniques that work on ducks don't always work on other geese and swans, and John Lynch describes the discovery that geese and swans could be counted on their wintering grounds where they are more easily seen than when scattered across their remote nesting areas.

In spite of the influences of airplanes and computers, almost all the critical facts have come initially from banding. And banding involves back-breaking manual labor. This chapter, however, tells the story of breakthroughs in technique that have made it possible for banding crews to be far more efficient. The invention of the airboat, the development of certain trapping techniques, and even something as simple as the use of dogs have all made their contributions.

In this chapter, only the surface of the techniques of waterfowl management can be presented. Yet all these efforts add up, in the estimation of Ross Hanson, to a "career hard to beat."

Taxonomy's Contribution

John W. Aldrich

The study of waterfowl taxonomy (the science of classification of diversity among organisms), although always recognized as supplying basic information for management, has seldom been included as an integral part of waterfowl management research. However, variations in biological characteristics of ducks and geese discovered in the course of incidental taxonomic research have played a significant part in guiding management programs, principally regarding the distribution, habits, and adaptability of those birds.

A case in point was the 1963 discovery by Harvey Nelson of the USFWS that giant Canada geese represented the only stock suitably adapted by nature for establishing new breeding populations in the eastern prairie refuges. The giant Canada goose was described as a distinct subspecies in 1951 by Jean Delacour, who thought that it had become extinct. Only recently, Harold Hanson of the Illinois Natural History Survey found it still extant in the wild.

Waterfowl biologists have generally been content to accept the classification of waterfowl species in the most recent edition of the American Ornithologists' Union (AOU) checklist as adequate basis for their work, and have looked with disfavor on conclusions of taxonomists that differ from that standard. However, waterfowl have produced their share of taxonomic problems that affect the validity of species classification on which hunting regulations and other management practices are based. Occasionally these problems have proved embarrassing to waterfowl management agencies. Among the taxonomic groups fitting this category are the whistling swans, brant, Canada geese, white-fronted geese, snow geese, mallards, and green-winged teal.

Probably the most studied, but still poorly

Museum skins are prepared and preserved for taxonomic research studies. Both geese in this picture are white fronts but note how much larger the Tule subspecies is as compared with the more abundant white-fronted goose. Photo courtesy of J. W. Aldrich.

known, example is the Canada goose group. These white-cheeked geese, which includes the largest and smallest of all geese in the world, have been considered at various times to include anywhere from one to four distinct species. Current taxonomic opinion favors the view that this is only one extraordinarily variable species. The last word will not be written on this concept, however, until it has been established by field observations — verified by examination of specimens — that the tiny quite-distinct cackling goose interbreeds with the larger lesser Canada goose where they have been found nesting together on the Yukon-Kuskokwim delta. Despite all of the work on geese in that critical area, no one has taken the trouble to verify that particular species relationship.

In 1926, boardman Conover of the Field Museum of Natural History in Chicago first reported, based on conversations with Eskimos, the nesting of cacklers with a larger variety of white-cheeked goose on the Yukon

Delta near Hooper Bay. Then, in 1929, George Sutton and Dewey Soper found a similar situation to exist between the diminutive Richardson's goose and a larger variety on Southhampton and Baffin Islands, respectively. In 1931, P. A. Taverner of the National Museum of Canada was prompted by these findings to recognize three species of the white-cheeked geese: Canada goose, cackling goose, and Richardson's goose. Taverner, one of the earlier taxonomists to become involved with Canada geese, was so impressed with their great geographic variation in size and color that he is alleged to have despairingly remarked about their classification, "If you split the difference, you double the difficulty."

The trend in splitting the white-cheeked geese into distinct species reached a climax in 1948 when Hellmayr and Conover, in their *Catalog of Birds of the Americas,* classified these geese in four different species: (1) a very dark West Coast population, now called *occidentalis,* together with the medium- to small-size northwestern population generally called lesser Canada goose including *leucopareia* and *taverneri;* (2) a small, dark species called *minima,* the cackling goose; (3) a small, pale species named *hutchinsii,* the Richardson's goose; and (4) a variable species with respect to size and color that combines populations that have been called *parvipes, moffitti, interior,* and *canadensis.*

W. E. Clyde Todd of the Carnegie Museum in Pittsburgh added significantly to our knowledge of the speciation in the white-cheeked geese when he characterized the eastern and southern Hudson Bay population *B.c. interior,* sometimes called Todd's Canada goose. This group is probably the largest and most studied population of all Canada geese and provides the bulk of the goose hunting in the eastern United States. Todd was most familiar with these geese on their breeding grounds because of his long interest in the birds of Ungava Peninsula. On his many trips to that area, the roly-poly little man, who always wore corduroy trousers in the field, became well known to the Eskimos.

They gave him a name that literally means "the egg-shaped man with pants that squeak."

The man who supplied most of the taxonomic information on the Canada goose complex was James Moffitt of the California Academy of Science. Unfortunately, he was killed in an airplane crash while on active duty in the Aleutian Islands during World War II, and never had an opportunity to publish his findings. In later years, Jean Delacour resurrected Moffitt's monographic manuscript on geese and, on the basis of it, published a revision in 1951 of the white-cheeked geese that, so far, is the most knowledgeable and perceptive treatment of this difficult subject. The revision classifies all of the known populations in one species called the Canada goose, *Branta canadensis,* with twelve subspecies. This is the arrangement appearing in Delacour's *Waterfowl of the World.*

Since Delacour's book there have been other important studies of the geographic variation of Canada geese, much of them unpublished. Particularly significant from the standpoint of management has been the work of Charles D. MacInnes on the west side of Hudson Bay; Douglas H. Johnson, Daniel E. Timm, and Paul F. Springer in the Pacific Flyway, particularly with regard to the Aleutian Islands population; and especially Harold C. Hanson, who has studied geographical variation throughout the entire range of the species and has much unpublished information that should be pertinent to Canada goose management.

The white-fronted geese have generated considerable speculation regarding their variability, but with relatively little success in solving the taxonomic problems posed. Hellmayr and Conover, in their *Birds of America,* pointed out that the big, dark, white-fronted goose wintering in the central valleys of California, called the tule goose by Harry S. Swarth and Harold Bryant in 1917, was the same as the race named *gambelii* by Hartlaub in 1852, based on specimens from Texas in the Berlin museum. Hellmayr and Conover speculated in 1948, as have other ornithologists since then, that the unknown breeding range of those big white-fronts was probably in Arctic America somewhere east of the MacKenzie Delta.

Later, in 1964, aviculturists Bob Elgas and Jack Kirocofe found the breeding grounds of part of the population of large-size white-fronts, specifically those that migrate through the Central Flyway to Texas, on the Old Crow Flats of Yukon Territory. However, there was no band recovery evidence that any birds from that area migrate to California. Furthermore, Bob Elgas, working with the California wintering tule white-fronts on the Sacramento refuge, was convinced that the whitefronts looked different from those he and Jack Kiracofe had collected on Old Crow Flats, some of which they had reared from goslings in their aviaries. Subsequently in 1975, based on Elgas' description of the distinctiveness of the California tule geese, Jean Delacour and Dillon Ripley published a diagnosis of those birds as a distinct subspecies that they named *Anser albifrons elgasi,* tule white-fronted goose, with wintering grounds in the Sacramento Valley but with location of breeding grounds unknown.

It was not until the summer of 1979 that Bob Elgas and Dan Timm of the Alaska Department of Fish and Game discovered the long-sought breeding area of the big California tules on the shores of Cook Inlet, not far from the Anchorage headquarters of the Alaskan waterfowl investigations. This important discovery should put to rest the wishful thinking of some regulatory agencies — fearful of the effect on goose hunting if a new and possibly endangered subspecies were added — that the tule goose represents unusually large individuals of a single, widely varying population of common white-fronts. It is significant that in the white-fronted geese (as in the case of Canada geese and bean geese of Europe), the large-size variants breed in the forest and grassland zones and the smaller-size races nest in the tundra zone.

Despite all of the studies of blue and snow goose distribution migration and abundance over the years, not until Graham Cooch investigated their behavior on their joint breeding grounds on Baffin Island was it learned that they are merely two color phases of the same species. Evidently people were impressed more by the visible differences in those geese than the snows and blues were themselves, since they interbreed freely, and thus no specie difference can be maintained.

No one questioned that the black brant of the Pacific Coast and the light-bellied Atlantic brant were merely well-marked races of the same species until the fifth edition of the AOU checklist in 1957 considered them specifically distinct. This action was based on Charles Handley's discovery that both types of brant occurred in summer on Prince Patrick Island in the Canadian Arctic. However, Handley's specimens later were considered to be intergrades, and the subspecific classification of the eastern and western brant populations was reestablished by subsequent compilers, particularly Ralph Palmer in his *Handbook of North American Birds.*

Until quite recently, the whistling swan was considered a species distinct from the other swans of the world. However, Peter Scott and other investigators at the Severn Waterfowl Trust began recording the extreme variation in the amount of yellow in the bills of Bewick's swans wintering at Slimbridge, England. The result has been the discovery of almost complete intergraduation of bill color between Bewick's and whistling swans; recent compilers, including Palmer, consider them to be merely races of a single circumpolar species appropriately named "tundra swan."

The mallards have offered one of the biggest taxonomic problems, particularly since Delacour, in his *Waterfowl of the World,* startled everyone by putting all mallard-like ducks in the same species. Reasons for and against such treatment have been argued back and forth up to the present, sometimes with more heat than light. It would appear that Delacour's arrangement is being accepted gradually on the basis of actual

Snow geese gather in huge concentrations along the flyways and on their wintering grounds. This one is at Tule Lake NWR in California. USFWS photo by D. B. Marshall.

knowledge of extensive interbreeding. On that basis, it is now apparent that the common mallard and the Mexican duck belong to the same species. That determination resolved a heated argument resulting from the banning of all hunting of mallard-like ducks in New Mexico, because the Mexican duck had been listed as an endangered species. Extensive specimen analyses by John Hubbard of the New Mexico Department of Game and Fish have shown quite conclusively that the Mexican duck and mallard are one species. Thus, a taxonomic conclusion based on a study of specimens saved legal mallard hunting in southwestern states.

On the other hand, studies of hybridization between the black duck and the mallard by Paul Johnsgard indicate that they are specifically distinct because hybrids make up only two percent of the population where the two species come together. Thus hybrids are relatively scarce compared with the pure-blooded types in the zone of overlap. Studies of the relationship to mallards of the mottled ducks of the Gulf Coast lowlands have not progressed to a point where it is possible to draw conclusions as to whether they are the same species, and there seems to be little interest at present in pressing the matter.

For many years bird watchers were excited by occasional observations of the European teal in American waters. Only recently was intergraduation between green-winged and European teal found in western Alaska. Thus, single-species status for the two forms was indicated, and the birders lost the European teal through a biological perversity. They were compelled to reluctantly scratch another species from their life lists. This is an event that seems to be happening more frequently in recent years, and it doesn't make taxonomists popular with bird-listers.

Thus, waterfowl taxonomy investigations have produced impacts with various values to the users and managers of the wildlife resource. Taxonomy has supplied information of species relationships and variations within species that has aided in recognition of populations from specific breeding areas when they were found in migration. Taxonomy has suggested racial stocks best adapted physiologically for establishing new populations in certain environmental situations. Taxonomy has continued to alter the number of separate species of ducks, geese and swans — to the pleasure or dismay of those engaged in the recreation of bird watching.

Estimating the Harvest

Samuel M. Carney

For several years prior to 1952, attempts to measure the hunting kill of waterfowl and the number of days spent waterfowl hunting consisted largely of bag-checks and interviews of hunters by field personnel. Although a large volume of data had been gathered, statistical analysis had shown it to be inadequate. The chief difficulty was one of sampling. How could information be obtained from a *representative* group of waterfowl hunters?

As Clarence Cottam, assistant director of the USFWS explained on April 24, 1952, "Currently, surveys are carried out in the breeding grounds for the purpose of determining indices to the annual fall flights of waterfowl. Once this has been determined, the next problem is one of translating the information into shooting regulations which will result in a kill commensurate with the size of the fall flight. This problem is creating difficulties which have not been satisfactorily solved to date. *No adequate method has yet been devised for obtaining data with regard to the annual kill of waterfowl or for measuring changes in the amount of hunting effort.*" Cottam was writing to the director of Stamps and Philately, U.S. Post Office Department, to arrange a meeting with Walter F. Crissey and Earl L. Atwood.

The problem Cottam faced becomes apparent when we recall that about forty species of ducks and geese (with a variety of breeding and migrating habits) are shot throughout the United States during a five-month period by two million hunters. Because information was needed about ducks and hunters that was too numerous and widely dispersed to be counted or contacted completely, statistical sampling was necessary. Information would have to be obtained from a small number of hunters regarding the waterfowl they killed; information that could, by inference, be related to all hunters.

For this to work, samples would need to have two characteristics: (1) they must be large enough to create confidence in the information obtained from them, and (2) they must be representative of all hunters and the ducks they bagged. Although mathematicians had formulated rules that made it possible to determine the size of sample needed to obtain reliable information, the Service would be more or less on its own when it came to selecting representative samples. came to selecting representative samples.

Because each hunter sixteen years or older was required to purchase a duck stamp before hunting waterfowl, Crissey and Atwood suggested that the logical solution to the problem would be to contact the hunters when they purchased duck stamps, rather than in the field. Cottam's 1952 meeting with them led to an agreement with the Post Office Department that made possible the first annual questionnaire survey of waterfowl hunters. It was started in the fall of 1952 under Atwood's direction. All states and Alaska participated in the survey, which was designed to reflect hunting pressure and harvest for each flyway. Although it was modest in scope, the procedures followed were similar to those still in use.

As now conducted, the Waterfowl Hunter Questionnaire estimates the magnitude of the annual harvest of waterfowl and hunter activity (day hunted) for individual states with enough accuracy for waterfowl management. Although the Postal Service maintains a list of post offices that sell duck stamps and the numbers they sell, no complete list of duck-stamp buyers exists. The first step for obtaining this list each year is to obtain the names and addresses of hunters to whom questionnaires can be sent. Postmasters at randomly selected post offices are mailed a supply of hunter-address cards (return postcards) with instructions to have postal clerks give one to each duck-stamp buyer. Approximately 75,000 of these cards are returned to the USFWS annually.

The next step is to send a questionnaire to

A "wing bee" at Poinette, Wisconsin. Waterfowl specialists check through thousands of wings submitted by hunters to gather important data on waterfowl harvests and age ratios in the populations. USFWS photo.

those persons who indicate that they intend to hunt. Answers from hunters are used to calculate the average number of ducks or geese bagged and days spent afield in each state. These averages, however, have been shown to be a bit high. During the formative years of the survey, Atwood sent postseason questionnaires to hunters whose kill and activity had been previously recorded at check-stations on public hunting grounds. He found averages calculated from the questionnaires to be somewhat higher than averages for the same hunters derived from check-station records. In a nutshell, hunters (like fishermen?) tend to exaggerate a bit. Armed with this information, Atwood developed a series of correction factors that allowed him to compensate.

The final step is to combine information obtained through the survey with that supplied by the Postal Service. Simply expressed, the number of stamps sold (excluding stamp collections) multiplied by the average duck kill, goose kill, and days hunted (each corrected for exaggeration) gives the total duck kill, goose kill, and days hunted for a given state or flyway.

While this may be "simply expressed," operating the survey is a substantial undertaking involving several hundred-thousand address cards and questionnaires. These must be numbered, sorted, bagged, mailed, edited, coded, and keypunched. At times our work rooms resemble a small post office. Because of the tremendous volume, everything must be fed into a computer. When the computer finishes digesting information and disgorges its findings, the USFWS has a good picture of the size and distribution of the waterfowl harvest and hunter activity throughout the United States during the previous season.

Although the Waterfowl Hunter Questionnaire gave the Service an excellent method for determining annual harvest and hunter activity, other needs soon became apparent. For one thing, the report of species bagged on the questionnaire was suspect. Many hunters had trouble identifying nondescript females and less common species. For another, more detailed information was needed on the productivity of individual species than could be obtained from aerial surveys.

At the Patuxent Wildlife Research Center, Dr. Aelred D. Geis reasoned that, since procedures had been developed that permitted gathering productivity information (ratios of hatching year to older birds) from the detached wings of several types of upland game birds, it was logical to consider a similar approach for ducks. Since ducks could be identified as species by their wings and, since early in the fall, the adult-juvenile ratios could be determined from their tail feathers, Geis initiated a small-scale pilot study involving about six hundred Minnesota hunters to see if they would be willing to remove these parts and mail them to the USFWS.

I began working with Al Geis in the summer of 1958 and was soon involved full-time on the project. It was clear from the onset that nationwide wing collections would not be feasible unless a method for determining age and sex of mallards was developed. By the end of October, Art Hawkins had examined large numbers of ducks in locker plants and had concluded that tail feathers were of limited use in determining age. By November, the pilot study had demonstrated that hunters were willing to do their part. But a method of age and sex determination had to be developed from wings.

Al had arranged for field collections of about two hundred mallard wings from birds of known age and sex. I was soon studying these samples while other drying wings festooned the walls and ceiling of my office.

Everyone got wind of the project. Injecting wings with formalin helped reduce odors, but breathing the fumes put me on sick leave for three days. Eventually, a method was developed whereby a trained observer (using a combination of feather shape, pattern, color, and wear) could correctly identify ages and sexes. I remember being so elated the day I knew the method would work that I wore a necktie!

To test the method, Al Geis, Art Hawkins, and Larry Jahn collected nearly twelve hundred wings from mallards they had examined in Missouri, Arkansas, and Louisiana. Each wing was numbered and shipped to Patuxent, where I had little difficulty correctly identifying more than 95 percent. The stage was now set for more ambitious studies.

Approximately eight thousand waterfowl hunters throughout the Mississippi Flyway were contacted in 1959 during a study jointly sponsored by the states and the USFWS. During the next year, similar studies were conducted throughout both the Mississippi and Atlantic Flyways. Concurrently, techniques similar to those used for mallards were developed that permitted age and sex of other species to be determined from detached wings. Flyway-wide studies explored the types of information that could be obtained and the various ways it could be used. This work also developed methods best suited for obtaining and classifying large volumes of wings and for summarizing information derived from them. These studies led to the establishment of annual waterfowl-parts collection surveys.

Waterfowl-parts collection surveys, as now conducted, are designed to obtain annual estimates of species, sex, and age in the waterfowl harvest and its geographic and chronologic distribution. The survey begins with selection of nearly thirty thousand hunters from respondents to the previous year's Waterfowl Hunter Questionnaire. Each of these hunters receives a packet containing envelopes suitable for returning duck wings or goose tails to a freezer storage site in one of the flyways. Goose tails, used to determine species and age (but not sex), have been included since 1962. Once the hunting season is over in a flyway, a group of state and federal biologists assembles at the freezer site for a "wing bee" and classifies the wings and tails. Numerical codes are assigned for the species, sex, and age, together with the place, date, and time of kill as recorded by the hunter. This information is shipped to Laurel, Maryland, where it is keypunched onto magnetic tape for computer processing.

Information from the two surveys is combined by dividing the total duck (or goose) harvest derived from the questionnaire by the number of wings (or tails) received from birds killed in the same area to obtain the number of birds each part represents. Because there is a record for each waterfowl part received, information is very flexible and can be sorted in many ways to examine various facets of the waterfowl harvest. It is possible to study variation in species, sex, and age composition among flyways, states, or even parts of states during different weeks, months, or years. Because of differences in wariness, migration habits, or hunter selectivity, some age, sex, and species groups are more vulnerable to the gun than others. In some instances, ratios in the harvest can be adjusted to reflect those that existed at the end of the breeding season. For example, if wing receipts indicate *twice as many* young as adult mallards have been shot but recoveries of birds banded before the season show that young were shot at *twice the rate* of adults, then equal numbers of each existed before the season.

Information derived from waterfowl harvest surveys relates to the season just completed. At the same time, twenty years of historical information has now been accumulated, data that can be related to a wide variety of regulations employed during both good and poor seasons. Such information gives the Service considerable insight into the probable effects of a given set of regulations.

Though they contribute a great deal toward our understanding of North American waterfowl, harvest surveys are but a part of a data gathering system. This system also includes aerial surveys of breeding and wintering grounds, pre-and post-season banding, and other programs. The gathered data is synthesized by computer into what has been called "the most sophisticated such effort in the annals of game management anywhere in the world." It has evolved to provide the maximum amount of recreational waterfowl use compatible with the well-being of the resource.

Calculators and Ouija Boards

Walter F. Crissey

The Migratory Bird Treaties with Canada and Mexico, and the Migratory Bird Treaty Act which implemented them, stressed the need for protecting the resource, particularly from hunters. Following passage of this act in 1918, the federal government began establishing annual hunting regulations. For regulatory purposes, states were grouped into east-west zones stretching across the country. Hunting season dates, in zones from north to south, were set to conform more or less with bird migration dates.

From 1918 until 1935, season lengths and bag limits were based on population information obtained from volunteers. This amounted to a "consensus of opinion" approach to setting regulations. Criticism of this method mounted as waterfowl populations dwindled during the 1930s. With passage of the Migratory Bird Hunting Stamp Act in 1934, which provided funds, an organized survey of waterfowl populations was initiated in January 1935 using airplanes, boats, and cars to cover wintering areas in the United States. Later the survey was expanded to include wintering areas in Alaska, Canada, Mexico, and the West Indies. The objective was to cover all wintering areas as completely as possible and count the number of birds present.

Waterfowl banding was launched around 1918. This was the beginning of the water-

Meeting of management biologists at Northern Prairie Wildlife Research Center in 1967. Shown are (front, left to right): H. Nelson, M. Smith, E. Chamberlain, C. Lostetter, W. Crissey, J. Smith, (2nd row): G. Jensen, D. Purinton, D. Combs, K. Baer, A. Weinrich, (3rd row): A. Brazda, H. Hansen, R. Smith, R. Mackay, J. Pospichal, K. Vermeer, K. Norman, (4th row): R. Hanson, H. Reeves, E. Wellein, R. Buller, (5th row): R. Slattery, P. Smith, J. Stoudt, R. Martinson and A. Hawkins. USFWS photo by J. Thompson.

fowl inventory program. Frederick C. Lincoln and others discovered that waterfowl traveled in well-defined corridors. He proposed the existence of four major flight routes and theorized that populations within each were more or less distinct. Based on this, he recommended that season lengths and bag limits conform to four north-south flyways rather than three east-west zones. The change from zones to flyways for management purposes was made in 1947.

With zonal management, a single bag limit and season length applied nationwide. With flyway management, a separate bag limit and season length was established for each flyway. Each state could select its opening date within a framework of dates for that flyway. It was assumed under the flyway management system that populations within each flyway were different, both in size and hunting mortality. In 1950, for example, it was judged that appropriate daily bag limits for ducks in the Atlantic, Mississippi, Central, and Pacific Flyways were four, four, five, and six birds respectively. Daily bag limits

for geese were two, four, five, and six birds; while season lengths were forty, thirty-five, forty-five, and fifty-five days.

From 1935 through about 1950, management decisions were based mostly on the results of the annual winter survey. Gradually the weaknesses in that approach became apparent. The winter survey provided an index to the size of the breeding population the following spring. However, the annual duck crop depended not only on the size of the breeding population but also on the success of the hatch, which is highly variable from year to year depending on breeding ground conditions. If hunting regulations in a given fall were based on "no change" in the wintering population as compared to the previous year, while the fall flight was reduced due to poor production of young, hunting regulations would be too liberal. The decrease would not be detected until the winter survey a year later. Therefore, when hunting regulations were based on winter survey data, adjustments were made the year after they were needed. This resulted in poor management, especially during periods when populations were decreasing due to adverse conditions on the breeding grounds.

Breeding Ground Survey

Recognition of the need for breeding ground information was prompted by drought conditions which reduced duck populations during the late 1940s. Exploratory investigations in North Dakota and western Canada were initiated in 1946 to determine the feasibility of conducting meaningful surveys of breeding populations and conditions. Promising results were obtained, and the investigations were expanded in subsequent years.

During the period 1947 through 1950, experimental population counts in the important prairie and parkland breeding areas of north-central United States and southwestern Canada were made from both cars and airplanes. As the years 1947, 1948, and 1949 were relatively dry, most of the roads that crossed the breeding areas were passable by car during May when the counts were made. But the spring of 1950 was so wet that many of the roads were impassable. By then we had learned that birds in the breeding areas could be counted and identified by species from low flying aircraft that were not impeded by road conditions. Further, exploratory surveys in northern Canada and Alaska had revealed the presence of important breeding populations of ducks and geese in areas not accessible by roads. It was decided that emphasis should be placed on developing a statistically reliable technique for conducting aerial surveys to determine population size and distribution as well as habitat conditions throughout important breeding grounds in the United States, Canada, and Alaska.

There was growing recognition that we knew too little about the factors that affected waterfowl production, especially in the important prairie and parkland breeding range of the north-central United States and south-central Canada. Therefore, study areas were established in the Dakotas and in each of the prairie provinces to conduct research on nesting success and brood survival. Most of these study areas were laid out as long, narrow transects to facilitate comparison of ground observations with those made from the air.

During the early 1950s, emphasis was placed on determining the numbers and distribution of breeding adults during May and early June. During July, survey crews concentrated on banding ducks, particularly on moulting areas. Information concerning probable breeding success came mostly from ground study areas combined with general observations concerning habitat conditions.

It gradually became apparent, however, that information from a few scattered ground study areas did not adequately represent average conditions throughout the many thousands of square miles of important breeding areas. Therefore, beginning in the 1960s, the aerial breeding ground survey transects were covered twice, once in May or early June to measure size and distribution of breeding populations, and again in July to measure production success.

Many special investigations accompanied the routine inventories in the early years of surveys. These revealed that aerial crews saw a higher fraction of the birds present during early morning hours than they did later in the day, and a higher fraction of some species than of others. They saw more birds when flying west (away from the sun) during morning hours than they did when flying east. They recorded a higher fraction of numbers present when water levels were low and withdrawn from border vegetation than they did during high water, when border vegetation was flooded. Of greatest importance, however, was the discovery of significant differences among aerial observers (as much as 30 to 40 percent) in both the number of birds recorded and the species composition. Changing a crew member from one year to the next could affect results as much as would an actual change in population.

An outgrowth of these discoveries was the initiation of annual air-ground comparison surveys to evaluate the characteristics of the aerial crews operating in the important prairie pothole region. Test transects were censused by both ground and aerial crews within a day or so of each other. The ground crew was assumed to have seen all the birds present on the transect and identified them by species. The proportion seen by the aerial crew was calculated as a visibility rate. If the aerial crew saw half the mallards recorded by the ground crew, the visibility rate was 2.0. The raw aerial count of mallards for the entire survey area then was doubled. This ground-air comparison automatically provided an annual correction for each survey crew.

At first each crew was given considerable leeway in developing methods for conducting the survey. This resulted in considerable divergence in collecting field data and analyzing results, making it difficult to summarize information. After much trial and error, standard operational procedures were developed which all the survey crews were instructed to follow.

As staff specialist for Migratory Game

Birds in the Division of Wildlife Research, my job was to analyze information from various sources and to improve survey methods. I soon realized that the USFWS was spending much more time and effort on collecting data than analyzing it. It appeared to me that data already on file could be used to solve many perplexing problems. This was especially true of banding records. In recognition of this, the Migratory Bird Populations Station was established in 1960 within the Division of Wildlife Research, and I became its director. The station was located at the Patuxent Wildlife Research Center. It had a staff of about one hundred people. Primary emphasis was placed on data analysis, including information from the waterfowl kill and parts collection surveys. The North American Bird Banding Office was attached to the station.

Waterfowl Harvest Survey

When I joined the USFWS in 1949, a kill survey of sorts was being conducted. It consisted of field personnel checking hunters' bags to determine average daily kill and species composition. After the season, hunters were contacted at sportsmen's clubs and asked how many times they had hunted that season. Using these sources of data, a total estimate of the waterfowl kill by hunters was determined by expanding the data. Probable biases in the data were recognized, but no one knew their magnitude. The kill estimates were used mostly for news releases giving the size of the waterfowl kill in the United States (which, looking back, must have been exaggerated). The information was not being used to determine any cause-and-effect relationships between hunting regulation and the resulting kill.

To improve the kill information, field personnel were instructed to collect names and addresses from waterfowl hunters contacted in the field during the early part of the hunting season in each state. Following closure of the hunting season, a questionnaire was mailed to each hunter asking the number of ducks, geese, or coots bagged and the number of hunting trips taken during the season.

Following the next two or three seasons questionnaires were sent to the same hunters as well as to hunters whose names and addresses had been obtained that year. We recognized biases of an unknown degree in this method, but hoped that the effect of changing regulations would be reflected in the replies of at least the group of hunters repeatedly sampled. But obvious inadequacies in the kill survey data, plus the need to evaluate the effectiveness of various hunting regulations, resulted in an effort to improve the representativeness of the survey. The obvious solution was to randomly select a mailing list from duck-stamp buyers; but the stamps were sold by the Post Office Department, over which the USFWS had no control.

At first, postal managers were unwilling to cooperate. A compromise was finally reached that allowed the Service to randomly select a small sample of post offices in each state and to provide each of them with a supply of self-addressed hunter contact cards. The postmasters were instructed to hand a card to each duck-stamp purchaser and to request that he fill it out with his name and address and drop it in the mail slot. Unfortunately, this was a voluntary program on the part of both the postmasters and the hunters. Over the years, names and addresses have been obtained from about 35 percent of the individuals who purchased their stamps at sample post offices. Thus, estimates of total kill over the years have had biases of unknown magnitude. We assume that the degree and direction of bias, at least as it related to selection of sample, has remained reasonably constant. In my opinion, the kill survey results have provided an adequate base for evaluating the effect of various hunting regulations on waterfowl kill under a variety of population and habitat conditions.

The post office kill survey initiated in 1952 had "growing pains" for several years. Experiments conducted to measure the biases that might exist in mail questionnaire responses determined that hunters exaggerate when reporting the number of birds they kill, over-report some of the common species, and under-report those that are less common. Exaggeration of total seasonal bag involved rounding upward to multiples of five and multiples of the daily bag limit. Tests showed that there were differences in bias from one flyway to another and from one year to the next, but methods were developed to compensate for the exaggerations and improve the comparability of kill estimates.

Initially, the Service's objective was to obtain an estimate of kill sufficiently accurate for practical management purposes within each flyway. With this objective, the sample of hunters in many states was inadequate to meet the needs of some states. During the early years of the kill survey, these states found it advantageous to contract with the USFWS to improve the accuracy of their kill estimates by increasing sample size. Some states had gathered waterfowl kill statistics for years through mailed questionnaire surveys to measure the kill of resident game. A few continued to do so after the Service's kill survey was initiated, particularly in the Central Flyway. Most state surveys used resident hunting licenses as a sampling frame. In some states estimates of waterfowl kill were surprisingly close to those of the Service's, but quite different in others. Examination of such similarities and differences led to increased understanding of questionnaire surveys to measure waterfowl kill and hunter activity.

Parts Collection Survey

Soon after breeding ground surveys were initiated, USFWS biologists began making forecasts of production success (the ratio of immatures to adults in the fall flight). These forecasts were checked by having field men determine the ratio of immatures to adults in hunters' bags. Most bag checks were made early in the season when successful hunters were easiest to find. It soon became apparent, however, that age ratios in the bag varied both by location and time periods. Needed was a method that spread the bagged sample in a more representative manner over place and time. Also, while checking hunter bags,

field personnel had discovered that most hunters were unable to identify the birds they had taken, particularly the less common species. Hence the species information on the kill survey questionnaire returned by hunters was largely unreliable.

Working with known-age birds, biologists at the Migratory Bird Populations station discovered that species, age (adult or immature), and sex of most ducks could be distinguished by examining wing feathers, while the species and age of geese could be determined from the tail feathers.

Based on these findings, a parts collection survey was initiated in the Mississippi Flyway in 1959, expanded into the Atlantic Flyway in 1960, and included in all four flyways in 1962. Hunters who had participated in the previous year's mail questionnaire survey and reported killing one or more birds were supplied with return addressed envelopes prior to the opening of the waterfowl season in each state. They were asked to put one wing from each duck and the tail feathers from each goose shot in one envelope, and record date, time, and place where the bird was taken. It can be argued that only the more successful hunters were being sampled, but experience showed that when previously unsuccessful hunters were supplied with envelopes, they were unsuccessful in subsequent years.

The parts collection survey complemented the mail questionnaire survey in many ways. The questionnaire survey provided an estimate of the total duck, goose, and coot kill within a state. The parts collection survey provided a basis for dividing that total into location, time during the season, and time during the day when the birds were taken, with that information capable of being divisible according to species, sex, and age. Since each hunter was assigned a number that appeared on each envelope, the average daily bag and number of times hunted successfully during the season could be tabulated. Because many of the parts collection survey respondents supplied information for more than one year, the effect of changing hunting regula-

Members of a banding crew work one of the hundreds of potholes in the Coteau area southwest of Moose Jaw, Saskatchewan. One crew member drives the birds toward land, where trained dogs will catch them for banding and releasing. USFWS photo by Fred Glover.

tions from one year to the next could be checked by using data from only those hunters who supplied information in successive years. In short, the parts collection survey provided a means of examining many aspects of the relationship between regulations, hunter activity, and waterfowl kill which previously had been only a matter of conjecture.

Banding Program

Shortly after the Migratory Bird Treaty with Great Britain (for Canada) was signed in 1918, it was proposed that a single banding system would provide more reliable information than two or more separate ones in North America. Meetings between representatives from the two countries led to an agreement under which the United States would operate the banding office and supply information for research and management purposes to personnel in both countries.

Numbers of birds banded were small in the beginning, so records were easily processed by hand. As interest increased, however, it became necessary to convert to machine methods. The first change involved a computer card on which information was both punched and written by hand. Duplication of cards with handwritten information soon became a problem, however, and codes were developed that allowed all of the information

to be punched on computer cards. After considerable effort, the files were converted.

At first, the primary purpose of banding was to relate the location of recovery to the location of banding. Data concerning the banding of birds was kept solely to process the recoveries when they were reported. Gradually, we realized that recovery rate information (the proportion of banded birds taken by hunters and reported) was at least as important as information on distribution. Again, with considerable effort, the banding schedules (which filled many file drawers in the Banding Office) were summarized and punched on computer cards so the number of birds recovered could be compared with the number of birds banded according to species, sex, and age.

By the early 1960s, the computer card system was no longer adequate. During a summary in the late 1950s of black duck banding data, one of the clerks estimated that she had passed several tons of cards through the sorters and tabulators. The physical space required to house records was huge, and the single set of cards we were able to maintain was filed according to location of banding. Thus, when a request came in for a listing of all recoveries of birds banded in a given state, it was relatively simple to retrieve the data; however, if the request was for all recoveries in that state regardless of where banded (a common request), all of the cards had to be sorted.

The obvious answer was to place the entire file on magnetic tape and use computer methods to file, retrieve, sort, and tabulate the information. After many negotiations and a great deal of effort, an IBM computer was installed at the Migratory Bird Populations Station in the mid-1960s, and the files were converted once again to the new system. Considerable retraining of personnel (particularly programmers) was required to operate the more sophisticated machines. The enormous volume of information that had to be maintained presented a unique problem that was hard to solve, even with modern computer methods. Coincident with the change, it was decided to machine process reports to hunters who had sent in bands (rather than by hand as had been done previously). At the height of the hunting season, we fell several months behind in replying to hunters who reported bands. Complaints were mailed to Congressional representatives. Once over the original hurdles, however, the new system provided an efficient means of maintaining banding files, handling responses, and retrieving information for research and management purposes.

Prior to the mid-1950s, about 1.5 million waterfowl had been banded. Determining distribution patterns was the usual motive, with relatively little thought given to specific distributional problems that needed to be solved. Rather, emphasis was placed on banding birds whenever and wherever the opportunity presented itself. This led to large numbers of birds being banded during the fall migration period on a few wintering areas and on several moulting areas scattered in the breeding grounds. In some instances, many more birds were banded in restricted areas than the solution to practical management problems would have demanded. For example, an all-time record 20,000 mallards were banded during the fall and winter in southern Illinois.

For management purposes, banded birds have little meaning unless they represent a known segment of the overall waterfowl population. For example, ducks banded during fall migration are going and coming at an unknown rate, so the size of the population represented by banding at a given site cannot be determined. Further, birds caught in bait traps during fall migration may not represent a cross section of the birds moving through. Once this was discovered, most banding was discouraged during periods when the birds were migrating. Summer banding on duck moulting areas was also discouraged. It was fairly easy to catch large numbers of birds when they were flightless, but the catch ran heavily to adult drakes. It was apparent that these birds had moved into moulting areas after pairing with females in unknown locations, possibly hundreds of miles away. Thus, they did not represent a population of birds whose size and location could be measured.

Once the aerial breeding ground surveys were well established, information was available concerning the number of birds in each of several strata into which the breeding areas were divided for survey sampling purposes. The problem, then, was to determine where the birds from each of these strata were being taken by hunters so that population changes could be properly assigned to each flyway when making fall flight forecasts. The solution involved banding females and ducklings before they were old enough to fly, to insure that the birds were related to the same areas where the breeding population changes had been measured during May aerial surveys. It was recognized that variations in distribution patterns occurred from year to year due to changes in weather and habitat conditions. Banding crews were assigned quotas based on the number of recoveries needed to solve the problem, and the banding effort in each stratum was distributed through a number of years so that recoveries would represent average conditions. It took about five years in most strata for mallard bandings, for example, to provide necessary information concerning distribution of harvest from various portions of the breeding areas to each of the four flyways.

Determining distribution is an important function of the banding program, but of equal or greater importance is the use of banding data to measure survival rates and differences in vulnerability to shooting among species and between age and sex groups. Much research has gone into developing techniques for estimating survival rates from waterfowl banding data; given a sufficient number of recoveries, present methods appear adequate for most management and research purposes.

To measure differences in shooting vulnerability among species and between age and sex classes, and to measure survival, a banding program was initiated in the early 1960s emphasizing capture of flying adult and immature ducks at a series of late summer and early fall concentration areas scattered across the breeding areas. Banding in August and September allows little opportunity for natural mortality to occur before initiation of the hunting season; thus, the number of birds banded will, for practical purposes, be the number exposed to shooting. Differences in the recovery rates (proportions of birds banded that are recovered) constitute a measure of the differences in vulnerability to shooting — and this will be true not only for the banded birds but also for the populations they represent. Soon after the pre-season program was initiated, experience demonstrated that vulnerability to shooting by species, age, and sex varied considerably from year to year. It also showed that young ducks were more vulnerable than adults to shooting. Hence wings received from hunters in parts collection did not reflect the true age ratio of the population. But vulnerability ratios obtained from the pre-season banding program provided a means of correcting ratios from the bagged sample. To obtain this information required an annual pre-season banding program. For these reasons, the banding of adults and immatures immediately before the hunting season — with

special emphasis on the mallard — has become a routine part of the annual fact-finding surveys.

At first, the USFWS encouraged any activity that increased reporting rates, assuming that more recoveries meant better data with which to work. Also, the cost per bird recovered decreased on paper when additional reports were encouraged. When faced with the results of promotional activities, however, we decided that a low-but-relatively-even reporting rate was far superior to a higher-but-uneven reporting rate. We considered mounting an annual publicity campaign that would stand a chance of getting to all hunters equally. But all proposals were judged to be inadequate, especially when it was recognized that hunters in Canada and Mexico were also involved.

Therefore, we discouraged in every way possible the sporadic publicity campaigns and band-collecting activities. Those who thought they had been helping resented this policy, but sporadic publicity to report bands gradually has become less of a problem. Most damaging to the program has been declining or erratic cooperation among hunters in the vicinity of banding stations where band recoveries are no longer a novelty. Hunters have become disgruntled because of opposition to hunting regulations or other reasons. In some instances, band loss due to wear or poor-quality materials has affected results. With all its problems, banding has maintained a prominent place in the waterfowl management program since its inception.

Data Analysis

One major responsibility of our office was to analyze and summarize information received from the breeding ground surveys in order to enable us to forecast changes in size of the fall duck flight in each of the four flyways. During the first decade of flyway management, improving habitat conditions resulted in an increased duck supply; our consistent forecasts of more ducks pleased both hunters and wildlife administrators. In

1957, however, the tables turned. Breeding ground surveys recorded a decrease in the amount of habitat, and the duck population began to level off. Conditions deteriorated rapidly in 1958 and 1959, improving somewhat in 1960. But by 1961 and 1962, a major drought enveloped the important breeding areas. It had become apparent that a direct relationship existed between the number of small ponds in the midcontinent prairie and parkland breeding areas and the number of ducklings produced in a given year. By then we knew that a simple count of broods in July yielded an unreliable measure of total production, but that a reasonably accurate prediction could be made during July by measuring other factors.

The necessary early termination date of field work was a constraint on production surveys. Administrative procedures required that hunting regulations be published in the *Federal Register* one month before they became effective. With the hunting season opening October 1, the publishing date was September 1. The states had to be given time to select season dates after the USFWS had reached a decision on season length, bag limits, and outside season dates. About two weeks was the minimum time required for the Service to summarize information and hold appropriate meetings to decide what the regulations should be. For these reasons, it was necessary to terminate field work around July 25. Most of the broods of the early nesting species would be on the water by late July in an early year. During late years, however, many broods hatched after surveys were completed. This was compensated somewhat by recording paired adults observed during the course of the July survey, as they were considered evidence that nesting was still in progress. Many pairs gave promise of strong late production. Habitat conditions such as frequent rains and large numbers of ponds provided another indicator of probable late nesting success, while a rapid drying of ponds suggested that few additional broods would be produced. After enough years of experience, we were able to compare current

survey data with those of previous seasons and make reliable forecasts. The accuracy of the forecasts was checked later by measuring the ratio of immatures to adults in the fall population, done either by bag checks or through the wing collection survey corrected by banding data for differential vulnerability of young and adults.

Before the mid-1960s, fall flight forecasting was perhaps more an art than a science. In most years, the accuracy was sufficient for practical management purposes, but mistakes were made. In 1960, for example, the forecast was for "no change in fall flight." The restrictive hunting regulations established in 1959 (because of drought) were continued in 1960. But production in 1960 was much better than we had forecast. Because 1959 was a dry year, many ponds refilled to a shallow depth in 1960. By midsummer most of the newly flooded ponds were choked with a dense growth of emergent vegetation — the first time we had experienced such a condition over a wide area. Neither aerial nor ground crews could see the hidden broods in dense cover. Age ratios in the fall production improved over the previous year, the kill increased, and the breeding population was up the following spring. With data from 1960 now on record, the chances of making a similar error in the future are reduced. By the mid-1960s sufficient data had accumulated to produce a statistically sound formula used with good results to predict the production ratio.

The two basic tools for managing waterfowl are preservation or enhancement of habitat and manipulation of hunting regulations. Habitat management is a long-term program. Regulating hunting is the only tool that has an immediate effect. Restrictive regulations will reduce both the total kill and the proportion of the fall flight that is harvested, while liberal regulations will have the reverse effect. Once the need for either reducing or increasing the harvest has been established, the problem becomes one of translating desired level of harvest into season length, bag limits, and so forth.

A precept of flyway management is that hunting regulations are geared to hunting pressure. Thus, the 1948 regulations, which were restrictive because of drought, allowed thirty-five- and forty-day seasons in the Central and Pacific Flyways respectively, with five-bird bag limits, while the Atlantic and Mississippi Flyways had thirty-day seasons, with four birds per bag. During the next ten years, the duck population increased due to improved breeding habitat conditions, so regulations were relaxed from the thirty- to forty-day range to the sixty- to ninety-five-day range by 1958. Accumulation of kill survey data during the period demonstrated that there was a direct relationship, at least in the three eastern flyways, between season length and both total kill and the proportion of the fall flight taken by hunters.

Spreading the Word

A just criticism of the USFWS' program during the early days was that we relied on cooperative effort to obtain data but furnished our cooperators only brief and very general summaries of the results. For example, the annual winter survey required a small army of field men, but only a few copies of the detailed report were duplicated, and these were given very limited distribution, even within the service.

An early effort to correct this deficiency was to publish a detailed summary of the breeding ground surveys in the form of a Waterfowl Status Report. A limitation, however, was that the report had to be approved by the editorial review board and the length of time required for writing, reviewing, and printing it was such that the report was not available for distribution until long after the information was of value for establishing current hunting regulations. Recognizing the need, I persuaded the director that it was feasible to summarize and duplicate a status report containing all of the current waterfowl survey information, making it available at the time of the director's Waterfowl Advisory Committee meeting in early August. Considerable "midnight oil" was burned in the process, but thanks to overtime help from a dedicated secretarial staff and special arrangements for duplicating, the survey data were available for current use.

The net major innovation was inauguration of a series of administrative reports. This occurred in 1962, after the Migratory Bird Populations Station had been in operation for two years. As anticipated, biologists at the station were able to pull much valuable information from current and accumulated survey and banding files. But because so much time was required for all the steps of publication, by the time the material could be distributed it was of historical value only. After considerable persuasion, the station was allowed to duplicate and distribute preliminary reports, each of which carried a proviso that "The primary purpose of this paper is to facilitate the prompt distribution of timely information. It is intended for administrative use only and is not for publication without permission of the Director, Bureau of Sport Fisheries and Wildlife."

Some of the reports were simple summaries of information, with little analysis. Others presented preliminary analysis of information related to subjects of current interest. For example, 43 of the more than 200 administrative reports issued during the next eleven years dealt with one or another of the many problems related to the management of mallards, 26 to black ducks, 27 to wood ducks, 16 to teal, 6 to canvasbacks and redheads, 9 to ringnecks and scaup, 9 to whistling swan, 5 to pintails, and 14 to Canada geese. A total of 44 reports dealt with some aspect of hunting regulations. For example, Report #160 discussed the "Probable effects of changes in the daily bag limit on wood duck kill during the 1967 hunting season in the Mississippi Flyway." Others included such subjects as trends in breeding population, estimates of kill, and age and sex ratios in the kill.

The reports were well received and, by the

end of the second year, over a thousand copies were being mailed to biologists and wildlife administrators in the United States and Canada, with a few being sent to interested individuals in Europe.

The Big Black Books

An outgrowth of the administrative reports was the gradual accumulation of tabular material organized in such a way that information concerning almost any aspect of the effect of regulations on hunting activity and kill could be quickly found. This material proved to be of particular value during meetings where hunting regulations and other management and research problems were being discussed. The data were placed in loose leaf binders, which happened to be black, and were looked on with favor by those whose ideas were being refuted.

Regardless, with information from duck-stamp sales, banding, breeding population and winter surveys, kill surveys, and duck-wing and goose-tail collections, it was possible to accumulate information concerning almost any problem that might be discussed. In some instances, particularly when a problem related to a restricted area within a state, too few data were collected in a given year to be meaningful. When this occurred it was often possible to accumulate information from several years and determine at least a tentative solution to the problem.

Data from the duck-wing and goose-tail collection surveys proved to be particularly useful. With information as to where and when each bird was taken, including hour of day, it was possible to determine the number of birds each hunter took each day he hunted successfully, the order in which he took them, and when during the day they were killed. Since each bird was identified to species, age, and sex, it was possible, for example, to examine the probable effects of either bonus birds or restrictions within the daily bag limit on the kill of various species, and the degree to which these effects varied from one location to another. With a record of time during the day when each bird was killed, it was possible to examine, for example, the effect on species composition and hunter success when shooting was allowed one-half hour before sunrise versus a sunrise opening. The effect of bag limit restrictions could also be examined; for example, it was possible to determine the proportion of the kill (either total or for any species) that was taken in particular daily bags. It is perhaps of interest to note that the effective range of bag limits as a tool for manipulating kill is discouragingly small. In the Atlantic Flyway, for example, over three-quarters of the total black duck kill occurs in bags that contain no more than one black duck. Since the average daily bag in the Atlantic Flyway is less than one bird, this is not surprising, but it means the factors that affect the amount of hunting activity (such as season length) have more effect on black duck kill than manipulation of the black duck bag limit.

Summary

For those of us in a position to observe the North American waterfowl situation over time, management by north-south flyways has been a definite improvement over management by east-west zones. The major advantage has been the ability to harvest the resource more efficiently: that is, to be restrictive in areas where the population was either very vulnerable to shooting or was in need of special protection while, at the same time, be more liberal in areas where the birds were in good supply. Further, flyways fostered cooperative effort on the part of states, since each state in a flyway shared in the harvest of the same population of birds and thus had common interests. Finally, the flyway concept provided a logical basis for refinement of the management system. As information accumulated, it was discovered that the waterfowl populations in the western portions of several Central Flyway states were more closely aligned with the Pacific Flyway than the Central, so the boundary between the two flyways was changed accordingly. Also, it was discovered that mallard populations in the Columbia Basin region in the Pacific Flyway and the "High Plains" portion of the Central Flyway were sufficiently different to warrant management as subflyways. Studies of Canada geese led to the discovery of several distinct flocks within the overall population, so separate management plans have been established for each flock.

Flyways — yes, but not just the four flyways as originally conceived by Fred Lincoln. Looking to the future, it is more than likely that further refinements will be made as additional information accumulates.

Ducks and Dogs

Fred A. Glover

"Look at this band report!" I said to my wife. I was returning from my mailbox with a card that turned my mind back over twenty years. I held a USFWS "Report to Bander" card. It showed that I had banded a hen mallard eleven miles south of Boharm, Saskatchewan, July 27, 1958, and that Buddy Rhodes of Lafayette, Louisiana, had shot the bird in January 1979, two miles southeast of Pecan Island, Louisiana. The bird was twenty-one years old when shot! I wondered if Buddy Rhodes found it a little tough to eat. Think of the experiences that mallard had! How did this hen happen to have been wearing band number 637-09411? My dog, Jet, had caught this bird when it was about one month old, and I had banded it.

The story begins in 1956 when the Migratory Bird Section of the USFWS undertook the apparently simple task of banding at least 300 birds for each one-degree block throughout the waterfowl breeding grounds. (Such blocks are now called a latilong — roughly a

rectangle forty by sixty-five miles.) However, accomplishing the task turned out to be both challenging and difficult.

The group reaching this decision consisted of the flyway biologists, flyway representatives, and the migratory waterfowl biologists at Patuxent, Maryland, where the data (banding and kill statistics) would be processed.

Why 300 birds per latilong? The thinking was based on a general band return rate of around ten percent. For reliability in small-number statistics, the minimum sample should be thirty. The banded sample would be of young-of-the-year, so the location of banding would represent the local area in which they were raised. Thus, when the biologists conducted their air and ground production surveys in July, the birds observed would be from the same general area as the sample banded, and recoveries from the birds banded (by areas) would represent the distribution and recovery rate of a population of known size. Ultimately this procedure would make it possible to forecast waterfowl fall flights throughout the flyways and to promulgate scientifically valid waterfowl hunting regulations each year.

Planning and organizing the breeding ground banding program was my responsibility, and I thoroughly enjoyed the assignment. However, there were times when I had my doubts, like that sixteen-hour drive through July heat and rain-slicked gumbo from Regina to Estevan, Saskatchewan, to deliver much-needed bands to a field crew.

We planned the banding program to be completed in five years, starting in 1957. The most important species to be banded was the mallard, since it formed a major part of the hunter's bag in three of the four flyways. Similar emphasis would be attempted on the black duck. Our first season saw banding crews working from Labrador west to Alberta, with most of the effort concentrated in the prairie provinces of Canada (Alberta, Saskatchewan, and Manitoba).

The crews operated independently most of the time, but on extensive marshes one or

A stellar team of duck banders, Fred Glover is flanked here by assistants Boy (golden retriever) and Jet (Labrador). USFWS photo by Fred Glover.

more crews would get together and put on massive drives — in which up to 5,000 flightless birds would be rounded up and banded. The banding crews were composed of USFWS and cooperating state game department personnel under the leadership of a crew leader, who was typically a federal game management agent personally interested in waterfowl.

Some of the most successful early crew leaders were U.S. Game Management Agents Floyd Thompson, Chuck Hayes, Milt Reeves, Joe Hopkins, Walt Price, Ed Bosak, Gus Bonde, Bob Meyerding, and Vic Blazevic. Biologists from the Canadian Wildlife Service and Ducks Unlimited also participated when the banding crews were in their areas.

About forty-thousand birds were banded that first year; but when we analyzed the banding schedules, it was apparent that we were not catching the mallards and black ducks desired. Most of the banded birds were molting adult pintail, gadwall, wigeon, greenwinged teal, blue-winged teal, and shoveler ducks. Unfortunately, these birds could not be associated with a particular part of the breeding grounds because no one knew where they had come from.

We resolved to try harder for the second year. More mobile trap equipment was developed and used. We tried more extensive drift-fences and net leads. Emphasis was placed on trying to catch mallards on the small potholes where they appeared to be more common.

Meanwhile a Canadian waterfowl biologist, Bernie Gollop, had been conducting a study since 1954 on mallards that fed on farmers' grain fields in central Saskatchewan. Bernie was interested also in banding and marking young mallards so he could associate their breeding areas with the places where waterfowl crop depredations were occurring. In his quiet, unassuming way, Bernie had been banding more young mallards than our ten five-man crews.

When I checked this out, I found Bernie was using a half-breed Chesapeake retriever and a couple of other hunting dogs to locate the young mallards in cover surrounding the potholes — not in the water. Also, one of our USFWS biologists, Jerry Stoudt, had been conducting research on a special study area in southern Saskatchewan. Jerry used a Labrador female, Dinah, to help him locate duck nests. While going about his regular research, Jerry noted that Dinah was having her own kind of fun catching and retrieving young ducks. A fair number of these were mallards, which Jerry banded and released. USFWS biologist Ed Addy had used his Labrador retriever, Sharky, a few years earlier to band a fair number of young black ducks in the Canadian Maritimes.

The results of the second big year at drive-crew trapping for mallards drew to a close with results no better than the first. We withdrew to the "moldy chambers" (Interior Building, Washington, D.C.) to contemplate what was happening and to develop new strategy. We were disgusted, tired, and somewhat baffled. However, the idea of using a limited number of dogs was beginning to gain favor.

We decided that for the next year the number of drive crews would be reduced and selected persons would be assigned to use dogs on an experimental basis. The major concern about using dogs to catch young mallards was the likelihood of mortality to the young ducks. Some of the more extreme opponents to using dogs referred to them as "duck-eating dogs," which raised the specter of bad publicity for the USFWS.

The toughest job facing me then was getting official agency approval to experiment with dogs for banding. Assistant Branch Chief John Findlay, my immediate supervisor, was reserved but willing to give the idea a try. Branch Chief Joe Linduska gave strong but cautious support, probably because he understood dogs; he and I trained our Labradors together on occasion.

The flyway representatives reacted differently to the use of dogs. Ed Addy (Atlantic) was supportive but skeptical since his experiences seemed to show that no such technique would work to catch large numbers of black ducks. Art Hawkins (Mississippi) and John Chattin (Pacific) took a wait-and-see attitude. Ray Buller (Central) was enthused and wanted to be personally involved as a crew leader. Dan Janzen, USFWS director at the time, supported the biologists' recommendations.

The major remaining hurdle was Wes Corbin, administrative officer for the USFWS. Wes felt it was just a boondoggle for a bunch of biologists to have fun with their dogs. He adamantly maintained that the idea was a waste of money (which USFWS never had much of). He could not believe the program would work. Needless to say, Wes and I had some pretty pointed discussions. However, he agreed to one year of experimentation if I would obtain insurance for the dogs, in case of injury or death, and if I would develop performance criteria for selection of the dogs to be used.

Obtaining adequate insurance was a challenge. After contacting numerous insurance companies with negative results, I telephoned the New York office of Lloyds of London. The representative listened politely as I explained the situation, then with a tremendous laugh responded, "What sort of joke is this? I've never heard of anything like it! If you're a practical joker, this is the best I've ever had happen to me." I closed out the conversation as best I could. I had gone to the ultimate insurance company and I couldn't even convince them I had a legitimate story. Maybe Wes Corbin was right.

For a couple of days I didn't know what to do. I was stumped. Over the weekend, a retriever field trial acquaintance suggested I call the president of the St. Paul Fire and Marine Insurance Company, in St. Paul, Minnesota. It seemed that the president was an avid waterfowl hunter who had his own retriever. On Monday morning I followed through, and by noon I had assurance that St. Paul Fire and Marine would, indeed, insure the dogs. Our congenial association with the St. Paul insurance company continued throughout the remainder of the banding program. Only one claim was ever filed. Without the help of the St. Paul Fire and Marine Insurance Company, man's best friend would never have had the opportunity to prove his abilities for banding mallards.

The performance standards adopted for selection of a dog to be used in banding work were: (1) a compatible personality, (2) an obedient and subservient manner, both on and off leash, (3) a "soft mouth" — as demonstrated by retrieving at least ten live birds (pigeons or ducks) under typical field cover conditions with less than 10 percent mortality, (4) a good nose — as demonstrated by ability to find birds in heavy field cover, and (5) good health (veterinary health certificate required). Under actual field conditions while banding mallards, a dog would be removed from the field and not used in the program when its daily mortality rate for ducklings exceeded 10 percent.

There were about twenty qualified dogs the first year. About one-third belonged to federal banding crew leaders, with the remainder borrowed (in some cases rented at a dollar a day) from interested duck hunters and retriever field trial enthusiasts. All insur-

©H. Tollas

ance, food, care, and veterinary costs were paid by the experimental banding program. Some of the early dog crew leaders were Jim Robinson, now retired and a professional dog trainer in the South; Al Niemeyer, deceased; and Chuck Cadieux, now retired and a freelance writer in Albuquerque. Other dog crew members were Bob Kinghorn, Harry Lyman, Fred Kreller, Carl Gruener, John Waters, Herb Duncan, Chuck Kniffin, Maurice Lundy, Dick Droll, Roe Meyer, John Perkins, John Eadie, and Bob Halstead. I may have forgotten one or two people after twenty-plus years, and I apologize if this has happened.

Dogs we borrowed or rented during the program came from the following interested private citizens: H. Wilson, Cheyenne, Wyoming; Don Burrill, Casper, Wyoming; Dale Oakes, Cheyenne, Wyoming; Carl Fratzke, Winona, Minnesota; Corby Losie, Winona, Minnesota; Bart Foster, Winona, Minnesota; Ernest Butterfield, Winona, Minnesota; Ben Grupa, Winona, Minnesota; Avery Borell, Denver, Colorado; R. W. Clinghorn, Denver, Colorado; and John Olin, East Alton, Illinois. USFWS employees who used their own dogs in the program were Jim Robinson, Al Niemeyer, Dick Droll, Roe Meyer, John Perkins, Jerry Stoudt, and myself. Harry Lumsden, a biologist with the Ontario Department of Lands and Forests, used his retriever to band black ducks in Ontario.

The dog crews typically consisted of a crew leader with an assistant (both USFWS employees), one to three dogs, and such miscellaneous equipment as a compartmented dog trailer, short-handled dip nets, and two or three nylon mesh laundry bags (to hold the birds until banding). Some of the crews camped out when operating in remote areas, but most favored staying in the small towns, making friends locally, and partaking of Canadian culture.

Our experimental year was a huge success. Many of the latilong block quotas for mallards were reached in the grassland areas of southern Saskatchewan, Alberta, and Manitoba. Approximately fifty-thousand birds were banded that summer in Canada. Most of the mallards were caught by dog crews. This is not to take any glory away from the drive crews, for they worked hard banding most of the other species. Additionally, the drive crews had been shifted to emphasize banding of scaup, canvasback, redheads, and equally important species.

It was not difficult to obtain further approval for the banding of mallards with dog crews. The first year of major use of dogs yielded some interesting statistics: (1) a two-man dog crew caught ten times more young mallards than a five-man drive crew; (2) mortality of young mallards caught by dogs averaged less than 5 percent; (3) a good dog crew in a productive waterfowl area regularly exceeded 100 young mallards banded per day; and (4) costs per young mallard banded were about one twenty-fifth of previous years. Bernie Gollop, the Canadian Wildlife Service biologist who pioneered much of the early use of dogs, figured that it cost about $1.50 (1956 dollars) for each local mallard banded.

In the next two years of dog-crew banding operations, the local mallard banding quota (300 birds) was reached in all of the latilongs accessible by auto in Alberta, Saskatchewan, Manitoba, and a limited portion of Ontario. In addition, a dog crew led by Al Niemeyer operated one summer in the vicinity of Yellowknife, Northwest Territories. On another special dog crew assignment, Al Niemeyer and I, with our dogs, flew an amphibian airplane to Fort Chipewyan to band young birds in the Athabaska Delta and Wood Buffalo National Park area for about two weeks. The Royal Canadian Mounted Police were most helpful in this assignment by providing a motor boat and sharing their intimate knowledge of suitable campsites in the bush.

Mallard escape behavior was the key to banding success by dog crews. As Bernie Gollop put it, "Mallards are upland waterfowl." At the first indication of intruders or danger, mallards leave the slough and head for dry land cover. This is why the drive

Searching for duck nests with the assistance of two Labradors on the Redvers Study Area in Saskatchewan.
USFWS photo by Rex Gary Schmidt.

crews were largely unsuccessful. Once the hen and brood reached shore they ran as fast as possible, not stopping until they found cover. Within a minute after a banding crew arrived on the scene, the mallards usually would be out of the water and in the weeds. Thus, it was important to get the dogs working an area as fast as possible.

On the short grass prairie in southern Alberta, cover for a fleeing mallard might be a cow chip, a tuft of grass, a cow's footprint in mud, a badger hole, or even a stick under which the young bird could slide its head, ostrich-like. However, most of the local mallards used snowberry *(Symphoricarpos)* or bunches of grass to hide in.

Knowing what the young mallards were likely to do, a crew would approach a slough or pothole from the side that had the heaviest cover, thus forcing the escaping birds to move into the light-cover areas. Each dog crew had its own method of operation, based on compatibility of dogs, probable number of mallards, amount of escape cover, and accessibility. Some crews drove roads and around fields, working all potholes in sight. Other crews would cover a general area on foot and use the car to go to another general area.

Typically, one dog was used by a two-man crew. Only one person would handle the dog. The second crew member would follow twenty to thirty yards behind the working dog and handler, or he would try to stay on the periphery of the area being worked by the dog. Both crew members carried dip nets, and each person had one or more of the nylon holding bags tucked in his belt or back pocket.

The dogs that had formal training retrieved birds faster directly to their handlers, while other dogs would give birds to the nearest crew member. The assistant usually handled the birds, examined them carefully for injury, placed them in the nylon holding bag, and was responsible for transporting and caring for them until banding started.

When typical dry July conditions were encountered, it was important that the young, bagged birds be kept cool and not crowded. As soon as the dog retrieved a bird to its handler, the handler would try to send the dog back after other birds. Before they learned better, some dogs on the early crews thought they were all done after they had made a single retrieve to the handler. When the dog was no longer able to locate birds, he was put back in the dog trailer, and the crew would commence banding. All birds were released to the nearest water area.

It seemed to take at least three, eight- to ten-hour days of fieldwork before a dog would perform correctly. Thus, it was important to work each dog every day. The dogs loved their work (play?). It seemed impossible to work the dogs too hard when banding local mallards if they were fed and cared for properly, although a dog might cover 50 to 100 miles in a tough day of catching over 100 mallards. Several of the crew members carried pedometers that registered twenty to thirty miles per day of walking following the dogs.

Some of the days were long and hot. For the long-haired breeds (golden retrievers, particularly) the discomfort was obvious. It was almost impossible to keep them out of the water, although it was important to get the dog on the scent trail as rapidly as possible. Typically, goldens are not overly anxious about spending time in water, but one summer I was working a golden named Boy that took special delight in mud baths and just sitting placidly in the middle of any slough, regardless of its character. One day he decided the rancher's watering trough was an ideal place to cool off.

Reports from the field crews showed their enthusiasm and success:

July 6 - John Waters - "Finished area B-1 this week with 212 mallards banded."

July 7 - Fred Kreller - "Rocky had a clean record. Not one dead or injured. This area (central Manitoba) much more difficult to work. Cover very dense."

July 14 - Carl Gruener - "Banded 114 mallards in BE-3 last week. Mac made 38 retrieves yesterday in heavy cover, almost phenomenal; tracks birds through brush and heavy going for considerable distances to come back with uninjured birds. Only 1 mortality so far. Rosie got 15 in heavy cover today."

July 21 - Al Niemeyer - "Finished off area B-7 today with a catch of 12 mallards. Banded 19 yesterday in B-17. Will be moving on to The Pas tomorrow."

July 29 - Jerry Stoudt - "Leaving area tomorrow. Got our 500th mallard today!"

The situation was not always the best, however. The dogs had encounters with skunks, badgers, porcupines, and ranch dogs. Some of the dogs received cuts from broken glass, injuries from barbed wire fences, and severe "swimmer's itch" infections. Home for the dogs was a specially compartmented dog trailer. The compartments were kept filled with dry grass and straw, but it was still hard on the dogs to ride in the trailers over rough, back-country roads. After a 100-bird day for a dog, it was not unusual to have to help the dog back into the trailer at night. The dogs got all the food they could eat as often as they wished. Adequate water and lots of dry bedding helped meet their needs. After a good night's sleep they all would be anxious and ready to go the next morning. If veterinary services were needed, the crew leader knew where to go for professional help.

A few of the dogs were credited with catching over 3,000 local mallards in a summer's operation. These dogs received special certificates of recognition signed by Director Janzen for their contribution to the banding program. Two of these dogs (Labrador retrievers) were handled by USFWS Game Management Agents Jim Robinson and Al Niemeyer. I am pleased to say that I worked with two dogs, Boy and Nugget (both golden retrievers) who came close to earning their certificates. And I'm very proud that my Labrador retriever, Jet, earned a certificate.

Which breed of dog was the best? It's impossible to say because the results were associated with the individual dog and not the breed. All kinds of dogs were used, as long as they could qualify. This included mixed breeds, one cocker spaniel, two pointers, three Brittanies, four springer spaniels, six Chesapeakes, eight golden retrievers, and sixteen Labrador retrievers. Most hunting dogs were alike in that they had good noses, soft mouths, and good dispositions. Big, short-haired dogs generally seemed to be best because they had the physical stamina to work heavy cover for long periods. They also dried off faster. The golden and Labrador retrievers had the best records in waterfowl banding operations.

None of the dogs were trained specifically for the banding work. However, it would not be difficult to do so. Basic commands like "no," "fetch," "sit," "stay," "heel," and "come" are adequate to meet most field situations. Perfect obedience is essential. A tough test we always used required the handler to call his dog off from a wing-tied mallard, flopping and running directly in front of the dog; the test required that the dog come directly to heel or sit position. Dogs that responded to whistle and hand signals turned out to be two to three times as efficient as the dogs that had not been so trained. We found that strict obedience saved ducks, time, tempers, and accidents. Once the dogs understood what was expected of them, they would bring ducks back all day.

One of the goldens I was using took his work very seriously. We were scouting the edge of a small slough one day when I noticed him sitting rigidly ahead of me about fifty yards. I called him in twice, but he just sat there. I was angry with his lack of response and went over to give him a few choice words. When I got there I found him holding down a duck with each of his front feet and another bird held tenderly in his mouth! *Good boy!*

Another day I was working with Jim Robinson and his Lab, Rollie. We had returned to the vehicles after working in a large slough and banding our catch. Rollie had been sitting patiently for the last fifteen to twenty minutes on the shady side of the trailer; but he had a strange, unnatural look to his face. Jim went over to Rollie to see what was wrong. Getting right in front of Rollie, he saw the little head of a one-or two-day old "puffball" duckling on one side of Rollie's mouth and just the tips of his paddle feet on the other! Jim took the little

duck from Rollie and returned it to the slough.

There are thousands of stories that could be told about the dogs involved in the banding program. Not all of them would be humorous or have happy endings. One of the best dogs, a Lab, was hit and killed by an auto. Another dog impaled its left front leg and shoulder on a dried, broken willow while in pursuit of a flightless duck. Fortunately this dog lived, though it was out of action for the rest of the summer.

Working with the dogs and crews on the waterfowl breeding grounds in Canada was one of the greatest experiences I have ever had. Never have I been associated with a harder-working, more dedicated group. And as for the dogs — it was probably the most fun they ever had!

Making Like a Bird

James G. King

One of the greatest breakthroughs in the study of birds was the airplane. The airplane allowed humans to operate in the unique aerial realm of birds for the first time and to get the "bird's-eye view" of the world which we share. The airplane has been particularly important to waterfowl management biologists working in the vast and often otherwise inaccessible northern nesting regions beyond the agricultural belt where most people live.

Not any airplane will do. Ornithological airplanes must have good visibility, which means wings above — not below — eye level; they must be capable of relatively slow flights at less than 100 miles per hour; and they must have a flight range of five to six hours. Amphibious planes are most useful, particularly in the north. The best airplane in existence for waterfowl surveys is *Anseriforme* a DeHaviland Beaver modified by Jerry Lawhorn, long-time USFWS mechanic in Anchorage, Alaska. *Anseriforme* is the only Beaver with a Garrett Air Research turboprop 331 engine. This engine, rated at 715 horsepower, provides 265 more horses than the standard Beaver. *Anseriforme* can climb 2,000 feet per minute, and cruise at any speed from 60 to 140, and the plane has superlative water and takeoff characteristics with the normally cumbersome amphibious floats. Special tanks allow the craft to stay aloft for seven hours; special windows provide maximum visibility; a slim engine cowling and lowered instrument panel further enhance visibility; and simplified controls allow wildlife pilots to devote most of their attention to the passing scene. Jerry Lawhorn understands the needs of wildlife pilots better than any other airplane builder. His airplane was christened *Anseriforme* by the waterfowl biologists, who eulogize it. Standard models by DeHaviland, Cessna, and Piper are also much used for ornithology.

Not any pilot will do, either. Most student pilots are taught that speed and altitude are the best friends of small-plane pilots, and they cringe at the thought of low speeds at low altitudes. The wildlife pilot knows that his mechanic is his best friend and that if the plane is well cared for, he can live — even while operating low and slow.

Having solved these airplane problems, neophyte wildlife pilots still find some hurdles to negotiate. Everything looks strange from above — especially birds, which we normally learn to identify from below or at eye level. Visual targets move past with startling speed even when flying slowly. Learning to make bird observations from the air is like learning speed-reading, trick-shooting or other activities that appear impossible at first but are mastered by persistent practice. Good aerial observers, like musicians, know they must practice regularly.

The best aerial ornithologists are pilots. The pilot can adjust automatically for speed, wind, sun, shadow, elevation, and direction, always placing himself where his eyes are most effective — advantages denied passengers no matter how great their experience. Trained wildlife pilots can develop a sense of ecology just as a taxicab driver develops a sense of the pulse of a big city denied to his often-mortified passengers.

Armed with aeronautical and ornithological proficiency, the wildlife pilot is still not ready to provide a scientifically acceptable product. He must have a system, a survey designed with means for recording and analyzing what he sees.

In Alaska, we have used five basic aerial survey systems for birds; (1) the complete census, (2) the random plot census, (3) the line transect survey, (4) random flight method, and (5) the exploratory flight method.

The complete census method works for large, easily seen birds such as eagles and swans that space themselves on territories for nesting. In Alaska we have plotted the location of virtually every trumpeter swan family in the state and every bald eagle nest along some rivers. Changes in population activity for these species can be measured from year to year. We tallied 2,847 trumpeters in Alaska in 1968 and 4,170 in 1975. It was this knowledge that allowed removal of the trumpeter swan from the endangered species list in 1968.

The random plot census can be used where populations are too large and widespread to make a complete census practical. Confidence limits can be calculated for this type census so that, even though the true total is not known exactly, one can fix outside limits within which the true total must occur. For this method, one grids the entire habitat into blocks, selects a sample, and makes a complete search of the sample. This method has been used to calculate the nesting population of bald eagles within the 40,000 square miles of land and water in southeast Alaska, disclosing a total of 7,287 birds, plus or minus 25 percent, in 1978. An equal number of younger eagles not yet ready to nest can easily be distinguished from the adults by their dark heads and tails. The same method was used in 1980 to calculate a breeding population of bald eagles in coastal British Columbia. Other possibilities for use of aerial plot censusing include calculating whistling swan populations and perhaps white-fronted geese in tundra habitats, and surveys of winter birds in coastal habitats.

Line transect surveys have been used to assess duck numbers in North America. Hunting regulations all over the continent have been based on this data for nearly thirty years. In Alaska we use sixteen-mile long segments, with the pilot and observer each recording all sightings within one-eighth mile of each side of the plane. This gives a sample of four square miles for each sixteen-mile segment flown. The total mean number of birds observed can be expanded for the total square miles of habitat in that area. In addition to the spring population of ducks, we get useful data on swans, lesser sandhill cranes, and loons. Line transects have been used to plot distribution of gulls, grebes, and even shorebirds on tundra habitats. This technique has also been used to plot distribution of birds at sea and even the distribution of lakes and ponds.

The random flight method can be used by those who are frequent passengers on flights across bird habitat. It is not necessary to direct the path of the plane so long as the elevation is suitable for seeing birds. Cal Lensink used this method very successfully to calculate weekly changes in the activities of whistling swans on the Yukon Delta. He was able to document spring arrival, nest initiation, peak hatching, brood size, first fledgling, premigration flocking, and departure from the nesting grounds over a period of years simply by recording all swan observations while flying over the area on other business.

The exploratory flight method can be used by observers flying over unfamiliar areas. It is similar to the line transect method, but is not confined to specific straight lines. Based on miles flown and width of observation swath, the observer simply calculates birds seen per square mile and expands the figure to the total square miles of habitat within the type. The pilot should fly over all portions of the sampling area and not linger too long in any one portion. The method, of course, is only valid for birds distributed over the entire

area. We calculated the number of whistling swans (800) and white-fronted geese (50,000) on the 23,000 square miles of Alaska's Arctic Slope this way in 1966. In spite of the lack of statistical credibility, subsequent surveys have shown these to be useful estimates.

USFWS personnel have now been using light airplanes for nearly fifty years. In that time planes have improved enormously, and good maps, voice recorders, cameras, computers, and other equipment have been added to the tools of the trade. Data collected from the air are often scientifically acceptable and crucial for the management of many species, particularly ducks. Even so, one must conclude that we are still in the pioneering phase of aerial wildlife work. We are just beginning to correlate human activity with wildlife distribution through aerial surveys. For instance, we can now correlate clear-cut logging and urban development with bald eagle distribution along the north Pacific Coast. We can correlate development with swan-nesting distribution. More exciting yet, perhaps, is the possibility of correlating movements and abundance of life in the ocean with distribution of the vast hordes of birds that live on and over the northern seas.

The second half-century of wildlife survey flying will doubtless prove even more exciting and productive than the first.

Alligator Airboats

G. Hortin Jensen

The great Bear River Delta in northern Utah is characterized by water and marsh, underlaid with a tabletop expanse of heavy clay soil. A gradient of one foot per mile has allowed the river delta to build slightly higher channel banks. In early days, before man's advent, with a more-or-less adequate river flow guaranteed by drainage from the Wasatch Mountains, the extensive marsh was nurtured. As the water pushed through the marsh and onto the flatlands, it would spread over vast areas, supporting lush growth of pondweeds and other aquatic plants. It is only natural that this area would attract large flights of migratory birds.

The first white people to utilize this area and its natural resources were waterfowl market hunters. They reached the area by walking or rowing boats where possible. These safaris were arduous experiences and required several days.

As time passed, the waterfowl resource of this area was reserved for human recreation, but access was still a barrier. One innovation used was the *Mud Queen*, a long boat with sufficient length and draft to allow mounting of an automobile engine and drive train, including the rear end axles. Propulsion was provided by paddles fixed to wheels that protruded laterally from the sides of the boat. Fenders were required to suppress flying mud and water. This was a cumbersome contraption that required some flotation above the substrate so that the paddle wheels could skim over the water. In shallower water, there was increased drag on the bottom, and eventually the wheels dug in until they could not propel the craft. This vehicle was used for a short period because there was little else available. The Kaille outboard motor, with its extended horizontal propeller drive, and the Wisconsin motor, with a similar horizontal screw drive, were also tried. They had limited success because of their slow locomotion, fouling of the propellers by pondweeds, and still other inadequacies in shallower water.

During the first quarter of this century, waterfowl populations losses due to "duck sickness" (later called botulism) reached epizootic proportions. To alleviate these losses and better manage the existing river flow on the Bear River marshes, the water was impounded in shallow-water units of several thousand acres. Low four- and five-foot dikes backed water as far as three or four miles, with water depths ranging from two feet to a thin feather edge. Approximately half the area of these man-made water impoundments was zero to six inches deep. The miles of dikes allowed access to this delta area in many places, but travel was confined to either motorized vehicles along constructed roads or to boats traveling only the deepest water and existing channels.

Although management of the area attempted to alleviate losses to avian botulism, that malady continued to ravage wild duck populations. To more fully understand the disease, a water-level manipulation experiment at Bear River Refuge was devised. A prerequisite of this study was the ability to traverse all parts of the habitat so that losses of sick and dead birds could be monitored while effects of water manipulation were evaluated.

Cecil S. Williams was assigned to this field project. I was to assist him. Early searches for a solution to the transportation problem had gone in several directions, but poling a boat or slogging by foot and pulling a boat remained the only access to much of the habitat. Our fantasies included multiple model aircraft engines and even air-thrust propulsion driven by a motorcycle engine.

Our frustrations culminated in a letter to Washington, D.C. specifying the capabilities of the boat required. The varied environment and the nature of the work made it essential for us to have a boat that could be operated in the field and also loaded off and on a trailer by one man. It would also need to carry men and equipment equally well over

Air thrust boats make ideal transportation on shallow waters and can even cross small mud flats. These boats proved indispensible in survey, banding, and waterfowl rescue work. Here C. S. Williams is at the controls at Bear River Refuge in 1946. USFWS photo by W. F. Kubicheck.

marshes, meadows, and mud flats covered by a few inches of water, as well as over deeper water areas filled with aquatic plants, *and* cover thirty or forty miles of each of the aforementioned environments in a day. Washington's reply to this request was a letter expressing grave doubts that we could accomplish any of the specifics. To cap it all, we were facetiously advised to get an alligator from Louisiana, saddle up, and ride the critter on our botulism studies.

As we were getting little help from Washington, Clarence Cottam, USFWS assistant director, gave carte blanche for anything we might like to try. The prerequisite of a small, versatile boat was still a necessity if our research plans were to proceed. Our thoughts were finally turned to small aircraft engines.

It was 1943. Because of the war, availability of most materials was a problem. An aircraft engine was located through a pilot instructor at an airport near Salt Lake City. This unairworthy, forty-horsepower Continental aircraft engine was purchased for $99.50. At this time, open-market government purchases were limited to $100.

With some trepidation, this engine was mounted on an old twelve-foot, flat-bottomed, duraluminum boat. Other bureau personnel were skeptical. Upon seeing the mounted engine, one viewer asked, "Who is going to wear the silver wings?"

Not knowing what success this combination would produce, we immediately tried the craft in the shallow water — even without directional controls. By sitting up front and using a canoe paddle for steering, we could manage reasonable directional control. Our spirits whetted by partial success, we were eager to complete the product.

We encountered other obstacles. As biologists, we were denied access to the government shop, with its tools and the refuge mechanic. This necessitated further work. At the local blacksmith's shop, we fabricated a propeller guard and a rudder with front steering and throttle control.

Materials came from assorted odd places. The iron hoop for the propeller guard had once been part of a large, wooden buggy wheel. The screen to cover it was found at a used-car wrecking business, and installed with pulleys and a rope to a combination air-and-water rudder. Additional flotation and lateral stability was provided by adding pontoons along each side. The improvised air-thrust boat was now ready for a trial run. This occurred in the spring of 1943 on Unit 5 of the Bear River Refuge.

The design proved even more versatile than had been anticipated, exceeding our expectations or even our fondest dreams. We could maintain any speed from trolling velocity to thirty-five miles per hour, moving over all types of terrain from a muddy feather edge to a deep marsh choked with aquatic vegetation.

We were so enthralled that we extended our trial run into the moonlight, probing through each and every challenge to the boat. Unknown to us, a police search and rescue team was looking for us. We finally made it home well after dark. We had constructed our own Louisiana alligator, so we christened it *Alligator I*. This makeshift, air-thrust boat performed admirably, insuring that the botulism research plans could go forth. For this innovation to marsh travel, Cecil S. Williams and I were cited by the Secretary of the Interior.

Alligator I served us well during the summer of 1943, but it was imperative that this first boat be replaced. We contacted Emil Johnson of Salt Lake City, who had built the hull of this first boat. At that time, he was the only person building small aluminum boats in the United States, and only then as a hobby. His boat-shaped bottoms and keels, rolled gunwales, streamlined transoms, and outboard and inboard motor recesses were indeed works of art carefully shaped in aluminum. His business had been brought to a halt by World War II when his metal workers left for more lucrative wages with the military, his materials went to those who had the highest priority, and even his Doberman pinscher went to the K-9 Corps. He had little left other than the option to retire. Late in the fall of 1943, Emil Johnson agreed to come to

Brigham City, Utah, and take a ride in our new mode of boat travel.

On a cool, blustery day in November, we clambered into *Alligator I* and took off from shore in Willard Spur. We hadn't gone more than fifty yards when Mr. Johnson motioned to be taken back to shore. He had seen enough to declare that he would build us a new aluminum boat. It would be up to us to get priorities from the Office of Price Administration to purchase the needed materials.

Within the hour Emil Johnson had returned to Salt Lake, but early the next morning he returned to Brigham City. He had committed himself to us, but he wanted our permission to build a boat for himself before constructing a boat for the USFWS. Thus, two aluminum boats designed for air-thrust were built in Salt Lake City during the winter and spring of 1944. Emil Johnson even flew to Denver to obtain an aircraft engine, a scarce commodity. We were able to obtain another forty-horsepower engine for the government boat.

Duraluminum was used to provide lightness and strength wherever practicable. These crafts were approximately fourteen feet long and fifty-two to fifty-six inches wide. For transporting cross country a special trailer was designed. Rear rollers easily permitted the boat to slip backward into the water and to be driven back on the trailer for transport.

Working with a craftsman like Emil Johnson and helping him work with metal was a revealing and interesting experience in itself. As I was hired as a biologist, this was hardly the type of work I was used to. To salve my conscience, I took annual leave and worked three weeks with Emil Johnson while the government boat was being built. It was exciting to observe skilled hands manipulate metal into required shapes. At this time, of course, hand labor was all that was available. Many rapid but light hammer blows produced the desired result, while one strong blow only resulted in a deep dent or a bend in the metal. I recall that the cowling across the front of the airboat was curved in two directions. Emil asked me how long I thought it took him to make it. Knowing how deftly we had formed

A duck trap called the "decoy" is used at the Delta Waterfowl Research Station to capture waterfowl for banding. The concept for this trap originated in Holland. USFWS photo by Rex Gary Schmidt.

other members, I estimated about forty-five minutes. To my amazement, he replied that it had taken the better part of two days. Gradually, our new air-thrust boat, *Alligator II*, took shape and reached completion in the spring of 1944.

With this new means of rapid water and marsh transportation, we were able to accomplish much waterfowl management work not previously possible. All parts of the habitat were accessible in minutes instead of hours or days. All field studies in research and management benefitted enormously, including nesting studies, plant studies, collection of botulism victims, banding, censusing of waterfowl, and others. The new boats aided all efforts to learn more about our aquatic environments.

For example, at Bear River Refuge in 1944, the management had a request to trap Canada geese for transplanting to midwestern

refuges. This was previously done with unlimited "foot soldiers" from the Civilian Conservation Corps acting as drivers to encircle the flightless geese. By wading through shallow water, the drivers could herd the geese into the trap; but it was a time-consuming operation. We were asked to assist with our airboat. On the appointed date, the refuge personnel had not assembled the materials necessary for the trap and leads. We went afield to see what could be done, not knowing how we were going to operate.

We circled the geese in the shallow water. While attempting to move them, we came upon a straggler slowed down by the profuse growth of pondweeds. It was easy to step out of the airboat and capture it. We soon learned that we could move in, cause geese to dive, and quickly catch them. We were able to catch the fifty geese required of the refuge in less than an hour. Needless to say, we didn't

Air thrust boats helped make a good catch of mallards and pintails at this marsh near Brooks, Alberta, in 1951. USFWS photo by R. W. Hines.

need the trap materials, just holding crates. Thus a new method for trapping flightless geese was discovered. For the several years that geese were needed for transplant, the request always came to Bear River Refuge, since we could readily supply the geese.

Since that time, breeding geese and their goslings have been banded at Bear River each season. It is possible for one airboat operator and two people on foot to catch 100 to 200 geese in one day for banding. This method of catching geese continues to be the standard procedure for banding geese on Utah's shallow-water federal and state refuges.

We also found it paid to set large and small nets made of aluminum rods, cotton netting, and poultry netting. This was done during the summer flightless period of ducks and geese in the shallow, weed-choked water that is usually their home. Drivers were positioned and repositioned by the airboat. This technique allowed us to congregate and trap waterfowl for management purposes. Over the years, thousands of ducks and geese have been caught for banding on the Canadian breeding grounds. Properly done, it is one of the most cost-efficient methods of banding waterfowl.

The versatility of the air-thrust boat led to other unique experiences. During the 1950s, many of the game management agents, I among them, were equipped with the new Ford six-cylinder automobile. Some of these agents were assigned to duty in Canada. As happens in field work, equipment can fail, and parts and repairs are needed. When our car failed, the field crew was at first stymied. Ford sixes were not found in Canada, so repair parts were unavailable. Resourceful people among us found the answer. The airboat was used to push the car from southern Manitoba to North Dakota for repairs. Farmers along the road, hearing the aircraft engine, would look skyward for a low-flying aircraft. They were startled to see a car being propelled through the Turtle Mountains by an air-thrust boat. It was a little slow at first, but when momentum was gained it was possible to push a car approximately thirty-five miles per hour this way.

On another day, Canadian Highway 21 around Buffalo Lake became a quagmire after heavy showers. Any car would have problems on that road on such a day. The pickup with our airboat in tow was in trouble. With little rear traction, the vehicle slid from side to side, hardly moving forward. We finally got stuck when tire ruts were filled with water over six inches deep. With conditions as they were on this Sunday afternoon, there was little chance of anyone coming by to help us. Our one hope was for an assist by air-thrust from the trailed boat. We soon found there was sufficient power to ease the truck along. In fact, there was power in surplus. By adding the traction of the truck wheels and careful manipulation of the throttle of the aircraft engine, we could maintain directional stability and move along this road until we reached improved conditions.

Such were these early days of flyway work — interesting, exciting, and never a dull moment. Challenged to new endeavors, we had the best days of waterfowl field work, which to me will never be recaptured.

Winter Productivity Appraisals

John J. Lynch

Life is a wonderful experience, but one that no living thing has been known to survive. So it is no wonder that biologists, including flyway biologists, are keenly interested in reproduction. Reproduction is needed to balance out the annual losses.

Flyway biologists, then, can be difficult to find in summertime; they're likely off in a remote corner of planet earth observing the nesting of migratory birds.

With some birds, however, the biologists have found it difficult to judge the success of the hatch — this, despite being camped right in the middle of nesting colonies. These especially problematic birds include geese, swans, brants, some of the long-lived sea ducks, and cranes. All need to be twenty-four months old before reaching sexual maturity. With these birds, unlike most waterfowl, the biologists began to realize that their nesting ground observations were highly incomplete since they were looking only at birds old enough to nest. That raised the question of where were the birds not old enough to nest.

Snow geese are an example, one we came face-to-face with in 1940 while working with snow geese, brant, and whistling swans in the Northwest Territories. We were suddenly struck with an idea that shouldn't have seemed so novel, but was. Why not go down to the wintering grounds to observe these birds? That way we'd see not only the sexually

John Lynch lectures on winter appraisal and productivity of the lesser snow geese at the Rockefeller Refuge in Louisiana.

mature birds with their young, but also the nonbreeding yearlings.

The case of the whooping crane offered a precedent. Winter surveys of whooping cranes began in the mid-1930s in south Texas at Aransas National Wildlife Refuge; at the time, no one knew where whooping cranes nested, so spring or summer observations were out of the question. I also had the personal precedent of having made some observations in 1936 of the greater snow geese that spent the winter along portions of the Atlantic coast. I found I could clearly distinguish the young produced the previous nesting season. In 1937, when I moved down to the Gulf Coast, I found I could make the same distinction with the lesser snow goose, in both the white and dark phase (then called snow goose and blue goose). The plumage of the young from the previous nesting was remarkably different from that of the adults.

With that background, we set up plans to survey the nesting of some birds, not during the summer nesting time, but on the wintering grounds. We began what came to be called the "winter appraisals of nest success" first with the lesser snow geese that spent the winter in that region, primarily in Louisiana and along the Texas coast.

The technique worked. We could see the young from the previous nesting season in the wintering flocks. We could also see the adult-looking birds, a group we knew included not only the parents but that group of adult-looking birds that were sexually immature the previous summer. We had another little bonus, in the form of birds we saw that had not spent the summer in North America; these were geese from the Old World, perhaps from Siberia. In those days, we had few ways of knowing what was going on with waterfowl in the Arctic regions of the Old World. For that matter, the top side of North America included many areas we couldn't get to. The new survey method had enormous promise.

Unfortunately, our nation got involved in World War II before we could make much progress with winter surveys. But after 1947, we went back to appraisals of nesting success along the Gulf Coast wintering areas. We began to reap additional benefits. The winter snow goose surveys produced not only ratios of young to older birds, but observations of what looked like families of geese.

We eventually worked out the details of the winter appraisals, though we had help. Flyway biologist Hortin Jensen made a special trip to Louisiana to see our procedure; of course, we reciprocated by going to California with Hortin to try our winter appraisals on the lesser snow geese that spent the winter there. Then, we were sure, we were seeing snow geese that had spent the summer in Siberia, although we couldn't tell what percentage of the snows we saw were Siberian birds. Nonetheless, we had a feeling for what the productivity had been for all those birds born in the Northern Hemisphere that spent the winter in North America.

We then branched east, thanks to flyway biologist Chuck Evans and flyway representative Ed Addy, to determine the productivity of the greater snows that wintered along the Atlantic coast. And, thanks primarily to the efforts of Bob Singleton of the Texas Parks and Wildlife Commission, we started getting good readings on productivity among the white-faced and specklebellies that spent the winter along the Gulf Coast. Subsequently, with help from Hortin Jensen, we had similar information for the specklebellies that spent the winter in the Pacific Flyway. The superb work of Bob Jones made it possible to get information on the black brant that spent the summer in Siberia and wintered along the coast of California and the western coast of Mexico. Before long, we tackled the swans. Many more birds remained to be studied with this procedure.

These winter appraisals enabled us to keep posted on the nesting success of birds that would have been difficult to study otherwise. We learned what we needed to know, namely whether or not these birds were cranking out enough young to make up for the losses their population had suffered the previous year.

The conclusion of a successful drive-trapping operation that netted over 1,100 mallards, plus many blue-winged and green-winged teal, and gadwall. This marsh and adjoining lake are near Swift Current, Saskatchewan. USFWS photo by Rex Gary Schmidt.

Duck Banding Methods

Henry M. Reeves

Coincident with the establishment of the aerial waterfowl survey program on the breeding grounds was the development of a large-scale banding program. Although aerial surveys provided an insight into the relative duck production over the expanses of prairie and parkland (the transition zone between the prairies and the forest), information from banding was needed to determine harvest areas affected by differences in annual production. Ultimately, the information would enable biologists to estimate the relative size of the fall flights of ducks to each of the flyways, and thus serve as a basis for developing the annual hunting regulations, particularly season lengths and bag limits, by flyways.

The duck trapping operation on the breed-

ing ground essentially went through three phases. Initially, attention was focused on moulting lakes because of the large numbers of ducks which could be easily captured. Between mid and late summer, drakes, followed by females, vacate production habitats to moult at large, relatively permanent lakes. During the postnuptial moult, ducks lose all their primaries (the large, outer wing feathers) and become flightless for several weeks. The same marshes are often used year after year, and ducks from tens and possibly hundreds of miles gather on them in large numbers. Some large moulting areas possibly attract upwards of a hundred-thousand ducks some years. More than ten-thousand moulting ducks have been banded during a single drive. Participants in these early drives often speak of concentrated moulters breaking through, or surmounting, the trap leads in their efforts to escape capture.

Most of the ducks caught by the drive

method are either flightless adults (moulters, sometimes called "flappers" because of their wing flapping to expedite escape) or ducklings which have not yet fledged, that is, gained their flight feathers and power of flight. Only ducklings older than two weeks of age are sought because they are large enough to retain bands. A funnel trap with a V-shaped opening is staked in the water or on the shoreline in a site conducive to duck capture. Often the trap is partially concealed in or behind emergent vegetation so it is not seen by the ducks until very near the end of the drive. "Leads" or "wings" of chicken wire or nylon mesh, held vertically by rods, are extended outward from the trap entrance to intercept and guide the ducks into the trap. The angle between the leads approximates ninety degrees so that the ducks naturally swim toward the trap, rather than fight the lead by trying to penetrate it. The lengths of leads vary by the size of the marsh, its configuration, and vegetation. Ideally, the ducks should be well inside the line between the outer ends of the two leads before they realize they are about to be contained. The trap may be preassembled or, particularly if a large capture is anticipated, constructed on the spot. Two or more assembled traps may sometimes be placed side by side. The trap is erected as quickly and quietly as possible to avoid scaring the ducklings from the marsh.

When capturing broods, it is important that crew members patrol the marsh edge, preferably from vantage points that insure the ducklings remain on the wetland. Otherwise the ducklings, especially mallards and pintails, may escape by fleeing overland.

Once the trap is erected, crew members vacate the trap site and join their comrades at the far end of the pothole or marsh so that the concentration of ducks is between them and the trap. The crew forms a line across the marsh, with members evenly apart, and advances upon the ducklings with much noise and disturbance, carrying dip nets for capturing straggler ducks. At this point, the activity resembles a Chinese New Year's celebration — or a national political convention!

The outer members of the line advance ahead of the other members to turn in those ducklings attempting to escape laterally. The fanfare increases as the ducks approach the lead and the trap entrance. However, care is taken not to stampede the ducks, as they will sometimes turn upon reaching the lead or trap and flap or dive back between the crew members to freedom. Only experience tells the crew where to place the trap and how persistently to drive the ducks. If all goes as planned, the ducks swim or waddle through the V-opening — not to freedom but confinement.

Although very large numbers of moulting ducks can be banded quickly and cheaply, the resulting recovery data has a major limitation in that the marked ducks cannot be attributed to specific breeding areas. The breeding area could be many miles from the moulting area where they were captured.

Consequently, emphasis shifted to banding flightless young on natal marshes, with special attention placed on the mallard. During the 1950s, banding crews were assigned to the Dakotas, Montana, and the three prairie provinces of Canada to band flightless mallards as well as other ducklings captured coincidentally with mallards. Crews were usually assigned annual banding quotas of 100 mallard ducklings per degree block of latitude and longitude. In southern Saskatchewan such a block measured about seventy by forty-five miles.

The crews, usually composed of a leader and four or five crew members, assembled in Regina in early July to receive briefings and pick up trapping equipment and bands. The crew leader was usually a U.S. game management agent who had previous experience in drive-trapping ducks, often in the same assigned area. Other USFWS and state conservation agency biologists or technicians rounded out the crew. Banding crews were frequently assisted on a daily basis by Ducks Unlimited biologists, provincial biologists, law enforcement officers, and occasionally sportsmen and farm youths.

Crews were often assigned two vehicles, one of which was often a pickup truck, and

A roundup for banding yielded this gathering of several species and age classes.

sometimes a trailer for carrying banding equipment. Other equipment and often a boat was carried on cartop carriers. A favorite boat was the seventeen-foot Grumman aluminum, square-stern canoe. It was easy to load and transport, carried a heavy payload, maneuvered easily on the water, and could be powered with a small outboard engine of five to seven horsepower. Major banding equipment included traps, aluminum rods anchoring the traps for holding the leads upright, chicken wire or lengths of nylon netting for leads, several sizes of bands, and pliers. The equipment was organized so that it could be quickly unloaded for use.

Banding crews usually operated every day, the only limitation being the rains which often made secondary roads impassable. The day began immediately after an early breakfast and often continued until dusk, which in midsummer on the prairies is often as late as 9:00 P.M. Crew members usually had specific assignments in the banding operation (note keeper; speciator, sexer, and ager; trap placer; and so on), but tasks were often rotated so that every member became experienced in all parts of the operation.

Crew members typically came from diverse geographical locations. For example, my crew in 1956 had members from Canada, Illinois, Louisiana, and Ohio, and I was at that time assigned in Texas. Members were young, strong, and highly motivated. The working conditions — slogging through marshes, wading in deep water, handling dirty trapping equipment, swatting mosquitoes, and freeing vehicles from mud holes — were often arduous and dirty. Nonetheless, many crew members reflect upon their banding days on the Canadian prairies as among their most cherished memories.

The greatest compliment that a crew leader could bestow was to permit a crew member to select the location for placing the trap. Not that a properly placed trap would always result in a large catch — but a poorly placed trap usually resulted in total failure or a poor catch of ducklings. The major challenges were first to locate substantial numbers of trappable ducks on a wetland that could be effectively worked by the particular crew and its equipment, properly placing the trap, successfully executing the drive, and quickly banding the ducklings with minimal mortality

Ducks, mostly pintails, in a holding pen after a trapping operation on Johnston Lake, Saskatchewan.
USFWS photo by Rex Gary Schmidt.

or injury.

Banding crews normally started in the southern portion of their assigned areas and followed the hatch progressively northward. Sometimes crews retrapped areas worked in previous years; but changing water and habitat conditions and changing duck densities sometimes caused areas excellent the previous year to be worthless for trapping the current year. Sometimes USFWS pilots provided information on potential trapping sites. As a last resort, the crew leader was forced to use maps, his general understanding of the terrain, and intuition to locate suitable drive trapping marshes. Two or three drives were usually made in a day, but sometimes a rather large area, lengthy drive, and sizable catch could consume the whole day. Our crew usually would not chance a drive unless prospects were good for capturing at least a hundred ducklings. The overall banding assignment usually lasted about five or six weeks.

The various species of ducks differed considerably in the ease with which they could be captured. Mallards were usually catchable if they could be kept on the marsh; but if they had opportunity to flee overland or hide in up-land cover, they quickly did so. Pintails were fairly easy to catch, although they also sometimes fled from the wetland if given a chance. Wigeons were also fairly easy to drive and capture. On the other hand, shovelers and gadwalls were notoriously obstinate, frequently turning near the lead or trap to flap through or dive past the advancing crew. Many a bander has been stared down and outmaneuvered by a gadwall that firmly resolved it would not be captured that day! Diving duck young were generally more difficult to capture, partly because they were found in deeper marshes where the logistics of placing traps and leads were more difficult. Divers could seldom be driven ashore into traps. Typically, the traps had to be fairly well concealed but with open water visible beyond. It was not unusual to have potentially catchable divers vanish by the time the drivers reached the trap. Of all the ducks, blue-winged teal were clearly the easiest to catch. Blue-wing broods often quietly watched crews erect the trap and leads, and then were easily guided into the trap with little fanfare. Crews usually ignored coots, even though they were abundant among duck broods. Generally,

Drive-trapping moulting ducks at Whitewater Lake, Manitoba, involved the cooperative efforts of fieldmen from the Manitoba Game Branch, Delta Waterfowl Research Station, the Bell Museum, Ducks Unlimited and the USFWS. They are: (standing, left to right) Jim Huston, Bob McCabe, Pete Ward, Lew Rowinski, Walter Breckenridge, Walter Crissey, George Brakhage, Chuck Southwick; (kneeling) Nick Neufeldt, Bill Elder, Lyle Sowls, Gene Bossenmaier, Keith Story, Art Hawkins. USFWS photo.

coots easily avoided capture by diving. On a marsh containing several hundred coots, it was not unusual to fail to catch a single bird. This usually pleased the crews because coots have very, very bad dispositions and fearlessly peck and scratch if held in hand.

Drive-trapping ducks is a highly chancy exercise. In time it became a compelling challenge to the crew leader and members alike. Better ways of outsmarting ducks, including unusual trap placements and equipment improvements were tried. Each concentration of ducklings on a marsh offered its own challenge as well as opportunity, and feelings of elation after a good catch were too often intermingled with days of frustration when few ducks were captured.

Special care was taken to avoid injury or mortality to ducks. Occasionally, unexpectedly large numbers would be captured in small traps. Crews then quickly divided the catch by placing excess birds in hastily constructed pens on land. Traps containing ducks were bodily moved ashore so that the birds would

remain dry and banding could be performed more quickly and safely. Bands were sometimes arranged for use by species and sex to expedite banding. For example, a "string" of 100 might be reserved for use on only male mallard ducklings, and another for female mallard ducklings. In later years, preopened bands on plastic tubes eliminated the need to individually open each band, speeding the process. During the era of preseason duckling banding, several hundred-thousand mallards were marked, along with tens of thousands of ducklings of other species.

Days off (rainy days) were used to check and repair equipment; service vehicles; prepare reports; plan the next few day's operations; and tend to personal needs, especially washing clothes and shopping. Most crews remained afield all day and consumed monstrous lunches of cheese, lunchmeats, salads, tea, coffee, and water at midday following a drive.

Normally we sought to obtain landowner permission before entering privately owned land. In many instances, however, the owner did not live nearby, or the ownership could not be readily determined. The main consideration in entering upon private lands was to be sure that gates were closed to prevent escape of livestock.

The drive capture program for banding ducklings wound down as the desired 300 duckling quotas in "latilong" (latitude-longitude) blocks were achieved. Recoveries from the bandings continued to be reported from successive hunting seasons, and eventually the band recovery file was available for analysis. These data were summarized in reports of extensive mallard study undertaken by the Service in the 1970s. The analysis gave much valuable insight into the distribution and derivation of the harvest, survival rates, and other characteristics of North American mallards. Of paramount value was the increased ability to relate changes in breeding populations and production to harvest areas during the following fall and winter. After the termination of the drive-trapping phase, banding shifted to the third phase, the capture of flying young at bait traps (a subject beyond the scope of this discussion).

In retrospect, our days spent trapping ducks on the Canadian prairies are fondly remembered and cherished.

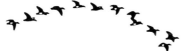

Diving Duck Banding

James G. King

Waterfowl banding began in Alaska, as far as I know, with Olaus Murie's work on the Yukon Delta in 1924. Banding was sporadic until the arrival of USFWS biologists after World War II. Aerial surveys became standardized in the early 1950s, showing substantial numbers of canvasback and a major population of scaup nesting in Alaska.

As the Alaska waterfowl program began to develop under Hank Hansen, he was urged to band diving ducks, particularly scaup, which loom rather large in the bag of some states. Banding crews of three or four people boated into the accessible wetland habitats of interior Alaska, but the results were meager. Goldeneyes and buffleheads we could catch, but somehow the scaup and canvasbacks evaded our small traps.

The breakthrough came in 1958 when we flew some chicken wire into Old Albert Lake near Tetlin. Hank, Bob Kelly, Amos David, and I built a wire trap in two feet of water adjacent to a little point and hung a 300-foot net lead off shore. We drove the flightless ducks with small canoes, making a sweep across the two-mile long lake. As we approached the trap, a mass of fowl were evident ahead. Unlike numerous past efforts, this time they hit the trap dead center. Birds began diving in all directions, fighting the net and portaging across the point. As we rushed in to close the trap entrance, it was clear we had a good catch. The surface of the water seemed largely covered with Barrow's goldeneyes, but a few canvasbacks, scaups, and wigeons were also evident.

Using a dip net we unloaded the trap, putting the birds into burlap sacks. We lost some birds when a hole developed in the trap. The air was soon full of flying water from the diving birds, rain began to fall, and we were all soaked by the time the trap was empty. We finally had some fifty sacks of ducks laid out in the woods. In the frenzy of emptying the trap, no one had much of an idea what our catch consisted of, other than the obvious goldeneyes. It was a pleasure to discover that the first sack held more than half lesser scaup. When the second and third sacks disclosed similar results, the level of excitement among the crew increased. A patter of jokes and speculations developed in spite of the steady rain. Our final tally of over 500 birds, more than half of which were lesser

This tent field camp in Alaska is practical in the drier regions, in contrast to the wet coastal areas. Lloyd Davis, a long-time Eskimo employee, peers from the mess tent. Photo by H. A. Hansen.

scaups, caused a high level of elation among the banders. It was a soaked, chilled, but happy crew that flew back to camp in the little Piper Pacer. We had, in one drive, caught more scaup and canvasback than had ever before been banded in Alaska. A memorable day for us all.

Recoveries of bands from these birds proved most stimulating. Tetlin scaup were shot by hunters in all four flyways, particularly the Mississippi Flyway, and canvasback bands were returned from both the Pacific and Atlantic flyways. This proved a great inducement for more banding.

We continued to perfect the techniques for banding diving ducks both near Tetlin for several years and later on the Yukon Flats, where the great waterfowl production areas were threatened with flooding by the proposed Rampart Dam on the Yukon River.

The law enforcement agents largely took over the banding work, and float planes were assigned to the project, leaving us with no need for the river boats. The use of float planes for carrying traps and canoes was a real emancipation. Crews were able to select the most optimum sites and reach them without the time-consuming and exhausting process of boating and portaging. The planes were used in the air to spot good locations and haul wire, nets, and canoes to the site. On the water they transported spruce poles and drove ducks. Agent John Klingbeil, with a

knowledge of fisheries traps, improved our duck trap designs. Agent Fred Robards, working with a Seattle boat builder, developed a twelve-foot fiberglass skiff with five independent, buoyant sections; these could be stacked like camp dishes for transport in a four-passenger Cessna 180 float plane, then assembled in five minutes into a craft capable of twenty miles per hour with a ten-horse motor. Agent Neil Argy, with agricultural know-how, developed a sheet metal funnel for sacking ducks as they were removed from the trap. We learned to load bands on welding rods for easy use, to make mauls from birch trees for pounding spruce poles into muddy lake bottoms while standing in the sectional boat, and to design traps that could hold a herd of moose or eight tons of ducks paddling vigorously with 20,000 little feet against our wire barriers.

The duck drives for divers on large lakes were a particular challenge. If we got close enough to see divers clearly, the would be diving under the drive line-up and escaping. On numerous occasions we would arrive at the trap to find that only a few grebes and goldeneyes had been outwitted. After such a drive, the trip back to camp tended to be silent, followed by a silent supper after which the crew tended to take little walks alone before bed. Though only occasionally expressed, the implication of the silence of each individual was that somehow his teammates had let him down. By contrast, a mood of conviviality followed a successful drive, and a jolly evening round the campfire was assured. After one unsuccessful drive we returned a day later to find a muskrat had built a home in the entrance funnel of our trap, providing himself with a network of entrance and departure tunnels around the wire. Someone suggested how much dumber ducks are than muskrats, which led to further conclusions about USFWS employees who could be outwitted by even the dumber ducks.

We learned to combat the drive problems to advising duck drivers that they should stay in line and watch the birds ahead with binoc-

Diving ducks caught at Ohtig Lake on the Arctic Circle during feasibility studies for the Rampart Dam.
USFWS photo by J. G. King.

ulars. Drivers were told to watch each other and to recognize that, if they saw someone who appeared to be out of place, he was probably having a problem and needed help, rather than that he was "fouling up." Eventually, we perfected the act of driving ducks on the water and placing traps so that we could make a clean sweep of all the divers on a lake.

Hank Hansen, under whose guidance the banding was conducted, rationed out bands in numbers he considered consistent with the ability of his crews. Herein was a challenge not to be taken lightly, and it became the goal of banding crews to use up all their bands so they could call Hank for resupply.

The payoff for our diving duck trapping system came at Ohtig Lake in 1962. Largest of the lowland lakes on the Yukon Flats, Ohtig Lake is about three and a half miles long and covers some five square miles. Though bisected by the Arctic Circle, summer water temperatures reach 75° F. Ohtig means "duck lake" in the local Athabaskan dialect, and Indians from several hundred miles around formerly congregated there to drive flightless ducks. When I asked an old Indian at Chalkyitsik how many ducks we could catch for banding at Ohtig, he shrugged and said, "All you want." We estimated more than thirty thousand ducks of fifteen species spent the summer there.

The 1962 trap was 100 feet wide and 300 feet long, with a 700-foot lead. There were 216 hand-cut spruce poles in the trap, and it took seven men four days to build. It took nine hours to drive the lake, using three float planes taxiing on the water and four boats. The catch was in excess of 10,000 birds. In the next three days, 5,050 ducks were banded, mostly lesser scaup, and 578 previously banded birds were recorded. Having met all quotas and exhausted all extra bands Hank had on hand, we released the rest of the birds. The entire project required 488 man-hours: 193 for trap building, 67 for driving, and 228 for banding. Ultimately, we processed 11.5 ducks per each man-hour of effort. The old Indian was right; we had all we wanted, and then some. Perhaps, too, there was some relief as well as triumph in finding Hank could not provide more bands.

Duck driving, led by agent Ray Tremblay, continued for several more years, then was dropped. More than 30,000 scaup had been banded since the gala day at Old Albert Lake, and the obligation to band scaup had been settled to everyone's satisfaction.

Information from banding, of course, is useful to management agencies in determining where and how heavily ducks are being harvested by hunters so that seasons and bag limits can be adjusted to safe levels. Some special scaup seasons in the Mississippi Flyway resulted from information derived from our banding.

The flood of duck bands we sent south from Alaska in those years produced some other interesting repercussions. As nearly every state (forty-three, I think) received some Alaskan ducks, it was not surprising that virtually every game department in America went on record opposing construction of the Rampart Dam because it would have a direct cost in terms of ducks lost for all. It now seems unlikely the Rampart Dam will ever be built. The interest in Alaskan ducks generated by the Rampart conflict continued, resulting in the establishment by the Carter administration of millions of acres of great new waterfowl refuges in Alaska at Tetlin, the Yukon Flats, and elsewhere.

During one of our big drives on Takslesluk Lake near Bethel, a crew led by agent Mil Zahn banded 1,784 old squaw ducks, 34 of which were recovered by Russian hunters in Siberia. This evidence of North America producing waterfowl for Russian consumption, balanced by their production of snow geese that we hunt, provided additional important impetus for the United States-Soviet Migratory Bird Treaty recently signed by our countries.

The value of diving duck banding in Alaska now seems obvious. However, it was not always evident to us. There were the cold and wet days, and others with ninety-degree-plus heat. It seemed we always had to contend with clouds of mosquitoes. Bears sometimes damaged our camps and equipment. Moose sometimes knocked down traps. Outboards and airplanes malfunctioned. There were days when even the most exhausting and carefully planned drive produced no ducks at all. There were a few injuries and some personality conflicts. And there were many, many work days that lasted on and on into the evening as the midnight sun dipped to the northern horizon and then began to

rise again. The USFWS can be justly proud of the several dozen people who participated in these projects. They served well the cause of conservation, the American public, and the waterfowl resource.

A Career Hard to Beat

Rossalius C. Hanson

For a person trained in biology who likes to fly, a career with the USFWS is hard to beat. I speak from experience. During thirty-one years with the Service, I logged 15,000 hours of flight time, travelling well over a million miles in assignments under three divisions (refuges, law enforcement, and migratory bird management). In pursuit of these various activities, I saw much of North America and had my share of memorable experiences, some of which I will share with you in the following pages.

After five and a half years of service as a navy pilot in World War II, I joined the Service in 1947 as a district refuge manager on the Upper Mississippi River Wildlife and Fish Refuge, stationed at LaCrosse, Wisconsin. My basic equipment was a boat, a five-horse outboard motor, and a pair of hip boots. Airplane duty came a year later, when flyway biologist Bob Smith and I picked up two surplus military J-3 Piper Cubs and returned them to LaCrosse. After it was modified for civilian use, I flew one of the planes to California — no mean feat in one of those slow, short-ranged and underpowered puddle-jumpers. It took two tries to stagger over the Rockies using the lowest pass I could find.

In California, I was assigned as pilot, based at the Sacramento refuge near Willows. My duties varied from censusing antelope on Sheldon National Wildlife Refuge to counting trumpeter swans in Yellowstone National Park. Although I had graduated to a Stinson L-5 by that time, I discovered, after some close calls, that a more powerful plane was needed for flying in mountainous areas.

At Yellowstone, for example, the airstrip from which we operated was located at 6,650 feet elevation, and some of the ponds to be surveyed were up to 9,000 feet, well above the limits at which the L-5 operated efficiently and safely. Also the L-5 was quick to ice up, as Dr. Ray Erickson and I discovered one day when we were counting muskrat houses on Malheur National Wildlife Refuge.

In 1951, I had a choice between flying a new 125 horsepower Super Cub outfitted to plant rice and spray undesired plants, or returning to LaCrosse as a law enforcement pilot-agent. I chose the latter. From then on, the rest of my career was tied closer to flyways and waterfowl management.

In August of 1952, I had just moved my family to LaCrosse when I was instructed to fly to North Dakota to combat depredation by ducks. The damage that field-feeding waterfowl can cause to agricultural crops is discussed in detail elsewhere in this publication. My work involved chasing the birds from the field being damaged and herding the ducks by aircraft. All USFWS pilots (refuges, enforcement, flyway biologists, and animal damage control) were conscripted to fight depredations when the situation got bad enough. Geese also were herded from grain fields. They usually responded better to our efforts than did ducks.

Herding from the air consisted of flushing the birds, usually from a swathed grain field, and driving them back to the refuge, where grain had been trucked in and dumped in a conspicuous place. On some refuges grain was grown for the birds and swathed to make it more attractive, thus holding the hungry birds away from the fields of nearby farmers.

To flush the ducks we buzzed the field and tossed out a bomb designed to burst before hitting the ground. Two other possibilities were that it might go off in the cockpit, or go off after hitting the ground and start a fire, alienating farmers already antagonistic toward ducks and those who sponsored them. Luckily, I escaped both of these alarming possibilities. Usually the pilot carried no passengers on herding flights because of the potential hazards, such as hitting ducks or stalling out on sharp turns and spinning in low to the ground. Two USFWS employees had lost their lives just two years previously when their plane stalled at a low altitude and went into a spin.

After the plane flushed the ducks, a 180-degree turn was made, giving the birds time to climb. The pilot then flew underneath the flock, boosting the birds still higher and pushing them toward the desired destination. This sounds easy, but sometimes the birds behaved erratically, seemingly intent on ramming the plane. Usually the birds outmaneuvered the plane, and collisions were fortunately rare. With persistent aerial pursuit and help from personnel on the ground who set off firecrackers and aerial exploders, the birds were sent back to the refuge. Since ducks fed late in the evening and early in the morning, duck herders made predawn takeoffs and twilight landings, often at short grass strips with no airport lights.

Goose herding always worried me more than rallying ducks. Geese were much larger than the ducks and less maneuverable. I considered the possibility that one might wind up in my lap after going through the prop and windshield. Canada geese were hard to move and to keep headed in the right direction. They didn't like to be pushed around and didn't cooperate. Fortunately, I never hit a goose with a plane. Snow geese, by contrast, were very nervous, and flushed when the plane was still miles away from them. They could be herded rather easily because I didn't have to get in close to make them respond.

The pilot-agent's duties involved a number of activities, including detecting illegal waterfowl hunting and apprehending the culprits. I could learn a great deal about illegal activities on the ground by flying slowly at altitudes from 300 to 500 feet. For instance, duck traps were visible; persons hunting out of season could be seen; cars parked in remote areas sometimes indicated that the occupants were hunting illegally in the vicinity; persons harassing and shooting ducks from motorboats were visible; waterfowl concentrations that might attract hunters could be located; hunters could be seen sneaking up on birds in open fields; decoys (live and artificial), were identifiable; and bait for ducks and geese could be observed.

Once agent Al Niemeyer and I were flying the Illinois River Valley in late fall a couple of days before the waterfowl hunting season closed. We were looking for baited areas. They were easily spotted from the air because the ducks muddied the water as they sought the feed deposited on the bottom of the pond by the hunters. The feed was usually placed in front of a blind so the hunters could shoot at close range. Al and I found several likely spots.

Next morning we picked the most promising site and waited in hiding for the hunters, but that day we picked the wrong site; no hunters showed up. However, on another baited site nearby, the hunters were shooting up a storm. It was too far away to reach by foot before the hunters quit for the day, so we drove toward the duck club gate in hopes of intercepting the hunters when they came out. Luck was with us. As we approached we noticed a panel truck about a half-mile ahead. We stopped our car and watched the action with field glasses. What we saw was startling. Two men were running back and forth from the roadside brush, loading bundles of ducks into the truck. Hastily, they finished loading, slammed the doors, and drove off down the road. Seconds later we were in hot pursuit, and we soon stopped the outlaws. When I opened the back panel doors I saw such a pile of mallards that I could hardly believe my eyes. We counted eighty-seven mallards. The culprits were soon on their way to see the judge to pay the penalty.

In 1955, I transferred to the management side of the Division of Management and Enforcement and gained the title of flyway biologist. The aircraft then available to us for surveys were mainly 135 and 150 horsepower Super Cubs. These constituted the entire flyway fleet for several years except for

the twin-engine Grumman (Widgeon and Goose) amphibians used for surveys in the Far North. These amphibious aircraft combined the versatility of being able to land on ground or water with the safety of two engines. Gradually, four-place, single-engine Cessnas were added to our air fleet, including the Cessna 170, 172, 180, 182, 185, 206, and 210. They all had their good and bad points, but the Cessna 180 and 185 series fit our needs best, and our fleet today is comprised mostly of those two types of aircraft.

One type of surplus aircraft acquired by USFWS from the military was the DeHaviland "Beaver." This large single-engine plane was quite expensive to operate but good for hauling bulky loads. It was used to facilitate waterfowl banding programs and operations in remote areas where aircraft were the only means of getting crews, equipment, and supplies in and out of the bush. The most recent aircraft to be acquired was the Cessna 337, a twin-engine, retractable-geared plane. It had a low stalling speed when we equipped it with a Robertson STOL (Short Take Off and Landing) kit, and it became a very useful survey aircraft. Over the years we progressed from make-do surplus military aircraft to modern equipment that had it all over the early models, being safer, easier, and cheaper to maintain, and more versatile and efficient as well.

I would like to tell one story to show that the flyway biologist's job is not always a bed of roses. Art Brazda, flyway biologist from Lafayette, Louisiana, and I were flying a waterfowl production survey in northern Manitoba and Saskatchewan in June of 1962. We made an overnight stop in Flin Flon, Manitoba, arriving quite late in the evening. Only the Flin Flon Hotel had any rooms left. It was an old frame building, a real firetrap. We were directed to a twin bedroom on the second floor. Being tired, we were soon asleep, but close to dawn something caused me to awake. I looked at the glass transom over the door to the hall . . . and it was bright red. Then I saw the reflection of flames dancing on the glass of the transom. I shouted at Art and grabbed for my clothes just as the transom blew in with a rush of smoke and debris. We kicked the screen out of the window and threw clothes, survey records, and gear out to the ground below before the smoke got too thick.

It was four o'clock in the morning, but a few townspeople were around. As soon as the cries for "help" and "fire" were heard, the town seemed to spring to life. The people in the street shouted at those of us in the hotel (now hanging out the windows, or sitting on sills or narrow railings) not to jump because the volunteer fire department was responding. In a few minutes (it seemed like an eternity) ladders were run up to us. We were down in no time at all, running to the far side of the street. As we stood there in our B.V.D.s, the fire department poured water on the fire. After the first shock wore off, we decided we should get some clothes on, although the ladies on the street didn't seem to be paying us any attention. It could have been a lot worse. Art and I were grateful for escaping without injury. The hotel burned to the ground, and two people died in the inferno.

Flyway biologists were involved in a number of programs in addition to waterfowl surveys. The term "duck counters" was used by many to indicate our profession. Sometimes it was easier to tell people what a duck counter did than go into a lengthy explanation about a pilot-biologist's position description. However, other surveys and duties entailed such things as a bush search one summer for nonbreeding whooping cranes.

Over a period of ten days one August a fleet of three USFWS aircraft flew sectors from Prince Albert, Saskatchewan, back and forth to Wood Buffalo National Park, Northwest Territories. Each sector was 35 miles wide and 400 miles long. The sectors were surveyed in two-mile-wide strips at the rate of about six strips a day. The result was no whooping cranes sighted, although miles and miles of moose pasture and spruce tops were recorded. We also documented the extent of a hugh tent caterpillar infestation that de-

nuded aspen trees over thousands of square miles from the Riding Mountains in Manitoba to Fort McMurray in Alberta.

Periodic Canada goose population surveys were run in the fall of the year to keep track of migration buildups, refuge use, and potential disease outbreaks. For a number of years, this was a regular procedure for me in northern and western Minnesota. Todd Eberhardt, Minnesota waterfowl biologist, was one of the most accomplished observers to fly with me on the Minnesota junket. He did it for a number of years with willingness and good cheer that many other good men could not muster. Anyone who can stand the rough rides at low altitudes and still do the job of counting waterfowl deserves praises sung on high. Todd is one of the many observers whose skill and courage have gone unrecognized.

Another observer who rode shotgun for years on duck surveys on the Upper Mississippi refuge and Canada goose surveys on the Horicon refuge was Dr. William Green. Known as "Doc" or "Bill" to his friends, he was a stalwart passenger and one of the best observers. I know of no rougher ride than one he and I often took, flying the 300 mile stretch of the Mississippi River from Lake Pepin to the Keokuk Pool on windy, rainy, overcast fall days. The valley lies between 500- to 600-foot bluffs on both sides of a one- to five-mile wide expanse of river, marshes, and timber. Often a strong northwesterly wind comes whooping down the side hills of those bluffs and proceeds to burble, swirl, and bump its way across the bottoms. It is one of the roughest survey flights that I know. Yet Bill was always ready to fly, never complained, and never got airsick. As soon as we climbed up out of the valley and went for a cross-country flight to another area like Necedah or Horicon, Bill would fall fast asleep, apparently having complete confidence in the pilot. Why he thought I couldn't fall asleep, too, always puzzled me.

I flew over many other areas in Mexico, the United States, and the Canadian prairies on a variety of waterfowl programs. I had some wonderful experiences on those stints. There is nothing more satisfying than circling the airport in the flight pattern just at sunset, preparing to land after a hard day of rough flying. You have missed a lot if you have never experienced the peacefulness of a late evening or a night flight in a small airplane. The air is smooth, the farm lights blink, the stars are out, and all is well with the world. You have left the worries of the masses and all earthly cares far below you, and the night sky envelopes your soul. Those moments, I believe, were why I was willing to assume the everyday risks of flying as a pilot-biologist, and why so many observers were willing to fly along with me.

My duties were expanded in 1965 to include regional pilot in the Great Lakes Region. In that capacity I supervised the aircraft operations in the eleven-state area. Aircraft use in the region included eagle nest and production surveys, timber wolf tracking, aerial hunting of depredating animals, waterfowl herding, aerial photography, monitoring pothole drainage, checking for disease outbreaks, assisting with enforcement projects, and other assorted management and research activities.

There are many tales I could tell about those experiences, but space will not permit. Over the years, there have been several tragic accidents that resulted in the loss of good friends. However, considering the hazardous nature of the low flying that was done, the overall record is good. In all the thousands of hours of USFWS flying done in Canada and Mexico, not a single person has been lost; the only fatalities have occurred in the United States and Alaska.

The life of the flyway biologist is never dull — sometimes hectic, hazardous, and nerve-wracking, but never dull. After almost thirty-eight years of flying (including World War II and the USFWS) a heart condition in 1978 stopped my flight activities.

If I had to do it over again, I wouldn't do it any differently.

1978-79 Hooded merganser *by Albert Earl Gilbert*

©J. Killen

National and International Partnerships

North American waterfowl management is unique in the world as an example of wildlife management reaching across state, province, and national boundaries. That is true, not because the bonds of cooperation have not been tested, but because those bonds have withstood all the powerful tests put upon them over the years. There is every reason to believe the years ahead will present new and possibly more difficult challenges to cooperative management.

This chapter explores the theme of this teamwork, as described by those who have done the actual work. In Canada, the critically important breeding area for most North American waterfowl, the partnerships have involved such private groups as Ducks Unlimited and the Delta Waterfowl Research Station.

A similar picture emerges when the spotlight is turned on the United States involving duck clubs like the Winous Point Club and organizations like the Max McGraw Foundation. While the state wildlife departments have operated under federal leadership, they have also made their unique contributions to the overall effort. An excellent example is Illinois, whose research arm, the Illinois Natural History survey, has a record of distinction. And because the problems of the state of Alaska are unique, they are treated here also.

Even within the federal government there is need for extensive cooperation. This inter-departmental coordination is discussed in the following chapter.

We should mention some groups not listed here, although they have made great contributions to the network of national and international partnerships aiding waterfowl. Because the stories of the national conservation agencies have been told elsewhere, they are not part of this chapter. The National Wildlife Federation, Wildlife Management Institute, National Audubon Society, and North American Wildlife Foundation have long supported the cause of waterfowl.

In the whole world of wildlife management, there is no parallel to the system by which North American waterfowl are managed. The continued well-being of those birds is the goal of a remarkable number of groups working together.

Canadian Connections

F. Graham Cooch

In the years following the signing of the Migratory Birds Convention in 1916, Canada produced a number of outstanding scientist-naturalists, including Robie Tufts, Harrison F. Lewis, J. Dewey Soper, and J. A. Munro. In a way, the development of the flyway concept was anticipated by the Canadian Wildlife Service (CWS), since Tufts worked the Atlantic provinces, Lewis worked in Ontario and Quebec, Soper worked the prairies and Northwest Territories, and Munro worked the Pacific. These men spent the years between 1920 and 1945 establishing sanctuaries, regulations, and enforcement programs. But most important, they studied and published articles on the natural history and distribution of birds in Canada.

At that time, what is now the CWS and the National Museum of Canada were in the same department. They performed functions quite similar to those of the U.S. Biological Survey and the U.S. National Museum. The CWS grew very slowly in the pre-war years. In 1931 the thirteen-man enforcement staff was absorbed by the Royal Canadian Mounted Police, but a bird banding office was created under the direction of T. S. Hennessey. The CWS was largely a clerical-administrative unit with four field scientists working under the direction of Hoyes Lloyd.

In the years immediately before World War II, USFWS employees began coming to Canada. Charles Gillham worked in the delta of the Mackenzie in 1939, joined in 1940 by John J. Lynch. Harold Peters worked with Harrison F. Lewis in the James Bay area also in 1940.

The real impact of the USFWS, States, and universities came in the immediate post-war years when a remarkably able group of men came north to undertake population surveys and studies of breeding biology of North American waterfowl. In 1947 there were no schools of wildlife management in Canada. The University of British Columbia,

under Ian McTaggart-Cowan, had begun to develop natural scientists and population ecologists, but not survey biologists and certainly not practitioners of wildlife management.

In 1947, the Dominion Wildlife Service, as it was called, and the USFWS began an annual cooperative waterfowl breeding population survey that covered large tracts of Canada. The CWS, which consisted of seven permanent migratory bird specialists, had to resort to supplying in-experienced students (like myself) to the tender mercies of flyway biologists, enforcement agents, and pilot-biologists. I have always felt that I was the most fortunate of these greenhorns, as I was assigned to Arthur S. Hawkins and based at Delta, Manitoba, in 1948 and 1949. O. H. Hewitt, then Dominion wildlife officer, Ottawa, wrote A. S. Hawkins on May 28, 1948:

> This will introduce Mr. Graham Cooch, who plans to arrive at Portage la Prairie on Monday, May 31st, at noon. He has completed his first year in biology at Queen's University, and while you will find him rather green for a short time, he is a keen observer, knows his ducks quite well, and I am sure he will obtain a great deal of valuable experience from working with you which will be of use in future surveys.

I remember arriving by train at Portage la Prairie, Manitoba, to be greeted by Art and Betty Hawkins; their son, Tex; Grace and Lyle Sowls; and Eloise Spencer. As an introduction, Grace Sowls handed me a box of twenty-four chocolate bars and said, "You'll need them working for Art. He never stops for lunch." How right she was. About 2 P.M. that same day, Hawkins, Dave Spencer, Chuck Evans, Lyle Sowls, and I headed west toward Gladstone and, among other things, I learned that the Hawkins method of beating out a pothole was to wade in it neck deep. Hawkins was built like an Ichabod Crane with long legs that could effortlessly straddle a barbed wire fence, while I had to clamber over as best I could. Furthermore, he was tireless. We kept this up until nearly 8 P.M. before heading back to Delta, then rising again at 7 A.M. the next day to head for the

Minnedosa pothole country. In the next eight days we beat out nearly two hundred miles of transects.

The main road from Winnipeg to Regina was paved, but all the rest were gravel or clay. Art always kept one eye on the ducks and the other on the rain clouds, because we couldn't afford to get caught off the gravel in wet weather. Manitoba gumbo was exquisite. On some occasions we had to jack up the car and cut the clay from the tires. The Minnedosa country was heavily wooded in the 1940s. We had to crash through poplars to get to the potholes. It was far different from the denuded landscape of today.

At night we either camped by the roadside or in the relative luxury of a schoolyard with a pump. Following an early morning cup of coffee we went to work, alternately driving between potholes and wading through brush and marsh. About midmorning, we would stop at a Chinese restaurant in some two-elevator town for a cup of coffee and breakfast. At dark we would hit a three-elevator town for our evening meal. Then we would head for the outskirts to camp. In the evening we would transcribe the day's records on permanent sheets and discuss the next day's work schedule, always with ideas for improvements, such as stratifying the surveys by soil type. In those days, prairie towns closed at noon on Wednesdays, a fact Hawkins never seemed to remember.

For the entire summer, work continued at the same frenetic pace whether in the field or at Delta. I was never permitted to stop learning. We worked up data, constructed bait traps, applied reward bands, took blood smears, beat out another hundred potholes to test some new survey scheme, and chewed plenty of pencils to nubbins. In 1949 Hawkins assigned me to the aerial survey portion of his team. Being young and naive, I flew aerial transects over the prairies and bush at under 200 feet in an unmodified SeaBee. Its airworthiness left something to be desired. Once when landing at Cadham Bay, Delta, the sheathed tip broke off the propeller and crashed through the bulkhead and hull, narrowly missing the passengers.

The living accommodations for students at Delta bore little resemblance to today's luxurious quarters. I shared a fisherman's caboose and a Coleman stove with Chuck Rawls, Chuck Evans, and Bill Kiel. That first year my field equipment consisted of patched woolen blankets that had been declared surplus by Dewey Soper and a pair of World War II German binoculars obtained before I had left Ottawa. This making-do was good training for my later experiences on Southampton Island where I lived in a borrowed, non-Arctic tourist tent for four months.

I had been raised in the museum world, working on Saturdays and during the summer holidays for P. A. Taverner, Austin L. Rand, and W. E. Godfrey, so my 1948 assignment was a cultural shock. Isolated in a museum, I had met Wetmore, Manning, Mayr, Vaurie, Clarke, Zimmer, Chapin, Allen, Porsild, Van Tyne, and Sutton. But I had never heard of Leopold, Cottam, Swanson, Sowls, Jensen, Williams, Peter Scott, Elder, Hochbaum, Glover, Bach, Lynch, R. Smith, J. D. Smith, Gutermuth, Hammond, Errington, Wellein, Marshall, Hickey, Davis, McCabe, Seth Low, Jess Low, Linduska, Ward, or Crissey — yet, these were leaders in wildlife management. It was my pleasure to meet and work with them all during the course of those first two summers at Delta.

I remember sitting in awe at a three-day meeting at Westhope, North Dakota, in 1949, listening to Wynn Freeman, Merrill Hammond, James Sieh, Cordy Henry, Hortin Jensen, J. D. Smith, and others. This was the period when almost everything that was being done was brand new. Thirty-two years later many of the players have changed, but the nature of many of the problems remain unaltered.

I'll never forget Stoudt, Hawkins, Bach, and Lynch arguing aerial survey versus ground study plots and the need for ground truthing. Lynch and Bach were the great free-thinkers of waterfowl aerial survey techniques. Lynch's typed manuscripts on regulation-setting, such as his "An Escape from

Mediocrity," are still treasured by those who worked with him. They should be required reading for today's technicians and bureaucrats, some of whom seem to take life too seriously. Thirty years later, his scheme for regulations is being largely implemented in western Canada.

The experiences which I have described in a purely personal way were shared by many others. Much of Canada was unknown, and exploratory work in isolated areas in Ungava, Labrador, Keewatin, Franklin, Mackenzie, Yukon, and northern British Columbia was fraught with danger. The underpowered Widgeons used in northern work required skilled and dedicated pilots. The stories from that era include such experiences as flying in clouds over a mountain range marked four thousand feet, only to have the clouds break and reveal mountains on both sides exceeding seven thousand feet. Maps and maintenance were woefully inadequate. As the CWS grew, more effort was spent working in the Arctic and sub-Arctic, principally on geese, while the U.S. crews concentrated survey efforts in western Canada and the Mackenzie valley. The use of students as CWS representatives on the survey teams began being phased out in favor of permanent survey biologists around 1950, although the summer student program continues to this day.

The CWS expanded rapidly in the late 1940s and early 1950s. D. A. Munro, J. B. Gollop. R. Mackay, H. Webster, R. D. Harris, G. M. Stirrett, V. Solman, J. S. Tener, L. Tuck, D. Colls, G. Moisan, L. Lemieux, and J. Kelsall became members of the CWS and worked in close collaboration with the flyway biologists, assisted by summer students.

The Wildlife Management Institute stations at Fredericton and Delta attracted many scientists and students, both Canadian and Americans, to work on many facets of waterfowl biology. Students like John Rogers, Milt Weller, Gene Bossemmaeir, Ted Dillon, Alex Dzubin, Bill Kiel, Chuck Evans, George Brakhage, Mike Milonski, Helen Hayes, Bob Smith, and Frank McKinney

made friendships which have endured. Who could forget Brakhage in a dark green tent sweating over a fluoroscope at Whitewater Lake, with his professor, Bill Elder, recording results in the shade, or Art Hawkins trying to demonstrate the newly developed Dill-Thornsberry "boom traps" to the International Association of Fish and Game Commissioners and suffering not one but three consecutive misfires?

In 1951 I worked in the Maritime Provinces with C. E. Addy, the Atlantic Flyway representative. Once again I was associated with a dedicated gentleman, this time one who smoked second-rate cigars and travelled in a new Detroit product called a station wagon. The wagon carried a canoe on top and a black Labrador named "Sharkie" inside. I camped out all over the Maritimes with Ed, who each night keyed out aquatic plants using Britton and Brown and Meunscher. I learned to work with tides and gained an appreciation for the black duck.

It wasn't all serious work. I can still see Bob Smith wearing hip-waders, bathing suit, bathrobe, and peaked cap as he walked to Delta Beach for a bath with a thermometer in his hand; after testing the water, he decided to drive to Portage for a "real bath" since Lake Manitoba was too icy. Another time, John Lynch, clad in white, descended from his Stinson L-5 to join the crews working on a stinking botulism outbreak at Whitewater Lake, only to slip and immerse himself in the gumbo . . . to the vast amusement of us footsloggers.

The four years I worked as a student assigned to the flyway biologists of the USFWS in the pothole counties and at Delta were the finest practical schooling imaginable. When I got to Cornell University for graduate work in 1951, Ollie Hewitt and Gus Swanson had preceded me and had joined the faculty. During the course of my snow goose research, in winter I lived in John Lynch's attic in Abbeville, Louisiana. We flew at dawn from Placquemines, Louisiana, to Winnie, Texas, watching the mist burn off the coastal marshes, talking theories of goose

Peter Ward, now Director at Delta Waterfowl Research Station, grew up at Delta. He is son of the first manager of the Bell properties, Ed Ward.

behavior.

As I followed the geese north along the Mississippi-Missouri to the north end of Hudson Bay, I constantly met friends from prairie Canada: federal agents Wes Newcomb and Charlie Horner in Missouri; Bill Elder and George Brakhage in Columbia, Missouri; Herb Dill at Swan Lake; Harvey Nelson at Sand Lake; Jerry Stoudt and Ev Sutton at Aberdeen, South Dakota; and back to Delta's Al Hochbaum and Pete Ward. More importantly, perhaps, the lessons learned from Hawkins, Addy, *et al* went with me to the north shore of the St. Lawrence and Labrador. The drive-trapping techniques learned in Saskatchewan and Lower Souris were transferred from prairie pothole duck to snow geese on the tundra. Lynch's Gulf Coast flock count methods proved useful at James Bay. Sowl's methodi-

cal nest search from Delta was applied to Boas River. Hawkins' careful recording of data and Addy's plant collection techniques were useful again and again.

I was not the only recipient of this biological technology transfer from the late 1940s to early 1950s. Many of the senior scientists of the CWS owe an enduring debt to our mentors from twenty-five or thirty-five years past. We hope that they remember those days as fondly as do we. It is hard to describe the close-knit nature of the class of the 1940s and early 1950s, but people like Ed Wellein, who flew fifty miles off course to drop cigarettes and newspapers to Tom Barry and me at Boas River, Southampton Island, Northwest Territories, in 1953, will never be forgotten.

In the early 1950s, the CWS had started to split research and operations components.

International co-workers, Ross Hanson (USFWS) and Nolan Perrett (CWS), check mallards as part of a food habit study. USFWS photo by Rex Gary Schmidt.

New permanent staff were added, including Harris, McKay, Perret, and Boyer. In the west, our close association with the USFWS continued unaltered and many of our efforts were directed toward regulation setting and population and production surveys. At the same time, Banfield, Cooch, Dzubin, Erskine, Fyfe, Flook, Gollop, Kelsall, Kuyt, Lemieux, Loughrey, MacPherson, Moisan, Novakowski, Reed, Stephen, Sugden, Tener, and Tuck all became species experts, and several of our publications won Wildlife Society Terrestrial Ecology Awards. The CWS was a curious blend of scientist-naturalist-wildlife technician, ably led by David A. Munro (birds) and Frank Banfield (mammals), and directed by H. F. Lewis and W. W. Mair.

The flyway concept which colours most of the attention of the USFWS and the states has never gained the same preeminence in Canada. This difference is a reflection of both political and biological reality. There are ten provincial and two territorial governments in Canada, and meeting with them either individually or collectively is a much simpler process than dealing with fifty states and three territories. Within Canada, populations of birds often have not consolidated themselves into flight lines by the time they reach southern settled areas, and populations of some species, like goldeneyes, cross west from north-central Alberta to New Brunswick and never do pass into the United States. Yet much of the data we provide is essential to U.S. and continental management efforts.

The Canadian contribution to continental waterfowl management has been in the areas of data flow and analysis in both research and management. CWS scientists and contractors have made major contributions to our understanding of snow geese (greater and lesser), Atlantic and black brant, Ross' geese, Canada geese, white-fronts, whistling swans, trumpeter swans, sandhill cranes, goldeneye, bufflehead, canvasback, mallards, black ducks, green-winged teal, common eiders, and common snipe.

Data collection and analysis for management purposes have many parallels in both countries. This has occurred not only as a result of the commonality of the problems but also because of the "old boy" network. The development of a hunting permit system in Canada has permitted the implementation of not only national kill and parts surveys, but has also provided a means of establishing specialized surveys for single species, and in discrete regions with a flexibility and precision not yet available in the U.S. The Canadian system was devised by D. A. Benson and A. R. Sen on the experience gained by the United States in their duck-stamp associated survey. Data on utilization of the migratory bird resource are shared on a continental basis. The bird banding offices are linked by a common system. The manual is largely written in the United States and is printed in Canada. Each year, cooperative breeding ground surveys are conducted within the western and northern region of the CWS, continuing the pioneering work of Hawkins, Smith, Lynch, Stoudt, et al. In the east, application of prairie techniques attempted by Addy, Chamberlain, Cool, and Kazcynski was not successful and has been replaced by quadrant studies developed by the CWS.

The deep friendships that resulted from contacts made during the postwar influx into Canada of USFWS biologists, federal agents, faculty, and students to Delta and elsewhere continue to last. The International Program Review Committee, cochaired by Harvey Nelson and Hugh Boyd; CWS representation at Flyway Technical Committee meetings; joint programs such as the West Hudson Bay Snow Goose program which brought together people from the USFWS, states, provinces, and Wildlife Management Institute; and Alex Dzubin's Kindersley white-front banding teams all serve to maintain the bond

of friendship and mutual cooperation begun in 1948.

The waterfowl resources of North America represent an incalculable heritage whose management and perpetuation requires increasing skill, dedication, and, above all, cooperation between countries. While the perception of this resource is viewed somewhat differently in Canada and the United States, there is no disagreement among friends as to the intrinsic value of migratory birds to the people of this continent or to the continued need for mutual trust and openess among the waterfowl biologists of North America.

Manitoba Joins the Team

Gerald W. Malaher

Many changes have taken place in wildfowl and waterfowl management in the fifty-eight years (1922-1979) since I first hunted ducks and geese in the great flood plain and delta of the Saskatchewan River. In those days, at least from The Pas northward, no one bothered about a license or with limits. Northerners still maintained "there ain't no law of God nor man goes north of fifty-three" (fifty-three degrees latitude) and acted accordingly, myself included. Hunting was by local people only and appeared to make no dent in waterfowl populations; the supply seemed inexhaustible. Migration was an unforgettable sight.

Then the Dirty Thirties drought across the Canadian prairie provinces took a major toll of waterfowl. In looking over the annual report of the Manitoba Department of Natural Resources for fiscal year 1933-1934, I came across the following item under "Comments on Waterfowl."

> The failure of the duck crop in the drought section of the Canadian Prairie Provinces is really a matter of greater concern to the United States than to Canada, as such failure affects only a limited area in Canada

while in the United States its influence is felt from the Atlantic to the Pacific excepting only the North-West coast of the New England States.

Maybe it was this "sage" observation, seen by some of our friends to the south, that led to the first real and exciting program in waterfowl research and management, in Canada at least. This of course was the annual survey of waterfowl across the prairies of Canada.

My first direct connection with this program came in 1943 while I was supervisor of Game and Fisheries for northern Manitoba. On the morning of August 10 of that year, a young and somewhat diffident USFWS biologist named Bob Smith called at my office and wondered out loud if he might borrow a canoe for a day or so to look over waterfowl conditions in the area around The Pas. As the area covered some million acres, I didn't think Bob would see much of it in a day or two, paddling by himself; and indeed he might even get lost in the myriad of channels and miles of tall phragmites. Heaven forbid the thought! So, to his evident delight, he was offered a canoe, motor, tent, and supplies, with a game guardian (conservation officer) to act as guide, and told to come back when he felt like it.

It was sometime after this that I received a letter from Ira N. Gabrielson — and I must here confess that at the time I had no idea who he was. To me the name Ira looked feminine, so to my shame I replied "Dear Madam." Gabe never mentioned this even when I got to know him well. This exchange of correspondence was the beginning of many discussions on waterfowl problems.

Manitoba in the early 1940s was busy with the development of the Saskatchewan River Delta. It was wartime, so funds were hard to get. I suggested to the deputy minister that we should argue for funds both on behalf of muskrats and waterfowl when recreating marsh habitat. Personally in favor of the dual idea and purpose, he felt that funds would be forthcoming on the basis of rehabilitating native trapper income by rehabilitating the muskrat, while both of us recognized the benefit waterfowl would enjoy. He was quite right; the dual purpose was fulfilled.

I was also corresponding with Aldo Leopold, and in January 1948 was invited to go to Madison and speak before the Kumlien Club on Manitoba's policies and techniques in waterfowl and muskrat management. It is Art Hawkins I have to thank for this wonderful opportunity. The resulting discussions with Dr. Leopold and many others at Madison on both waterfowl and muskrats were an inspiration to me.

Later in the spring of 1948, there was a meeting in Regina among representatives of the USFWS, the Canadian Wildlife Service (CWS), and the Prairie Provinces of Canada to discuss, encourage, and formalize Canadian cooperation and participation in waterfowl surveys across the Prairie Provinces. Up to this time Ducks Unlimited (Canada) had provided virtually the only Canadian information on waterfowl abundance through its keeman organization, of which I had been a member. This information was not considered to be sufficiently accurate, so there was need to move forward on a more scientific basis.

Manitoba was the first province asked what cooperation might be forthcoming. We pledged twelve to fourteen conservation officers, or game guardians as they were then called, to run ground transects to determine the breeding population of ducks and, later, nesting success. This offer, I think, surprised the other provinces and perhaps led to more participation on their part than had been earlier contemplated. Manitoba stipulated that its contribution was contingent on the USFWS undertaking to train our men in the work so that information obtained would be fully consistent.

Nearly all the men involved were veterans of World War II, young men who had already received general training but had no experience with transect work. They were keen as mustard and entered enthusiastically into the new program. They were encouraged to observe and make notes on other

A planning session for a waterfowl survey brought this group together in the late 1940's. The group includes representatives of USFWS, CWS, Ducks Unlimited, and the Manitoba Game Branch. They are: (standing, left to right) Peter Ward, Bill Leitch, M. Hammand, Bill Keil, Gene Bossennaier, Ed Wellein, Glenn Parsons, Tommy Schindler, (unidentified), Herb Krentz, Joe Roberston, Joe Roberston, Arnold Davie, G. W. Malaher; (sitting) Bernard Gollop, Al Hochbaum, Nan Mulder, Gerald Pospical, Art Hawkins, John Lynch, Red MacIntosh, Alex Reeve, Ray Gilmore, Joe Serafin, W. J. Goody, Barry Iliffe, Herbert Henderson. USFWS photo by Rex Gary Schmidt.

wildlife seen during waterfowl surveys and soon branched out into upland bird and other wildlife surveys important to our department.

Their first waterfowl transects were run in 1948 to the satisfaction of the USFWS, whose biologists spent some time with each one of them, planning transects and demonstrating correct procedures. As the studies spread northward from the Manitoba prairies, other staff participated, and by 1950 a total of twenty-three field workers were involved.

Manitoba was very fortunate in those early days in the quality and quantity of waterfowl studies conducted in the province. Much of this emphasis emanated from the Delta Waterfowl Research Station under the guidance of Al Hochbaum, whose enthusiasm and experience were of great value. Delta was the center of the Manitoba program and, indeed, home base to the men of the USFWS. The CWS, probably because their men at that time lacked full training in waterfowl surveys, did not play a prominent part but did participate in work undertaken in Canada.

Two studies undertaken by the USFWS in Manitoba, separate from the waterfowl breeding studies but invaluable for the information they provided on waterfowl and other wildlife resources, should be acknowledged here. These were undertaken by the USFWS because Canada had no experience in river basin studies such as those contemplated.

The first of these was a reconnaissance survey headed by W. A. Elkins in 1947 and reported under the heading *Manitoba Central Basin Project.* Manitoba Hydro was examining the feasibility of diverting the Saskachewan River into Lake Winnipegosis, through Lake Manitoba and Lake St. Martin, and then across to Lake Winnipeg where a large hydroelectric plant would be installed. It was of vital importance for both Manitoba and the United States to know what the probable effects of such a vast project would be on the fish and wildlife of the area. The purpose of the report was to examine and

analyze these effects. Though Manitoba Hydro later abandoned the idea of development, the fish and wildlife study produced a wealth of new information of permanent value to Manitoba.

A second survey project covered the probable effects on fish and wildlife resources of the Grand Rapids Hydro-Electric Project. It encompassed the entire delta of the Saskatchewan River in Manitoba and its tributary waters, documenting wildlife values both with and without the hydro project. The study was conducted under the leadership of Yates Barber, with a number of Manitoba agencies and disciplines providing background information.

Other more intensive individual studies of waterfowl were being carried out at Delta, Whitewater Lake, and in the Minnedosa pothole country which, though not part of the annual breeding ground survey, provided much basic information to it.

The Manitoba Government Air Service provided many flights into north Manitoba for waterfowl investigations. A number of these were in support of Harold Hanson's study of the Canada goose. It has always seemed a bit ironic to me that Harold had to come up to Manitoba to rediscover the continued survival of the greater Canada goose in the province, with the Delta station already long established.

Gene Bossenmaier and Al Pakulak were also transported in the survey of goose nesting along the Manitoba coastline, particularly in the Cape Churchill region. Art Hawkins made a reconnaissance flight over much of northern Manitoba in 1947.

In 1946, Hawkins and Lyle Sowls made a trip through the delta of the Saskatchewan River in the *Musquash,* a cabin boat used to supervise the muskrat project. By all accounts they had a pretty good time on this trip under the guidance of Norman MacKenzie, the senior game guardian. Art's only complaint was having to make a smudge in a tin can whenever nature dictated that he go ashore, due to the voracity of the local mosquito population.

One did not have to rely on the honking of wild geese overhead to know that spring had arrived in Manitoba, for each year at this time Art would arrive to talk over the year's program. Sometimes I wondered if he hitched a ride with the geese and, with a "thanks for the lift," stopped off in Winnipeg for these discussions.

In my sketchy recollections of the beginnings of the joint United States-Canadian waterfowl breeding surveys in Manitoba it has not been possible to name and give credit to all Manitobans and "Yankee birdmen," as Art called them. I hope that those not mentioned specifically will forgive me and realize that they too played a significant part in this outstanding example of international cooperation toward the better understanding and management of migratory waterfowl. In preservation of this resource our two nations are mutually and inevitably interdependent. Who can blame the birds if they seek refuge from our severe Canadian winters by traveling to southern climates (as many Canadians do)?

One thing is certain, the men of the USFWS who took part in the waterfowl breeding studies across the prairie provinces of Canada were, and are, some of the best ambassadors the United States ever sent to Canada.

Saskatchewan's Part in the Early Program

Ernest L. Paynter

In 1946 when I first joined the Saskatchewan Department of Natural Resources, the Game Branch, which I headed, was in its embryonic stage, short of funds and personnel. I soon discovered that waterfowl matters were to occupy a major share of my time.

Post-war waterfowl surveys in Canada were just beginning, and the use of aircraft in making these surveys was a new approach. The biologists from the USFWS who did the flying must have gotten tired of driving our dusty roads and preferred risking their necks in tiny aircraft even though the pay was the same on the ground as in the air. Their flights covered the duck-producing areas of the province, but they also made forays for observational purposes into the more isolated north country. It seemed to me that they were flying fools — not because of their daredevil acts but because of their early and long hours, flying just above ground level.

John Lynch and some of the other members of the survey team taught me a great deal about ducks. For example, I learned that the key to sustained production of shootable ducks from Canada lies with water conditions on the prairies and parklands of Manitoba, Saskatchewan, and Alberta. The area, comprising only 166,400 square miles, in past good years has contributed from 50 to 80 percent of the total North American duck crop. If one considers only the ducks most sought after and harvested by hunters — mallards, pintails, blue-wing teal, redheads, and canvasbacks — the percentage is considerably higher, probably up to 95 percent.

This area contributes to all flyways and can rightfully be called "the great duck factory." Unfortunately, it is most vulnerable to boom-and-bust production cycles. The number of ponds present in May varies from about 6 million in wet years like 1955 to less than 2 million in dry years like 1961. By July of each year about half the ponds are dry in a normal year, while during droughts only about a half million depressions may still hold water. The ups and downs in duck numbers and in pond numbers usually are strikingly similar.

Our interest in ducks extended beyond the duck surveys. Crop depredations were increasing every year, and wildlife administrators were getting the heat. At that time, the grain was harvested by swathing and pickup, rather than being packed into sheaves by a binder. Hungry ducks found a plentiful table of wheat or barley laid out for them to feed on; they shelled and trampled it especially during wet weather when the harvest was delayed. Farmers complained bitterly about

Commissioner of the Wildlife Branch, Ernest L. Paynter (left) discusses plans for the 1957 Canadian survey with J. W. Churchman, Deputy Minister for the Natural Resources Department of Saskatchewan and Fred Glover (right), USFWS Director of Canadian surveys. USFWS photo by Rex Gary Schmidt.

the losses. At the Game Branch our response was to issue out-of-season Crop Protection Permits which allowed farmers to kill or scare the offenders. Our limited staff demonstrated the use of scarecrows of various types and the "Zon Gun" scaring device that had just been introduced.

After considerable research in our worst damage area, Saskatchewan introduced, in 1953, the first crop damage insurance program in North America. To underwrite the program, most hunting licenses were assessed an extra dollar. Farmers, to participate in the program, had to apply for coverage on the crop they wished to protect and pay a small premium. Crops could be insured for five to twenty-five dollars per acre; premiums cost from ten to fifty cents per acre. When damage occurred, trained hail adjusters inspected the areas to determine the amount. The program was successful for some years except in heavy loss years when the Saskatchewan

government had to underwrite it.

As migratory birds are managed under a treaty between the United States and Canadian governments, we felt that our federal government had a firsthand stake in the problem. In recent years the insurance has evolved into a compensation program, whereby farmers are paid up to fifty dollars an acre for crops damaged by waterfowl. This represents the cost of production but does not provide a margin of profit.

The government now has lands sown purposely as "lure crops" to attract ducks. Crops are planted and left unharvested, at least until the grain on nearby land is harvested. Or, lure crops may be harvested and the grain moved to other areas where needed. The Fish and Wildlife Branch also supplies about five-hundred scaring devices on loan to farmers to help control damage. With good harvest weather in 1979, there was a minimum of damage. The cost of the program was about $1.4 million, shared between the federal and provincial governments. Many farmers believe that sportsmen, rather than they, should pay for crop damages caused by waterfowl. Obviously, we still do not have an airtight solution to this problem, and if we expect agriculture to fully cooperate in maintaining satisfactory waterfowl populations better solutions must be found.

Through the 1950s and 60s, a comprehensive duck survey system was developed. The spring and summer aerial surveys were augmented by the ground studies near Redvers, Saskatchewan, where Jerry Stoudt and others waded hundreds of potholes annually counting the birds and determining nesting success.

For years a drive-banding program was carried out under the direction of U.S. Game Management Agent Floyd Thompson. Floyd was a hard worker, as my younger son, Bill, discovered when working with his crew one summer. Foul weather and slough itch were among the minor discomforts. One day a small tornado came their way. It tossed some farm machinery around, but the show went on. Thousands of moulting ducks and geese were captured and banded during these drives, and much was learned later about ducks in relation to the flyways from recoveries of these banded birds.

One annual event in Saskatchewan that became popular among the wildlife administrators of North America and flyway-concerned delegates was the "show me" tour. Fred Glover would brief a small group of big and lesser wildlife VIPs prior to showing them firsthand, by air, what the "big duck factory" looked like. I took the trip once, and it reminded me of briefings in the Air Force before a bombing raid. Everyone attending these briefings also had a chance to tour pothole country. Without exception, participants were high in their praise of this crash-course in duckology.

I remember once when Johnny Lynch dreamed up a better way to run the surveys. We cleared the floor of his room, and he proceeded to unfold a large number of sheets of paper which opened in several different directions. There wasn't enough room, and I think we had to move out to the airport runway to complete his thesis.

Flyway biologists were sometimes diverted from their regular duties. In the fall of 1952, a crippled whooping crane was found in southern Saskatchewan. Fred Bard, director of the Museum of Natural History in Regina, had it brought to his property on Wascana Marsh in that city. Dr. Bard is one of the founders of the Whooping Crane Conservation Association and is still an active member. For many years, he and his staff traced their birds' migration, spring and fall, through the province. They took excellent photos and movie film. He gave many releases to the press, radio, and television to inform the public of the importance of protecting these cranes. About November 1, 1952, it was decided to send the crippled bird, nicknamed "Queenie," to the San Antonio Zoo. Ross Hanson, with considerable help, loaded Ralph Stueck and Queenie into the backseat of his Piper Cub. Ralph was one of our best-known naturalists. It was a long, tiresome, crowded trip, and I think he more than once wondered about the vocation of a naturalist.

Sometimes, the air over Saskatchewan gets pretty choppy. On one "show me" trip, four of us flew west to Calgary, northeast to Prince Albert, and south to Regina. When we reached Calgary, we had to land three times before the plane would stay on the runway. I had a couple of packages of candy in my shirt pocket. Talk about bumps — twice before we got home I had to pick the candy out of the air and put them back into my pocket. One would have thought that an experienced pilot like Fred Glover could have done better.

Bill Hyshka, who participated in a number of surveys for our department, has related some of his memories in the following letter.

I look back on the duck surveys as the "good old days," and certainly they have been the highlight of my work with the government to date. I'm not certain that I can add anything more than what probably has already been written and still be printable, but a couple of incidents do stand out. I was flying with Johnny Lynch at the time, and we had completed our part of the July survey. We had written up our reports, recuperated from the pounding we took in the Super Cub, and recovered from a lost weekend, when John decided to fly mail out to Floyd Thompson's crew, who were banding ducks near Kerrobert. As we arrived on the scene, Floyd was using the airboat to drive five to ten thousand ducks into a trap on shore, when suddenly the airboat gave out and the ducks began to filter through the drivers wading in the water. John cranked up the Cub and we proceeded to drive the ducks into the trap with the airplane. This involved skimming above the water at about five feet and then doing a tight cotton duster's turn and back over the water again. We carried this on for about twenty minutes, which was about nineteen minutes too long for me, but we did drive the ducks toward the trap. I figured I'd never be able to walk or fly after that deal but Floyd, who was eternally grateful to us, drove to Kerrobert, brought back some refreshments and we had a celebration. I managed to fall off the top rail of the corral that night, but other than that a good time was had by all.

I was involved in an unfortunate aircraft accident over the family farm near Payton, Saskatchewan. I'll never forget it because it just about cost us. Immediately after the crash, I wasn't so concerned about my condition as I was about trying to explain to Art Hartwell, my superviser, what I was doing at home without being on authorized leave.

The survey lines ran through some pretty remote country and it was a constant challenge to our navigational abilities. During one run in which we encountered high winds and bad weather, we were heading for The Pas and running short of fuel, when we spied a town. I wasn't sure it was The Pas. A closer look, which proved embarassing, showed we were at Barrows, some ninety miles north of our destination. I think the one thing that strikes me about the whole operation is the dedication of fellows like Ross Hanson, John Lynch, Joe Perroux, Joe Matlock, Vern Conover, and the late Don Smith — the pilots with whom I flew. It was a pleasure to know them.

There are no doubt many other incidents that could be mentioned but space I'm sure wouldn't permit — like doing the survey by road in a beat-up half ton with Art Benson and later Jerry Pospichal or banding ducks and geese and dealing with the slough itch, and the many, many hours spent in the back seat of a Piper Cub. I appreciate the opportunity to add my recollection to your

story. Thanks, Ernie.

The flyway biologists were a dedicated group. Men like Art Hawkins, Bob Smith, Jerry Stoudt, Ross Hanson, Fred Glover, Joe Matlock, Walt Crissy, Ed Wellein, Vern Conover, Don Smith, Floyd Thompson, and the daddy of them all, John Lynch, did a wonderful job. In addition, they were goodwill ambassadors to Canada. Many of us who worked on either side of the border became lifelong friends.

Recollections of a Stump Sitter

William G. Leitch

When Ducks Unlimited Canada began operations in Canada in April 1938, a breeding survey of waterfowl was established as an annual operation following the pattern of *The 1935 International Wild Duck Census* (described in Chapter 1), but omitting the United States portion. B. W. (Bert) Cartwright, a participant in the 1935 survey and then chief naturalist of Ducks Unlimited (DU), headed the operation. Together with the assistant general manager and public relations officer, E. S. Russenholt, he organized a force of group observers, or "keemen." By the end of 1938, they numbered 3,200. Keemen came from all walks of life — farmers, small town businessmen, and professionals. They reported on water conditions and migration in the spring, made actual duck counts on their assigned areas in July, and submitted final migration reports at freeze-up. The keeman organization is still active but with reduced numbers.

Bert Cartwright was charged with compiling the ground reports, but his greatest love was the complementing aerial surveys. These he organized and flew from 1938 to the mid 1950s, except for the war years when gasoline shortages curtailed activities. The routes followed were roughly the same as the pioneering 1935 survey and covered the important

Angus Gavin, former general manager for Ducks Unlimited (Canada) wishes Bert Cartwright (naturalist) and Tom Sterling (biologist) good luck as they begin their 1951 aerial duck survey. The pilot is Gordon Hoffas. Photo by Ducks Unlimited.

waterfowl marshes and lakes between the northern fringe of agriculture and the Pre-Cambrian Shield as far north as the Peace-Athabasca Delta.

A variety of DU people flew with Bert until 1946. Then the second observer spot became my permanent assignment until I took over the surveys in the mid-1950s.

Bert, all five feet of him, was a remarkable flyer. He didn't always know where he was (fortunately the pilot usually did), but he could hang in there in the roughest air and maintain a keen interest in his duck counting — even after a bad night. And rough it usually was! For the surveys followed the shorelines of marshes and shallow lakes where the wind, sweeping across the open water, boiled up over the tree line, producing a turbulence at the 100-foot level where the surveys were flown, which seemed certain to tear the wings off the aircraft. Sometimes the stall horn seemed to be making more noise than the engine! Flights would be postponed if the wind was too strong at takeoff, but if it rose after departure the observers could only look forward to a bad day.

Although Bert was able to maintain his enthusiasm in the rough going, it was a little different in the back seat, which was usually occupied by me or Tom Sterling (a long-time DU biologist), neither of whom are good flyers. Aerial logs from these pre-Dramamine days show frequent gaps. After all, it isn't easy to count ducks with one's face in a bag! I never lost less than five pounds during the surveys, which usually lasted about ten days.

From 1946 through the mid-1950s, pontoon aircraft — a Norseman, then a Fairchild 24, a Cessna 170, and finally a Cessna 180 — were supplied by Lamb Airways from The Pas, Manitoba. Later, when the survey was organized on a roughly provincial basis, Athabasca Airways from Prince Albert, Saskatchewan, provided a Cessna 180 for the Saskatchewan and eastern Alberta sections; Walter Staheli, a Ducks Unlimited Canada director, used his personal aircraft to fly the western part of the Alberta section with Fred Sharp, a long-time DU employee, as observer.

Sharp was as big as Cartwright was small. His first aerial survey was in Manitoba when, for experience, he was assigned to fly the Manitoba section with Bert Cartwright. Lamb Airways sent its Fairchild 24 to Winnipeg for the survey, but they were unable to get airborne with 250-pound Fred in the back seat! They had to send a Norseman down from The Pas. Fred's coworkers never let him forget that incident!

The famous bush pilot pioneer Tom Lamb, from The Pas, flew the early surveys with Bert Cartwright and was at the controls in 1938 when the survey plane, after taking on a bad batch of gas, crashed on takeoff at Cumberland House, west of The Pas. Fortunately, there were only minor injuries. It certainly didn't bother Bert Cartwright very much. His log describes the crash and then states laconically, "I am now going at 11:15 A.M. to study birds on the beach at Cumberland Lake." It took more than an air crash to divert Bert from his passion for birding!

After the war, Gordie Hoffus flew most of the surveys until the mid-1950s when Greg Lamb, Tom's eldest son, flew with me. Both Sterling and I also flew with Floyd Glass, owner of Athabasca Airways, who enjoyed the surveys enough to always fly them himself, rather than assigning them to his pilots.

Ducks Unlimited survey crews were indeed fortunate to have pilots who were not only skillful and bush-wise, but almost as interested in the surveys as the observers. Knowing what was required, they were able to put the aircraft in the best possible position for the work.

Tom Lamb was a joy to be with, full of stories of the bush and extremely knowledgeable of his area. But his enthusiasm was sometimes a bit of a strain for me. The pretakeoff conversation often ran something like this:

"Tom, you know I don't fly all that well — so please take it easy in the turns."

"Okay, Bill. I know. I'll take it easy."

Minutes after takeoff, however, we were inevitably fifty feet off the ground in a vertical bank around a particularly outstanding bull moose or a new beaver lodge, whose occupants had had the temerity to build in that particular place without Tom's permission.

Fear wasn't the problem. Tom was an exceptional pilot. But the effect of repeated tight turns on an unsteady stomach tends to destroy interest in most wildlife experiences!

With so many hours of low flying under difficult conditions, it is surprising that there were no accidents other than the 1938 incident. There were, however, plenty of "hairy does." Sterling recalls a series of emergency landings in small lily-pad lakes when the carburetor of the Fairchild 24 insisted on malfunctioning at unpredictable times. I remember interrupting a rural telephone conversation when Greg Lamb and I cut a telephone wire across a narrow valley north of Prince Albert, Saskatchewan. And, of course, there were some shaky takeoffs when heavily loaded aircraft seemed to stagger into the air at the last minute and then had difficulty staying there. Several times ducks were hit but no forced landings resulted, although on one occasion the wing was holed and on another, badly dented. Once over the Peace-Athabasca Delta a goose zigged when he was expected to zag, whereupon I claimed the distinction of being the first biologist to sex a goose in midair!

Most DU people developed a love-hate relationship with the aerial surveys. It was rough going. Air sickness was no fun. But there were substantial rewards. There was the thrill of low flying over wild country and along the canoe routes of the early fur traders, places like the Methy Portage between Methy Lake and the Clearwater River which links the Hudson Bay and Arctic drainages — and was the key to exploration of the McKenzie River and the Arctic by canoe. Nights were spent in historical settlements — Ille-a-la-Crosse, Buffalo Narrows, and Fort Chipewyan — at that time not too much changed from the fur trading days. There was the excitement of masses of ducks, geese, magnificent moose, caribu, and buffalo in the Peace-Athabasca Delta.

Tom Sterling expresses this feeling most eloquently when he reflects on his experiences while banding moulting, large-type prairie Canada geese, in cooperation with the Canadian Wildlife Service, in the interior barren grounds along the Back, Dubawnt, Kazan, and Quoich rivers from 1963 through 1969. He had similar reflections during exploratory flights of other northern moulting areas. He knew that Samuel Hearne had reported these geese in his explorations from 1769-1770 and Captain Back in 1833-1835 had said carts could have been loaded with the discarded quills, and that the landscape and the behavior of the geese was unchanged from that time. All that historical backdrop lent a particular poignance to standing at the same place early explorers reached only after unbelievable hardships.

"In reflecting on the surveys I was involved with," Tom says, "my most profound feeling — which I can't really express — was of being privileged to cross and follow some of the trails of the first white explorers of that area. The country was relatively unchanged from when they saw it — except that there were even fewer natives. The explorers were going into unknown territory, whereas we knew the boundaries, the major land forms, and river and lake systems. But you could still dredge up that feeling of aloneness and stepping back in time. We saw the herds of caribou, musk oxen, grizzlies, wolves, foxes, as well as the localized breeding and moulting geese."

The aerial surveys were discontinued after 1967.

With an increase in biological staff after the war, ground transects were laid out for the agricultural areas of the three prairie provinces. These were run experimentally in 1949 and became operational in 1950, and were designed to augment data from keemen, who were no longer asked to make an actual count in their areas. Instead, they were requested to provide subjective reports on local conditions. This required fewer partici-

pants, and keemen numbers declined by attrition to about four hundred.

The transects were laid out on roads that were expected to be passable in the spring and would give an overall provincial picture of waterfowl populations and water conditions. Fieldmen swore that those who laid them out were much more concerned with distribution than the quality of the roads!

As a result, in wet springs cars bogged down repeatedly, and some transects were completed on horseback, tractor, or foot. George Freeman, who ran the transects in southwestern Alberta for twenty-three years, recalls how frustrating it was to be hopelessly stuck in the mud and see Horten Jensen and Al Smith of the USFWS roar overhead on the same transect (it was being run for air-ground comparison) to land at Calgary in a few minutes, while the best he could hope for was to be home before dark.

The names associated with the ground transects in the early years in Manitoba were Frank Ward, Ted Dillon, and Charles Lacy. In Saskatchewan, it was Tom Sterling, Bob Caldwell, and Gordon Staines. In Alberta, Fred Sharp, George Freeman, and Francis and Keith Williams ran the transects. And finally, in Winnipeg, it was Doris Kuntz who shared the agony of putting it all together.

At the time Ducks Unlimited began its ground-transect program, the USFWS was inaugurating its aerial transects and the ground study areas to complement them. While formal meetings between biologists of the two organizations were convened to discuss mutual problems, cooperation, and techniques, the real interaction took place in second-rate hotels all across the prairies. Firm friendships were bonded that exist to this day. It is not without amusement that those of us who leave our fishing, whittling, and stump-sitting long enough to mingle with the present crop of biologists find that many of the "new" waterfowl management ideas were proposed, discussed, and disposed of many years ago in the Tremont in Minnedosa, the Kings in Regina, the Seymour in Kindersley, the Healy in Swift Current and

This bizarre aircraft is a Junkers, used by Ducks Unlimited for hauling equipment to remote areas. Photo by Ducks Unlimited.

the Brooks Corona, and Mayfair hotels in Edmonton.

Ducks Unlimited also established ground study areas in the early 1950s. The Caron Pothole Study Area in southern Saskatchewan was closely monitored from 1947 to 1974 by the writer, and an area in the parkland north of Regina received similar attention by Tom Sterling from 1952 through 1957. At the request of the USFWS, two ground transects were established in southern Alberta in 1953 and run weekly to provide data for air-ground comparison studies. The transect east of Brooks, Alberta was of short duration. But the one between Strathmore and Calgary was run through 1973 for its value to Ducks Unlimited itself. George Freeman, who ran the transect all those years laughs (but no doubt with some regret and nostalgia) that the western end of the transect is now in the City of Calgary!

In addition to cooperation and free exchange of information on the prairies, I accompanied Bob Smith and Everett Sutton of the USFWS on their annual survey of the western Arctic in 1955. In turn, Ross Hanson flew the northern Saskatchewan and Alberta sections of the Ducks Unlimited aerial survey with me in 1959. Horton Jensen and Al Smith showed Ducks Unlimited field men how to drive-band geese, and Ducks Unlimited projects provided good duck banding situations for USFWS crews.

Fishing, whittling, and stump-sitting are fine pursuits for old waterfowl biologists. They give unlimited time for reflection on old friends and old experiences, and even permit the warm satisfaction that comes from the realization that together we have served waterfowl well — perhaps just when the resource most needed us.

Delta Waterfowl Research Station

Charles H. Bell and Peter Ward

The Delta Waterfowl Research Station was born in the dust of the Dirty Thirties, as a result of concern about waterfowl. The chain of circumstances which produced it was as "erratic as the flight of a teal," as Aldo Leopold put it. But throughout history there have been times when things come together to allow impossible achievements. In Delta's case there was a coming together of the scientific community, which at the time had only faint glimmerings of knowledge about avian ecology, and a man with a conviction. The catalyst was James Ford Bell of Minneapolis, Minnesota, founder of General Mills, conservationist, layman scientist, and board member of the Carnegie Institution. James Ford Bell was convinced that waterfowl were a renewable resource best perpetuated through a scientific understanding of their behavior.

Perhaps what would ultimately produce Delta was set far back in time within the physical structure of the marsh itself. Ever changing, always beautiful and seemingly limitless, the marsh was first described by Alexander Henry, the Younger, in his diaries of 1802: " . . . Lake Maninthonoban [sic: Manitoba] where wildfowl breed in prodigious numbers . . . round the south end of this lake . . . a low broken, marsh country extends from one to three miles before we come to terra firma — these extensive morasses being the great resort for wildfowl of all kinds." One hundred and thirty-eight years later Hochbaum would describe it thus in *A Canvasback on a Prairie Marsh*:

> Lake Manitoba, in south-central Manitoba, is a great shallow pool in the bed of ancient Lake Agassiz of glacial times. Each spring for countless years the north winds, whipping across the open expanse of water, have thrown broken ice hard against the shoals of the southern shore line, casting up a low, narrow ridge of sand. The ridge, now, is covered by a tangle of poplar,

James Ford Bell, crica 1936, was an enthusiastic sportsman, as well as a leading Minneapolis businessman, who donated the land now occupied by the Delta Waterfowl Research Station. Photo courtesy of Delta Waterfowl Research Station.

maple, ash and willow. Behind these woods, extending to the south, east and west, nearly as far as the eye can reach, is a sea of Phragmites, tall, plume-topped, yellow cane, reaching to far-off groves, the farm "bluffs" on the wheatlands of the rich Portage Plains. This sea of yellow cane is the Delta Marsh.

The Delta Marsh is one of the largest in the Canadian wheat belt. Some 19 miles long east and west, and as much as five miles wide between lake ridge and wheat prairie, it embraces about 36,000 acres. It is the largest of several marshland units in the Lake Manitoba basin, and is one of the finest waterfowl breeding places on the Canadian Prairies. It is also the home of the Delta Waterfowl Research Station.

James Ford Bell, like so many others, before him and since, was drawn to the Delta Marsh in response to the immense autumn gathering there of canvasbacks. No one is exactly sure, but the best guess is his first visit took place around 1923 when he stayed with Dr. Fred Cadham who had a summer cottage and hunting lodge at Delta. It is only natural that the early stories of the Delta Marsh are found in the writings of hunting experiences. All of them speak of an abundance of ducks. The following account is from the writings of Dr. Bigelow, who, as a young man, was spending the month of September camped with Dr. Cadham on the south shore of Lake Manitoba.

I recall most vividly, an interesting incident which happened about the 1st or 2nd of October — three miles off Water Hen Bay. We ran into a flight of canvas-backs which we had been watching for several days, but had been unable to make our way to the location with our canoe. This was our last day out and finally we found a pass through and we immediately paddled to our "Hide". We were very busy as canvas-backs were coming in from all directions. *Then,* a most *unusual* thing happened. We could hear to the west of us a medley of talking, laughing, singing and paddles hitting the gunwales of the canoe. During the three years we were there, we had never heard a shot in this part of the swamp while we were there, except our own and those fired by two old hunters and trappers, Mr. Atcheson and Mr. Smith, who resided in that neighborhood. The situation was funny, as each of us thought we were having hallucinations. The sounds were passing one-quarter mile westward and we could see nothing through the reeds. When we broke silence, we assured ourselves of our sanity and started shooting again. In a few moments a canoe came through the reeds in front of us and Jack Atcheson with two English Gentlemen, who were sitting in low chairs in the canoe. Atcheson, knowing us, said that the Dominion Government had been placing barley and other feed on this shallow slough and that the Duke of York was to shoot there at daybreak the next morning. There were abut 18 or 20 of them in the company together. Atcheson ordered us away.

A shack had been built on the Lake by Senator Kirchoffer to accommodate this Royal Party. The Duke of York was to shoot on the same place where we were and Atcheson told us to "leave at once." This did not go down very well with us, so, we told him we had never heard of the Duke of York and promptly to go to --- and kept on shooting. One of the *Gentlemen* in the canoe immediately got very "fussed-up" at our language and immediately asked Mr. Atcheson to take them out of there, *at once,* away from *those men* and they went.

Then, we found that in our haste we had forgotten to mark our exit out of the swamp so with the shadows of the reeds on the water at sundown, we could not find our way out of the swamp. We spent an uneasy night huddling together in the canoe to keep warm, but also did a lot of paddling all night to keep warm; as the ice would form on our paddles (it was down to freezing after dark) and with water in the canoe, from 117 wet canvas-backs, it was cold without even sweaters. At daybreak we paddled to the reeds to see where the Royal Gentleman was to shoot. They tied in

about fifty feet from where we had shot the night before. We pushed our canoe to the edge of the reeds so we could watch the Duke shoot. The shooting was not difficult. There were three men in the canoe, the Duke of York in the centre, Atcheson in the stern and the third man, who loaded two Greener, ten bore shot guns, for the Duke. The flight was fast. We watched him shoot for half an hour and he never missed one shot. He centered every bird and they just crumpled and dropped straight.

An interesting sidelight to this story is that Senator Kirchoffer had a much more pretentious lodge built in anticipation of hosting the Duke once more on the marsh. But he never returned. Today, Kirchoffer Lodge sits on the site of the Delta Waterfowl Research Station, serving as unmarried student accommodation.

Both authors of this short history saw Delta first when we were small boys. As we grew older we watched the transformation from one man's hunting lodge to perhaps the best-known waterfowl research station in North America, if not the world. Charles Bell recounts his experiences first.

Charles Bell's Memories

Back around 1921 my father, who had been shooting for many, many years at Heron Lake, along with a small group of his friends, had secured the rights on the famous Ten Mile Pass at Dalton, Minnesota, since it seemed to be evident that the Heron Lake shooting was beginning to deteriorate. However, at the same time, Father, as I recall it, seemed to be convinced that the same thing would happen in the northern part of Minnesota as happened in the southern part, and he felt that if he wanted to secure shooting for himself and his family in the years to come that he would have to go further north into the Canadian area where the majority of the waterfowl are raised.

I don't know how he came to select the Delta Marsh area, but with the help of a certain Captain Cecil Gunn, a lawyer in Winnipeg, he was able by about 1925 to put together a large part of the lakeshore property from Delta up toward the Clandeboy Bay gap. He subsequently secured the bal-

Kirchoffer Lodge, at Delta, annually houses students and visitors from universities and conservation organizations from many foreign countries, as well as all parts of the United States. USFWS photo by Rex Gary Schmidt.

ance of it except for about a quarter of a mile which is government-owned, right at the Clandeboy channel.

My first experience at Delta was in September of 1925, which was the year that Father completed the present York Lodge. Back in those early days — 1925 and afterward — the roads to Delta left something considerable to be desired. In fact, during the rainy period they were impassable — gumbo mud — so for a number of years Father had arrangements with the railroads to rent one of its automobiles on rails for the hunting season. Many times that is how we were able to get from Portage la Prairie out to Delta when it otherwise would have been impossible.

Those were big high-wheeled, awkward vehicles, and I remember tales of Father, Guy Northrop, and some of the other friends taking that car on the rails up the line on the west side of Lake Manitoba for sharptail shooting. One of the problems on that kind of a trip was how to turn the vehicle around and get it headed back home when they were finished shooting. Apparently the renowned way was to jack the car up on a center point, keep it balanced properly, rotate it around, and drop it back onto the rails heading the opposite direction. The only trouble was that it had such high freeboard and, if the wind

was blowing, they very often couldn't get it back on the rails. Then there was all the devil to pay to get it hoisted back up and lined up on the rails.

I remember very clearly that Father and I shot on opening morning of the 1925 duck hunting season in Manitoba. At daybreak we departed by canoe from the lodge through the gap and hunted just east of that. We were back at the dining room table in the lodge at 7:15 P.M. with forty-four ducks. The limit in those days was twenty a day from the early opening in September until the first of October, then forty a day. Our forty-four birds came as a result of picking up four cripples on the way home after we had stopped shooting.

Interestingly enough, as we arrived at the dock we were greeted by a game warden who asked us what luck we had. We told him we had forty-four birds, and that we had picked up four more than our limit because we found cripples on the way back that we hadn't known were there. He said he understood; that was perfectly normal and nothing to be worried about. Obviously, situations have changed today from those days back in 1925.

In any case, Father, as a foreigner in Canada and as a conservationist, felt it was his duty to try to compensate for the privilege of being able to shoot in Canada. Therefore, he decided to replace at least as many ducks each year as he and his friends shot during the hunting season. To do this, he secured permission from the necessary authorities in Canada to import some hatchery equipment. He got a permit for the Indians to go out on the marsh and take eggs off the wild nests, bring them into the hatchery, raise them to six weeks, and release them on the marsh. My recollection is that between 1933 and 1937 the number was 9,798 ducklings released.

When Father moved up into Canada, he was looking for a competent person to manage the property and run the hatchery. Luckily, he employed Peter Ward's father, Ed whom we of my generation all called Uncle Ed. Ed Ward had been a sergeant in the Northwest Mounted Police in the Yukon Territory.

It was a fortunate selection, for Ed Ward was a very wonderful and observing person. As a result of his observations, some important knowledge came to us which might otherwise have been delayed for a long time, if ever known. A particular example dealt with difficulties they had yearly in the hatchery with wild canvasback ducklings. They could hatch them, get them into the small indoor pens, and get them into the pond connected with the pens; but they couldn't get them to eat. They tried everything — all different kinds of food, but nothing was successful. The ducklings all died of starvation.

After a couple of years of this, Uncle Ed got the idea that maybe these diving ducks had to be in the water to eat since that was their natural way of eating. All he did was go quietly into one of the pens and, with his foot, slid the pan of food carefully over until it was touching the edge of the water tank. Almost instantaneously, the ducklings started to feed! Before that they would run through these feeding pans and never would touch a thing. That was how the first knowledge of how to raise canvasbacks in captivity came about.

After a considerable period of time, Father

realized that there was much that should be studied about waterfowl, and that he and Ed Ward were not trained to really get down to the basics. With the advice and counsel of Aldo Leopold, Dr. Rowan, and Dr. Cadham, he decided to turn over the land and the hatchery buildings to the predecessor of what is now the North American Wildlife Foundation. At Dr. Aldo Leopold's suggestion, he hired Al Hochbaum to come up and provide the research and management direction needed to develop serious knowledge of waterfowl and their behavior. That was in 1938.

At the same time he persuaded a small handful of his personal friends who were interested in shooting and conservation to provide the necessary finances to run the station. They continued to provide the necessary finances for a long time. I believe it wasn't until somewhere in the late 1950s or early 1960s that the North American Wildlife Foundation began to organize its own fund raising. I am happy to say this important waterfowl research station has *always* been privately financed and privately managed, with no governmental interference either from the Canadian authorities or from the USFWS. As far as I know, it is the only privately operated waterfowl research station on the North American continent.

Peter Ward's Memories

My own recollections go back to 1926 when, as a boy of six, I accompanied my family to Delta. My father, after two previous visits — one on foot, the other on horseback both of sixty miles distance — became manager of the newly acquired Bell properties on the Delta Marsh. In those early years we were intruders in a community that existed on a natural resource base by fishing, trapping, guiding, and hunting. They resented the boundaries imposed by the Bell properties, boundaries that on more than one occasion were defended physically by Father.

To him, however, such encounters were of little consequence. He was an accomplished boxer. Indeed, his skills had once resulted in his transfer as a mounted policeman from the plains of Saskatchewan to the even more remote Yukon Territory. There one of his annual assignments was to carry the winter mail packet from Fort McPherson to Dawson City, a thousand miles of unmapped wilderness. And now in 1926, with World War I behind him, he had accepted and begun consolidation of what later became known as the Bell Property.

My first impressions of Delta at age six were of a vast green morass, the smell of freshly varnished canoes, the huge fish that came from the marsh, and the chokecherry trees that intertwined across the sand road into Bell's Lodge and made it all but impassable for a Model T Ford. In 1926 there was a twice weekly train service that increased in summer acording to the traffic of summer cottage vacationers. Everything needed to sustain life came in and was hauled from that train, unless in good weather you were prepared to face the seventeen miles of dirt road into Portage la Prairie. There were no services such as indoor plumbing, running water, or automatic heat — niceties considered essential today.

The Delta we came to know consisted of two parts. Along a three mile strip of the lake ridge adjacent to the water were some 120 summer cottages. The second (and much more ancient ridge) on which we lived was the site of most of the permanent residents. These primarily were people who made their living from the marsh and lake by trapping and commercial fishing.

Summer was a time when vacationers descended on Delta by the hundreds. Among the usual activities of such people, the most exciting was to gather at the local store twice weekly for mail. The same train that brought the mail also included moonlight specials from Delta to Portage la Prairie.

But the bustle of summer ended after mid-August when the cottages were deserted for reopening of school. About then, as well, the wind swung into the northwest; summer, for all intent and purposes, was over. For the next month Delta lay deserted except for the few local residents on the second ridge. The sounds of summer gaiety were replaced by those of the north wind and rustling of endless phragmite beds of the marsh.

The solitude of late summer ended in mid-September with the opening of duck season, broken by the sound of shotguns near and far, even in the center of town. Local boat rentals were swamped on weekends, and strangers wearing hunting clothes and paddling canoes seemed to be everywhere. This was heady stuff for a boy locked away from such sights and sounds in a one-room country school. By age fourteen I had persuaded my father to let me be a part of that atmosphere. Armed with a single box of shells that had to last over two weekends, I began to learn the art of wing shooting without benefit of any instruction. Many were the times I returned with nothing. And many were the times I returned home early for want of ammunition. However, on some days little ammunition was needed. By this time we were well into the drouth of the thirties, and the waterfowl flights that had made the Delta Marsh so famous were no longer as abundant .

The thrill of autumn ended in late October or early November when the marsh froze over and returned us to the solitude of wind and reeds. For a time there was a new excitement in the village as the commercial fishermen readied for winter out on the ice of Lake Manitoba. This ended as they dragged their ten- by twelve shacks with horse teams eight to ten miles offshore, not to return until spring. Winter then set in in earnest, a lonely, long period of blizzards and snowdrifts. The road to Portage was a thing of the past, and the only link to the outside was the twice-a-week train.

James Ford Bell, writing about his impressions of Delta, said: "When I first went to Delta there were no limits except those which were self-imposed. Despite this freedom, we did set limits, both as to amount and to the number of shells to be used in getting that limit. Still it troubled me to think that we

Delta's first graduate student, later to become director, was H. Albert Hochbaum (right), who poses here with his advisor, Aldo Leopold, in 1935.

326

were destroying without making some effort at replenishment. It occurred to me that it would be possible by artificial means to put back into the air as many or more birds as were killed." In 1933 Mr. Bell took the first positive steps toward making that effort by constructing the hatching and rearing facilities that still exist. At the time no one knew it, but this move would make a significant contribution to the knowledge by which waterfowl are managed today.

Delta's wild duck hatchery had fulfilled by 1937 the original objective set by Bell, and he realized that "we must go much deeper into the matter to have an understanding of the various phases of their lives." In part, he had begun to look deeper by testing the effects of various hormonal and ultraviolet light treatments on reproduction, working under the direction of Professor William Rowan of the University of Alberta. By today's standards these were, to say the least, primitive tests with electricity supplied by a 110-volt generator driven by an old car motor.

Of the many people in the scientific world who responded to Mr. Bell's enquiries about how to gain a better understanding of waterfowl ecology, none had more impact than Dr. Miles D. Pirnie of Michigan State University who visited Delta in 1938. Pirnie was amazed at the facilities and the opportunities to conduct waterfowl research. He talked to his friend, Aldo Leopold, father of modern game management. Leopold in turn visited with Bell in Minneapolis in April of 1938. Leopold learned that Bell was not "interested exclusively in artificial propagation. What he desires is to offer his plant and property for any research on waterfowl." Leopold made representation for support to other members of the Technical Committee of the American Wildlife Institute, and they agreed to put up $1,000 in support of a graduate student at Delta. In June of 1938, H. Albert Hochbaum, a graduate of Cornell University who was working under Leopold, arrived on the Delta Marshes. The present-day Delta Waterfowl Research Station was born. In 1949, Bell donated the original hatchery to the North American Wildlife Foundation, which was initially established as "More Game Birds in America" early in the century by a group of public-spirited conservationists. Subsequent gifts added 4,000 acres of the Delta Marsh to the foundation's property, thus ensuring research without interference.

Four decades later, from this humble beginning, the Delta Waterfowl Research Station has become the premier organization of its kind in the world. That prestige is enhanced by more than 250 students from thirty-three United States and seventeen Canadian universities who have undertaken seventy masters of science and forty doctorates at Delta. From all this work have come 300 scientific publications and 6 books, the Wildlife Society Literary Award three times, the Brewster Medal of the American Ornithological Union, and the Wildlife Society Group Achievement Award. Graduate associates of Delta are found in leading positions in federal, state, and provincial resource management agencies. Others work for Ducks Unlimited or have remained in university research and now send their own graduate students to Delta. In this manner, the station's program has threaded a legacy through all levels of waterfowl biology and management. And knowledge gained at Delta is so routinely applied that its origin and value are often not questioned by present-day managers.

The Delta station remains today a project of the North American Wildlife Foundation, a group of Canadian and United States businesspeople drawn together in mutual concern for the welfare of North American wildlife. Through support of imaginative research, the foundation transforms concern into action. The foundation recognizes universities as the centers of knowledge from which stem most major theoretical and practical advancements in science. Secondly, it perceives that university graduate students have the maximum potential in terms of commitment and ability to generate new knowledge. In the case of waterfowl, Delta is the center where foundation support, university advancements in science, and areas of research need are brought together.

Over all the years, the North American Wildlife Foundation has consistently guarded the station's prerogative to study freely, as the foundation has been certain that pushing back the frontiers of knowledge proceeds best in an atmosphere of complete freedom made possible through private funding. They have asked of Delta only that its objectives be the discovery of new scientific knowledge useful in waterfowl management, and the development of well-rounded scientists specializing in waterfowl and wetland ecology.

In September of 1938, Aldo Leopold wrote that "it is certain that Delta set-up is rich in possibilities for work on important problems not yet visualized by other organizations."

Perhaps nothing more fitting can be said for the vision of those who founded Delta than the words of Hugh Boyd, director of the Migratory Birds Branch of the Canadian Wildlife Service: "At the age of forty the Research Station promises to have a future brighter than its distinguished past — and who of us can claim as much? As a center for sustained excitement about research on waterfowl and wetlands and as an independent source of advice and wisdom, it has no equal in North America."

©H. A. Hochbaum

The boat house and dock of the Winous Point Club as they appeared in 1864, shortly after the club was organized.

Winous Point
Club's Contribution

John M. "Frosty" Anderson

Returning from an extended European visit, courtesy of Uncle Sam, I stopped in Cleveland, Ohio, in late 1945 to call on the President of the White Motors Company. I intended to explain to Windsor T. White why I was not interested in the job as manager of the Winous Point Shooting Club. My reasons were that I was en route to the Illinois Natural History Survey to resume my pre-war job in waterfowl research with such characters as Art Hawkins and Frank Bellrose, and also that I considered marsh *management* a questionable concept since most

of the information on which to base management was still buried in the marsh.

On the subject of food habits, I explained my lack of confidence in the veteran hunters, guides, old Indians, outdoor writers, and other qualified experts. If I wanted to know what ducks ate in southwestern Lake Erie marshes, I would ask the ducks. Before I planted any more wild rice, I would try to figure out why it was disappearing and how valuable it was as duck food. I allowed as how age ratios determined in the fall migration could give us a handle on production rates which, in turn, might provide a basis for hunting regulations.

I took it for granted that the average duck hunter would say "that's all very interesting, but I can't see how it would do much for our duck shooting."

Mr. White was not an average duck hunter. He listened intently with a faintly quizzical smile which I was at a loss to interpret. I was about to reach for my hat when the old gentleman said, "I first went to the Winous Point Club when I was eleven years old. The punters, the manager, and the club members were arguing about the very same questions you have raised. About sixty years later I became president of the club and I realized the same questions were still being debated. I now think it's time we got some answers. Miles Pirnie has advised me to see if you or Charlie Gillham would be interested in helping us out."

As it turned out, Charlie had other fish to fry, so I was at Winous Point for the next twenty years, the first three as consultant, then seventeen as manager.

Windsor White, Howard Prescott, Hall Kirkham, Robert Gale, and other officers of the club proved to be very easy to work for. White was a member of the Wildlife Society. All were familiar with Herb Stoddard's work on the bobwhite quail and Val Lehmann's work on the King Ranch. Using age ratios as an index of production and band recovery rates as an index of harvest rate made sense to them. They could see that comparing the relative abundance of plants growing in the marsh with that found in gullets would give an index of food preference.

They also thought their young duckologist should meet and compare notes with Miles Pirnie, Aldo and Frederic Leopold, Joe Linduska, Art Hawkins, Frank Bellrose, Logan Bennett, Clarence Cottom, John Lynch, and other students of the flat-faced fowl. Prime Lake Erie muskrats were sold in the New York fur market as "Hudson seal." Since every dollar from the hide of a muskrat was one that need not come from theirs, they thought it wise for me to pick the brains of Paul Errington, Herb Dozier, Bill Hamilton, and Dan Lay to study the lives and times of those sweet-smelling Microtines.

My first summer as an employee of the Winous Point Club was spent at Delta, Manitoba. In those days, there were conflicting reports reaching the club members about the status of ducks on the breeding grounds. Al Hochbaum's classic, *The Canvasback on a Prairie Marsh*, intrigued men such as Windsor White. On the other hand, a prominent outdoor writer, who ran a commercial duck camp on the Delta Marsh, claimed Hochbaum was deliberately painting a false picture of the status of canvasbacks and that Al was a real enemy of duck hunting. The outdoor writing fraternity, by and large, looked askance at biologists who made interesting reading of cold, hard facts about waterfowl. Windsor White and Howard Prescott decided I should spend the summer of 1946 gaining a firsthand look at the situation.

That summer, I worked primarily with Art Hawkins, Al Hochbaum, and Paul Springer. We learned — the hard way — how to trap and band broods and develop drive-trapping techniques for flightless adults. Bob Smith was the other Mississippi Flyway biologist, and he and his amphibious Widgeon got us up to The Pas, over to Saskatchewan, and around Manitoba.

Other biologists working in and out of Delta that summer included Frank Bellrose, Dave Spencer, Lyle Sowles, Bill Elder, Nina Leopold, Estella Leopold, Glen Sanderson, and Pete Ward. Most of our cabins had no running water and no electricity, but no one seemed to mind.

I managed to inspect every Ducks Unlimited project in Manitoba in 1946. In contrast to the well-engineered projects of 1980, those built prior to 1946 contributed very little to the overall duck population. In fact, the Big Duck Factory seemed to be running well below capacity for lack of parts.

It's said that ancient rulers had a nasty habit of slaying the messenger who brought bad news. But my report on the rather disappointing picture for Manitoba in 1946 was received by the Winous Point Club with no show of dismay. As one member pointed out, "We may have an unbiased appraisal of the situation for this season, but we don't know what it means because we don't have much to compare it with."

In the mid-1940s, marshland owners around the west end of Lake Erie had a quaint habit of supplementing their decoys with yellow dent corn. In the lacustrine soils of glacial Lake Maumee, land that was too poorly drained for consistent crop production but not wet enough to support a productive marsh and widely distributed, usually dominated by blue-joint grass. When such areas were diked in, flooded, and sprinkled with corn, they made good shooting holes that could be rented at a handsome profit. Small granaries were a common sight on the levees in those days.

The local federal game warden did not discourage this practice. He explained that the wild rice and wild celery were gone; nothing grew in the marshes except cattail; ducks would not eat cattail; therefore, if they were not fed, the Lake Erie marshes would be duckless.

This line of reasoning was widely accepted with much enthusiasm. But for some reason, the USFWS did not agree. The new federal wardens, such as Curtis Allen, Fred Jacobsen, Rex Tice, and Chuck Kniffin essentially put a stop to baiting in the region in the early 1950s. The ducks continued to make out very well on the abundant smartweeds, millets, rice cut-grass, orange jewel weed, and other wetland species, plus the hundreds of acres of waste grain on nearby farms. Since the Winous Point Club had not adopted the practice of artificially boosting the food supply of the flat-faced fowl, their marsh management program was not affected by the change in enforcement policy. (It was suspected, of course, that Winous Point was bribing the game wardens and baiting like everyone else.)

For the waterfowl biologist, attendance at the Midwest or the North American Wildlife conferences in the late 1940s was quite different than today. The duck boys would gradually congregate in somebody's room to have a few nips and talk shop. On one such occa-

sion in 1947, the idea of forming a waterfowl research committee with a meeting scheduled for the next Midwest Wildlife Conference was born.

Eventually the Mississippi Flyway Waterfowl Research Committee was formed, and I was the first chairman. This was the forerunner of the Technical Section of the Mississippi Flyway Council.

Among our first cooperative projects were age and sex ratios and biweekly censuses in the various states so we could trace migration peaks of various species and delineate the major wintering areas. When the Mississippi Flyway Council was established in 1952 we already had a fair amount of baseline data to build on. The development of the other flyway councils followed a similar pattern.

Meanwhile, back at Winous Point, the flyway concept of waterfowl management was viewed with much interest. Throughout the Mississippi Flyway, bag inspection data gradually accumulated, usually gathered by state or federal personnel. In the Ohio marshes, gathering these data was paid for by the Winous Point Club.

Many hunters do well to tell one duck from another, let alone drakes from hens. But as for separating old birds from young of the year, "Well, that I gotta see." And see they did. The bursa of Fabricius, the open or closed oviduct, the sheathed or unsheathed penis — these anatomical features, once displayed, never failed to attract attention from duck hunters. Invariably, the comment was "Well, I'll be damned. But it does make sense."

Ohio mallards and blacks averaged about four ounces heavier than Illinois River birds, and about the same as Parker River Refuge (Massachusetts) black ducks. In some years, young of the year would concentrate along southwestern Lake Erie, giving an abnormally high age ratio. As more data from bag inspections, banding, periodic censuses, and harvest estimates accumulated, the basis for flyway management gradually became more stable. It became apparent that birds from the Mississippi and Atlantic flyways were crossing paths around western Lake Erie. Admittedly, there is still much to learn about the effect of various regulations on the longevity of the average duck, but we have come a long way since 1946.

When he hired me, Windsor White emphasized the need for periodic reports on various aspects of the waterfowl picture:

> I don't think we'll ever get back to limits of twenty-five ducks per day, but this club has had a history of being interested in other aspects of the marsh besides just the shooting. In 1880, Dr. Frank W. Langdon, who was a widely known physician, and J. Bonsel Porter, a son of one of the members, during the week which ended July 4, 1880, surveyed the birdlife. They published a list entitled *Summer Birds of a Northern Ohio Marsh* in the *Journal of the Cincinnati Society of Natural History*. Then in 1930, John Semple, a member of the club, and Bayard Christy, an ornithologist, repeated the study and published the comparable lists in the *Auk,* Vol. XLVIII, No. 3. (With Karl Maslowski, Woodrow Goodpaster, and Jay Shepherd, I repeated the survey in 1950.)
>
> Dr. Josepth T. Wearn, dean of Western Reserve Medical School, is also an amateur ornithologist. But, most of us prefer to look at birds over the front sights of a Purdy or a Greener. I think we'd get a log more kick out of hunting if we knew what happens to the ducks before and after they are at Winous Point. Some say most of our ducks are raised around here, but I question that. Anyway, that's something I want you to study and report on.

It so happened that Judge Day, of the nearby Toussaint Club, had published a paper in 1932 stating that his marsh of 1,500 acres produced 10,000-15,000 ducks annually. Alas! My first nesting survey came up with an estimate of only 51.5 pairs per square mile. Practically no nests on the many miles of dikes in Ottawa County were successful. Raccoons, skunks, opossums, foxes, dogs, and juvenile humans traveled the dikes, and very few nests went undetected. High water during northeasters was another adverse factor.

Once again my report was disappointing; but instead of skepticism, or an immediate demand for predator control, some thought was given to possible means of coaxing the ducks to nest in safer places. About ten years later, a graduate student named Chuck Hanson gave artificial nesting platforms their first trial in the marsh. They are now widely used in the region.

Speaking of graduate students, the first one to do research toward an advanced degree at Winous Point was an ex-bomber pilot named Karl Bednarik. Karl made a detailed map of the vegetation and muskrat houses on a seventy-acre block of marsh, ear-tagged young muskrats in their nests, and trapped the study area in winter. Compared to the old Frenchmen in those parts, he wasn't much of a trapper. But he learned a lot about muskrats and marshes, and so did we.

Bednarik not only added to our knowledge of muskrats, he also proved that a college degree did not rule out the possibility of becoming a competent punter. As the postwar economic picture changed, men who were born and raised in the Lake Erie marshes and depended on them for a living became relatively scarce. It was gratifying to discover that young wildlife biologists could learn to handle a duck boat, lay out decoys, call ducks, and identify them a mile away. In short, they made good punters in addition to gathering needed information.

After Bednarik left to eventually become Ohio's waterfowl biologist, Ralph Andrews appeared on the scene. His study of waterfowl nesting in 1951-1952 was published later by the Ohio Division of Wildlife and is a valuable reference to this day. Ralph later became a research biologist for the USFWS. Bob Donohoe compared muskrat production on managed and unmanaged units of the marsh. He is now Ohio's forest game biologist, and returns to Winous Point to punt on the opening day of every duck season. Leroy Bandy earned his Ph.D. doing a nesting structure study, and is now teaching at the University of Maine. Bob Meeks studied the effect of draw-down data on wetland plant succession for his master's thesis. For his Ph.D. dissertation, he traced ring-labeled DDT through the marsh ecosystem.

The list of graduate students who worked at Winous Point before and after Bob Meeks

Winous Point Club, photographed about 1960. The club has flourished for nearly 120 years, making it one of the oldest clubs in the nation. USFWS photo by J. D. Smith.

is too long to dwell on here. Suffice it to say, they all made a significant contribution to management of southwestern Lake Erie marshes, and to my knowledge all are doing well in their chosen profession.

Bob Meeks took over as manager when I left in 1966 to become director of the Wildlife Sanctuary Department for the National Audubon Society. From the Winous Point Club's standpoint, this was an extremely fortunate turn of events. In 1972, with Lake Erie standing at an all-time high, a vicious northeaster smashed most of the levee system. Fortunately, Meeks is not only an outstanding biologist and mathematician, he is a natural-born construction engineer. When the clubhouse, boathouse, fur shed, science lab, and every other building was flooded, the levees obliterated, and the continental duck population well below its former levels, many observers believed that the duck club that had stood for 116 years would surely fold. Such was not the case.

An aerial photo of the Winous Point marsh in the summer of 1980 shows crystal-clear water, impounded by levees that are

built to last. Outside the levees, Sandusky Bay is so muddy that submerged aquatics are nil. The managed marsh supports a healthy growth of smartweeds, millets, and rice cutgrass. Equally interesting, if not more so, is the concentration of mallards, blacks, blue-winged teal, wood ducks, and even the odd ruddy duck in breeding plumage.

The Winous Point club is now more than a century and a quarter old. The marsh has never been used for anything except wildfowling, fur trapping, fishing, birding, and biological research. In one sense, Winous Point symbolizes the love of humans for marshes. If private institutions — in cooperation with biologists and state and federal wildlife administrators — can maintain the sport of wildfowling, then the future of the sport seems secure.

Our defense against massive environmental degradation such as acid rain, stream channelization, lowered ground-water tables, increased salinity due to irrigation, and hazardous waste disposal may or may not be sufficient to save the ducks and the duck hunters. We can only hope that keen young minds who continue to use the Winous Point marsh as an outdoor laboratory may be able to stave off this latest threat. At least, they can be sure of the club's support.

Over the years, the research effort has involved cooperation with Ohio State University (OSU), the North American Wildlife Foundation, the Ohio Division of Wildlife, and the USFWS. Early in the game, the club was fortunate enough to gain the cooperation of Eugene Dustman, leader of the Ohio Cooperative Wildlife Research Unit. He was followed by Tony Peterle, and presently Ted Bookhout serves in that capacity. Over the years they have carefully selected graduate students who could be turned loose in the marsh to gather valid data without immediate supervision.

My recent opportunity to visit the club again and be brought up to date by Dr. Robert L. Meeks, one of the OSU students who became club manager after I left, brought back many memories of this fine old duck club.

Max McGraw's Legacy

George V. Burger

"To many, he will ever symbolize the dignity and strength of the individual in a free enterprise society." This tribute to Max McGraw appeared shortly after his death in a memorial issue of *Public Service.* Friends and coworkers tell us more about the man, calling him "reserved," "unassuming," and "soft-spoken," while at the same time he was "a leader" with "a toughness of character" and "a subtle wit."

Max McGraw left enduring marks in the fields of business and conservation. The story of his life, his achievements, and his legacy to wildlife is replete with drama and coincidence. It seems altogether fitting that a man to whom waterfowl meant so much should enter this world in Clear Lake, Iowa (1883), and leave it after a heart attack in Utah's Bear River marshes.

Young Max grew up in Sioux City, Iowa. For six years, starting at the age of eleven, he arose at 3:30 A.M. daily to deliver newspapers, on horseback, over a seven and a half mile rural route. Herein, another twist of fate: the paper was the *Sioux City Journal,* and the youngster's supervisor was the *Journal's* circulation manager, J. N. "Ding" Darling, who would become a Pulitzer Prize winning editorial cartoonist, a pioneer conservationist, and chief of the old U.S. Biological Survey.

Many years later, McGraw would write in a letter accompanying a volume of Darling's cartoons sent as a gift to friends, "He was my first and only employer preceding my sixty-four year venture in the electrical industry." Young McGraw supplemented his paper-carrier income by helping out at the Sioux City Congregational Church where Darling's father was pastor: "I little thought when I was a boy pumping the organ in the church of Ding's father that either of us would see the changes in this world of ours which Ding so meticulously records in this fine selection of old cartoons. . . . Through the Max McGraw Wildlife Foundation I am striving to realize Ding Darling's dream of perpetuating our depleted wildlife by practical research."

Their careers took separate paths after the Sioux City days, but Max and Ding remained close, bound by a shared dedication to wildlife conservation. After Darling's death in 1962, McGraw would serve as a trustee of the J. N. "Ding" Darling Foundation.

But all this lay far in the future of the young man riding in the predawn hours in western Iowa. His mind was filled with thoughts of an exciting new field — electricity. He enrolled in a correspondence course in electrical engineering, and used some of his hard-won dollars to purchase the latest books on the subject. By 1900 he had garnered enough expertise and saved enough cash ($500) to apply for and receive Sioux City's "Wiring Permit #1" and rent space for an electrical shop in a drugstore basement on Fourth Street. He was seventeen.

In January 1964, less than a year before his death, Max McGraw presented a painting to Secretary of the Interior Stewart Udall, in recognition of the Secretary's conservation work. Chatting after the ceremony (left to right): Stewart Udall, Max McGraw, Judge Russell Train, and Ambassador Adlai Stevenson. Photo by G. V. Burger.

That first year was tough; it ended in the red (by $37.50), and McGraw continued to carry papers to make ends meet. But in the second year his career was well and truly launched. The young man's combination of ability, enthusiasm, integrity, and salesmanship landed two major contracts: installing the first electric and power plant at the Sioux City stockyards, and the lighting for the city's opera house.

By 1912 McGraw merged several business interests into the McGraw Electric Company. As the company expanded, various utility properties were acquired and put together as a separate corporation, later to become the Western Power and Gas Company. Also in the 1920s, McGraw learned of an automatic pop-up toaster, manufactured by a Minneapolis firm and called "Toastmaster." Because of costs and design, the manufacturers felt there was little future for the appliance beyond commercial restaurants —

a market easily saturated — and most major electrical companies agreed. Not Max McGraw; he acquired the firm and got busy with his staff solving design problems and production costs. The result: the Toastmaster became a home appliance and a household word, and the McGraw Electric Company took another giant step.

In 1957 the company merged with Thomas A. Edison, Inc. as the McGraw-Edison Company, of which Max McGraw later became president. Following his death in 1964, *Public Service* magazine noted of the one-time newsboy, "Two great enterprises . . . , Western Power and Gas Company and Telephone Subsidiaries, and McGraw-Edison Company, remain as tangible monuments of his business and organizational acumen."

There was another legacy. That story, in McGraw's own words, "all began in the spring of 1937 when we moved McGraw

Electric Company, Toastmaster Division, from Minneapolis to Elgin (Illinois) and made it our corporate headquarters. The first land I purchased was a 60-acre tract on which were the springs that now . . . supply our lakes with pure spring water." Thus the beginnings of what would become the Max McGraw Wildlife Foundation.

It took time. First came the acquisition of additional land, to eventually total over 1,600 acres on the east side of the Fox River between Elgin and Dundee, in Kane County. Much of the land was in crops, open pasture, and grazed woodlands. So next came major "remodeling" of that landscape, always with an eye for improved terrestrial and aquatic wildlife habitat in a pleasing setting. Twenty-eight lakes and ponds were carved out of the bluffs overlooking the river; grazing was halted on the remaining tracts of native woodlands; and 750,000 trees and shrubs were planted, most of them in a reforestation effort on marginal soils formerly pastured or cropped, but many along the forty-lines of 500 acres of fertile farmland.

In this work, McGraw was to prove as meticulous as he was in his business career. An old-timer, who was a member of a planting crew forty years ago, still remembers with awe the replanting of a single pine seven times until "Mr. McGraw" was fully satisfied with its placement.

In the beginning it was primarily a hobby, an opportunity for a successful businessman in the prime of life to create an area, close to office and home, where he could hunt and fish, favorite leisure activities. By 1941 the hobby was expanded to include friends and business acquaintances, becoming the Fin 'n Feather Club. The club secured one of Illinois' first shooting-preserve permits and built a modest game farm to produce pheasants for upland hunting and mallards for "flighting."

Inspired in part by his frequent conversations with Ding Darling, in part by the writings of Aldo Leopold, and in part by leading conservationists who visited the soon-famous Fin 'n Feather, McGraw became deeply in-terested in national and international aspects of the budding new "art" of wildlife management. He met Al Hochbaum and was fascinated by the Delta Waterfowl Research Station's twin challenges of training professional waterfowl biologists and opening new vistas in waterfowl research and management.

He also took note of potholes and other wetlands in duck production country where breeding waterfowl were rare or absent. His response was typically direct. No professional biologist, McGraw *did* know the ins and outs of hand-rearing waterfowl — witness the excellent strain of mallards developed and produced at Fin 'n Feather. Why not tackle the problem at the source, by producing high-quality waterfowl on game farms and stocking them directly into underpopulated habitat?

It was not a new idea, of course. Mallards probably were hand-reared for hunting in England as early as the seventeenth century, and it's likely that descendants of English colonists followed similar practices in North America. In 1930, the U.S. Department of Agriculture (USDA) produced a booklet on aquatic game bird propagation. In the 1934 USDA *Yearbook*, Fred Lincoln stated that restocking with hand-reared mallards was impractical, since birds he tested did not migrate.

Other, larger-scale studies and stocking programs had been concluded or were well under way at the time Max McGraw became interested. The state of New York had released over 23,000 hand-reared mallards between 1946 and 1952; in Wisconsin results were at least tentatively established from a major mallard-release study by Dick Hunt, Larry Jahn, and associates; Pennsylvania was embarking on a large-scale stocking program; and George Brakhage had published results of twenty-one years of data on waterfowl hand-reared from wild-gathered eggs and released at Delta.

Conclusions were mixed. These projects clearly demonstrated that hand-reared waterfowl could and would migrate in patterns similar and sometimes identical to those of

©J. Raedeke

wild birds. Further, survival to the first hunting season after release was sufficient to produce hunting harvests approaching and at times surpassing those from wild, banded "locals." But there were serious, often substantiated doubts about the subsequent survival and return of released waterfowl. True, the mallard was becoming established as a breeding bird on suitable waters throughout New York (and elsewhere in the Northeast); but wild mallards were extending their range eastward simultaneously, and it was not (and may never be) clear whether establishment was due to stocking or to natural range extension.

These were the facts in the early 1950s as presented to Max McGraw. Many people were quick to interpret the data negatively in response to his proposed solution to the "duck problem." But this was a familiar situation to McGraw, whose business career was studded with instances where his insight and persistence had scored major success when others said it couldn't be done. Remember the Toastmaster?

And so was born the McGraw Mallard

Program. It was initiated, appropriately enough, at Delta, with the release of a few hundred banded mallards, produced at Dundee. The release was studied by a young graduate student named John L. Rogers. In an unpublished manuscript, John noted that the data were thin, but indicated that McGraw birds did migrate (though perhaps later and not so far south as wild mallards) and demonstrated a high first-season hunting recovery rate, but did not appear to contribute importantly to breeding populations in subsequent years.

Undeterred, Max McGraw went on to larger-scale efforts. These included stocking privately owned waters in the upper Lakes states and Texas in conjunction with his many friends; releases on several national wildlife refuges, with cooperation from the USFWS and the Boy Scouts of America; and, at the time of his death, involvement with youth groups and sportsmen's clubs in a stocking program in Minnesota.

Meanwhile, in Dundee other significant developments were under way. McGraw's interests were too diverse and his energies too great to be limited to the McGraw Mallard. The Fin 'n Feather Club became the McGraw Wildlife Preserve, and Max was a trustee of Ducks Unlimited and president of the North American Wildlife Foundation (NAWF), parent organization for the Delta Station. An ardent fisherman, he was instrumental in the construction of eighteen one-acre fisheries research ponds at the preserve, working cooperatively with the NAWF and with the Illinois Natural History Survey.

Although his skills with fly rod and shotgun were little diminished, the one-time newsboy was by then in his late seventies. Concerned for the future of the conservation programs to which he had devoted his energy and skills, and for the lands at Dundee which were by now a dream (of woodlands and lakes, upland waterfowl coverts, and sparkling trout waters) come true, McGraw took a major step. In 1962 he formed the Max McGraw Wildlife Foundation (MMWF), which was certified as an Illinois nonprofit corporation and later granted federal approval as a private, charitable foundation.

It was typical of the man that he acted in time, for a fatal heart attack in a Bear River marsh duck blind came in October of 1964. He was buried beneath a native stone at his favorite spot at the foundation — an oak woodland overlooking the Fox River valley.

In his will, McGraw left to the foundation the land (1,350 acres) it presently holds, buildings and facilities (including a newly completed and expanded modern game farm), and some capital. Goals had been spelled out clearly in the bylaws previously established for the foundation: "To engage in . . . scientific and educational activities in furtherance of the public welfare and which tend to promote . . . the conservation of fish, game and wildlife . . . to the end that such resources of this character as the nation now possesses may be conserved and expanded in the public interest." Under leadership of three presidents (Richard Aishton, who succeeded Max McGraw; Crowdus Baker; and currently Boyd Simmons), the board of directors has worked diligently since 1964 to achieve those goals.

I came aboard as general manager in 1966, replacing Colonel Jack Y. Canon, who had resigned. A top priority was a review of the McGraw Mallard release program; should it be continued and, if so, on what course?

Prior results at MMWF, and in similar programs elsewhere, clarified certain points. Long-time (and McGraw Mallards by 1966 were well over four generations "removed from the wild") game farm mallards might survive well enough after release to beef up hunting opportunities, but seemed to contribute little toward long-term breeding populations. Further, there was more than a reasonable doubt that hand-reared birds could overcome environmental resistance factors (ranging from declining habitat quality to over-harvesting of local populations) responsible for the decline of wild mallards.

Despite this prognosis, there were still many as yet unanswered "ifs." If the long-line game farm mallard couldn't "hack it" (in building breeding populations) in the wild, what about birds with a sizeable infusion of wild "blood?" In altered habitats, might such birds not combine the tolerance of human interference and the egg-laying and renesting tenacity characteristic of game farm origins with the wiliness, nest-site selection, and brood-rearing talents of wild birds?

If over-conditioning to humans was a problem (and there's no duck deader than the greenhead who identifies with a hunter after being imprinted on a friendly hatcheryman), why not test the impact on survival of birds reared in isolation?

One more big question: If hand-reared mallards, even improved strains, failed to enhance breeding populations in traditional production areas (which was becoming more apparent), what might be their potential outside traditional waters? As rapidly as natural potholes and marshes were drained in the northern United States and Canada, farm ponds and reservoirs were constructed in the United States. Could these become new duck factories?

The "ifs" were many, the odds against success high. Yet the potential was mind-boggling. With this, and the memory of the persistence of "Mr. McGraw" in mind, we decided to give the mallard-stocking program our best shot. Many people besides the MMWF staff aided us in this endeavor. Art Hawkins facilitated MMWF representation on the Mississippi Flyway Council's Technical Section. Milt Reeves and George Brakhage helped us participate in the Minnesota FFA project, the first effort to evaluate the importance of varying degrees of genetic "wildness" to the survival of released hand-reared mallards. Al Geis, Forrest Lee, Bob Jessen, Dick Hunt, Bob McCabe, Rich Bishop, Harvey Nelson, Vern Stotts, and George Arthur were but a few whose understanding and cooperation contributed to our projects.

And there was input from the private sector: Fred Armstrong, of Anoka, Minnesota, a successful shooting preserve operator, was the first to produce "half wild" mallards for the Minnesota Future Farmers of America (FFA) program, and made other important contributions to that program. Jack Frost, from Coloma, Wisconsin, beat the MMWF to the punch by supplying USFWS with "environmentally conditioned" mallards for release.

The year 1971 was a landmark in the history of waterfowl stocking activities. In February, representatives of federal, state, and private organizations met at MMWF for a symposium sponsored jointly by USFWS and the foundation on the "role of hand-reared ducks in waterfowl management." The symposium included discussions and evaluations of propagation and release programs in Canada, New York, Pennsylvania, Wisconsin, Maryland, and Minnesota, together with research projects at MMWF, Delta, and USFWS' Northern Prairie Wildlife Research Center.

In an introduction to the informal transactions of this symposium, Allan Studholme noted that the presentations "ranged from a rehash of knowledge gained a decade or two ago to material hot off the line." Newer issues

— some of which were clarified or aired formally for the first time on this occasion —included acknowledgement that different strains of hand-reared birds were needed for different purposes. Where put-and-take hunting is the goal, for instance, long-term survival ability is not important (and may not even be desirable); a mallard that is reasonably similar in appearance to a wild mallard and able to fly well suffices. Such a strain, used for flighting on shooting preserves, exists on commercial game farms and can be produced in nearly any quantity at reasonable cost, depending on demand.

But for introduction into new areas or replenishing existing habitats, hand-reared birds should resemble wild stock as closely as possible. This was especially important in the light of another issue raised at the meeting: possible negative effects if game farm birds could "contaminate" the wild mallard gene pool. This concern was eased somewhat when geneticist Bob Shoffner noted that there seemed little likelihood of problems unless game farm releases increased to a much more massive scale than existed in 1971 or drastic environmental changes placed the wild genotype at a distinct disadvantage.

Results of a mail survey of waterfowl propagation and release programs at the state level was included in the symposium transactions. Of the forty-four states responding, twenty-two had engaged in release projects in the past, but only ten were currently (1971) active. With the exception of Pennsylvania, such projects involved relatively small numbers of waterfowl (often species other than mallards) in specialized situations.

Since this landmark symposium there have been, in general, more sophisticated studies and release programs, aimed at answering specific questions, with improved scientific design. The "pump 'em out and see what happens" approach characterizing some earlier efforts has largely (and fortunately) disappeared.

Some of the studies in which the MMWF participated following the symposium included completion of the Minnesota FFA project (of which one accomplishment was successful refinement of techniques to hand-rear mallards of varying degrees of genetic wildness) and a Maryland program (which tested survival of mallards of varying wildness strains reared under isolation conditions and "environmentally conditioned"). Other MMWF release projects, in cooperation with state agencies and universities, included studies of various wildness strains and the effect of isolation rearing on mallards stocked on man-made waters in Oklahoma, Iowa, and Illinois, and on managed wetlands in Wisconsin.

Offshoots of this work included development of the alula-clipping technique (in cooperation with Ray Greenwood at Northern Prairie) as a means of identifying wings of hand-reared birds in parts collections. Most recently, our biologists have developed a system of measurements useful in distinguishing day-old and older mallards as to game farm versus wild origin. In recent years, a major emphasis at MMWF has been studying procedures for efficient production of significant numbers of wood ducks, pintails, and other dabbling ducks under game farm conditions.

By no means have we been alone in such studies. The Delta Station investigated production, release, and survival of hand-reared mallards of wild origin on Canadian potholes and marshes. Delta also made (and continues to make) major contributions toward developing and refining propagation techniques for other waterfowl species, including the canvasback.

The USFWS' Northern Prairie Wildlife Research Center led the way in the scientific investigation of a number of propagation and stocking questions. The center's accomplishments range from development of standardized physical measurements for mallards and studies of comparative physiology, morphology, and behavior between game farm and wild birds, to documentation of the efficiency of the gentle-release system in stocking and the potential for restoring or establishing new breeding flocks of wood ducks

and giant Canada geese using hand-reared birds and specific management techniques.

Most recently, Kim Cheng, a student of Bob Shoffner, is completing a series of studies (partially funded by MMWF grants) on early imprinting and mate selection in wild and game farm mallards. This work should shed further light on the "gene pool contamination" question.

So where does artificial propagation and stocking of waterfowl stand today? One answer comes from examining the degree to which the current state of the art has fulfilled four major functions attributed to this management technique.

First, artificial propagation *has* made a major contribution by furnishing appropriate stock for experimental research. A good share of the scores of thousands of mallards donated by MMWF to public agencies, for example, have been instrumental in studies of disease, pesticides, physiology, and behavior.

Second, artificial propagation *can* supply birds to increase hunting opportunities on a put-and-take basis, and put those birds in the bag much more cheaply than can habitat management. Yet, it seems unlikely that put-and-take programs will expand significantly on public-agency levels or beyond current use by shooting preserves and some private clubs. There are too many problems, of which cost is one. While habitat acquisition and management are more expensive, they benefit a host of wildlife and plant species —a critical factor in today's public-opinion climate. Add problems of enforcement and the still-possible threat of gene pool contamination with massive releases of game farm mallards, and the difficulties become clear.

Third, releases of hand-reared waterfowl have been successful — at least in the case of the giant Canada goose — in reseeding certain habitats where overharvest, habitat changes, or other factors depleted native populations. But such instances are the exception, not the rule. Any objective overview must conclude that no significant success in reseeding has been achieved with the

1974-75 Wood Ducks *by David A. Maass*

mallard — the most-tested species — in range where wild populations have been reduced by habitat, harvest, or weather factors. Nor is such success feasible (as suspected long ago) unless and until the causes of such population reductions are solved.

Finally, the role of artificial propagation and stocking to expand breeding populations beyond historic range has met with some success. Wood ducks in North Dakota, Canada geese in many areas, and small numbers of mallards in central Illinois and southern Iowa are cases in point. One might add the so-called "urban" or "suburban" mallard populations in the Chicago area and other metropolitan centers, plus some possible influence on the rate of spread of mallards into the Northeast. Yet again, the important breakthroughs that were once envisioned have not come to pass. Here, too, environmental resistance seems a root cause — more severe (in terms of predation and lack of cover, nesting habitat, and food source for ducklings) on farm ponds and reservoirs than I, at least, had imagined.

So the hand-reared waterfowl story currently adds up to some important successes and some major failures. Even in the failures, however, much of value has been learned and many questions resolved. A storehouse of knowledge has been (and is still being) accumulated on the morphology, physiology, behavior, and genetics of wild and game farm mallards. Techniques for propagating and releasing many species have been developed or refined, including methods for improving genetic wildness and for rearing birds to minimize imprinting and conditioning to man. In this context, it is our opinion at MMWF that strains of hand-reared mallards can be and have been produced that can "make the grade" on release where environmental resistance is not overwhelming. In brief, we have progressed to the point that one no longer need fault "the bird" for reseeding or range-extension failures.

Professional wildlifers have rarely if ever viewed artificial propagation as a major management technique. But the work of the past forty years, culminating in the past decade, has established propagation and stocking as a valuable and useful management tool when applied wisely and reasonably. Many professional waterfowl biologists and managers contributed to this progress. With them stands one layman — Max McGraw.

At the foundation that bears his name, we like to think that we've "kept the faith" with "Mr. McGraw." While not all of his dreams for hand-reared waterfowl have come true, his foresight has been responsible for significant additions to man's knowledge of waterfowl and waterfowl management. Those contributions include the fact that nearly 50 percent of the $500,000 awarded by MMWF to date in grants-in-aid for research has gone toward waterfowl studies (many of them supervised by Bob McCabe at the University of Wisconsin), including projects centered on wild populations and their management.

All in all, not a bad legacy from the newsboy on horseback.

One State's Contribution

Frank C. Bellrose

Illinois' fame for waterfowl and waterfowl hunting extended far and wide during the early part of this century. The notoriety of mallard populations in the Illinois River bottoms elicited this remark from a member of the U.S. Bureau of Biological Survey (USBS): "When all other ducks are gone, there will still be mallards on the Illinois River."

Doubtless, the fame of Illinois River waterfowl induced Frederick C. Lincoln — head of the Bureau's new bird banding office in Washington, D.C. — to journey to Browning, Illinois, to band ducks during spring and fall of 1922. His base was the famous Sanganois

Club on the Sangamon River several miles upstream from its confluence with the Illinois.

In the Sangamon Bottoms, Lincoln banded 1,667 mallards, the first large-scale trapping of waterfowl in the United States. Recoveries from mallards banded there numbered 314 in 1922-1923, and 183 in 1923-1926. Lincoln returned to the Illinois River to band mallards again at nearby Crane Lake during January of 1926. He banded 952 mallards; 83 were recovered the same season.

Following Lincoln's visits, there was little waterfowl inquiry along the Illinois River until Aldo Leopold began his game survey of the north-central states in 1928. In the Illinois Valley, Leopold saw the "phenomenal success of resting grounds or refuges" owned and maintained by private duck clubs. He attributed the concentration of waterfowl on the lower Illinois River to both baiting and large rest lakes. Three lakes rested a maximum population of 6.5 million ducks. At Beardstown, Illinois, "the baiting capital of America," clubs and commercial shooting grounds in 1928 put out as much as 7,000 bushels of corn per season on a twenty-acre tract. Elsewhere, baiting rates were as high as 450 bushels per acre. One baited dry-land commercial club killed 4,000 ducks in sixty days on forty acres.

Francis Uhler investigated the effect of live decoys and baiting on waterfowl of the Illinois and upper Mississippi river valleys in 1933. He found the most sophisticated use of live decoys and baiting amid the sand hills of western Mason and Tazewell counties, Illinois. From a plane, Uhler counted 250 pens of live decoys along with the corn bait used to attract mallards to shooting stands. Most of the ducks enticed to these dry-land clubs came from Clear, Jack, and Crane lakes — one to ten miles away. Largely as a result of Uhler's report, the USBS prohibited baiting and live decoys in 1935.

As a part of his study, Uhler examined eighty-seven mallard gizzards for food items. These gizzards were collected in November 1933 from the Duck Island Club, noted for

A major thrust of the work of the Illinois Natural History Survey has been banding. Photo by Illinois N. H. Survey.

its dependence upon natural foods and limited use of bait. Four plants made up 83.5 percent of the food items: Longleaf pondweed (*Potamogeton nodosus*) seeds, 36.7 percent; corn (*Zea mays*), used as bait, 21.1 percent; rice cut-grass (*Leersia oryzoides*) seeds and rootstocks, 20.6 percent; and duck potato (*Sagittaria* sp.) seeds and tubers, 5.1 percent.

Severe drought in the early 1930s sent the continent's waterfowl population plummeting to alarming levels that necessitated further major cuts in hunting. Dry-land clubs were wiped out, and duck kill severely curtailed at large private duck clubs in the Illinois River valley.

Because of the drastic effect of these many factors upon waterfowl hunting in Illinois, Dr. T. H. Frison, then chief of the Illinois Natural History Survey (INHS), inaugurated

studies of waterfowl and their problems in the state. Early in 1938 he gave Arthur S. Hawkins and myself carte blanche to select projects and goals needed to clarify waterfowl problems and management in the state. Because wood ducks were the only important breeding duck in Illinois and were particularly abundant in the Illinois Valley, the first project, begun in the spring of 1938, was a nesting study of this species. The high use of natural cavities and some unusual nest sites prompted us to develop the first practical nesting house, made of rough-cut cypress with a four-inch entrance hole. When raccoons decimated wood ducks using these nesting houses, I developed predator-proof models after 1943. The breeding ecology, population dynamics, and evaluations of various types of nesting houses have been an important research project of the survey up to the present. Findings of the forty-three-year-old investigation of the wood duck — probably the longest continuous study of a bird species in the world — have been reported in several papers and will be covered in a book now being prepared.

A study of the ecology of aquatic, marsh, and moist-soil plants of the bottomland lakes of the Illinois River valley was begun in summer 1938 and continued on and off over a period of forty years. During this study, the tragic effect of sedimentation upon the lakes of the Illinois Valley became apparent. Marsh and aquatic plants declined as lake beds rose from the deposition of clays and fine silts. The size and depths of these lakes are being rapidly diminished by sediments. At the current rate, most of the 70,000 acres of water surface in the Illinois Valley lakes will be gone within the next 100 years.

Other studies that early contributed to management of wetlands in Illinois concerned waterfowl food habits and the productivity of aquatic, marsh, and moist-soil plants.

Harry G. Anderson was employed in June of 1939 to analyze food items contained in gizzards collected in 1938 and those that would be procured in 1939 and 1940. By the end of June 1941, when the project terminated, Anderson had analyzed the contents of 4,977 gizzards of seventeen species of ducks, identified plant and animal foods utilized by waterfowl, and assessed the value of native plants to waterfowl by relating availability to use.

Dr. Jessop B. Low, INHS Survey game specialist, 1941-1943, participated in many studies and inaugurated two: the seed and vegetative yield of waterfowl food plants in the Illinois River valley, and a study of aquatic and marsh plants and breeding waterfowl in the Glacial Lake district in northeastern Illinois.

Studies that yielded vital information about migrating waterfowl were initiated by Hawkins, myself, and later associates. Most data were gathered in autumn when Illinois is host to several million waterfowl migrating from prairie breeding grounds to major winter concentrations.

Waterfowl populations in the Illinois River valley were censused in the fall of 1938 and subsequent years with binoculars or spotting scopes from various vantage points, such as cars, boats, valley bluffs, and trees. When these somewhat primitive methods were replaced with light aircraft in the fall of 1946, the time required to census waterfowl was reduced from approximately one week for the Illinois Valley to one day for the Illinois Valley plus a large area of the Mississippi Valley.

Light aircraft have enhanced researchers' censusing capabilities. Waterfowl have been censused weekly each fall since 1946 over the Illinois River valley (Spring Valley to Grafton) and in the Mississippi Valley (Moline to Alton). Coverage of Illinois wetlands has been expanded to include southern and northeastern water areas in recent years. Much of Illinois has been flown each January for the national winter waterfowl inventory, and spring migrations have been censused at various intervals between 1954 and 1980.

The Illinois Department of Conservation has financed most of the aircraft costs from 1956 to the present. At times other agencies have provided funds to increase surveillance of wetlands outside the Illinois and middle Mississippi valleys. I conducted the waterfowl population censuses through 1970; since then Robert Crompton has been responsible for them.

Waterfowl population data derived from census estimates have been incorporated into numerous studies. An early study I made compared the effect of population chronology and the setting of the open season. Optimum shooting dates, season lengths, and shooting hours were considered. Moreover, studies have evaluated the effects of the bag limit, laws for depleted species, three-shell regulation, and the prohibition of bait and live decoys on the duck harvest.

In the 1930s and early 1940s, Illinois duck hunters clamored incessantly for a return to live decoys and baiting, so the regulation prohibiting their use was appraised. The kill was eight to eleven times greater in 1933, when bait and live decoys were permitted, than in 1941, when these enticements were prohibited. One of the most expedient methods of regulating the duck kill was to alter the season length. Bag limits were effective at low population levels, but as populations expanded, bag limits were progressively less effective in controlling the harvest.

The role of waterfowl refuges in Illinois was determined from waterfowl banding and population data. Refuges enhanced the optimum use of local food resources by waterfowl, and hunters near refuges benefited by an increased harvest.

The effect of changes in the food supply on waterfowl populations is shown by census data. A catastrophic decline in fingernail clams in the Illinois River during the 1950s resulted in a comparable decline in diving ducks. As plant food resources varied in the bottomland lakes of the Illinois River, so did population levels of certain dabbling ducks and coots.

John M. Anderson joined the Illinois Natural History Survey staff in the fall of 1939 and began its banding program. Over the years many persons participated in this activity, which was most intensive from 1939 to 1952. During that period over 75,000 ducks, about 85 percent of which were mallards, were banded by survey personnel at four locations in the state. George Arthur, former waterfowl biologist with the Department of Conservation, began banding waterfowl at Union County Wildlife Area in southern Illinois in 1954. He and his associates banded almost fifty thousand ducks there and on the Mississippi River at Nauvoo, Illinois.

Banding data have been used to analyze varous waterfowl problems: population mortality in mallards, black ducks, and bluewinged teal; migration patterns of mallards and black ducks (this study demonstrated that mallards and black ducks return to the same migration area in succeeding years);

and defining waterfowl migration corridors. In addition to banding data, radar surveillance and population and kill distribution also entered into these analyses.

Banding provided a means of evaluating the importance of lead poisoning as a mortality factor among mallards in the Mississippi Flyway. Band recovery rates were compared between birds dosed with lead and those free of ingested lead. Recovery rates in the subsequent fall were markedly higher for birds free of lead, indicating higher mortality at higher levels of ingested shot.

Data from bandings were applied to sex and age ratios obtained from checking hunters' bags to evaluate hunter selectivity. Intentionally or not, most hunters selected slightly more drakes. The low proportion of hens in duck populations was attributed to losses incurred during the breeding season. Diving ducks had the greatest disparity in sex ratios; among dabblers, mallards had the most balanced sex ratio.

Age ratios in mallards followed a yearly variation in magnitude that was related to prairie pond abundance. The yearly proportion of juveniles appeared to reflect a density-dependent relationship between the size of the returning population and the availability of water areas.

Canada Goose Investigations

Both populations and the kill of Canada geese were escalating in the area of Horseshoe Lake Game Refuge in extreme southern Illinois during the early 1940s. Because of developing problems, Arthur S. Hawkins and John M. Anderson spent the winter of 1940-1941 making observations and banding 315 Canada geese, the first ever in Illinois. Shortly thereafter Hawkins and Anderson were inducted into the armed forces.

Dr. William H. Elder directed the Canada goose research at Horseshoe Lake from December 1941 until March 1943. His studies resulted in a paper on techniques for aging and sexing Canada geese, as well as an analysis of weights by age and sex classes.

Dr. Harold C. Hanson took charge of the

research at Horseshoe Lake from fall 1943 until spring 1947. A classic paper on Canada geese resulted from Hanson's intensive studies; Robert H. Smith, a flyway biologist with the USFWS, collaborated with him and provided extensive data on geese in the Mississippi Flyway. Other papers from Hanson's studies at Horseshoe Lake included trapping and handling Canada geese, methods of determining age and sex, and interfamily dominance in Canada geese.

Later, Hanson evaluated the effect of stress on Canada geese — an important contribution to waterfowl management. His discovery of the giant Canada goose, its characteristics, ecology, population dynamics, and management was chronicled in a book on this race. In a masterful evaluation of the occurrence of twelve elements in the keratin of primary feathers of geese, Hanson and Jones demonstrated that these elements could be used to trace the geographic origins of a population.

The Future

Although we have accumulated much knowledge about waterfowl and their problems in Illinois since Lincoln, Leopold, and Uhler visited in the 1920s and early 1930s, there is never sufficient information for all of management's needs. Some aspects of the problem are that waterfowl and their habitats are dynamic, as the birds shift their pattern of distribution to accommodate changes in habitat and food resources. Data often remain in files unanalyzed and unavailable for decisionmaking. And, as always, insufficient funds and manpower limit research.

Agriculture, transportation, and electric power developments have brought rapid changes to waterfowl and their management in Illinois. Much of the waste grain in harvested fields that was formerly available to mallards and geese has all but disappeared because of better combines, less lodging, and fall plowing. Increased soil erosion from intensified row cropping has increased sedimentation in most wetlands, thus reducing the wetland area and degrading its quality for fish and wildlife.

On the other hand, the construction of cooling lakes for power plants has increased the water area available for waterfowl. Large numbers of waterfowl use certain cooling lakes during migration and to a lesser extent during winter. Waterfowl food resources in these lakes should be investigated so that the role of cooling lakes in waterfowl management can be properly evaluated.

Increasing barge traffic on the Illinois and Mississippi rivers is having an effect. So, too, are new highways that permit intensive use of formerly inaccessible water areas. An unexpected benefit from the interstate highway system are the ponds created by removal of fill for overpasses. Moderate use of these ponds by migratory ducks during spring encourages researchers to believe they are of some benefit to waterfowl.

FWS Operating Branches

Henry M. Reeves

Nearly all organizational units and programs of the USFWS and its predecessor, the Bureau of Biological Survey (USBS), have been directly or incidentally involved in some aspect of North American waterfowl management. Prominent among these have been the National Wildlife Refuge System, the Law Enforcement Division, and the federal aid to wildlife restoration program. In addition, the Cooperative Wildlife Research Unit Program, which is described elsewhere, has played an extremely important role. The roles of the first three activities warrant further elaboration here.

Several major federal wildlife programs arose or were greatly enlarged during the Roosevelt administration of the 1930s. This occurred because of the perceived deterioration of many species of wildlife and their habitats in the United States, and, in the case of waterfowl and other migratory game birds, in North America.

Fortunately, a group of outstanding conservationists — many of whom were also ardent sportsmen — in the USBS, state conservation agencies, private conservation organizations, on Capitol Hill, and in the press were prepared and eager to meet the challenge. Through their efforts the public also learned of the resource need variously called "conservation" or "restoration." The public, in turn, vigorously gave these conservation advocates the support through Congress to fund and mount several major conservation programs for America's natural resources, including its wildlife. Nearly all of these "Dirty Thirties" conservation programs in some way contributed to an improved status of waterfowl or their habitats.

Although we cannot acknowledge all the leaders who contributed to these early conservation programs, we would be remiss not to mention some of the truly outstanding individuals. Fortunately, President Franklin D. Roosevelt took a keen personal interest in the conservation movement. On January 8, 1934, he appointed the "Beck Committee" to study and propose means for establishing a "wildlife restoration program." In 1936 Roosevelt summoned conservationists to the first of what were to be known as the annual North American Wildlife Conferences.

Key congressional leaders during or preceding the Roosevelt administration who took leading roles in waterfowl conservation legislation were Senators George P. McLean (Connecticut), Charles McNary (Oregon), Peter Norbeck (South Dakota), Key Pittman (Nevada), Elihu Root (New York), and Frederic C. Walcott (Connecticut); and Representatives August H. Andersen (Minnesota), Daniel Reed Anthony (Kansas), Richard Kleberg (Texas), John F. Lacey (Iowa), A. Willis Robertson (Virginia), and George Shiras III (Pennsylvania).

Through the efforts of Senator Walcott, the Select Special Committee on the Conservation of Wildlife Resources was organized. Senator Walcott became its first chairman and Carl D. Shoemaker its secretary. A companion Special Committee on Wildlife Conservation was established in the House of Representatives in 1933.

T. Gilbert Pearson of the National Audubon Society and William T. Hornaday and Madison Grant of the New York Zoological Society were particularly prominent in the early waterfowl conservation movement. The Boone and Crockett Club, especially through the efforts of John M. Phillips, John C. Phillips, Charles Sheldon, and George Bird Grinnell, was an effective lobbyist for waterfowl conservation. John B. Burnham and William S. Haskell, both of the American Game Protective and Propogation Association, were also effective advocates of waterfowl conservation. Several writers and editors were instrumental in informing the public and molding public opinion and support. "Ding" Darling's nationally syndicated conservation cartoons are noted elsewhere as in Thomas Beck's role. George Bird Grinnell, a magazine editor like Beck wrote prolifically of the conservation movement in *Forest and Stream.*

The extraordinary John C. Phillips, a physician and founder of the American Wild Fowlers, found time to co-author *American Waterfowl, their Present Situation and the Outlook for their Future* with Frederick C. Lincoln in 1930 and then wrote the unsurpassed four-volume monograph *A Natural History of the Ducks.* Also, the influence of Aldo Leopold, an emerging professor of wildlife management at the University of Wisconsin, was evident in the Beck Committee report to President Roosevelt, and in several "New Deal" wildlife conservation programs. State support centered in the International Association of Game, Fish and Conservation Commissioners. And in Canada and Mexico, colleagues were espousing similar concerns for the North American waterfowl resource.

We wish to shift our attention to several of the major activities of the USBS and the legislation which made these programs possible.

Law Enforcement

In general, the early conservation movement in the United States focused upon the regulation of hunting activities, and such was the case with waterfowl. Prior to the negotiation of migratory bird treaties, the states and lesser governmental units had sole responsibility for establishing wildlife protection laws and regulations.

The federal government's first mandate for enforcing wildlife laws arose from passage of the Lacey Act on May 25, 1900, with authority assigned to the Division of Biological Survey, U.S. Department of Agriculture. The Lacey Act provided for the conservation, preservation, and restoration of "game birds and other wild birds" by prohibiting their illegal transportation in interstate and foreign commerce.

The first legislative effort providing federal protection specifically to migratory birds occurred on December 4, 1904, with the introduction of a bill titled "An Act to Protect Migratory Game Birds of the United States" by Congressman George Shiras III. The bill reflected Shiras' remarkable but politically premature perception of the need for federal protection of the migratory bird resource, evidenced as follows:

> Whereas, experience has shown that laws passed by the States and Territories of the United States to protect game birds within their respective limits have proved insufficient to protect those kinds and classes of said birds which are migratory in their habits . . . .
>
> And whereas the absence of uniform and effective laws and regulations in such cases has resulted in the wholesale destruction and the threatened extermination of many valuable species of said game birds . . . .
>
> Be it enacted . . . in Congress assembled,
> That all wild geese, wild swans, brant, wild ducks, snipe, plover, woodcock, rail, wild pigeons and all other migratory game birds which do not remain permanently the entire year within the borders of any State or Territory shall hereafter be deemed to be within the custody and protection of the Government of the United States . . . .
>
> That the Department of Agriculture is hereby authorized to adopt suitable regula-

tions to give effect to the previous section by prescribing and fixing closed seasons, having due regard to the zones of temperature, breeding habits, and times and lines of migratory flight, thereby enabling the Department to select and designate suitable districts for different portions of the country within which said closed seasons it shall not be lawful to shoot . . . kill or seize and capture migratory waterfowl within the protection of this law.

Unfortunately, Shiras' concepts in the far-seeing legislation were well beyond the political and public sentiments of the day, and no action was undertaken on it or the revised bill submitted in 1908.

Nonetheless, Shiras' efforts later came to the attention of Congressman John W. Weeks and Senator George P. McLean. On March 4, 1913, the Federal Migratory Bird Law (Weeks-McLean Act) became effective, and the first federal migratory bird hunting regulations were adopted on October 1, 1913. The Weeks-McLean Act declared that certain designated migratory birds, including wild geese, swans, brant, and wild ducks were within the custody and protection of the federal government, and that they shall not be taken contrary to regulations established under the act. Unfortunately, the possible unconstitutionality of the act limited its effectiveness as the legality question was placed before the courts.

The legality of the Weeks-McLean Act became moot, however, with passage of the far more comprehensive Migratory Bird Treaty Act on July 3, 1918, which implemented the "Convention Between the United States and Great Britain for the Protection of Migratory Birds" (Canada at that time was a dominion under Great Britain), signed on August 16, 1916. The act provided for the development and promulgation of hunting regulations, including means, season times and lengths, areas open to hunting, and daily bag and possession limits. A key provision was that no hunting (or other taking) was permitted unless appropriate regulations were expressly promulgated. The act's constitutionality was sustained on April 21, 1920, in the landmark case *Missouri* v. *Holland* decided by the Supreme Court and read by Associate Justice Oliver Wendell Holmes. The Migratory Bird Treaty Act has been amended to implement subsequent migratory bird conventions signed with Mexico, Japan, and the Soviet Union. States may enact additional waterfowl regulations as long as they are more restrictive than the federal regulations.

On March 16, 1934, the Migratory Bird Hunting Stamp Act became law. It provided desperately needed funds for acquiring waterfowl habitats by requiring that all waterfowl hunters sixteen years of age or older purchase an annual federal duck stamp. The enforcement of this and the earlier legislation was assigned to the USBS.

Prior to 1919, the enforcement of various regulations relating to the USBS' administrative functions was decentralized. In that year, enforcement of the Lacey Act and administration of the new migratory bird law and regulations first became the responsibility of a single organizational division. Also, the division administering the eighty national game refuges and bird reservations then in existence was abolished and combined with the division administering the Migratory Bird Treaty and Lacey acts. The new unit was named the Division of Game and Bird Conservation.

In the late 1920s, Congress was appropriating only enough money annually to support twenty-five to thirty U.S. Game Protectors to cover all forty-eight States. The new division was directed by the United States Game Conservation Officer, assisted by two deputy officers, four administrative assistants, two biologists, and clerical support. In 1928 the chief officer drew a salary of $5,600. Full time U.S. Game Protectors were located at twenty-three field locations. At that time, their salaries ranged from $2,200 to $2,600 annually. In addition, between 600 and 700 Deputy U.S. Game Wardens were placed on duty during busy times of the year. They were paid on a per diem basis. A number of state game wardens were also empowered to act as U.S. Deputy Game Wardens.

Slow but steady progress was made by federal officers and their state colleagues in stamping out illegal hunting activities. However, of grave concern was the persistent illegal sale of waterfowl. Jenks Cameron summarized the market-hunting situation in the late 1920s as follows:

It has been well said that the charging of the survey with the enforcement of the Lacey and Migratory Bird Treaty Acts is really only a nominal charging in view of the fact that Congress has never appropriated funds for more than twenty-five to thirty wardens to cover forty-eight states, a thing that would not be an easy job for a force four times as large. It is also well known to those in a position to know that contraband game has not entirely disappeared from the markets of the larger cities. A great deal of it changes hands in a certain great midwestern city. It is not unobtainable for a consideration in many Atlantic seaboard cities. In the national capitol itself, it is not impossible to obtain it.

From the foregoing it might be gathered, at first blush, that the national and state legislation which has been enacted during the past thirty years, aimed at trafficking in wild fowl and other game birds, and the administrative effort which has been put forth thereunder, have constituted a mere essay in futility. But this is by no means the case. To be sure, the laws are violated, and violated to no mean extent. They will continue to be violated so long as human nature is what it is: so long as there exist in numbers in our large cities so-called ladies and gentlemen longer on cash than on character who are willing to compound law-breaking in order to give a "smart" dinner. So long as the game continues to be thumpingly worth the candle, there will be found shack-dwelling beach combers about our flats and marshes and estuaries, who will gun for market in spite of the game warden.

But this is only one side of the picture. If you look at this illegal leakage from the wild fowl flocks, and look at it alone, it bulks somewhat alarmingly large. When you compare it, however, with the leakage of the good old days, when the business arrangements between the city buyers and the feeding-ground shooters were "open covenants openly arrived at," you note that the comparison is between a trickle and a torrent.

Furthermore, it is a leakage that is getting progressively more difficult. As the years go by, there is coming to pass an improvement in enforcement both as regards to quality and quantity. Game wardens, both state and national, are getting to be better game wardens, and they are

Confiscated punt guns being inspected by USFWS biologist Hortin Jensen and Mexican officials in Mexico City. USFWS photo.

becoming more numerous, though they still — and especially the federal ones — are far from being numerous enough. Cooperation of the enforcing officers is improving. Finally, there is to be reckoned the great and growing force of sportsmanship among the great mass of our citizens who gun for pleasure and recreation. Unselfishness, consideration for the rights of the shooting fraternity at large, self-restraint, and an intelligent comprehension of the fact that the real reason for our game laws is the perpetuation of sporting opportunity — these things are not yet as universal as they might be. But it can be laid down most emphatically that the improvement along these lines in America during the past quarter century has been very great, and that no

signs exist of any reactionary tendency.

Upon cooperation between national and state game authorities has depended much of that attained in the enforcement of the federal wildlife statutes in the past, and is depending more and more on the success being attained at the present time. This cooperation, taking the country as a whole, is not yet one hundred percent perfect, but it can safely be said to be a thing that is constantly on the make; reflecting, in its trend, the improving ideals of sportsmanship and the increasing comprehension on the part of the public at large of the necessity for the replacing of the heedlessly wasteful ideas of the past with the conservational methods made imperative by the increasing complexity of civilization.

On July 1, 1934, a Division of Game Management, under the direction of Stanley P. Young, was established in the USBS. It contained a Section of Reservations and Game Agents under W. E. Couch and a Section of Law Enforcement under F. P. Callaghan. The title of the enforcement officers was changed from U.S. Game Protectors to U.S. Game Management Agents. Increased emphasis was placed on the enforcement of the migratory bird hunting regulations. In 1934, the number of apprehensions for waterfowl regulations increased by 100 over the previous year.

The bureau's annual report for 1935 stated that the regular force of twenty-two game management agents had been increased to twenty-five, and that thirty-two deputies were employed on a seasonal basis. For enforcement purposes, the country was divided into eight regions in the charge of regional directors who supervised the operations of game management agents and deputies. The deputy agents were organized into eight mobile units, or "flying squadrons," of four men each, to patrol major waterfowl concentration areas. The annual report also stated that forty-eight "duck sellers" had been apprehended along the Illinois River alone. The first national conference of the U.S. Game Management Agents was held in Chicago, Illinois, during September 24-26, 1935, to discusss law enforcement policies, court procedures, and individual and district problems.

In 1935, with the continued diminution of the waterfowl flights, the USBS, under "Ding" Darling's leadership, imposed the most restrictive hunting regulations on record. The hunting season was slashed to thirty days, the bag limit for ducks reduced to ten birds, baiting and use of live decoys were prohibited, sinkboxes and batteries were declared illegal, and shotgun capacities were reduced to three shells. An anguished outcry arose from some hunters who believed the restrictions far too severe. According to James Trefethen, "Ding" replied, "The regulations will stay as long as they are needed to bring back the ducks; and if tougher restric-

tions will help the course, we'll find some tougher restrictions."

The 1936 annual report noted that the number of U.S. Game Management Agents had been increased to thirty, and that they had at last been provided with adequate equipment for covering their assigned districts. This included cabincruisers for larger waterways, lighter boats and outboard engines for inland waters, automobiles for land patrol, and auto-trailers for transporting lighter boats. The report went on to explain that the officers had been issued badges of a new design and that they wore a distinctive uniform when on patrol, attending court, or representing the bureau at meetings. It noted, however, that uniform was not worn during "special duty or undercover operations."

On July 1, 1939, the USBS was transferred to the Department of the Interior; on June 30, 1940, the USBS and the Bureau of Fisheries were consolidated into the Fish and Wildlife Service. Fish and Wildlife Service Director Albert M. Day announced on November 15, 1951, the expansion of the enforcement and management program for migratory waterfowl and the establishment of the Branch of Game Management. Another reorganization on November 15, 1956, placed wildlife enforcement responsibilities of the Branch of Management and Enforcement in the newly formed Bureau of Sport Fisheries and Wildlife. On July 1, 1972, the waterfowl management responsibilities of the Division of Management and Enforcement were assigned to the new Office of Migratory Bird Management, while the enforcement responsibilities were placed in the new Division of Law Enforcement on September 28, 1972. On July 1, 1974, the Bureau of Sport Fisheries and Wildlife became the U.S. Fish and Wildlife Service.

The titles of the federal officers responsible for enforcing the federal wildlife laws and regulations also changed over the years. They include: Inspector, Interstate Commerce in Game (1900-1918); U.S. Game Warden (1918-1928); U.S. Game Protector (1928-1934); U.S. Game Management Agent (1934-

1973); and Special Agent (1973 to present).

Efforts of federal wildlife law officers generally focused on those regulations that posed the greatest threat to the waterfowl resource. These included using illegal means of taking waterfowl (such as trapping, shooting over bait, use of live decoys, use of sinkboxes), times of taking (such as out of season and after permitted hunting hours), and the extent of taking (taking protected species and exceeding allowed daily limits). However, much effort was directed to stamping out the commercialization and sale of waterfowl.

Market hunting of waterfowl was prohibited by the Migratory Bird Treaty Act, but this ingrained exploitation of the waterfowl resource persisted for decades thereafter on a reduced but, nonetheless, serious scale. Commercialization often persisted wherever local abundance of waterfowl and an affluent segment of society mingled. Personal courage, dedication, and innovation of wildlife law enforcement officers were taxed to the utmost as efforts were made to eliminate this most nefarious type of violation. Often, officers had to resort to undercover operations to gain the evidence required to sustain convictions in the courts.

U.S. Game Management Agent Hugh Worchester wrote in 1955 of his efforts to eliminate market hunting in the Central Valley of California during the 1930s and 1940s. Special Criminal Investigator Tony Stefano was notably successful as an undercover operator in California, Texas, and the upper Mississippi River valley during the 1950s, and his exploits in Texas were described in articles appearing in *Field & Stream* articles in 1956 and 1957. Many other successful undercover programs have not been publicized, but they nonetheless contributed to a reduction in market hunting and commercialization. Albert Day described some of the notable enforcement efforts of the "Wildlife G-men" in his 1949 book, *North American Waterfowl.* Hopefully other exploits will eventually be made public. Needless to say, the very lives of these undercover operators,

as well as those of their colleagues who functioned publicly were frequently placed on the line.

Even less well documented and described are the other management activities of the federal law enforcement officers. They routinely participated in an array of management and data gathering programs including local and regional waterfowl surveys, the national winter waterfowl survey, banding, bag checks of waterfowl hunters, investigating crop depredations, and promoting public education and relations. While these activities were chiefly limited to the United States, game management agents were routinely assigned to waterfowl studies in Canada as early as 1934. There they and bureau biologists comprised teams that annually evaluated waterfowl breeding and production conditions; information from these studies was used by both U.S. and Canadian administrators for developing the hunting regulations for the following autumn and fall. For many years, supervision of the operational waterfowl surveys and the banding program was assigned to the Branch of Management and Enforcement.

In their enforcement activities, federal agents have been fortunate in having the cooperation of state and local officials, and often the assistance of sportsmen and other citizens. Hopefully, the full story of the federal law enforcement officer's role in North American waterfowl management will be told so that these remarkable individuals will receive the recognition they so richly deserve.

National Wildlife Refuges

The USFWS' National Wildlife Refuge System is the most comprehensive and diverse assemblage of habitats managed for wildlife that exists in the world. Although these tracts were acquired for the benefit of many forms of wildlife, most provide primary or secondary values to waterfowl. Nearly all have some value for breeding, migrating, or wintering ducks, geese, brant, and swans.

The first national wildlife refuge was the

three-acre Pelican Island in Florida, which President Theodore Roosevelt had created by executive order on March 14, 1903, for the protection of brown pelicans and other colonial birds. The first caretaker, deputy game warden Paul Kroegel, was paid the salary of fifteen dollars per month — and had to furnish his own boat and firearm!

Space does not allow us to describe in detail the fascinating story of how the national wildlife system came into being and, nourished by public support, grew to its present size and diversity. The story, however, has been told well many times. Outstanding treatments of the topic can be found in Albert Day's *North American Waterfowl*; James Trefethen's *An American Crusade for Wildlife*; the section on "Federal Refuges" (written by J. Clark Salyer II and Francis G. Gillett) in *Waterfowl Tomorrow*, edited by Joseph P. Linduska; and a special issue of *Fish and Wildlife News* that appeared December-January, 1978-1979. Additionally, much of Ira Gabrielson's book, *Wildlife Refuges*, focuses on the National Wildlife Refuge System. Though the details are to be found elsewhere, we would be remiss not to recognize some of the major events relating to the establishment of wildlife refuges for waterfowl.

Initially, most federal wildlife refuges were created by executive orders. These refuges were usually small in size and designed for some particular species or group of birds, often colonial nesters, or big game. In 1924 Congress appropriated the unheard of amount of $1.5 million for acquisition of bottomlands along the upper Mississippi River for the Upper Mississippi River Wildlife and Fish Refuge. This complex extended from Wabasha, Minnesota, to Rock Island, Illinois. This was also the first national wildlife refuge on which public hunting was specifically authorized.

In 1928 Congress appropriated $350,000 to establish the Bear River Migratory Bird Refuge in Utah. A major objective was to reduce waterfowl losses to botulism by impounding and regulating the waters of the Bear River before it emptied into the Great Salt Lake.

The Migratory Bird Conservation Act, became law in 1929. It authorized establishment of a migratory bird refuge system, appropriated monies for habitat acquisition, and created the Migratory Bird Conservation Commission. This commission was given the authority to review tracts for inclusion in the refuge system, a power usually limited to Congress. Members of the commission included the Secretaries of Interior (who served as chairman), Agriculture, and Transportation; two members each from the Senate and House of Representatives; and an ex officio member from the state in which acquisition is being considered. The amended act also provided for rental or acceptance by gift of areas suitable for the National Wildlife Refuge System.

Salyer and Gillett's section in *Waterfowl Tomorrow* tells us that 1929 also marked the beginning of the great drought that wrought havoc on North America's waterfowl. The drought gradually grew worse, reaching its peak of severity in 1934 and continuing for about four years before relief came. Waterfowl populations dwindled as prairie wetlands became dry or unsuitable for breeding.

The Beck Committee, appointed by President Roosevelt in 1934, identified the need to preserve habitat if the waterfowl resource were to be salvaged and restored. The committee recommended that a $50 million program to purchase and rehabilitate nesting wetlands be undertaken. As is related elsewhere, Ding Darling was chosen by Roosevelt to direct a revitalized USBS, one of whose new programs was the expanded national refuge system. "Ding" aroused much public support for the new program and in 1934 alone he was able to garner $8.5 million from emergency acts relating to the retirement of submarginal farmlands, drought relief, and Works Progress Administration programs, and a special fund of $1 million.

Refuge acquisition centered in the eighteen states that had been specifically designated for drought relief. Many of these states had also been major producers of waterfowl. The initially appropriate funds for land purchases was obligated by June 15, 1935, and Congress voted another $6 million to extend the refuge acquisition program. This time lands for refuges could be acquired in the Atlantic coastal states and the lower half of the Mississippi Flyway. Appropriated funds were augmented by revenues derived from the sale of federal waterfowl hunting (duck) stamps.

Civilian Conservation Corps (CCC) camps were established on many refuges and thousands of CCC workers undertook much of the work to develop and improve the new refuges. Some assisted in biological studies. Many CCC enrollees, aroused by their experience, went on to become wildlife refuge managers, biologists, and administrators.

The Fish and Wildlife Coordination Act of 1934 expanded the scope and authority of the USBS and its successors by recognizing wildlife and recreation values on federal water development projects. Several new federal refuges and state management areas were established by this means. In addition, at least seven national wildlife refuges were created from submarginal lands transferred to the Biological Survey by the Resettlement and Farm Security Administration. Salyer and Gillett credit Congressmen McNary, Norbeck, Pittman, Andresen, Anthony, Robertson, and Shiras for passage of much of the key legislation leading to the expansion of the National Wildlife Refuge System. Many of these same congressmen were instrumental in the passage of other wildlife legislation during the 1930s.

At this point, we should also recognize the great contributions of J. Clark Salyer II to the national refuge program. Darling first met Salyer when the latter participated as an ornithologist in the biological survey of Iowa. When Darling became USBS chief, he selected the thirty-two-year old Salyer to head up the burgeoning national refuge program. Long afterward, "Ding" wrote that the young Salyer was among the two "most competent, efficient and courageous members of his staff" (the other being Clarence Cottam). Without Salyer, "Ding" asserted,

the success story of the national wildlife refuge development program could not have been recorded. During his lengthy career, Salyer visited nearly all the national wildlife refuges, and knew the character and management problems and opportunities of each intimately. Late in his career, after his loss of sight, he was still able to vividly recall details of the various refuges, to his co-workers' astonishment. By 1961, when Salyer left his post as supervisor of the Division of Wildlife Refuges, the system had grown to 279 refuges, encompassing some 29 million acres. Fran Gillett succeeded Salyer as the head of the refuge system until his retirement. Breaking with tradition, one of the gems of the system, Lower Souris National Wildlife Refuge in North Dakota was renamed J. Clark Salyer National Wildlife Refuge.

With inflation, particularly in the cost of land, it was not surprising that the expenses in acquiring land for national wildlife refuges would outstrip available funds. Consequently it was necessary to increase the cost of the duck stamp. The price increased as follows: original cost in 1934, one dollar; two dollars in 1949; three dollars in 1958 (with the provision that up to 40 percent of a refuge could be opened to public hunting); five dollars in 1971; and seven dollars and fifty cents in 1979. In addition, the Wetlands Loan Act of 1961 (extended in 1967 and 1976) allowed the Service to draw upon anticipated revenues from the future sale of duck stamps as a means of expediting the acquisition of wildlife refuges and a new program for acquiring waterfowl production areas in major waterfowl producing states of the upper Midwest. The later program was designed to protect by purchase or easement key waterfowl producing areas that were under threat of drainage for agricultural production. Countless thousands of acres of valuable wetlands had been drained in the prairie pothole region of the two Dakotas and Minnesota since the conclusion of World War II.

Passage of the 250 million dollar Bicentennial Land Heritage Program in 1976 gave impetus to the National Wildlife Refuge Sys-

Pilot John Ball is on the wing of the Grumman Widgeon, while in the background is a Grumman Goose at Kodiak Island in Alaska. These two aircrafts were the workhorses for survey work, starting shortly after World War II. USFWS photo.

tem. The five-year program was designed to upgrade the system by providing money for construction and rehabilitation of refuge facilities, and strengthen the refuge staff.

The National Wildlife Refuge system is an extensive network of Federal lands providing habitat valuable to wildlife. The Refuge System encompasses 89.9 million acres and includes 418 refuges, 149 waterfowl production areas, and 58 wildlife management areas. Some 392 refuges are categorized as principally migratory bird areas and 25 are managed primarily for their mammal and non-migratory bird values. Units of the National Wildlife Refuge System are found in 49 states (all except West Virginia), Puerto Rico, the Virgin Islands, and the Pacific Trust Territories.

In addition to managing habitat for waterfowl, refuge personnel have banded countless thousands of ducks and geese, cooperated in various waterfowl surveys, participated in public education and relations programs, enforced hunting regulations, and assisted in controlling waterfowl depredations on private lands. As with U.S. Game Management Agents, the story of their contributions to the overall waterfowl management program has not yet been fully told.

Cooperative Wildlife Restoration

Many earlier conservationists of the 1930s foresaw that a truly effective wildlife restoration program of national scope would have to be cooperative in nature. This was envisioned by Aldo Leopold, "Ding" Darling, and Thomas Beck, all members of FDR's Committee on Wildlife Restoration. Too often excessive concern about the alleged rights of federal and state prerogatives and responsibilities had interfered with progress in wildlife conservation. Lacking was a formalized means of undertaking a cooperative wildlife program of national significance. And especially absent was the funding required to support such a program. Both obstacles were to be overcome by the Federal Aid to Wildlife Restoration Act, often known as the Pittman-Robertson or PR Act.

In addressing the first North American Wildlife Conference in 1936, Darling, former Chief of the Bureau of Biological Survey, identified three common aims in restoring wildlife populations, noting "that the restoration of wildlife is synonymous with restoration of the environment." Senator Key Pittman, later cosponsor of the wildlife restoration act, also exhorted sportsmen and women and conservationists to join forces with others in pressing for needed legislation. Ira N. Gabrielson, then USBS chief, outlined a seven-point national wildlife program. The second point outlined the need for a cooperative federal-state program for restoring wildlife. Gabe candidly stated:

> Furthermore, I see no reason why the Federal Government should not assist the States in some of their wildlife problems. To me one of the great tragedies of the whole conservation movement is the financial uncertainty in State game agencies. Most of them are dependent on license fees for hunting and fishing, and those license fees fluctuate tremendously. This uncertainty seriously cripples many conservation activities, and as if the commission's own financial hazards were not enough, the ingenuity of other interests in chiseling money from the fish and game organizations is something to marvel at if it weren't so tragic. I have known of money to build statues, to build highways, and to do all other kinds of things that might be of political advantage to someone, being taken from the State game funds. Because of this and other handicaps, the State agencies have hesitated in many instances to embark on any kind of a refuge or land ownership program.
>
> They simply haven't done it. The Federal Government does cooperate with existing State organizations in other fields in helping them solve this problem. I offer as a suggestion that the Federal Government might well make provision to help State agencies finance wildlife restoration programs and refuge-acquisition programs where it is necessary for the perpetuation of their wildlife or the development of their conservation activities. If it is possible for the Federal Government to help finance highways, to help finance the acquisition of forest lands, and to help set up agriculture experiment stations and acquire lands for that purpose, I see no reason why it shouldn't do the same thing for wildlife.

The notion that the hunter should carry part of the financial burden for supporting the migratory bird resource had been advanced previously. For example, a private foundation named More Game Birds in America proposed a-cent-a-shell tax on shotgun ammunition as a means of funding the establishment, improvement, and management of waterfowl breeding grounds and refuges, and financing increased administration cost and additional research work. The foundation estimated that such revenues would approximate more than $3.5 million annually, more than ten times what had been spent in past years for waterfowl. More Game Birds in America admonished sportsmen to lobby for the adoption of the tax, noting that the choice was between "less hunting or more paying! The longer the cure is deferred the larger the dose required and the heavier the doctor's fee. If it is postponed too long, well, there simply will not be any use of trying to save the patient."

The Federal Aid to Wildlife Restoration Act, which took effect on July 1, 1938, authorized appropriations not to exceed the annual revenue from the 10 percent excise tax on sporting arms and ammunition. On that same date, Albert M. Day took charge of the Biological Survey's new Division of Federal Aid in Wildlife Restoration. Under the cooperative program, states paid 25 percent of the cost of completed approved projects, while the federal agency contributed 75 percent of the cost. At the close of the first year, forty-two states had enacted the necessary "assent" legislation to permit them to participate in the program, and thirty-seven of these had submitted approvable project proposals. The apportionment of money to the states was based on the land area and number of hunting license holders in each state. The initial appropriation was for $1,000,000 of which $890,000 was apportioned to the states.

At the third "North American," details of the recently passed Pittman-Robertson Act were explained. Albert M. Day flatly stated that it was "the most forward-looking conservation measure since the Migratory Bird Treaty Act was approved in 1918." He noted

The official opening of the Northern Prairie Wildlife Research Center, in September 1965. Officials present (left to right): C. Edward Carlson, Chief of Wildlife Research; Stanley Cain, Assistant Secretary of the Interior; Harvey K. Nelson, Center Director; John Gottschalk, Director for USFWS. USFWS photo.

that "the language throughout the entire act speaks in terms of restoration of the natural environment habitat. It is meant to provide a means for the states to acquire and improve lands so that wildlife may reproduce normally and supply a surplus to be harvested by hunters. The act also emphasizes the need for additional research into problems of wildlife management."

Many states used federal aid monies to initiate the acquisition and development of waterfowl management areas, and to undertake comprehensive waterfowl investigations. Two years later, Al Day was able to report further progress in the Pittman-Robertson Program. On July 1, 1939, an additional $1.5 million had been made available to states, and in the following year the amount had been increased to $2.5 million. The forty-three states that had established eligibility for the program had submitted a total of 232 projects for funding. While these included a broad spectrum of wildlife activities, many directly involved waterfowl habitat acquisition, management, and research. An incidental benefit of the program was the employment opportunities made available to professional wildlife graduates, many of whom were recent products of the Cooperative Wildlife Research Unit Program.

During the first fifteen years of the Pittman-Robertson Program, thirty-eight states acquired and improved habitat for waterfowl. By 1961, 912,739 acres had been acquired and developed for waterfowl. Some areas were designated as refuges, some as public

hunting areas, and other served dual functions.

Other PR-supported state management and research investigations — chiefly involving surveys, banding, biological examinations, and habitat inventory and evaluations — have contributed greatly to the national waterfowl management program. The following key figures reflect the large contribution to waterfowl managment and research made by state conservation agencies during the period 1938-1979. In that period, over $208 million was spent. Over $1.6 million acres of habitat were purchased at a cost of nearly $43.5 million. The greatest expenditure, $134.6 million, was for land development, with over $30 million going for research.

These expenditures do not include states' funds which are obligated in the ratio of one dollar for every three dollars in federal aid monies. Gabe's and Al Day's fondest expectations have been fulfilled.

Research

From the early days of the USBS, when new emphasis was placed on the economic value of wildlife, research has been a major activity of the USFWS. Earlier waterfowl investigations were conducted by two major facilities: the Denver Wildlife Research Center, Denver, Colorado, and the Patuxent Wildlife Research Center, Laurel, Maryland. Several substations were established to concentrate on special studies such as those on

Cooperative Wildlife Research Unit Leader, Jessup B. Low, examines a muskrat house as a potential Canada goose nesting site. The setting is Ogden Bay Waterfowl Management Area in Utah, in 1950.

botulism at the Bear River Refuge in Utah. As waterfowl management intensified, the need became evident for a facility that could devote full time to the study of waterfowl problems. In 1963, such a station was established in North Dakota, the Northern Prairie Wildlife Research Center at Jamestown. Harvey K. Nelson was the first director. Shortly thereafter, a research station with similar responsibilities, the Prairie Migratory Bird Research Centre, was established by the CWS at Saskatoon, Saskatchewan. These two research centers have continued in close cooperation to conduct research on a variety of waterfowl populations and habitat problems in North America.

Additional research on waterfowl has been conducted through the cooperative program described in the next section.

Other Contributors

As noted earlier, nearly all organization units and program activities of the USFWS relate in some manner to waterfowl. The Division of Realty plays a major role in the habitat acquisition program by negotiating purchases, easements, and rights ascertaining fair market values, and overseeing and performing the many necessary functions associated with the transfer of lands and rights to the federal government for wildlife purposes. The Division of Engineering performs the necessary surveys for locating and marking boundaries of the areas being acquired. Public Affairs people perform important functions in informing the public of current developments and producing informational booklets, books, and films. Among the most popular of all publications produced by the Government Printing Office is *Ducks At A Distance*, a waterfowl identification guide showing color illustrations of most North American waterfowl. The office also supervises the annual duck stamp contest; in 1980 more than 1,400 entries were received. The Division of Wildlife Management provides technical support to farmers experiencing crop depredations from waterfowl, and to other individuals having nuisance bird problems. These examples illustrate the broad importance of waterfowl in the USFWS' activities.

Cooperative Wildlife Research Units

Jessup B. Low and Daniel L. Leedy

C. Hart Merriam, the director of the USBS, wrote in this 1909 annual report: "Cooperation with state game officials and others interested in game and birds continues to be an important part of this work." But it was not until many years later that cooperation on the scale we now know it occurred.

In 1934, in a reorganization of wildlife research, a Section of Distribution and Migration of Birds was established under the direction of Frederick C. Lincoln, a section of the Division of Wildlife Research. Although a Section of Cooperative Wildlife Research Units was not yet a reality, plans for it were being made.

In the late 1920s and early 1930s waterfowl populations were plummeting because of drought, drainage, and other factors. During that period "Ding" Darling — a nationally syndicated cartoonist, dedicated conservationist, and member of the Iowa State Fish and Game Commission — recognized the need for more facts upon which to base sound conservation programs as well as the need for trained personnel to carry out those programs. He also recognized that at Iowa State University (then Iowa State College of Agriculture and Mechanical Arts) there were knowledgeable individuals, such as Paul L. Errington, who were interested in conducting wildlife research and who could help train students in the wildlife field. Accordingly, by enlisting the support of the state Fish and Game Commission and by using some personal funds, Ding promoted the inauguration of an expanded cooperative wildlife research and training program at the university in 1932.

One of the initial projects of this program was a study of the blue-winged teal. This study was conducted primarily in the most important remaining duck breeding region of northwestern Iowa by a student named Logan J. Bennett. As part of the investigation, however, Bennett and Charles Friley, Jr. obtained additional data elsewhere in Iowa and in Nebraska, South Dakota, North Dakota, Wyoming, Minnesota, and Manitoba. Also, to learn more about conditions on the wintering grounds of this species, Bennett spent four weeks in Mexico in December 1936 and January 1937.

Meanwhile, Ding Darling — still convinced of the value of combining the resources of universities, state fish and game departments, and private organizations in a cooperative wildlife research and training program — was appointed chief of the Bureau of Biological Survey (USBS) in March 1934. On November 8, 1934, Darling visited Utah State University where, in the school year of 1930-31, Professor T. G. Taylor had inaugurated the school's first course in wildlife management. During Darling's visit, Professor Taylor suggested the establishment of an "Intermountain Wildlife Experiment Station" at Logan. His suggestion was not to go unheeded. Although he was bureau chief only until November 1935, Darling obtained congressional and other support for initiating the national Cooperative Wildlife Research Unit Program.

The USBS' annual report for the fiscal year ending June 30, 1935, stated, "Plans were completed at the end of the year for initiating nine combined wildlife research, demonstration, and educational units in various representative regions, in cooperation with land-grant colleges and State game commissions. These projects will be for the purpose of conducting fundamental investigations, applying the results to local wildlife-management conditions, and carrying them to landowners, both public and private, by demonstration and extension methods.

The 1936 annual report of the Bureau listed as "established and at work," units located as follows: Alabama Polytechnic Institute, Auburn, Alabama; Connecticut State College, Storrs, Connecticut; Iowa State College of Agriculture and Mechanical Arts, Ames, Iowa; University of Maine,

359

Orono, Maine; Ohio State University, Columbus, Ohio; Oregon State Agricultural College, Corvallis, Oregon; Agricultural and Mechanical College of Texas, College Station, Texas; Utah State Agricultural College, Logan, Utah; and Virginia Polytechnic Institute, Blacksburg, Virginia.

The 1936 annual report also described the initial arrangements for funding as follows: "Project leader's salary, by the Bureau of Biological Survey; $3,000 in cash, by the American Wildlife Institute; not less than $6,000 in cash or its equivalent in services, equipment, or facilities, by the land-grant college; and not less that $6,000 in cash or its equivalent in services, equipment, or facilities by the State game department."

Federal funding for these cooperative units was accomplished under existing authorizations of the USBS and (later) under the USFWS by means of language in the annual appropriation bills of Congress until 1960, when Congress passed the Cooperative Unit Program Act. This act gave added status to the program.

Over the forty-five years the program has been operating, units in Connecticut and Texas were disbanded, many of the institutions and agencies have been given different names, and many additional cooperative wildlife research units have been established. The Wildlife Management Institute, successor of the American Wildlife Institute, continued to support the wildlife units through regular grants and grants for special projects. The cooperative fisheries units were patterned after wildlife units.

Research and training objectives for each unit were established by a coordinating committee made up of a representative from the unit's cooperating agencies. The annual objectives were set within a framework of the broad goals of the unit program to accomplish research needs by the cooperators, to provide training for biologists for professional careers through conduct of this research; and to disseminate research findings to resource management agencies, the scientific community, and the general public. The

projects were by no means limited to waterfowl. To paraphrase former flyway biologist Charles E. Gillham, they dealt with analysis from "A to izzard" of "any critter from an earthworm to a polar bear." However, many are concerned with waterfowl and their management.

Establishment of the Cooperative Wildlife Research Unit Program in 1935-36 was timely in that its primary products — professionally trained personnel and research findings — could be put to use immediately in the expanded programs resulting from a series of federal acts. For example, the "Duck Stamp Act" of 1934 provided funds for the acquisition of more wildlife refuge lands and waters for which both management methodologies and management personnel were needed. Similarly, the Federal Aid to Wildlife Restoration Act of 1937 (Pittman-Robertson Act) required many new employees for implementation, particularly at the state level.

Although the federally employed wildlife research unit leaders served as faculty advisors to many of the graduate students and often conducted seminars, special classes, or assisted in the development of new wildlife-oriented courses, the universities — with their professors and specialized, as well as supportive, courses in many disciplines — had the major role in training. Therefore, it is appropriate to speak of "unit school graduates" when discussing the personnel coming out of the program. Without detracting from the importance of the unit schools, we should note that other universities, such as the University of Wisconsin and Cornell University — neither of which had cooperative wildlife research units early in the program, nonetheless were actively engaged in wildlife research and training.

The remainder of this section will be devoted largely to some observations on waterfowl-related research activities and accomplishments of the wildlife units, and to the roles of some of the students following graduation from the unit schools. These accounts can in no way be considered as comprehensive but, rather, as illustrative.

All of the cooperative units have been engaged to some extent with waterfowl research. Some of the studies have been brief, while others have been carried out over long periods of time; likewise, some of the research results or observations have been published as brief scientific papers or notes and others as books. Many graduate student theses and dissertations were never published, but, nevertheless, are available in university libraries for the serious waterfowl researcher or manager. Also, the experience gained by the student working under the supervision of qualified unit leaders or university professors constitutes a part of the student's training.

Among the earlier established units, those in Iowa, Maine, Missouri, and Utah, especially, gave considerable attention to waterfowl. Later, established units such as Colorado, Idaho, Montana, and New York also investigated many waterfowl management-related problems.

Beginning where we left off, with the student Logan Bennett in Iowa, let us comment on some of the major waterfowl publications resulting from cooperative unit investigations. Bennett's doctoral thesis was published in 1938 as *The Blue-Winged Teal: its ecology and management* when the author was leader of the Pennsylvania Cooperative Wildlife Research Unit. This 144-page book is still referred to frequently.

In Maine, prior to 1943, studies of the ring-necked duck were incidental to other waterfowl investigations of the unit; but from 1943 through 1955, they constituted one of the Maine unit's major research projects.

The findings from this long-term investigation by Unit Leader Howard L. Mendall were published in 1958 as a 317-page University of Maine Bulletin, titled *The Ring-Necked Duck in the Northeast*. This well-written book contains a wealth of information on the ring-necked duck and its management.

Arthur S. Einarsen, former leader of the Oregon unit, wrote the following in the preface to his book, *Black Brant: sea goose of the Pacific Coast*:

> In everyone's mind there are recollections so vivid that he can easily relive past experiences. How clearly I remember a day in late November, 1903, when the smell of burning peat moss was in the air. I was a little boy standing on the barrier beach of Livingston Bay and looking out across the water to Mt. Rainier. The incoming tide lapped softly against the massive driftwood piled high on the beach, and the glassy surface of the bay was broken only where widgeons cruised leisurely, cutting V-shaped ripples as they searched for food. Cattle were lowing in the nearby meadows; cowbells tinkled as the dairy herd moved toward the barn, urged by the shepherd dog; and from the sea came a compelling and eerie call, vibrant and reedlike.
>
> Thoughtfully I wandered back to my home at the edge of the meadow, and in the glow of the kitchen lamp I tried to tell my parents about the mysterious music I had heard over the water. "It must have been some bird," said my mother. To this day these haunting notes stir within me mental pictures of the sunset, the sea, the burnished water of the bay, and the silhouette of flying birds against a deep rosy sky.

It was some years later on this same Washington bay that Art Einarsen learned that the bird he had heard calling was the Pacific black brant. His fascination with the bird remained undiminished, and in due time he undertook to bring together the scattered information available on the species and supplement it with his own observations made from the Arctic to Mexico.

Although special mention has been made of these three books based upon early unit projects, many scores of other waterfowl-related reports of varying length have been published in professional journals, as bulletins, or in other forms. These have contributed substantially to the knowledge of waterfowl, to research techniques, and to management methods.

From the High Latitudes

Henry A. Hansen

Within a day or so of my arrival in Alaska, I overheard an associate pleading with a Washington office figurehead who insisted on conformity. "But Alaska is different. You can't compare us with stateside situations." During subsequent years, I not only heard that assertion repeated often, but I learned to use it myself as circumstances warranted.

On my first field trip to the interior, I experienced a very basic difference between life in the high latitudes and the "lower forty-eight," as they were called (sometimes with condescension). Following a long day of flying in mid-June, I landed at Fort Yukon, eight miles north of the Arctic Circle. Wanting to get an early start the following morning, I bedded down at 9:30 P.M. on the upper level of Cliff Fairchild's roadhouse in a sparsely furnished, north-facing room.

My deep and satisfying sleep was suddenly interrupted by brilliant sunlight flashing through the window. I checked my watch and wondered how I could possibly have slept until noon. I threw on my clothes, raced out into a sleeping village and then saw the sun hanging on the northern horizon in a saddle of the Brooks Range. Since I was already awake and wanted an early start anyway, I reluctantly began my day at midnight.

Those long summer days represented quite an adjustment for a midwestern farm boy brought up to think that daylight is for working and darkness is for sleeping. This and other differences facilitated a departure from the normal way of doing things, administratively and operationally.

Prior to 1941 sporadic and cursory ornithological studies had been conducted in Alaska for about 150 years, usually the afterthought of a broader investigation of natural resources as a whole. Probably the more important contributions to our general knowledge of waterfowl came between 1920 and the beginning of World War II from O. J. Murie, Frank Dufresne, Ira N. Gabrielson, H. W. Brandt, and C. E. Gillham.

Gillham initiated in 1941 what was probably the first specific waterfowl study on the Yukon Delta near Hooper Bay. This was interrupted by the war, and no more waterfowl work was attempted until 1948. When I arrived in May 1955, I was given a broad mandate to organize and supervise a program to learn all about waterfowl — without guidelines, instructions, employees, equipment, or long-range objectives — but with $22,500 per annum to do the job.

Conforming to government policy, the areas in which my budget could be spent were clearly identified. The money would cover my salary and expenses, plus those of any temporary summer employees I could indenture into service. It would also pay for flight time and any equipment that could be purchased out of year-end funds. Equipment accumulated slowly, and employees rotated rapidly.

During territorial days prior to 1959, the USFWS administered fish and game programs for Alaska in lieu of a state government. Pittman-Robertson funding was allocated to Alaska with essentially the same guidelines and regulations that applied to the states. To insure that the moose and caribou projects in Alaska did not inadvertently allow any federal aid money to revert, I quickly learned how to tap those funds to supplement my meager waterfowl budget. Within two years the waterfowl project budget was swelled to $30,000, where it remained for about ten years — a period of significant accomplishment. Much manpower, equipment, and flight time were generously provided to the waterfowl program by other activities, particularly through the Branch of Management and Enforcement. These contributions enhanced the productivity of the waterfowl program far more than its meager budget would allow.

By the time the waterfowl program was established in Alaska under its own identity in 1955, survey and banding activities were well standardized and progressing rapidly elsewhere on the continent, including northern Canada. Funding, as well as line and technical supervision, for that large endeavor came directly from the central office in Washington.

I was an exception, designated supervisor of Waterfowl Investigations in Alaska as opposed to my flyway biologist counterparts elsewhere. At the suggestion of a distraught typist, my six-word title was soon condensed to waterfowl supervisor. My line supervision was delegated to the regional office in Juneau, but technical supervision was retained in Washington to maintain quality control of data gathering. This had both advantages and disadvantages that were frequently frustrating. In retrospect the advantages probably tipped the scales favorably, covering an error of omission here and possibly a sin of commission there from time to time.

There is an axiom that seemed to culminate in its ultimate application in faraway Alaska; namely, the attention a problem receives varies in an inverse ratio to its distance from Washington, D.C. In the financial structure of the USFWS, my waterfowl project was identified in the Alaska regional budget. But because of the split jurisdiction between Alaska and Washington, neither seemed to feel responsible for adequate financing of the waterfowl project. Because we insisted that Alaska was different, we were apparently expected to work out our own salvation in different ways. Hence, the necessity of tapping other activities on an ad hoc basis.

The standard operating procedures of air and ground surveys applied to Alaska as elsewhere; however, for additional flexibility, we adapted some of the procedures to our different circumstances: 1) survey transects were laid out in whatever direction necessary to cross the river valley and coastal tundra habitat at right angles, rather than the precise east-west pattern of the prairies and northern Canada; 2) transects were divided into sixteen-mile segments instead of the standard

eighteen-mile segments used elsewhere; 3) surveys were conducted early in the morning when possible, but not always, because of logistics problems and highly variable wind and weather conditions; and 4) aerial brood surveys proved entirely unworkable as a means of measuring production and were eliminated after experimentation. As long as the breeding population survey was conducted in a timely manner to provide data for the annual hunting regulations, there was wide latitude to "learn all about waterfowl."

Toward this end, goals and objectives were needed to establish an orderly, long-range program. The ultimate goal was to save and protect a maximum amount of Alaska's prime waterfowl habitat in pristine condition. This was a vision of two former regional directors under whom I worked, Clarence Rhode and Pete Nelson. To achieve the goal, substantial data were needed to document the extent of this habitat, the numbers and kinds of waterfowl using it, and the resource's values to the people of North America. This was needed to counter inevitable pressures for development. An array of objectives designed to build on previous work and to gather additional necessary information was developed. In conjunction with aerial and ground surveys, a massive banding program became the cornerstone of our waterfowl project.

Ground studies of a rather general nature, as well as more specific research projects, were conducted in several diverse areas over a period of years. These were usually in support of our goal, but were sometimes a response to questions raised by researchers to the south. For example, we verified yearling breeding in lesser scaup and documented the fate of ducks displaced from the prairies during years of severe drought. In the aggregate, these studies produced an impressive array of information that will continue to pay dividends long into the future, although none was pursued as long as a biologist would desire.

During early aerial surveys from 1949 to 1954, biologists located all major breeding areas and delineated boundaries. At some locations extensive banding had been done (black brant and cackling geese on the Yukon Delta), and breeding population surveys on the more imporant areas had been conducted. In 1949 Dave Spencer made the first limited aerial survey on the Yukon Delta and experimented with a workable randomness-of-sample as opposed to a textbook approach. He quickly demonstrated that distribution of waterfowl on tundra habitat and distribution of beans in a laboratory jar have little in common. When I designed an extensive aerial survey for all of Alaska, I adopted Dave's common-sense approach to randomness in the interest of economy and out of logistical necessity. This didn't appear to compromise the validity of our data.

One of the basic weaknesses of the waterfowl survey in Alaska was its constantly changing cast of observers. In 1955, for instance, there were thirteen observers at different times and in different locations. Most were untrained and some could not realiably identify waterfowl. At times it seemed that individuals were assigned to the survey merely to provide ballast in the right seat. Usually these were one-day "pickups" from the geographic area of the survey, because one individual could not be spared from his primary job for the full three-week period. In 1956 the number was reduced to eight observers, and it was further reduced to six and five in 1957 and 1958. After that the survey was conducted with only one or two observers each year, but very seldom was the same person available for two consecutive years. This game of musical chairs with observers introduced a recurring bias of unknown proportions into the waterfowl index. On the prairies this was worked out by standardizing crews. As there seemed to be no prospect for permanent observers in Alaska, an effort was made to standardize whoever landed in the right seat against a common denominator, the pilot-observer.

The waterfowl supervisor became the common denominator, designated "observer X." In comparing the other observers it was assumed that observer X was a constant throughout and was assigned a par value of 100. The other observers were given a value above or below 100, depending on the number of ducks they counted relative to observer X. This difference in observers was designated a "vision factor" as opposed to "visibility factor." The first has to do with different people's ability to see, and the latter reflects various species' inability to keep from being seen because of coloration, choice of loafing sites, or other factors. Of six observers tested, one of them for a four-year period, the counts ranged from a low of 59 percent of par value to a high of 131 percent, with an overall average of 95 percent.

Our research statisticians viewed this exercise with a range of opinions from "mickey mouse" through "interesting" and "worth pursuing further, but not at the expense of doing something worthwhile." Be that as it may, I continued to correct our annual breeding population estimates with a little of the "English" that the vision factor provided as long as observers continued to spin in and out of the revolving door. What the exercise really pointed out was the need to develop good air-ground comparison studies in the north that would show by species the number of ducks on the ground that were missed by aerial observers, so that a corrective factor could be developed as had been done on the prairies.

Subsequently, Rampart Dam gave us the opportunity to complete such a study for the spruce-muskeg habitat of the interior. A companion study has never been done for the open coastal tundra, however, which constitutes seventy-two percent of our total 87,000 square miles of waterfowl habitat. We can't escape the biologist's basic creed: "additional research needed." The bottom line of the study on the Yukon Flats was that only thirty-three percent of the ducks are counted from the air in interior Alaska, ranging from a low of nine percent for green-winged teal to essentially 100 percent for canvasback and scoters.

In contrast to the great fluctuation in production of ducks from the prairie areas following the vagary of weather cycles, production of ducks out of the north is reasonably dependable year-in and year-out; this is not necessarily so for geese. A lack of water never seems to be a limiting factor. Because permafrost prevents percolation, the low annual precipitation can maintain surface water levels. There are no serious nest predators in the north and heavy plant cover in the absence of agricultural disruption gives better protection to nesting hens and their broods. Brood studies from several areas in Alaska show consistently larger broods reaching flight stage for all species of ducks. Only a catastrophically late spring seems to have the capacity to decimate a year's production, particularly of dabbling ducks.

The axiom that an early season is a good production year and a late season is a poor one is especially true in the Far North. An early season in the north still does not allow for nesting until well into May, and shallow ponds may start to freeze by early September. Some late-hatched diving ducks are still flightless at freeze-up. The breeding population survey in Alaska traditionally does not begin until about May 18. In the intense but abbreviated Arctic summer, there is just not time for renesting to effectively compensate for early failure.

Casual observations led many biologists to believe that waterfowl in the Arctic grow at a faster rate than in the southern part of their breeding range, thus allowing for the possibility of successful renesting. With the results of previous studies from the southern prairies available for comparison, a growth-rate research project was set up in Alaska. Karl Schneider, a graduate student from the University of Alaska, was assigned to do the field research. What he discovered in two summers of research was an optical illusion. Feather growth in the Class II stage is faster in the north, but the duckling spends more time in the downy stage designated Class I. The time it takes a given species to achieve flight is essentially the same both north and south. Schneider's conclusion: "While the

length of time required to attain flight for mallards was similar for both Tetlin and South Dakota, the rate of body feathering of Tetlin birds was considerably faster." In addition to the mallard, Schneider's study of canvasbacks and lesser scaup led to the same conclusion. In an earlier project for his graduate research, Pete Shepard determined the trumpeter swans require the same time to develop in Alaska as those on the southern breeding areas. These studies lead to the conclusion that too much midnight sun can distort a casual observer's view.

Because practically all of the field work in Alaska depended entirely upon aerial transportation in a float plane, field camps were kept simple and equipment was modified or developed to meet our minimum needs. The rat canoe was an early staple of transportation. It is a narrow, pointed, willow-framed craft, eight to ten feet long and covered with canvas. It is normally used by Indians in their spring muskrat harvests. Its main features are its small size and light weight for easy portaging. Unfortunately, the rat canoe is unstable and terribly unforgiving of carelessness. Some of us never mastered its art.

Because it was necessary to have wider, more stable boats for banding in remote areas, we developed a ten-foot, sectional craft that could be nested in its entirety and carried inside a Cessna 180. This five-section fiberglass boat was built by Marine Fiber-Glass and Plastics, of Seattle. The five sections, bolted together with wing nuts, weighed 140 pounds and could be disassembled and loaded inside the airplane in five minutes. After developing this boat we were much less inclined to carry canoes lashed to airplane float struts. Wherever landing conditions permitted, we tried to supply field camps with the large-capacity, twin-engine Grumman Goose.

Since the USFWS was responsible for monitoring all wildlife in those days, and perhaps to satisfy my own curiosity, I took advantage of waterfowl transects and other flights to record a great deal of information. Some was given to other researchers for their use, some was analyzed, some was tabulated and filed for future use, and some suggested the need for new tools or techniques. Without adding to the time, expense, or complexity of the waterfowl surveys, I tried to record all wildife within the one-eighth mile strip on my side of the transect, by segment, so that locations could be mapped. Although the sampling intensity for waterfowl was adequate to show trends within prescribed limitations, it could be debated whether my samples were adequate for other species; yet, my intent was the same. For instance, during my first two years of record keeping in this manner, a fantastic buildup of ptarmigan was recorded on the Yukon Delta. During the following winter a crash occurred in the ptarmigan population. Our summer transects recorded fewer than half a dozen birds where hundreds had been counted the year before. The rate of population recovery was similarly documented over the next several years until a new peak was reached.

In the same manner, black bear, grizzly bear, moose, caribou, wolves, and foxes were tabulated. Too few of the canines and grizzly bears were recorded to do more than arouse scientific curiosity, but a comparison of prestatehood moose populations and distribution with a replicated count today could be both enlightening and relevant to management purposes.

From 1961 to 1963, I conducted a supplemental breeding population survey in my spare time to help satisfy a curiosity carried over from my early days working for the State of Washington. Despite longer seasons and more generous bag limits in the Pacific Flyway, waterfowl populations, especially mallards, seemed to hold up much better there than elsewhere, even during periods of prairie drought. The source of these birds had long been a matter of speculation.

British Columbia had been considered a possible source, and some surveys had been conducted in the southern part of the province. Because of the mountainous terrain, much of the province had not previously been considered sufficiently significant water-fowl habitat to warrant the continued expense and effort of surveys. Having casually looked at much of the northern part of British Columbia and the southern half of the Yukon Territory after several years of intensive waterfowl surveys in mountainous Alaska, I came to the conclusion that British Columbia had considerable potential for waterfowl production and merited closer examination.

Coverage in 1961 was extended into Canada within a 200 mile radius generally east of the north-south line through Whitehorse, Yukon Territory. Most of this country was mountainous like Alaska, but there was a surprising number of ponds and lakes in the river valleys at the lower elevations. In a total survey area of about 56,000 square miles, there were approximately 22,500 square miles of river valleys, lake systems, and scattered potholes constituting waterfowl habitat. Forty sixteen-mile transects were laid out at random through these irregular areas and censused for the ensuing three years.

Applying the air-ground correction factors developed in Alaska, we estimated a breeding population of about 625,000 ducks, primarily lesser scaup, mallard, and pintails.

The combined size of the Yukon Territory and British Columbia is roughly equivalent to that of Alaska. Assuming the ratio of waterfowl habitat to be the same for both areas and applying the waterfowl density from the Whitehorse survey area, the total breeding population for Yukon-British Columbia would be between 2.5 million and 3 million ducks, of which more than 1 million would be mallards and pintails. Based on distribution patterns from surrounding banding stations, the mallards would be essentially all Pacific Flyway birds, as would most of the other dabbling ducks.

What seems like an infallible rule-of-thumb is that any waterfowl field investigation conducted in the Far North will produce results much slower than a comparable effort on southern breeding grounds. A lack of roads and alternative transportation, difficult logistical support, the need for specialized equipment, a compressed season, an adverse climate, and much greater costs all contribute to slower progress. When the incentive is great enough, however — whether it is a threat to be repelled, a prize to be attained, or an impasse to be compromised — adequate data of sufficient quantity and quality can be gathered in a timely manner to provide administrators with needed ammunition.

A case in point was the Rampart Dam proposal. The interior region of Alaska is generally mountainous but is bisected by three major rivers and many of their tributary streams. In several locations the river valleys expand into broad floodplains containing innumerable lakes and potholes that comprise Alaska's best waterfowl habitat — over 22 million of 55.7 million total acres in the state. At intervals these rivers are constricted between high rock walls that make ideal potential hydroelectric sites. The largest of these is located on the Yukon River in the Rampart Canyon immediately below the vast floodplain known as the Yukon Flats.

In 1959 the Army Corps of Engineers was directed to conduct a feasibility study for a hydroelectric structure in the Rampart Canyon. An integral part of its overall feasibility study, as provided for in the Fish and Wildlife Coordination Act, was an assessment of the fish and wildlife resource that would be affected by construction of the project. We knew from past aerial surveys and limited ground studies that the Yukon Flats produced "a lot of ducks." The river supported large and unique runs of salmon. That was nebulous information, however, that would certainly never suffice to document the real value of the Flats. Within two field seasons we were expected to provide detailed information that would withstand very rigorous scrutiny. Our objectives for waterfowl were to determine accurately the amount and quality of habitat; the species of ducks and geese, and the numbers of each and their productivity; and the continental distribution of waterfowl from the Yukon Flats.

The waterfowl project budget was sup-plemented each of the two years by about $21,000 from Corps transfer funds — nowhere near enough to attain our objectives. Nevertheless, we put together a team of enforcement agents, research biologists, river basins biologists, refuge managers, college students, and Indians from the local villages. The field work was to be accomplished in 1960 and 1961 including data analysis, with the final report to be completed in 1962. Both phases were later extended by one year. In addition to the waterfowl research team, other groups were gathering fisheries data and upland game and fur-bearer information with Corps funds allocated for those studies.

To accomplish the objectives in the allotted time, all phases of the field work moved ahead simultaneously with various segments assigned to different teams. New techniques were devised for the spruce-muskeg habitat of the Arctic, and equipment was developed for quick deployment in a roadless wilderness far from a center of supply. The prospect of losing more than 10,000 square miles of prime waterfowl habitat if we failed to document its worth was enough to spur the dedicated group into long, exhaustive periods of work.

Certainly the construction of Rampart Dam was seriously considered and strongly promoted by its advocates. But it was not built. In the final analysis its demise was attributed to economic infeasibility, but a major factor in that equation was the value of fish and wildlife — both its initial loss and replacement cost through mitigation. Perhaps the dam would not have met the cost-benefit test even if no fish and wildlife data had been injected into the formula. But there is a band of warriors — siphoned daily by hordes of mosquitoes and other indignities to the flesh, but never yielding in spirit — who will remain convinced forever that their contribution helped turn the tide. What did their effort reveal?

The Yukon Flats is Alaska's most productive habitat and is probably the largest solar basin anywhere in arctic North America. It is an area of 10,800 square miles of prime habitat that produces an average fall flight of about 2.1 million ducks and geese of seventeen species. Ducks banded on the Yukon Flats have been recovered in forty-three states, Canada, Mexico, Panama, and the Dominican Republic. Of particular significance is the secure retreat the Yukon Flats and other Alaska habitats provide for displaced ducks during the years of severe drought on the Canadian prairies.

Is Rampart dead? I think not. It is like a dormant volcano that could erupt again when the pressure for energy grows strong enough and economic factors change in its favor. To whatever extent the value of the natural resources of the area may influence any future consideration of a Rampart Canyon dam, at least they have been well documented and are available when needed.

Alaska's coastal Eskimos have long maintained that they need waterfowl in the spring (outside legal season dates) for subsistence. They further claim an aboriginal right to these birds. In March of 1956, I attended the first of the public hearings on acquisition of what is now the Clarence Rhode National Wildlife Refuge on the Yukon-Kuskokwim delta. Then and in subsequent years I visited native villages in early spring prior to arrival of the first waterfowl. There is no doubt in my mind that the people in many of these isolated villages desperately need food, particularly fresh meat, during these hungriest of all months. Not that a benevolent government with its multiplicity of welfare programs would let them starve, but fresh meat self-acquired may be as much a necessity for the spirit as it is for the stomach. In the devastation of a culture, who is to judge which is more important?

I can see the need for legalized, regulated spring hunting of migratory birds wherever needed by the native people of the Arctic. Toward that end, I worked for an amendment to the Migratory Bird Treaty with Canada after I transferred from Alaska to the central office in Washington in 1964, so that spring hunting could be legalized and controlled. From a legal standpoint, a solu-

tion seemed simple; but for understandable political reasons, an amendment was not possible. During that long interim since my first visit to a pauperized native village, spring hunting of waterfowl has been a continuing source of controversy.

Proponents of native rights have advocated unrestricted spring hunting, legal aspects of the Migratory Bird Treaty notwithstanding. To them, moral right should be transcendent. Wildlife administrators, though many may have been sympathetic to the needs of the natives, were compelled to view the legalities of the treaty literally. Organized waterfowl hunters in the states, totally unacquainted with conditions in Alaska's rural areas, have tended to use subsistence hunting as a scapegoat for their own lowered success, which in all likelihood was directly associated with loss of prairie production areas to agriculture. Thrust into the middle are game management agents, who must enforce the law.

Imbued with the philosophy that you are either guilty or not, the agents tried to play it straight. This has led to situations both comic and tragic, but always generating mistrust and ill will that makes an ultimate solution more difficult. In the summer of 1958 an agent was sent to Point Barrow to stop the hunting of king eiders on their southward migration prior to the opening of the legal hunting season on September 1. The Eskimos were busily gathering their winter supply of birds at a traditional site when one was arrested, presumably as an example to the others that would cause them to cease and desist. But the next day over 100 Eskimos brought in one eider each, laid it gently at the feet of the agent, and demanded to be arrested. When this mound of evidence was presented to the U.S. Attorney in Fairbanks, he declined to prosecute — after long and presumably careful deliberation.

During the next few years the situation among the Eskimos on the Yukon-Kuskokwin delta became tense and much more serious as attempts at enforcement intensified. Shots were fired at agents in aircraft and on the ground. Their presence in the area gave me a bit of apprehension at times because the Eskimos couldn't necessarily differentiate between USFWS employees or our respective jobs. When threats were made, my unattended aircraft was as vulnerable as an enforcement agent's. Fortunately, enough cool heads prevailed among the more militant that serious injuries never occurred, although there were scuffles.

Soon after these threats and encounters became serious, the agents were instructed to stay away from potential trouble spots in the spring. But the entire situation still needed to be corrected — legally, sociologically, and biologically. With respect to the latter, we had been accumulating evidence that some species were being adversely affected by spring hunting and egg gathering. As Eskimos improved their equipment and mobility with automatic shotguns and large outboard boats, they took more birds and eggs in ever-enlarging circles surrounding the individual villages. Brant, cackling geese, and white-fronted geese were particularly susceptible to this activity, especially when some of them were being hunted heavily at the southern end of their range as well. On the other hand, there were several species hunted or lightly or not at all any place else that could sustain greatly increased pressure both fall and spring if necessary. These included emperor geese, old squaws, and several species of scoters and eiders. Greater scaup probably fit this category as well.

So the next thrust toward solution of our probem became biological education and social rapproachement in Alaska, while in Washington we continued trying to solve the legal aspects of the treaty.

As an educational gesture, the Service sponsored show-me trips for selected groups of Eskimos to the waterfowl wintering areas in California. One rumor circulating among Eskimos explained the dwindling supply of breeding birds close to their villages as the result of heavy shooting in California. After all, Eskimos have access to the latest Eddie Bauer catalogs, too, and how else does Eddie get enough down for all his fine parkas unless it comes for "their" ducks and geese? The objective of the trip was to demonstrate that "their" birds were not all being shot, but rather that the people down south, through state and federal programs, were spending a lot of money and were working hard to insure an adequate breeding supply within a framework of enforced regulations. Having accompanied the Eskimos on the first of these tours, I can attest to their awe in viewing the impressive flocks of ducks and geese resting within the boundaries of Tule Lake, Sacramento, Grey Lodge, and other refuges. Whether or not the proper message was conveyed to these individuals while in California, or their friends when they returned to the home village, little change in action or attitude was apparent on the tundra.

Meanwhile, substantial progress was made to legalize subsistence hunting and thereby institute controls necessary to protect those species on the breeding grounds that cannot withstand additional pressure in spring. New migratory bird treaties with Japan and Russia provided for subsistence hunting, and the original treaty with Great Britain (for Canada) is finally undergoing limited amendment to legalize subsistence hunting which, from today's perspective, was an obvious oversight in the original deliberations.

Progress toward the ultimate goal of saving Alaska's prime waterfowl habitat based on solid information culminated in Section 17d(2) of the Alaska Statehood Act. With a steady accumulation of data from the aerial and ground surveys, banding projects, and special research studies, a waterfowl profile for Alaska was developed sufficiently to delineate boundaries for an extensive waterfowl refuge system of more than 50 million acres. The best analysis for planning purposes showed an average Alaskan fall flight of more than 13 million ducks, geese, and swans of thirty-eight species and subspecies; of these, various species disperse to all fifty states, Russia, Canada, Mexico, Central America, and the Carribean.

During the past three decades much has been learned about waterfowl in Alaska, but as much more remains to be learned.

Western Canada

BAFFIN BAY

Foxe Basin

Baffin Is.

Southhampton
Is.

HUDSON STRAIT

Chesterfield

Coats Is.

LABRADOR SEA

Eskimo
Point

Mansel Is.

Ungava
Peninsula

UNGAVA
BAY

HUDSON BAY

Churchill

Belcher
Islands

York
Factory

Fort Severn

Cogaluk R

Severn R

Fawn R

JAMES
BAY

Port-Harrison

Attawapiska R

Albany R

Akimiski Is.

GULF OF
ST. LAWRENCE

St Lawrence R

Moose
Factory

Prince
Edward
Is.

L. Superior

L. Huron

L. Michigan

Ottawa

BAY
OF
FUNDY

ATLANTIC
OCEAN

Eastern Canada

©R. Plasschaert

Waterfowl Flyway Councils

This book is about the *biological* flyways established many centuries ago by the birds themselves. But this chapter concerns the *administrative* flyways designated by waterfowl managers only since the 1940s.

The four administrative flyways end at the United States borders, but their biological extension into Canada is compelling reason for Canadian biologists and administrators to participate in decision-making regarding waterfowl management of each flyway. Canadian delegates to flyway council meetings, therefore, participate in all activities except the setting of U.S. hunting regulations.

The Federal Aid in Wildlife Restoration Act, also called the Pittman-Robertson or P-R Program, became effective in July, 1938. The act soon generated enough funds to allow every state to employ at least one full time waterfowl technician and to commence large-scale habitat acquisition and research programs.

Although World War II slowed progress, the waterfowl program made great strides right after the war, as individual states became more highly involved in research and management of the migratory waterfowl resource.

In Canada, a similar increased interest in waterfowl occurred among the provinces immediately after the war.

With increased state participation came a demand for a greater voice in the setting of regulations. In 1947, the FWS divided the nation into four flyways for the purpose of setting hunting regulations, recognizing the great differences in hunting conditions across the country.

After several years of working in the flyway system, the states decided they could most effectively achieve their objectives by organizing by flyways rather than operating individually. The formation of flyway councils was accomplished in 1952.

This chapter presents the story of the founding of the four flyway councils and looks at their work since the early 1950s.

Origin and Role

Laurence R. Jahn and Cyril Kabat

Establishment of the flyway councils was inevitable. Both hindsight and foresight attest to this. The wide-ranging seasonal movements of waterfowl among countries and strong human interest in these migratory birds left no alternative.

Precise tracking of the evolution of the flyway councils, however, is difficult because records are scattered and incomplete. Understanding the legal and factual framework for effective waterfowl research and management, including the role of the flyway councils, also is difficult because it spans more than eight decades; those involved in laying the foundation blocks, as well as many others who contributed substantially later, have departed. This understanding is imperative to strengthen the foundation of knowledge and authority to improve management of migratory waterfowl, especially to those with primary responsibilities for the program.

For purposes of this brief review, it is not practical or necessary to identify the countless actions and dates when each stone was laid paving the way to the establishment of flyway councils. Rather, we identify some of the major events in the formative process to provide an overall perspective of change over many decades. In the same respect, it is not necessary or practical to detail all functions of the flyway councils, but we should cite some of the major current responsibilities, activities, and challenges for the future.

As will be seen, the flyway councils evolved, almost step by step, with comprehensive waterfowl management. Rather than progress being sequential, according to grand design, steps in the process frequently were opportunistic. The interest of key individuals, progressive identification of informational and management needs, and support of key decision makers all played an important role in advancing waterfowl research management. But of paramount importance was the eventual formation of the four flyway councils — Pacific, Central, Mississippi, and Atlantic — as well as the National Waterfowl Council, to serve as the administrative vehicles to forge cooperative efforts among the provinces, states, and federal agencies to improve waterfowl programs.

The historical record is summarized generally in a chronological sequence according to five convenient categories: 1) protection and use of waterfowl; 2) surveys and research to provide facts for management; 3) establishment of flyway councils; 4) developing international biologically based plans for waterfowl species and populations; and 5) some current challenges to flyway councils and agencies responsible for waterfowl research and management.

Waterfowl Protection and Use

Among the first legal authorities to protect wildfowl, as early as 1776, were regulations enacted by the colonies of New York and Massachusetts. Spring shooting of waterfowl was prohibited in Rhode Island in 1846, but the law was repealed later. Between 1850 and 1885, wildlife legislation received considerable attention and, by 1880, there was some legal protection for wildlife in all states and territories. Many of these statutes were important to waterfowl.

Much of the progress in the last sixty-four years (1916-1980) rests on the first substantial federal authority for managing migratory birds in both Canada and the United States — the Migratory Bird Treaty of 1916. It specifies that there shall be a closed season on migratory game birds between March 10 and September 1, with certain limited exceptions for subsistence purposes. It also requires, among several stipulations, that prescribed open seasons should not exceed three and one-half months in any one region.

The implementing Migratory Bird Treaty Act of 1918 made the sale of migratory birds

These Winous Point Club wildfowlers have just returned from a successful hunt. In return for days like this, they willingly invest thousands of dollars to preserve and maintain habitat for the birds. USFWS photo by J. D. Smith.

illegal, a practice that had stimulated the taking of many thousands of waterfowl. The act also completely prohibits hunting of all migratory birds, including waterfowl, except as permitted by regulations such as those adopted by the U.S. Secretary of the Interior. This meant that waterfowl hunting was no longer an absolute right of the citizen; rather, through the act it became a privilege to be exercised only as permitted by the regulations. In the absence of regulations, there would be no open seasons.

This historic treaty and associated act laid part of the legal foundation to which government agencies, organizations, and citizens have been responding ever since. The principal demand is that the status of waterfowl populations and conditions of their habitats be known. Within the philosophy that the welfare of the populations must be considered first, the harvestable waterfowl surplus may be taken within prescribed times and by certain methods. Throughout the years, the goal has been to permit hunting without threatening or endangering the breeding stock.

Lack of courses in higher institutions of learning, and the consequent lack of trained personnel, as well as shortages of funds, constrained development of fact-finding programs to establish the annual status of waterfowl populations by scientific methods until 1947. Prior to then, observations from limited areas of North America and personal opinions of field observers were used largely to set annual hunting regulations.

For many years, the waterfowl hunting seasons were established on a nationwide basis. Later, they mostly were prescribed for three or four latitudinal zones extending across the United States. The northern zone customarily opened in late September or early October, the central zone about mid-October or later, and the southern zone about mid-November or later. All states in each group were permitted a specified number of shooting days beginning on a uniform opening date for a particular zone. Length of seasons varied, according to the supply of waterfowl. Under this system, waterfowl hunters along the Atlantic Coast were given the same number of shooting days and the same bag limits permitted on the Pacific Coast, although the abundance of waterfowl and the number of hunters often differed considerably. These general, largely nationwide regulations were a step in the right direction. But they also had some disadvantages. The most liberal regulations were applied to broad areas and many populations, some of which could have benefited from more restrictive measures.

As a first step to understanding waterfowl regulations, beginning in 1946 the USFWS invited representatives of federal and state wildlife agencies and the public to regional informational meetings held throughout the United States. Albert M. Day and Clarence Cottom — as USFWS director and assistant director, respectively — held many of these pioneering sessions. Most involved warm debates over one phase or another of the waterfowl hunting regulations. They were among the first experiences with public participation in decision making, an exercise later required by various U.S. laws, especially since 1970.

Overall, however, these regional meetings were well received. In a 1947 formal resolution, the International Association of Game, Fish and Conservation Commissioners (now the International Association of Fish and Wildlife Agencies) commended the USFWS for holding the sessions on proposed migratory bird regulations. They were considered to be of great benefit in disseminating information on conditions affecting migratory game birds, promoting a better understanding of the problems of management and regulation, and enlisting the cooperation of state agencies, sportsmen, and the public in a sound, long-range program for conservation of waterfowl. The International Association strongly recommended that such meetings be continued. The soundness of that position is reflected by the record. Similar, though considerably more formal, meetings have been held annually from 1946 to date.

Waterfowl Surveys and Research

In 1885 Congress included $5,000 in the Agricultural Appropriation Act to establish a new unit to study birds. Dr. C. Hart Merriam, chairman of the American Ornithologists' Union's Committee on Migration and Geographical Distribution of Birds, was selected as the first chief of the new unit. This unit subsequently became the Bureau of Biological Survey, and was expanded to take on new functions in wildlife research and conservation. From that early beginning nearly 100 years ago, this small unit evolved into the U.S. Fish and Wildlife Service. Over the entire period, migratory birds — especially waterfowl — have received priority attention.

In the 1940s, especially after World War II, proposals were received by the USFWS to strengthen fact-finding and coordination mechanisms to determine the waterfowl supply and harvest. There also were requests to set annual hunting regulations to ensure proper management of migratory waterfowl. In September 1946, the International Association of Game, Fish and Conservation Commissioners recommended through formal resolution that the USFWS:

1. Enlarge and expand its migratory bird survey forces.
2. Supplement its own surveys with additional information on conditions affecting migratory waterfowl by seeking cooperation of all appropriate agencies of the federal government, states, governmental authorities in Canada and interested private organizations.
3. Hold open discussions each year in each region constituting a major waterfowl flyway to obtain advice and recommendations on proposed regulations; invited representatives at each meeting should include all state wildlife and fish or conservation departments and other state agencies concerned, sportsmen's and conservation organizations, and other interested groups in the regions.

This resolution was prompted by the state fish and wildlife agencies wanting to participate more closely and effectively in migratory waterfowl management. Overall curtailments in the U.S. waterfowl seasons for 1946-1947 included reduction of season length from eighty to forty-five days and closing the season on Canada goose shooting in the Mississippi Flyway. These, the most restrictive waterfowl hunting season regulations since the drought of the 1930s, prompted considerable comment.

In one exchange, Ernest Swift (later the boss of the writers when we worked for the Wisconsin Conservation Department) stated:

Every time the state or the federal government attempts to put across something that is different, your sportsmen will tell you that if you changed the law in some respect, or did a little more advertising, and so forth, they would have accepted it more readily. That is true whether it is in relation to something done by the state or something done by the federal government. The real question is whether the action taken was or was not the best thing to do for the good of a certain species, regardless of what the sportsmen think. As a matter of fact we

have to be realistic and remember that periodically in conservation we have a pill to swallow, and that regardless of how much molasses you put on it, it will still be bitter to some people. No matter how your public relations work, it isn't going to satisfy everybody. We should be realistic and keep that in mind.

Later at the same meeting in 1946, Harrison F. Lewis, superintendent of Wildlife Protection for Canada (now the Canadian Wildlife Service) stated, "Sound waterfowl management practices should be based on and modified by the results of careful scientific research." In 1948, he emphasized that the surface of many waterfowl research problems had hardly been scratched. He also emphasized land-use impacts on waterfowl habitats and populations, and the need for coordinated waterfowl banding in many areas.

These and other similar post-World War II statements continued to keep the pressure on the USFWS, Canadian Wildlife Service, and other units in both federal governments to strengthen considerations and programs for migratory waterfowl. One of the initial responses was to advance the concept of managing waterfowl according to four geographic flyways. Although this initial concept was framed largely on biology of waterfowl known then, two decades later both administrative and biological flyways were recognized. Waterfowl within the Atlantic Flyway, encompassing the seventeen eastern seaboard states, were recognized as not being biologically isolated and independent. Therefore, a waterfowl management plan could not be limited to the administrative flyway boundaries, which had been marked conveniently by state lines.

Helping to stimulate and encourage a more effective North American waterfowl research and management program were officers and field representatives of the Wildlife Management Institute, especially Ira N. Gabrielson, C. R. Gutermuth, and Philip Barske. From the 1940s to present, the institute has assisted all of the agencies and groups involved with waterfowl to advance

United States. The gray area indicates the prairie pothole region.

Participants at the First Inter-American Waterfowl Conference held at Watertown Lakes in Alberta in September 1948. Participants shown are (left to right): J. Stoudt, A. Smith, R. Anderson, R. Bowman, E. Heustis, O. Hewitt, A. Hawkins, A. Bourquingnon, G. Jensen, R. Benson, F. Bryant, C. Gutermuth, G. Fansel, G. Spargo, G. Watt, C. Cottam, D. Munro, W. Ranson, R. Mackay, W. Rodrey, E. Cunningham, M. Cowan, A. deVeber, A. Munro, F. Thompson, J. Kerr, R. Smith and C. Williams.

1939-40 Green-winged teal *by Lynn Bogue Hunt*

census, banding, and other needed projects. The institute's objective is to help ensure sound scientific management of waterfowl and other wildlife populations and their habitats.

With strong support from the Institute, Ducks Unlimited, other conservation organizations, and the newly organized flyway councils, new projects were developed to assemble facts required to improve waterfowl management. Among the first to receive attention were breeding and harvests surveys. Remarkable as it seems now, decisions about appropriate hunting regulations were made for almost a century without any broadscale, systematic colletion of data on the numbers of waterfowl or hunters and their harvests. These problems were recognized fully in the 1940s and 1950s, with cooperative efforts to solve them promoted through the flyway councils and among countries. Following exploration of aerial surveys begun in 1947 by pilot-biologist Robert Smith and observer-

biologist Arthur S. Hawkins of the USFWS, a large-scale annual monitoring program became operational in 1955. It involved federal, state provincial and private personnel and has continually been improved throughout the more than twenty-five years since its inception. Nationwide waterfowl harvest surveys also have been operational in the United States since about 1950, and since 1966 in Canada. Quality of harvest characteristics in both countries depend on cooperation of hunters to provide the essential information. Their assistance has been most helpful in obtaining remarkably reliable information. These waterfowl harvest and population data, combined with other information from banding and habitat analyses, are the principal ingredients for building additional understanding required to improve waterfowl management.

Establishment of Flyway Councils

It was from this frame of need for immediate action, particularly on regulation-setting, that the proposal for establishing flyway councils was advanced. Needs also included action to maintain aquatic habitats, strengthen coordinated and cooperative efforts to improve biological and ecological information on waterfowl, and exchange that information among wildlife biologists and managers from different geographic areas. Other necessary and immediate actions were to review the entire system of waterfowl regulations in order to modify it, to recognize regional and local differences, waterfowl population, and to improve public understanding of and support for waterfowl management programs. The need for more intensive management of waterfowl hunting regulations was prompted by the four-fold increase in numbers of waterfowl hunters from the mid-1930s to the mid-1940s. This rather sudden increase in demand for recreational opportunities, combined with the recognition that the waterfowl supply was not inexhaustible, encouraged conservation administrators, biologists, and managers to seek a firmer foundation of information on which to base waterfowl management. Subsequently, many waterfowl research projects were initiated and carried out, many by veterans of World War II who completed their course work and manned field studies in various areas in North America. Most states, provinces, and territories reorganized their fish and wildlife agencies to meet expanding program needs, including land acquisition and restoration projects for waterfowl and other wildlife.

It also was in the mid- to late-1940s that the first groups were established to exchange information on waterfowl research and management needs, research findings, law enforcement problems, and overall coordination among agencies, private groups, and citizens. One of the first comprehensive programs developed by agreement among the states and other agencies and organizations interested in waterfowl arose from the Joint Black Duck Committee. It was organized in the mid-1940s to hasten restoration of eel grass on the Atlantic Coast. Similar embryonic groups were being established in other regions of the United States. In what was to become the Mississippi Flyway, for example, waterfowl technicians started assembling informally about 1946, primarily to share information on waterfowl production, migration, and harvests, as well as to discuss habitat losses and acquisition needs.

Conservation administrators considered the formation of these technical flyway committees one of the most progressive steps taken at the time. Competent biologists in many states devoted considerable time to waterfowl matters and, through these committees, coordinated their waterfowl census, banding, migration, and harvest studies. Nevertheless, some complaints continued to be registered, primarily that not all agencies and groups working with waterfowl were coordinating their efforts. Despite such reservations, these early cooperative efforts had far-reaching impacts on approaches developed to improve waterfowl research and management.

That the road toward advancing and improving waterfowl management was bumpy and filled with political detours should be evident. As C. R. Gutermuth put it in 1948, "Approximately half of the states still use their conservation funds more or less to pay political debts and to give political rewards to the faithful who have worked for the incumbent governor or party." Though this biopolitical situation prevailed, it then was considered much better than it had been in prior years.

In further discussion of the political situation, Harrison F. Lewis of Ottawa, Ontario, Canada, provided appropriate insight:

> In the course of the panel several references have been made to politics. We all know what is meant. But I should like to say that politics, if you use the term in its proper sense, are not in themselves objectionable. The function of truly democratic govern-

Technical committees of the flyway councils hold annual workshops to discuss how each agency can contribute to the waterfowl management program of the flyway. This meeting of the Mississippi Flyway waterfowl technicians was held at Louisiana's Rockefeller Refuge.

ment must be in a large measure political. What we need is not absence of politics, but honest, intelligent, patriotic, far-sighted, self-restrained politics. In a waterfowl program there is plenty for the national governments to do, plenty for the states and provinces to do, plenty for private individuals and organizations to do. The work must be coordinated in an orderly and cooperative fashion.

To some experienced conservation administrators, as well as biologists with experience in the first flyway committees, the time seemed right to develop an organization that spanned North America to deal more effectively with migratory waterfowl research, management problems, and programs. Discussions were held among waterfowl biologists and conservation administrators. Agreements were reached and Resolution Number 10 was drafted, presented, and adopted at the Forty-first Convention of the International Association of Game, Fish and Conservation Commissioners in September 1951. It reads:

> WHEREAS, the flyway plan of administering the waterfowl resources of the Continent has been adopted by the U.S. Fish and Wildlife Service as the basis for migratory waterfowl regulations; and
>
> Whereas, each of the states within the several flyways should participate more actively in annual surveys, both on the nesting grounds and in wintering areas, to determine the status of waterfowl and especially the development of more adequate midwinter inventories; and
>
> Whereas, the state wildlife agencies within the several flyways bear a major share of the burden for enforcing migratory bird hunting regulations in the shaping of which they have practically no voice; and

> Whereas, conditions prevail in each of the flyways which present difficult problems for both the states and the federal government, including waterfowl depredations on agricultural crops in some flyways; and
>
> Whereas, in order to bring about better understanding and cooperation, representatives of the official state agencies should participate fully in the formulation of the annual migratory bird hunting regulations of the United States,
>
> Now, therefore, it is hereby recommended that there be established a flyway council in each flyway composed of representatives of the official state wildlife conservation agencies; and that each flyway council in turn appoint or elect two of its members to serve on a national waterfowl council, and that the federal government departments of Canada and Mexico in charge of waterfowl management each be invited to appoint two advisory members, without voting powers, to meet with this national waterfowl council; said national waterfowl council to meet with the U.S. Fish and Wildlife Service to recommend annual regulations and such management practices and policies as they deem fitting.
>
> Be it further resolved that coordinators be selected and assigned to each flyway by the U.S. Fish and Wildlife Service to act as liaison agents for the coordination of research and management work of the various states and the federal government, and to combine state and federal findings and make such findings available to the respective flyway councils.

In 1952 actions were taken promptly to establish the four flyway councils: Pacific, Central, Mississippi, and Atlantic. State representatives who contributed substantially to establishing each council were Ben Glading, California Division of Fish and Game; Philip W. Schneider, Oregon State Game

Department; C. N. Feast, Colorado Game and Fish Department; Charles A. Dambach, Ohio Division of Wildlife; Ernest Swift, Wisconsin Conservation Department; Charles B. Belt, New York Conservation Department; and Clyde Patton, North Carolina Wildlife Resources Commission. These were the individuals who took the recommendations of waterfowl biologists and fought for agreement at a time when diversity of views on waterfowl management was prevalent. They visualized more effective cooperation, teamwork, and mutual understanding among Canada, the United States, Mexico, and other countries to build a stronger continental waterfowl program.

In recognition of a new era of closer working relationships, the USFWS appointed waterfowl coordinators or representatives in each flyway in the early 1950s. They serve as advisors to the states and aid in coordinating waterfowl censuses, surveys, banding projects, and other multiorganizational efforts. After nearly thirty years of continuous service, their invaluable contributions have been demonstrated many times.

USFWS' support and confidence in the flyway councils was articulated in March 1969 at the National Waterfowl Council meeting in Washington, D.C. by then-director John S. Gottschalk: "The flyway councils established about twenty years ago were formulated for the express purpose of better waterfowl management. Next to the Migratory Bird Treaties, their creation is the most significant step that has ever been taken in waterfowl management. They have been an excellent forum for communication for seeing and understanding the situation and problems throughout the flyways and tackling problems in a cooperative, scientific way to husband the resource and the sport. The concepts and understanding developed by and through the councils are vital to proper waterfowl management."

Developing International Waterfowl Management Plans

As the record shows, the flyway councils initially focused on waterfowl hunting regulations. Then, as accumulating information permitted use of population-oriented harvest regulations, increasing emphasis was placed on other dimensions of the total waterfowl program. This was a logical evolution of events from limited manpower and funds. Maintenance of thriving waterfowl populations was considered first, after which increased attention was given to the needs of more than 2.5 million North American citizens who annually seek recreational and subsistence opportunities associated with waterfowl. Meshing supply-demand situations led to concerted efforts to develop international waterfowl management plans.

Evidence of the flyway councils' efforts to place waterfowl management in an overall planning perspective is illustrated by pioneering efforts of the Mississippi Flyway Council. In 1953, a planning committee was appointed in the council's Technical Section. A first draft plan, consisting of sections on waterfowl production, distribution, harvest, and habitat management, was presented to the Technical Section in June 1954. This initial draft was received with interest, but no action was taken on it because it was considered too general.

Subsequently, in the process of preparing a second revised draft plan, the planning committee identified the need for first developing a national waterfowl management plan framework. It was to be designed to serve as an umbrella under which each of the four flyway councils could generate individual plans calling for specific activities. A request for this proposed national waterfowl management plan was registered with the Mississippi Flyway Council in August 1955. No action was taken. The request was considered as asking for actions too complicated to be achieved.

Despite obvious hurdles of various types, the Mississippi Flyway Council's planning committee continued its struggle to produce a waterfowl management plan for its flyway. After several drafts and revisions, a plan was approved and published as *A Guide to Mississippi Flyway Waterfowl Management.* For practical reasons, the publication focused on concepts for making decisions and planning future activities, and was tabbed as PART I. Work was begun on PART II, but became submerged by the council's preoccupation with actions on numerous individual components of waterfowl management; PART II never materialized. PART I stood the test of time, was found useful and, with certain appendices and amendments added after 1958, remains the council's guide today.

In addition to these pioneering efforts in individual administrative flyways, plans were developed and continue to be developed that span biological flyways. The latter include the daily, seasonal, and yearly travels of waterfowl species and populations. Through this approach, plans have been prepared for some Canada goose populations. Specific population goals have been identified and achieved through joint management efforts.

For other species and populations, much remains to be accomplished. Still to be met, for example, are needs of the eastern segment of the North American canvasback population. A well-designed, coordinated, biological-based management plan remains to be completed for canvasback that breed in Alaska and Canada, stop on migration in the Central, Mississippi, and Atlantic administrative flyways, and winter primarily in the Atlantic Flyway. Nevertheless, there is no reason to delay developing plans for administrative units — whether they are territories, provinces, states, public lands, or other areas — to maintain and restore habitats important to waterfowl and their users. Use by waterfowl signals that aquatic areas are valuable, usually to perpetuate an array of

Members of the U.S. Fish and Wildlife Service, Canadian Wildlife Service and Ducks Unlimited prepare to inspect waterfowl production areas in Saskatchewan on a typical "show-me" trip. Shown here are (left to right): F. Glover, J. Matlock, J. C. Shaver, T. Evans, P. Schneider, E. Fry, E. L. Paynter, B. Hesterberg, T. Harper and F. Phipps. Saskatchewan Government photo.

hydrological, ecological, social, and economic values important to society.

To aid in further focusing on needed cooperative activities, the Canadian Wildlife Service and the USFWS — in conjunction with provinces, states, and others — completed in 1980 drafts of waterfowl management plans for their respective countries. Both plans will be open for public comment. They represent the first effort toward preparation of each country's position prior to entering into joint discussions (possibly with Mexico) to develop a North American Waterfowl Management Plan. Much more effort is needed to satisfy the objective of sustaining waterfowl populations, including those of individual species, at desired levels to meet recreational and subsistence demands.

Current Challenges

That those responsible for managing waterfowl will continue to face challenges is exemplified by two actions in 1980. First, Inuit delegates assembled at the first Inuit Circumpolar Conference formally requested through a resolution to maintain their subsistence, aboriginal hunting rights in the Arctic, and urged all their people to behave in such ways to avoid endangering those historic hunting rights. A protocol to amend the Migratory Birds Convention — contemplating a regulated spring and summer hunt by native people for "nutritional or other essential needs" — was signed by Canada and the United States in 1979. It does not have the force of law in either country. The challenge that must be faced is implementation of subsistence harvest regulations without causing damage to waterfowl populations or significantly compromising the interests of other users.

Second, Defenders of Wildlife, the Sierra Club, the Humane Society of the United States, and Friends of the Earth petitioned the USFWS to charter the Atlantic, Missis-

sippi, Central, and Pacific Flyway Councils and the Fish and Wildlife Service Regulations Committee as advisory committees, pursuant to the Federal Advisory Committee Act. The petition also asked the Department of the Interior to institute proceedings for the control and disclosure of ex parte communications during informal rule makings which affect migratory birds, including waterfowl.

The intent of the petition is clear. It seeks to give equal representation in the rulemaking process to citizen membership organizations, and place the organizations on a par with the Fish and Wildlife Service and the state fish and wildlife agencies. These federal and state wildlife agencies have trust responsibilities for migratory waterfowl and legal responsibilities for their management.

Both subsistence taking and the threat to the very successful regulatory process — involving close working relationships among the U.S. federal and state wildlife agencies — remain to be resolved.

As these challenges are being faced, Canada, for 1979-1980, and the United States, for 1980-1981, initiated "stablized" hunting season regulations for ducks, with adjustments to be made to produce desired changes in harvest. The objective is to provide consistent regulations for a five-year period, while allowing optimum recreational hunting opportunities. Members of flyway councils, as well as others, eagerly look forward to findings from the evaluations proposed of these new approaches to waterfowl harvest management.

The hope and promise for the 1980s and beyond is that the waterfowl management plans, now in draft form in Canada and the United States, will focus attention on accumulating additional needed facts, using available facts, and accelerating the pace of making biopolitical decisions to further strengthen research on and management of North American waterfowl. There are many economic and social benefits from flourishing waterfowl resources, a number of which extend beyond those realized by immediate users. Recent Canadian Wildlife Service surveys show that 75 percent of Canadians pursue an active interest in migratory birds, including waterfowl. A similar strong interest in waterfowl prevails in the United States. There is a substantial aesthetic value to waterfowl and other wildlife beyond dollar expression. Full recognition of this value must be built into future considerations, evaluations, and decisions.

Nearly a third of a century of valuable efforts by the flyway councils emphasize significant accomplishments in advancing waterfowl programs. The trail through the biopolitical maze has not been without numerous challenges and some outright roadblocks. The continuing challenge is to establish more jointly supported federal-state-province-territory projects, and work to ensure that those partnership efforts yield substantial dividends for waterfowl, their habitats, and citizens.

Atlantic Flyway

C. Edward Addy
and Warren W. Blandin

©W. Breckenridge

Perhaps the most significant influence in building a basis for establishing flyway councils was the establishment of the Federal Aid to Fish and Wildlife program in 1938. This act made it possible for all states to establish their own waterfowl research and management programs and to cooperate with federal and private agencies concerned with waterfowl. Many states soon got started on banding programs, surveys, and land acquisition.

Then came World War II, during which time most programs were temporarily terminated, reduced or had plans shelved for the duration. Immediately after the close of hostilities, there was a period of intense activity during the latter part of 1945 and during 1946 when personnel returned to their jobs, and others were hired, and efforts were made to get various projects underway.

At that time many administrators, technicians, and sportsmen were concerned about the poor status of waterfowl populations. Ducks Unlimited (DU), which came into being in 1937 as a result of deteriorating production habitats and low populations of the 1930s, initiated an ambitious habitat restoration program in prairie Canada. However, for the northern part of the east coast area, from which Ducks Unlimited received substantial funds, nothing was being done for the all-important black duck. Furthermore, what to do in eastern Canada to improve production of black ducks was not readily apparent. Therefore, in 1945, Ducks Unlimited set up and financed a research station based at Fredericton, New Brunswick, in cooperation with the University of New Brunswick, and hired Bruce Wright as director.

To further implement the black duck program, on April 5, 1946, DU established a Black Duck Committee whose job it was to recommend and coordinate a DU black duck program. At a meeting in New York, December 13, 1946, the Black Duck Committee was enlarged and its name changed to the Joint Black Duck Committee. This new committee included representatives from several state game departments, the USFWS, DU, and certain other private organizations.

Under the encouragement and guidance of the Joint Black Duck Committee numerous banding, survey, and acquisition projects got underway in eastern Canada and the Atlantic coastal states. Later, to give more attention to special programs, the Northeast Region Waterfowl Committee and a similar committee in the southeast were formed.

Management by flyways began in 1948, creating a more definite need for cooperation among all agencies in the flyway and the establishment and coordination of broad flyway-wide programs.

On September 10-11, 1951, in Rochester, New York, the International Association of Game and Fish Commissioners passed Resolution Number 10 calling for the formation of flyway councils. At Edgewater Park, Mississippi, October 24, 1951, the South Atlantic Flyway Waterfowl Committee in implementing Resolution Number 10, called for the union of the southern and northern committees of the Atlantic Flyway and requested that the Fish and Wildlife Service appoint an Atlantic Flyway coordinator. C. E. Addy served as coordinator under the title of "Flyway Representative" until he retired in 1972. He was replaced at that time by Warren W. Blandin.

Under the sponsorship of the Wildlife Management Institute, a joint meeting of the southeastern and northeastern groups was held January 28-29, 1952, at the Hotel Statler in Washington, D.C. The purpose was to form an Atlantic Waterfowl Council and draw up a constitution and bylaws. After many hours of work the proper documents were prepared and the Atlantic Waterfowl Council became an official entity. The first officers were: C. B. Belt, chairman; Clyde Patton, vice-chairman; Philip Barske, secretary; assistant secretary, T. S. Critcher; member of the executive committee, Norman Wilder; southern representative, Clyde Patton; northern representative, R. A. Wells.

The first meeting of the National Waterfowl Council, which included the two Atlantic Councils representatives, took place in Washington, D.C. on August 5, 1952.

From its establishment in 1952 to the present time, the Atlantic Waterfowl Council has grown in stature, becoming an aggressive and positive force in the planning and development of programs in cooperation with the USFWS, the Canadian Wildlife Service, and other agencies and organizations.

Several technical publications have been published by the council, including: the *Small Marsh Manual, Waterfowl Techniques Handbook, Techniques Handbook of Waterfowl Habitat Development and Management* (a revised and expanded version of the techniques handbook), *The Atlantic Flyway Council Waterfowl Identification Guide,* and *The Black Duck, Evaluation, Management and Research — a symposium.* In addition, a popularized version of the flyway's management plan, *The Atlantic Flyway Waterfowl*

Management Guide, was produced in 1964. Allan Kennedy, council secretary-treasurer, and C. E. Addy collaborated on a history of the council in 1969.

In addition, the council established the Charles Banks Belt Award in 1954 to be given to those who accomplish the most outstanding achievement in behalf of waterfowl in the flyway. The winner receives a bronze medallion, and the organization which employs the winner receives a suitably inscribed scroll. Four council members have received the award: Robert A. Wells, New York; James W. Webb, South Carolina; George W. Davis, Vermont; and Lester G. MacNamara, New Jersey. These gentlemen, along with Norman Wilder, Clyde Patton, Stuart Critcher, and Chester Phelps, were among the most influential members in the early years of the council.

The Atlantic Flyway Council, in cooperation with the Wildlife Management Institute and the Fish and Wildlife Service, pioneered pooling of federal aid funds for conducting waterfowl banding projects in eastern Canada. Council members since 1965 have supported three five-year Eastern Canada Cooperative Banding Program segments, both financially and through contributions of manpower and equipment. Financial support for waterfowl research includes banding data analysis projects on the wood duck and the black duck, and Canada goose parasite studies. This council, in conjunction with the other councils, assisted the Service in getting the Post Office Department to obtain the names and addresses of duck stamp buyers.

During the regular annual council meeting, May 2-3, 1960, in Baltimore, a formal Technical Section was organized. Duties of the section were stated, committees were established, meeting dates outlined, memberships specified, and duties of officers indicated. The first elected officers of the Technical Section of the Atlantic Waterfowl Council were Vernon Stotts, chairman; Dirck Benson, vice-chairman; and Jay Harmic, secretary.

The Technical Section has fulfilled its role as a technical advisory group to the council, and has pioneered several kinds of experimental waterfowl seasons, research projects, and waterfowl management techniques.

Mississippi Flyway

Kenneth E. Gamble

and Arthur S. Hawkins

The Mississippi Flyway Council was organized in St. Louis on January 24, 1952; its formal Technical Section was organized on July 14, 1952. For three decades the same fourteen states and three provinces have continued as members, except for eight years (1968-76) when Louisiana dropped out and several months in 1975-1976 when Alabama and Mississippi also withdrew.

In the early years, conservation departmental directors took a much more active part than they have in recent years. Ernie Swift of Wisconsin, Harry Ruhl of Michigan, Charlie Dambach of Ohio, Gerry Malaher of Manitoba, Bruce Styles of Iowa, I. T. Bode of Missouri, and T. A. McAmis of Arkansas personally saw to it that the council got off to a strong start. In recent years, game division chiefs usually represent their states at council meetings.

Five years before the council came into being, the waterfowl technicians of the flyway already were informally organized as the Mississippi Flyway Waterfowl Committee. Organizers of this embryo Technical Section were J. D. Smith of the Minnesota Conservation Department, Tom Evans (fieldman for the Wildlife Management Institute), Frank Bellrose of the Illinois Natural History Survey, and Frosty Anderson of Winous Point Club. Two university professors, Bill Marshall (University of Minnesota) and Joe Hickey (University of Wisconsin), were enthusiastic supporters. Strong USFWS backing came from John Lynch, George Saunders, and from Bob Smith and Art Hawkins, who were the flyway biologists at the time.

Whenever the opportunity permitted, as

1976-77 Canada geese brood *by Alderson Magee*

many as possible of this group gathered in someone's hotel room to "talk shop." On March 1, 1948, the committee issued its first newsletter to keep members informed of the various data-collecting programs. The advantages of gathering data cooperatively were apparent to this highly motivated group of biologists and to them the goals of management were remarkably clear for that early date.

Committee members agreed that whether one was managing domestic livestock or wild game, the same kind of vital statistics must be gathered if the species is to be managed successfully. Therefore, uniform data-gathering procedures were established to survey breeding stock, determine numbers, kind, ages, and sexes of birds taken by hunters, and to gather other vital statistics.

Up and down the flyway, the data-collect-

ing team of the late 1940s included Al Hochbaum, Lyle Sowls, and Peter Ward in Manitoba; Harry Lumsden in Ontario; Don Smith, Grady Mann, and Bill Marshall and his students in Minnesota; Ralph Hopkins in Wisconsin; Herb Miller in Michigan; Frosty Anderson in Ohio; Russ Mumford in Indiana; Frank Bellrose in Illinois; Parker Smith in Tennessee; and Dick Yancey in Louisiana.

In adjacent states of the Central Flyway, Merrill Hammond in North Dakota, Jerry Stoudt in South Dakota, and John Wampole and Harvey Miller in Nebraska made important data contributions.

The upshot was that by the time the Mississippi Flyway Council was organized, the waterfowl technicians of the member states and provinces were ready to step in as a group experienced at working cooperatively, with a data bank already well started.

Flyway council business includes special meetings on waterfowl problems. Concern over the canvasback led to this meeting in April 1976, at the Northern Prairie Wildlife Research Center. Pictured (left to right): Jerome H. Stoudt, Larry R. Jahn, Art Hawkins, William E. Green, and J. M. "Frosty" Anderson. USFWS photo by John Lokemoen.

The council's business got off to a rousing start thanks to the strong leadership of Ernie Swift and Cy Kabat in Wisconsin and Charlie Dambach of Ohio. The council's primary role was to support a sound waterfowl management program, thinking and acting as a flyway unit rather than as unorganized individuals or separate states, in recognition of the fact that all members were sharing a common resource.

It soon became evident that, at least on matters related to regulations, the members didn't always agree. Canadian members of the council decided to abstain from voting when United States regulations were discussed. This left fourteen voting members; on many occasions, the vote was tied, usually due to a north-south split with the southern block favoring the more liberal hunting regulations. Frustration over this situation finally led to the withdrawals from the council mentioned earlier; however, procedural differences were resolved in 1976, and the council once again includes all flyway states.

It was clear from the beginning that the flyway needed a management plan, a blueprint to help guide its actions. A start had been made by the waterfowl committee even before the council existed. On August 3,

1952, the council named a management plan committee which produced a first draft for the council's consideration at its July 1954 meeting. It was not accepted for various reasons, and two years later a new committee was named with instructions to prepare a new and more complete plan. Finally in March 1958, the council adopted the plan produced by the second committee (A. S. Hawkins, C. Kabat, Parker Smith, G. B. Saunders, and J. D. Smith, with a Council Review Board of T. Evans, J. Kimball, and A. Hyder). It was edited by Clay Schoenfeld and Ruth Hine of the University of Wisconsin and Wisconsin Conservation Department, respectively. In 1960 the council's planning committee prepared a state-of-the-flyway report telling of progress made and challenges remaining. Then, a decade later, the planning committee updated the original management plan in a sixty-three page report called *Lessons from the Sixties and Challenges of the Seventies in the Mississippi Flyway.* This report contained appendices prepared by three other committees: Law Enforcement, Information and Education, and Research. The latter report listed the primary council fact-finding activities of the decade, highlighted a dozen major accomp-

For several years, Canada and United States officials hosted a waterfowl "Show Me" tour. These allowed fly-way council members, outdoor writers, and other interested parties to see typical waterfowl breeding habitat in Canada. One such group is shown here. Saskatchewan Government photo.

lishments, and foresaw fourteen challenges in the decade ahead.

Waterfowl management issues addressed by the council during the 1960s included subjects both basic and far-reaching. A 1961 planning committee report, *Waterfowl Management and Quality Hunting,* concerned the problems associated with sustaining recreation quality in the face of ever-increasing demands on the resource. A year later, the planning committee's report, *The Forward Look,* dealt with the future of waterfowl hunting as it was envisioned at that time. A 1965 report, Wasted Waterfowl, addressed the long-standing problem of lead poisoning among waterfowl.

Habitat surveys and preservation programs have been from the first strong rallying points for the council, consistently commanding support from all members. Most council members have supported fact-finding programs, often involving out-of-state travel

even to remote goose nesting areas in Canada. Improved enforcement efficiency and public relations have been other areas in which close cooperation has been achieved.

All things considered, the flyway council system in the Mississippi (as well as the other three flyways) has been a positive force on behalf of waterfowl management. There have been agonizing moments for those who support the principles on which the councils were organized and which all members pledged to support. Sometimes, states'-right-isms seem to have gained the upper hand over the unity required in sharing a common resource. Part of this problem has been due to the rapid turnover rate which directors of departments of natural resources share with football coaches. During the two decades that Hawkins served as flyway representative with the Mississippi Flyway Council (1953-73), there was a complete turnover of state conservation department directors and, in some cases, he worked with several directors from a single state. Unfortunately, some directors lost their jobs before they fully understood what the council was all about.

Another problem has been the increasing complexity of almost everybody's jobs in the areas of resource management. This has focused attention toward single-purpose activities, such as managing one class of game bird resulting in undue emphasis on the regula-

tions-setting process at the expense of perhaps more meaningful reasons for the council's existence.

Even so, we hate to think of what waterfowl management in the flyway might be like today had it not been for the existence of the Mississippi Flyway Council these past twenty-nine years of hectic development and economic progress.

©J. Killen

Central Flyway

Harvey W. Miller

The "central flyway" was first a biological term that became meaningful in the mid-1930s. The terrible drought had just begun to moderate and waterfowl populations were still at an ebb when Dr. Frederick C. Lincoln announced the discovery of four major migration routes of "flyways." His findings were based upon the early results of some pioneering banding programs; hence some of the routes were not too well delineated. What

he called the Central Flyway was essentially that area between the Pacific coastal states and Mississippi valley flyways. This biological Central Flyway persisted until after World War II.

The return to peacetime in the mid-1940s saw greatly increased interests in waterfowling. Many states found that duck hunting rivaled pheasant and big game hunting in popularity. Accordingly, more resources, enriched with funds from the Federal Aid in Wildlife Restoration (Pittman-Robertson) Program, were directed into studies of waterfowl. As the states learned more about waterfowl, they began to clamor for a role in establishing hunting seasons. In the fall of 1947, for example, the Western Association of Game, Fish and Conservation Commissioners (representing eleven western states) recommended management by flyways because, in the opinion of the members, it was not sound management to have the same seasons and bag limits across the United States.

One of the participants at that meeting was C. N. Feast, director of the Colorado Game and Fish Department. Feast returned to Colorado and invited representatives of the states in the biological Central Flyway to meet and "work out an organization to develop a uniform and cooperative Central Flyway management program." The meeting was held at Glenwood Springs, Colorado, on August 12-13, 1948. Representatives of nine states, the USFWS and the Wildlife Management Institute participated.

Much of the discussion at the meeting dealt with what the organization would accomplish. A major consideration was to provide more and better information on breeding and wintering populations, harvests, and migrations. There was concern over how this information should be reported and whether or not the necessary surveys could be financed through the Pittman-Robertson Program. There was special concern over whether or not the USFWS would use the information after it was made available. C. R. "Pink" Gutermuth, representing the Wildlife Management Institute, was a staunch advocate of a flyway management system throughout the discussions.

Naming the new organization was something of a challenge. It was called the Central Flyway Committee at the outset of the meeting; however, it was argued that a committee is a part rather than the whole of an organization. "Association" was not acceptable because the word connoted dues and fees. "Council" was preferred over all other choices. Hence, the Central Flyway Council became a formal organization with the unanimous adoption of a statement of aims and purposes. It included the following statement of objectives:

> The purpose of the Central Flyway Council shall be to assemble factual information, endeavor to encourage the adoption and use of more uniform practices and techniques, correlate and coordinate the migratory bird program and activities of the several governmental agencies throughout North America, to determine the migratory bird production in the states within the Central Flyway, collect additional mortality return data, conduct more widespread bird banding operations, augment participation in the annual censusing work, and otherwise assist in the efforts to increase the continental waterfowl populations and to effect better utilization of this valuable natural resource.
>
> The aim of the Council shall be to provide the U.S Fish and Wildlife Service, the Dominion Wildlife Service and the Mexican Government with urgently needed management data, and to supplement the work of the Federal, Dominion, and Latin American agencies in the restoration and management of waterfowl and other migratory birds.

The organization got off to less than a whirlwind start. The minutes of a subsequent meeting indicate that a second meeting of the council was held in Denver; however, it must have been an innocuous session, as no record of the proceedings are available.

The next recorded meeting of the Central Flyway Council was July 6-7, 1950, in Wichita, under the chairmanship of Dave Leahy, director of the Kansas Forestry, Fish and Game Department. There were detailed discussions of information on breeding populations, harvests, and banding. Frederick C. Lincoln was there to defend the hunting regulations prescribed by the USFWS and to explain the processes by which they were developed. A noteworthy action was to "petition and urge the U.S. Fish and Wildlife Service to assign a full-time coordinator to the Central Flyway."

The problem of getting started and keeping an organization going were illustrated at the fourth meeting, held August 16, 1951, again in Wichita, in conjunction with the 18th Annual Meeting of the Association of Midwest Fish and Game Commissioners. Early during his term as council chairman, Kelly DeBusk had been "relieved of his posi-

This excellent nesting and brood pond, located in Manitoba, provides both cover and food.

tion as director" of the Oklahoma Game and Fish Department. Paul T. Gilbert, executive secretary of the Nebraska Game, Forestation and Parks Commission, had agreed to fill out that term; however, an emergency precluded his being at the meeting. C. N. Feast of Colorado, the organizer and first chairman of the council, was there and stepped in to handle the meeting.

The expanded studies of waterfowl during the late 1940s had greatly improved the definition of the biological flyways. In the early 1950s, other flyway councils were being organized within the newly defined boundaries. By June 25, 1952, when the fifth meeting was held in Bismarck, North Dakota, membership in the Central Flyway Council had been narrowed to that of today: Alberta and Saskatchewan; Colorado, Kansas, Montana, Nebraska, New Mexico, North Dakota, Oklahoma, South Dakota, Texas, and Wyoming; and Mexico.

One highlight of the fifth meeting that must be noted was the unanimous adoption of a recommendation to establish a committee, made up of one technical representative of each member state and province, to serve the needs of the council.

Organization was firmed up in 1953. Meeting in Oklahoma City on May 8, the Central Flyway Council reaffirmed its organizational structure. It authorized a Waterfowl Technical Committee. USFWS acknowledged the council as a partner in management of waterfowl in the Central Flyway and announced the selection of Cecil S. Williams to serve as the first Central Flyway representative. Williams served in that capacity until he retired and I replaced him. Thanks to the persistence of leaders like Feast, Leahy, DeBusk, Gilbert, H. R. Morgan of North Dakota, Robert Aldrich of Oklahoma, Lester Bagley of Wyoming, and a host of others, the Central Flyway had been organized, come of age, been recognized, and gotten its own coordinator in the remarkably short time of five years.

The Central Flyway Council has lived up to expectations. It has a long-range management plan which was requested by the council in 1955, adopted in 1957, and subscribed to by the USFWS that same year. It has pioneered studies such as those which lead to the development of species management programs as exemplified by the High Plains Mallard Management Unit. It has provided manpower and funds for cooperative efforts in Alaska, arctic and prairie Canada, and throughout the flyway. The aims and purposes of the Central Flyway Council have been exceeded. The results have amply demonstrated that management by flyways certainly is the better way.

©R. Plasschaert

Pacific Flyway

James C. Bartonek

Active and organized participation by states in managing this nation's waterfowl resource had its beginning with the Pacific Flyway Study Committee — or at least that's the way we westerners view it. At the Western Association of Fish and Game Commissioners' meeting in Santa Fe in June 1947, it was probably Oscar Johnson of the USFWS, Wiley Ben Williams of the Western States Federated Sportsmen, and Emil J. H. Ott, Jr. of the California Division of Fish and Game who unwittingly provided the catalyst. The state-federal relationship (or lack of it) in establishing waterfowl regulations and the concept of managing waterfowl by flyways were recurrent topics throughout their presentations and the ensuing discussions. During an "evening session" over beers, a group of conferees continued on in this same vein discussing the pros and cons of their states acquiring basic information to be used in formulating regulations. While there were obvious reasons why each state should go its own way in collecting waterfowl information, there seemed more to be gained if many states were to conduct somewhat similar investigations and pool their information. Ben Glading from California and J. Burton Lauckhart from Washington were among those who thought such a cooperative effort would provide far superior information upon which to manage waterfowl than that which was in use.

Organizing that envisioned way of managing waterfowl into a working program was surprisingly difficult, considering the times. In those postwar years state wildlife agencies, having been bolstered by release of withheld Pittman-Robertson (PR) funds, were rapidly expanding their programs. Biologists, managers, and enforcement officers, some recently schooled and some eager to apply certain military-acquired skills to wildlife management, were readily available. Obstacles to this new program came from both state and federal agencies. The USFWS had never encouraged and at best was lukewarm toward states initiating PR projects related to waterfowl investigations. Some Service administrators perceived waterfowl management as being exclusively within their agency's purview. Some state directors did not overly object with this arrangement, because they wanted their funds and manpower to go toward resident species and the necessities of habitat acquisition and development, rather than the luxury of "studying" ducks and geese. Only a few states had modest state-funded waterfowl programs, though not of the nature desired.

The California Division of Fish and Game gave the cooperative program the needed push by inviting representatives from agencies and colleges along the Pacific Coast to attend a two-day "Waterfowl Conference" at the Orgeon Fish and Game Commissions' office in Portland on February 17-18, 1948. Participants included James F. Ashley, John E. Chattin, and Robert N. Hart from California Division of Fish and Game; Frank B. Wire, Phillip W. Schneider, Melvin Cummings, A. V. Meyers, and William B. Morse from Oregon Fish and Game Commission; J. Burton Lauckhart, Carl N. Crouse, and Robert G. Jeffrey from Washington Game Department; James G. Cunningham from British Columbia Game Commission; Jay Long from Oregon State College; Charles F. Yocum from State College of Washington;

and Stanley G. Jewett, Leonard M. Springer, Kenneth F. MacDonald, Ralph H. Imler, and Robert P. Boone from the USFWS. James Ashley was elected chairman of the conference and directed the group in discussions about accomplishments and proposed waterfowl management programs. The group concluded that certain basic information was urgently needed, including: 1) inventories of resident (i.e., locally breeding) and migratory waterfowl; 2) estimates of harvests; 3) estimates of production within states, provinces, or regions; and 4) banding programs that would identify migration routes and relationships between production, harvest, and wintering areas.

Chattin, Cunningham, Meyers, Lauckhart, and Boone were appointed to a standing committee to prepare a preliminary work plan detailing the kinds of information needed and how it should be obtained. John Chattin, assistant chief of Game for California Division of Fish and Game, presented the committee's plan to the other agencies at the group's meeting in Salt Lake City, June 2-4, 1948. In a paper titled "Outline of Pacific Flyway Studies," he described the values and the inevitability of management of waterfowl by flyways. (Later that same year, federal waterfowl regulations were segregated for the first time by flyways.) The program called for obtaining the four basic types of information identified during the Portland conference, and for an inventory and evaluation of waterfowl areas. The virtue of this program was that the surveys and investigations would be conducted and reported in a similar manner, with information being sent to a clearinghouse — the Federal Aid Division of USFWS — for compilation and redistribution to all contributors.

Response to Chattin's presentation was mixed. Most biologists and administrators thought that the approach was desirable and possibly even necessary, but a few thought it was too costly in light of other ongoing or proposed projects. Montana, Idaho, and Utah, however, thought the program was worth the effort; their representatives and those from the five Pacific Coast agencies met in Portland in August 1948 to work out details of the program and to standardize methods.

While most states had a desire and interest to participate in the Pacific Flyway waterfowl program, the wherewithal was sometimes lacking. For this reason I believe that a portion of credit for the cooperative program's success should go to Bob Boone, the regional supervisor for the federal aid program who broke the USFWS' long-standing but unwritten taboo by allowing and even encouraging states to have PR-funded projects on waterfowl investigations. Importantly, these new PR projects followed the outline recommended by the committee and allowed project personnel to travel its meetings.

The Pacific Waterfowl Flyway Committee (in 1952, whether purposeful or not, the council called the group the Pacific Flyway Study Committee, by which it is known today) held its third meeting in Portland on February 23-24, 1949. Its ranks were growing, with Nevada, Colorado, and Arizona expressing interest but unable to participate in that particular meeting because of travel constraints. Policies and procedures for conducting the investigations were dominant topics. The format and schedule for reporting information were finalized, although some changes manifest themselves even yet in the *Pacific Flyway Waterfowl Reports*, with eighty-four volumes being compiled between 1948 and 1980.

The Committee formally requested that the USFWS assign a man to handle the workload of compiling, analyzing, and reporting the data being collected and to coordinate the interstate activities. Up to that time those tasks had been undertaken as an additional workload by Bob Boone. In response to the Committee's request, Director Al Day announced in June 1949 that Leo K. Couch would be the Service's coordinator for the cooperative waterfowl studies in the Pacific Flyway. Couch served in that capacity until mid-1951. After a hiatus in the position of more than a year, both the newly formed council and its study committee urged the USFWS to fill the vacancy. John E. Chattin was hired in September 1952 to fill the vacancy. While John's title was variously assistant regional supervisor of game management (Law Enforcement), waterfowl management biologist, flyway manager, migratory bird coordinator, and others, his duties were always — as the most enduring title implies — the Pacific Flyway representative. John well served the waterfowl resource and waterfowlers during his twenty-five years (1952-77) in that capacity.

Although administrators from a few of the western states and from the USFWS met informally in Milwaukee, Wisconsin, in March 1951 at the request of Al Day to discuss cooperative waterfowl management within the Pacific Flyway, the notion of a Pacific Flyway Council did not materialize until the International Association of State Game, Fish and Conservation Commissioners passed a resolution on September 10, 1951, calling for the establishment of the four flyway councils and a national council. The Western Association of State Game and Fish Commissioners had theretofore served as a forum for states to discuss the various waterfowl management issues, but it did not allow for effective participation in decisions leading to waterfowl hunting regulations.

At the urging of the International's president, George W. Davis, the first Pacific Flyway Council meeting was convened on January 16, 1952, in Pendleton, Oregon. Ben Glading was elected both president and secretary of that meeting. Arizona was represented by O. N. Arrington who was proxy for Director Thomas Kimball. In addition to Glading was E. L. Macualay from California. Others present were Bob Salter from Idaho; Phil Schneider, William Morse, and Delbert Gildersleve from Oregon; R. L. Turpin from Utah; and John Biggs, Burton Lauckhart, and Raleigh Moreland from Washington. Frank Groves, Nevada, could not attend because of a storm, but telephoned the group. Robert Lambeth, Montana's director, and Robert Cooney expressed that state's continued interest in the Pacific Flyway Study Committee but said that, where policy matters were concerned, it wished to be part of the Central Flyway. (From 1948 through 1959 for Montana and through 1961 for Wyoming, Colorado, and New Mexico, the USFWS regarded those states as being wholly within the Central Flyway. Therefore, Montana's voting membership in the Pacific Flyway Council was of little consequence until 1960, when the western portion of the state was placed in the Pacific Flyway.)

At that first meeting, there was a discussion of the relationship of the existing Study Committee to the newly organized council. There was a consensus that the two groups were to remain separate; the Study Committee was a fact-finding organization, and the Council would be a policy-making organization that would rely heavily on factual information furnished by the Study Committee.

Membership and governing rules of the Council and Study Committee are different. The study committee in 1950 had representation from the states of Arizona, California, Idaho, Montana, Nevada, Oregon, Utah, and Washington; the Territory of Alaska, the Province of British Columbia, and the USFWS through the flyway representative. It has functioned with a relatively simple and flexible organizational structure and without bylaws since its inception. Wyoming and the Canadian Wildlife Service are now regular participants in the committee meetings, with Colorado, New Mexico, Alberta, and Yukon Territory being irregular participants. Virtually anyone who could contribute to the understanding and management of the flyway's waterfowl has been welcomed and even encouraged to attend and participate to varying degrees in the committee's meetings.

The Council's membership is more limited than that of the Committee's, and its activities are governed by bylaws. Originally, only those states within the boundaries delineated in 1948 by the USFWS for administrative purposes were members — Arizona, California, Idaho, Nevada, Oregon, and Washington. Usually the director, a commissioner, or both, represented each state; therefore, decisions made by the Council were made without delays for consultation and carried clout. British Columbia was not invited to participate because most issues dealt with by the Council were of political importance to the United States and not Canada. Participation with the province in other waterfowl matters was still possible because of its membership in both the Western Association of State Game and Fish Commissioners and the Pacific Flyway Study Committee. Alaska was admitted to the Council in 1959. Montana, which repeatedly sought representation after being placed partially within the administrative boundaries of the Pacific Flyway, was finally granted membership in 1980. Wyoming became a member in 1982 without debate. Hawaii, where mourning doves are the only hunted migratory birds, had no need for the affiliation.

Ben Glading found the activities of the Council during his thirteen-year affiliation to be for the most part an annual tug-of-war between the states and the USFWS over regulations, with both sides doing a lot of preening and posturing. Carl Crouse characterized the process for establishing the annual waterfowl hunting regulations as following the adversary system, whereby regulations were arrived at as a compromise between two unrealistic positions instead of by joint efforts toward realistic objectives. What must be a major accomplishment and a credit to both was the agreement between the Council and the Service to stabilize duck hunting regulations for a five-year period. Except for minor changes, framework for duck hunting regulations were made stable from 1975 through 1979 and uniform throughout the flyway. The Study Committee, which proposed the standardization of regulations, sought to determine hunting's effect under fixed regulations upon duck populations that were subject to the uncontrolled vagaries of nature. Frank Kozlik, Al Regenthal, and John Chattin designed the evaluation. In 1980 the Committee reported to the Council that under the prevailing conditions and duck populations, these particular regulations had no apparent adverse impact upon ducks. Concurring with the Committee's recommendations, the Council and the Service agreed to continue with these same regulations for another five-year period of evaluation. For Alaska, Dan Timm developed new regulations covering all waterfowl and cranes that were acceptable to both the Council and the Service, and which were stabilized in a five-year evaluation beginning in 1977. The stabilized regulations have lessened the number of "spirited discussions" and "warm debates" of past meetings, and enable both the council and the Service to devote more attention to other deserving issues.

The Study Committee's coordinated banding program paid dividends early when it could be demonstrated that the Pacific Flyway mallards and canvasbacks were not part of those more easterly populations that were undergoing periodic declines. These two species, therefore, should be managed by flyway rather than over their range. J. Burton Lauckhart, Chester E. Kebbe, Elwood Bizeau, and John Chattin summarized the information on the build-up of mallards in the Columbia Basin and concluded that more liberal regulations were warranted, both to alleviate present and future problems with crop depredations and to increase hunting opportunities. The Study Committee's report, which was endorsed by the Council in 1961, encouraged the USFWS to permit bonus limits of mallards that year and allowed for further increases in bonus limits, season length, and shooting hours in 1964. The Columbia Basin still retains a one-week-longer season than the rest of the flyway, but bag limits and shooting hours are now the same. Increasing acreages of circle-irrigation farming and expanding populations of geese in the basin will continue to provide management challenges in the years ahead.

California's problem of crop depredation by waterfowl was a recurring topic discussed at Council meetings during the early 1950s and was reason for some of the innovative bag limits within the flyway. Most states were opposed to California's use of depredation orders to kill the marauding waterfowl and preferred to see those birds taken by hunters in all states of the flyway. John Biggs suggested that Washington hunters could help California farmers by having a season on pintails in September. The Study Committee, at the Council's request, evaluated the proposed pintail hunt and concluded that the disadvantages outweighed the advantages, citing among the disadvantages that banding showed that most Washington pintails were local and would not go to California. Miffed by the report, Biggs stated that the committee far exceeded its duties in this matter by reporting "conclusions" and that it should only report findings. Bonus limits on both pintails and wigeons from 1952 through 1958 and progressively longer seasons did much to placate sportsmen and California farmers throughout the flyway, although other simultaneously employed management practices and changes in farming were more important in reducing depredation losses.

John Biggs from Washington and Phillip Schneider from Oregon regularly did verbal battle with Californians William J. Silva, Seth Gordon, and Ben Glading and the USFWS (whomever was there from Washington, D.C.) over what was perceived by them to be preferential treatment of California hunters who could "feed" waterfowl, whereas hunters in other states "baited." The USFWS was further castigated for what was viewed as poorly defined baiting regulations and policy. California's regulations on the waterflow feeding program and the USFWS' antibaiting regulations have been controversial for nearly thirty years. After early skirmishes in court, which were won by Californians, the commission tightened up its feeding regulations and limited the program to nine southern counties. When the USFWS advised clubs that they would not be allowed to feed after the 1974 seasons, that decision was taken to court by California's game department, its commission, a farmer whose crops would allegedly be in jeopardy, and the newly formed Waterfowl Habitat Owners Alliance (WHOA). Conditions for a settlement included a study of the role of feeding in waterfowl management and its relationship to depredations. Leigh H. Fredrickson, director of the University of Missouri's Gaylord Memorial Laboratory, conducted the study; his findings were reviewed by a blue-ribbon panel of experts, who, in turn, gave their recommendations to the USFWS. The next episode in this continuing story is yet to be written.

As the Pacific Flyway Council knows and the Atlantic Flyway Council will learn, hunting the regal swan is far easier than gaining the authority to do so. At the request of J. Perry Egan from Utah and Frank Groves from Nevada, in 1955 the Council asked the Study Committee to give consideration to limited hunting of whistling swans within the flyway. Utah's Noland Nelson took the lead in gathering and evaluating information on the status, distribution, and migration of swans. In later years, Don Smith and then John Nagel, also of the Utah Department of Fish and Game, continued to report the status. Not all states wanted seasons for themselves — public sentiment against shooting swans and the mingling of whistling swans with the then-endangered trumpeter swans were principal reasons. Glen Sherwood, in a Utah Cooperative Wildlife Research Unit-sponsored study of swans in the Great Salt Lake Valley, concluded that even a limited hunt was not warranted. However, because of the Study Committee's persuasive evidence and the Council's persistent requests, the USFWS allowed permit hunts in Utah in 1962, in Churchill County, Nevada, in 1969, and in Teton County, Montana, in 1963. During the period 1970-1978, when the three states were annually authorized a total of 3,500 permits, hunters bagged an average of 1,234 swans per season and, importantly, the population increased by about 900 birds per year. Alaska's one-time bid in 1973 to join

the three states permitting swan hunts had not been endorsed by the Council and was not approved by the Service.

Homegrown honkers usually attract the attention of biologists long before those geese that nest in distant arctic lands become of interest. Such was the case with the Great Basin Canada goose in our flyway. The Study Committee recognized the honkers' importance to sportsmen, particularly those of the inland states, and implemented cooperative management programs to increase their numbers. Honkers were easily captured and banded; they lended themselves to being transplanted into vacant habitat; and they responded well to habitat improvements. These big geese were subjects of many university and agency studies, with a resulting plethora of theses, reports, and publications.

It was one such study by William B. Krohn and Elwood Bizeau that identified the Great Basin Canada geese as being comprised of the two populations by which they are now called — Rocky Mountain and Pacific populations of Western Canada geese. With the improved information on rates and location of harvest, migration routes, and habitat requirements, the Study Committee has sought since 1955 various restrictive regulations that would best benefit a particular flock. While not developing a formal, written management plan until recently, the subcommittee on these geese would meet each July in Jackson, Wyoming, to work out the needed regulations over the flocks' ranges. The years of restrictions and intensive flock management will soon reap the benefits of increased limits and seasons because the 1981 midwinter waterfowl inventory of these birds was the highest recorded.

Management plans, management plans — the flyway is up to its collective ears in them. Beginning in 1978, biologists from state and federal wildlife and land-managing agencies, university students and faculty, and others gathered in a series of workshops to develop twenty management plans on Pacific Flyway geese, swans, and cranes. Biologists from the Central Flyway, Canada, Mexico, and

U.S.S.R. have contributed to these plans. For most of the participants the effort was educational because it was the first opportunity they had been given to consider the management needs of a particular group of birds over their range. While there may be delays in official endorsement of the plans, managers of state programs, managers of USFWS regional and refuge programs, and university researchers have already begun to implement those aspects deemed of greatest importance.

The flyway has had management plans before, but not as many. The Study Committee prepared for the Council and the Service in 1954 the *Pacific Flyway Waterfowl Management Plan,* which was in 1959 revised to the *Pacific Flyway Waterfowl Management Guide.* The guide calls for maintaining widely distributed populations of waterfowl at levels that could be enjoyed and used by both hunters and nonhunters. A program of habitat preservation, surveys and investigations, management of harvest, and evaluation of management functions and programs was outlined.

The dusky Canada goose in 1973 became the first group of birds to be bestowed with its own management plan. There was concern for the race's status. Its restricted nesting grounds on the Copper River delta in Alaska had undergone marked changes from the 1964 earthquake; it wintered only in the Willamette Valley of Oregon; and it was probably the smallest population of geese that was hunted, numbering less than 10,000 in the early 1950s. The plan was the product of state, Service and university biologists in Oregon and Alaska. It called for cooperative efforts that would allow the population to achieve and be maintained at not less than 20,000 nor more than 25,000 geese as measured by the midwinter waterfowl inventory. The plan and its cooperative implementation has been an unqualified success. With the advent of ever-increasing numbers of lesser Canada geese into the wintering range of the duskies, new approaches to managing both races must be considered for the future.

Other early management plans include those for black brant, Aleutian Canada goose, and Mexican-like ducks. The brant plan calls for restoring numbers of brant wintering in the three coastal states to levels comparable to those prior to their abrupt decline in the late 1950s. The Aleutian Canada goose plan seeks to remove the race from the endangered status and return it to a hunted population by establishing new breeding populations in the Aleutian Islands. California hunters, because of curtailed hunting, have borne much of the burden of the recovery efforts. The plan for Mexican-like ducks, prepared by Arizona, New Mexico, Texas, and the USFWS, recognizes that the birds in regions of these three states are hybrids, and that Mexican ducks in the principal part of their range are not endangered.

Lead poisoning of waterfowl and the required use of steel shot in certain areas are the topics that have livened meetings of both the Council and the Study Committee since the annual regulation hassle was put aside. Noted for its adamant opposition toward aspects of the USFWS' nontoxic shot problem, the flyway has some notable "firsts" in solving the problem. Oregon was among the first states in the nation to join that program when in 1974 it required the use of steel shot on its Sauvie Island Wildlife Management Area where poisoning was a serious problem. The Council, in March 1980, adopted the nation's first flyway-wide criteria for monitoring and reducing lead poisoning in waterfowl.

Members of the Study Committee, perhaps more than those of the Council, have felt budgetary constraints on travel to their meetings. Nevada, either in Reno or Las Vegas, has become a traditional meeting place because some participants can travel to an adjacent state without special travel authorization. When the meeting was in Reno, the California contingent could "stay" in nearby Truckee, California, without traveling out-of-state. None of the members' travel requests, however, quite got the attention as did that of Al Regenthal's, whose proposed travel to Reno was reviewed at a very, very high level and even reported in the *Salt Lake Tribune*. It seems that Utah's governor and secretary of state were split in their decision to allow Al to travel, but the attorney general broke the tie in favor of the trip by the toss of a coin.

Hugh Boyd, that barbed-tongued observer and skilled practitioner of waterfowl management in North America, noted that waterfowl management is a very conservative activity with any concept less than twenty years old being "too novel" to merit consideration. Such may seem the case to those biologists and administrators, both state and federal, whose suggestions for providing new or increased hunting opportunities, hasten-

ing recruitment of depleted populations, and reducing wastage of waterfowl are either ignored or rejected. Hugh might have added, but did not, that also in waterfowl management quite a few hare-brained schemes are initiated with haste and little forethought. The interaction and debate on issues among the Council, Study Committee, Service and public is necessary and desirable if the better concepts are to survive and the poorer ones rejected. The Pacific Flyway Council and Pacific Flyway Study Committee have each in their different ways fostered truly cooperative management of all migratory birds which know no political boundaries. If it was to be done over again, I would not suggest a different approach.

Among their other uses, large marshes serve as moulting areas for ducks during their flightless period. Here a banding crew attempts to take advantage of the concentrated "flapper" stage ducks. USFWS photo by R. W. Hines.

Upon being assigned the task of writing this article, I gained empathy with those paleontologists who must visualize and then characterize the habits of a twenty-three-ton brontosaurus based upon examining a few of its bones. I hope that in this characterization of the Pacific Flyway Council and the Pacific Flyway Study Committee I did not mistake a caudal for a cervical vertebrae. The minutes of the various Council and Study Committee meetings and the periodic and special reports suggest to me that there were easily thirty "stars," one-hundred "regulars," fifty "substitutes," and a host of others participating in flyway activities during the past thirty-three years. Not all participants have been or could be given the recognition due them — for that and to them I apologize. I thank the three secretaries to the Pacific Flyway Council who collectively served that group for twenty-nine years — Ben Glading, 1952-1965; J. Burton Lauckhart, 1965-1974; and Albert F. Regenthal, 1974 to date — for sharing with me some of their recollections. Robert P. Boone, John E. Chattin, Carl N. Crouse, Frank M. Kozlik, John R. LeDonne, and William B. Morse provided me with perspectives of certain issues that were not obvious or well stated in the minutes of meetings. I especially thank John Chattin, my predecessor of twenty-five years, and Henry M. Reeves for reviewing and commenting on this manuscript.

©C. Pearson

CHAPTER

10

Habitat Case Histories

In the last analysis, habitat — and not the gun or any other agent — determines the fate of the waterfowl resource. Almost since the first pioneers pushed westward, however, North America's waterfowl habitat has been deteriorating.

Plows were soon devised that could break the tough prairie sod, but the innumerable small wetlands dotting the landscape remained a nuisance for far longer. Ultimately, draglines, subsidized by governmental subsidies, made destruction of the potholes feasible. The process, once begun, snowballed until it became evident that what once had been the most fertile waterfowl production area in the world was now quickly losing its ability to raise ducks.

In this chapter, three champions of prairie pothole preservation reflect on the struggle to shift public policy from pothole eradication to pothole protection.

The first major inland marshes encountered by pioneers were those along the Great Lakes. A particularly interesting story concerns efforts to modify the great Lake Erie marshes. Those efforts foretold the fate of many great marshes lying farther westward.

Another kind of habitat and another kind of story is provided by the mighty Mississippi, important waterfowl habitat both in its upper reaches and where it slows and spills into the Gulf of Mexico.

These stories are, in a sense, not finished. The many encroachments of man's activities on waterfowl habitat continue today and continue to modify that habitat in ways that are both planned and unintentional. No one today can predict the ultimate effect of all this, but the stories in this chapter give us important insights.

Welcome Back Potholes

Clay A. Schoenfeld

At midnight in the bitter depths of mid-winter 1948, a Chicago, Milwaukee, St. Paul and Pacific milk-run train deposited a brash, young reporter at the windswept, deserted depot of a small town in eastern South Dakota. His assignment: to investigate a mass murder. Shivering with both cold and uncertainty, he trudged a half-mile to the town's one hotel and set up shop in a dingy room where steam banged and rattled and hissed in a vain attempt to pump some warmth into a reluctant radiator.

I was that reporter.

Early the next morning, I located an old Army infantry buddy from Anzio and hitched a ride through swirling snow squalls to view the scene of the crime, inspect the graves of the victims, and interview the perpetrators. It was a cinch. The countryside was figuratively strewn with dried blood at every hand, and the executioners literally marched up happily to me to tell their accounts of what had happened — and what, indeed, was continuing to happen.

The resulting story became what has been termed an "earth-shaking" lead article in the April 1949 issue of *Field & Stream* magazine under the title, "Good-By Pot-Holes." The subtitle read: "Is the Soil Conservation Service destroying waterfowl habitat faster than Ducks Unlimited and Fish and Wildlife Service can restore it? Conditions on one of our most important breeding grounds indicate need for closer cooperation."

Arthur S. Hawkins, then a USFWS flyway biologist, says the article "unleashed a chain of events like a nuclear reaction. It was the leaven that started the ball rolling, if I can combine metaphors, toward today's wetland preservation programs, [and is] your greatest contribution to wildlife and humanity."

That's laying it on pretty thick, but Art and I go 'way back, and a writer needs fans like that. (It was with Private First-Class Hawkins that I had hunted Wisconsin mallards the last weekend before shipping overseas in 1941.)

The South Dakota saga all started with a phone call to my office at the University of Wisconsin in Madison from Hugh Grey, executive editor of *Field & Stream* at the time. Hugh had had a tip that there might be something tragic going on in the prairie states, the greatest "duck factory" in the continental United States. I was a parttime graduate student in journalism and wildlife management and part-time assistant to the president of the university then. I had done quite a bit of freelance outdoor writing for *Field & Stream* and other national magazines of the type. Anyway, Hugh thought I might be a guy to go out and "do some solid investigative reporting."

Hugh was operating in the great tradition of American sportspersons and their communication media in defense of fish and wildlife habitat. Beginning as early as the 1870s, it was the hunter, fisher, and birdwatcher in search of recreation, serenity, and science in the out-of-doors who first sensed the ill effects of what Eric Sevareid would later call "the mis-development" of America. Outdoorspersons saw the ravages of logging and forest fires, of farm soil erosion, of lake and stream pollution — and the resulting destruction of fish and wildlife habitat. Those sportspersons and bird lovers began to call insistently, through voluntary organizations and campaign literature, for government help.

The Woodward and Bernstein of that early conservation movement were outdoorsmen George Bird Grinnell and Emerson Hough, Grinnell as editor and publisher of *Forest and Stream,* a high-class New York weekly, and Hough as his prize investigative reporter. Through a long series of exposes and editorials, they helped educate the public to support pioneer state and federal legislation affecting parks, forests, and wildlife.

Later, the combination of Robert Underwood Johnson, as editor of *Century Illus-*

trated Magazine, and John Muir and John Burroughs, as his nature writers, helped lead directly to legislation setting up national parks. Bringing the new National Park Service to the attention of the public was the work of two former New York *Sun* reporters-turned-conservationists, Stephen Mather and Robert Sterling Yard.

In the mid-1930s, himself no slouch at conservation communication, Franklin D. Roosevelt picked to get his revamped Biological Survey off the ground an Iowa journalist, Jay N. "Ding" Darling, whose pungent cartoons had been harpooning the ditchers, drainers, dammers, and despoilers of duck habitat. It had been in the spring of 1948, just before his untimely death, that one of my professors, Aldo Leopold, had put most of the finishing touches on his *Sand County Almanac and Sketches Here and There,* the little book that was to become the bible of the environmental movement thirty years later. And in Washington, Rachel Carson was already hammering away at the terrible, swift sword of her *Silent Spring* manuscript.

So as I set out for the Dakotas I unconsciously had as quiet companions a distinguished cohort of writers serving the cause of conservation.

To get a feeling for what I might be facing, I stopped en route at the Twin Cities in Minnesota to chat with the regional USFWS chief, Dan Janzen, later to become USFWS director. Dan, in his reserved way, was hopping mad. The waterfowl in his care were literally going down the drain. Taking me to a big wall map, he sketched the situation.

In the 5,000 square miles in eastern North and South Dakota, there was an average of twenty potholes to the square mile, ranging in size from one-sixteenth of an acre to one-hundred acres. Together with surrounding sloughs, lakes, and uplands, the glacier-made kettles constituted one of the prime waterfowl breeding areas on the continent. Yet in just one Dakota county alone, 1,400 of those potholes had recently been drained, and there was talk of more and bigger regional drainage to come — a major threat to the Mississippi Flyway duck population, which Dan was charged with protecting, using in part the special taxes paid by duck hunters.

Who was doing all that draining? Well, farmers, of course. But there was more to it than that; just what, Dan was not at liberty to say.

With expense money for only five days, how could I possibly cover 5,000 square miles? Why don't you concentrate on one typical county, Dan suggested. Did he have one in mind? Yes, Day County, in eastern South Dakota — the county seat, Webster.

So I headed for Webster with its wind-swept depot.

No less an authority than the past director of the USFWS, Lynn Greenwalt, says, "You really started something when you went to Webster that winter so many years ago."

As I've said, it was easy to find the scene of the crime. Those 1,400 representative drained potholes were in Day County. Ranging in size from one-eighth of an acre to ninety acres, a total of 6,285 pothole acres had been drained by thirty-eight miles of ditches. Some 350 farms were the sites. All you had to do was drive down any country road, get out of the car, climb a fence, and stand in a slight depression in a big wheat field, a depression that yesterday had been one of the homes of an incredible 33.2 breeding pairs per square mile — of teal, gadwalls, mallards, and pintails.

It was easy to find the graves of the victims, too. With the help of local biologists, I made some rough calculations. Even assuming that only 60 percent-plus acres of drained potholes in Day County had held breeding pairs producing an average of seven ducklings each, that would still mean that Day County drainage to date had lessened duck production by some 26,000 ducklings a year. The famous Delta (Manitoba) Marsh had produced only one-tenth that many ducklings in 1947. Plenty of Dakota duck graves, in other words.

What is more, as the vice president of the Wildlife Management Institute, Larry Jahn, pointed out, "Ducks are members of a com-

There is no more persistent problem than habitat destruction, exemplified here by a prairie pothole being drained. USFWS photo by J. Stoudt.

munity; the graves represented losses of entire aquatic communities," with their varied plant and nongame wildlife species.

Now ordinarily when you have a mass murder like that, the criminals are conspicuous by their absence. Not so in Day County. They were simply delighted to identify themselves and talk for public consumption. Their crime turned out to be an amoral alliance, funded by your federal tax dollars and mine.

First, of course, there were the farmers. But they were just doing happily what society asks farmers to do — raise bigger and better crops as efficiently as possible and sell them as cheaply as possible to feed a hungry country and a starving world. With the price of wheat encouraging and the cost of arable land mounting, there was nothing in the equation to deter turning "nuisance puddles" into cropland — and Matt Mallard be

damned: "If hunters would just stop shooting so many, the ducks will do all right, anyway."

Second in line, there was the United States Department of Agriculture's (USDA) Soil Conservation Service (SCS), born in the Depression to bring a halt to dust bowls. Supposedly the SCS was set up to promote such salubrious land manipulations as grass-legume rotation, check-dam building, wind-break planting, strip cropping, contour plowing, and so on. But not in Day County in 1948. At the top of its "approved farm practice" list was "the construction of drainage ditches (to alleviate) depressional areas where continuous cultivation cannot be practiced because of periodic harmful accumulations of water." Did a farmer want to drain a pothole but didn't know how to go about it? "Why, we SCS engineers will lay out your ditch for free."

Next was the USDA Production and Marketing Administration (PMA) (formerly the Agricultural Adjustment Agency, now the Agricultural Stabilization and Conservation Service (ASCS)). The PMA listed drainage ditches high among its "approved construction practices" in Day County. A farmer could collect eight cents a cubic yard for ditching, and another seventy-five cents a thousand square feet for grassing the waterway. In 1947 the PMA had paid the farmers of Day County $17,285 for digging forty-three miles of drainage ditches.

"We're the bread-and-butter agency in this country," the Webster PMA director told me, proudly thumping his chest.

Fourth member of the conspiracy was the Cooperative Extension Service (CES), that remarkable link among the USDA, each state land-grant university, and the agriculture committee of manifold county boards, with a ubiquitous "county agent" in every court house. From the state college at Brookings, the CES was sending out bulletins extolling the merits of pothole drainage, and the Day County agricultural extension agent was serving as the very efficient secretary of the pivotal local Soil Conservation District, gleefully signing up "approved practice" farmers, meaning ditchers and drainers.

Last but by no means least were the manufacturers, distributors, and dealers of earthmoving equipment. In the best tradition of the free enterprise system, they were passing out calendars and caps in a push to sell, lease, or rent bulldozers and backhoes: "We geared up to win World War II, and we aren't about to miss out on a fast buck now."

As a matter of fact, there was another member of the conspiracy — the local public, represented, sad to say, by the editor of the Webster *Reporter and Farmer*, who told me frankly, "Pothole drainage is one of the finest things that has happened to Day County agriculture in years. Besides, in a region where the economy is based entirely on farming, nobody opposes what the farmers are all for."

Well, hardly anybody, anyway. On my last day in Webster, I did find some opposition that chose to be anonymous. An astute old game warden who showed me one grain field in which the surface area of the ditch equalled the surface area of the reclaimed pothole. A devout Audubon Society member who said, "They're crazy. In another five years the dust will blow their ditches shut." A courageous state game biologist carrying on a "stop the ditching" campaign. An editorial writer for the Aberdeen *American-News* calling for "no more draining of sloughs and swamp lands. Any program that would rob South Dakota of its water reservoirs is short-sighted." And an USFWS refuge manager with those devastating statistics already cited.

That USFWS man deserves special mention because it was really he who blew the whistle on the ditchers and drainers. He was Fred Staunton, manager of the Waubay National Wildlife Refuge. In his first "early warning radar" letter dated March 18, 1946, Fred reported to Regional Director Johnson in Minneapolis that "the local office of the Day County Soil Conservation Service is embarking on a drainage program that may seriously affect the migratory waterfowl population in this locality." On April 21, 1947, Fred recommended that USFWS personnel "examine each area in the proposed drainage plan and tabulate the number of nesting birds using the areas, the character of the habitat, and the potential revenue from fur-bearing animals produced and harvested."

That got a May 7, 1947, response from Director Janzen, thanking Fred for his "alertness" and suggesting that Fred spend "whatever time you have available from your other duties this spring" on the inventory. By July of 1948, subsidized wetlands drainage in the prairie pothole region began to command the attention of Dr. Ira N. Gabrielson, then chief of the USFWS. His concern found its way to *Field & Stream*, and that's where I got in the act.

The records clearly show that Fred Staunton was one of those fellows always bugging his superiors about what was happening to his beloved wetlands. By the time I got to

Day County, he had hard data.

So I got my facts. They were incontrovertible. But putting them down on paper for publication represented a certain hazard. After all, I was an employee of a land-grant university somewhat in league in Wisconsin with much the same sort of cabal I had discovered in South Dakota. For assurance I checked with my boss, the inimitable University of Wisconsin President E. B. Fred. As a lifelong scientist pledged to the defense of academic freedom, he told me in effect to let the chips fall where they may.

Some of them fell on my head.

I had wound up my article with a ringing quote from Leopold: "All in all we have a beautiful piece of social machinery — the Soil Conservation District — which is coughing along on two cylinders because we have been too timid and too anxious for quick success to tell the farmer the true magnitude of his obligations. Obligations have no meaning without conscience, and the problem we face is the extension of the social conscience from people to land."

That obviously had some bite to it, and through the CES the SCS petitioned that I be censured. Nothing came of it, of course, but I remained *persona non grata* to the SCS for many years. Time has a way of healing wounds, however, or at least of fading memories. At any rate, a person invited to speak at last year's Soil and Water Conservation Society convention in Toronto was none other than the author.

Nationally, as you've heard Hawkins and Greenwalt say, "Good-By Pot-Holes" did produce some reverberations. At the very least, it gave the USFWS a public hook on which to hang a drive to get wildlife values considered more fully in federal projects and programs, a drive that led more or less directly to a considerably strengthened federal Wildlife Coordination Act in the 1950s. Certainly today wetland preservation has a higher priority nationally and locally than it did thirty years ago.

Milt Reeves of the USFWS calls "Good-By Pot-Holes" "one of the landmarks in popular conservation literature." Art Hawkins asks, "How could one man with a sharpened pen create so much havoc as you did?" Because there was a lot of follow-up. Mounting concern about federally subsidized drainage of wetlands in the prairie pothole region led to the establishment of the USFWS' Wetlands Habitat Preservation (WHP) Program, changes in drainage policies and criteria by the USDA, and passage on October 4, 1961, by Congress of the Wetlands Loan Act which provided authority and means for the USFWS to acquire migratory waterfowl habitat, especially in the prairie pothole region. No small credit should be accorded Refuge Manager Fred Staunton in first identifying and documenting the drainage program which was decimating the wetland habitat base so essential to United States waterfowl production in the prairie pothole region.

"Good-By Pot-Holes,'" says Hawkins, "showed me the power of words, for it stirred up a hornet's nest." In a recent anniversary issue, *Field & Stream* reprinted "Good-By Pot-Holes" as an example of its tradition of no-holds-barred reportage over the years in the cause of wildlife conservation. My current students in environmental communication at the University of Wisconsin were duly impressed.

Perhaps the most significant fallout from that 1949 magazine expose came in 1972 with the passage of the federal Water Bank Program, after many years of persistent lobbying on the part of the National Wildlife Federation. The Water Bank Program has put a total of 590,367 acres of wetlands and adjacent land under protective management for wildlife. The Water Bank Program is administered in selected areas of the country by local offices of the ASCS. Planning and technical assistance is provided by the SCS. The areas are chosen by state ASCS committees in consultation with SCS and state wildlife agencies. The program offers landowners annual payments under ten-year agreements for protecting wetlands and adjacent nesting cover important to a broad array of wildlife. Since 1972, 5,227 landowners have participated in the program.

Currently (1980-1981) the Water Bank Program is authorized by Congress to receive only $10 million annually. Last year, however, Congress reauthorized the act and increased the limit to $30 million, beginning in fiscal year 1982. It also expanded the program to include all wetlands, rather than only three types. Annual payments to protect the 590,367 acres total about $7 million. Most of the protected acreage is in the northern parts of the Central and Mississippi Flyways, the major routes used by many migratory birds. The program is most active in Minnesota, North Dakota, and South Dakota, the prairie pothole region.

Success of the Water Bank Program indicates that attitudes toward America's wetlands have changed radically in the recent past. Farmers and the general public have taken a second look at the lands long considered wasted and useless, and have found that these wetlands serve many vital roles in maintaining our environment and managing water resources. Aside from wildlife production, wetlands control pollution by filtering out nutrients and toxic materials that otherwise would enter streams.

Yet the SCS, ASCS, CES, and agribusiness are still a threat in the Day Counties of the country. Before they altered their policies somewhat, more than a million acres of potholes in the prairie states were drained between 1943 and 1961. Surveys in the Dakotas and Minnesota indicate that about 125,000 acres of wetlands were drained from 1965 to 1968 in those three states alone.

Lynn Greenwalt, former director of the USFWS, described the situation in 1980:

> The SCS has had a change of direction, but effecting that change in ways that mean something to ducks and other critters is a long-term effort. It's being made, I'm happy to say, but it will be long after a week from Wednesday before the impact is evident.
>
> We're spending more money than ever to buy potholes and other lands — and those lands cost more than ever. While we have more money than before, we find new complexities we've never faced before: curious legislation in North Dakota, for exam-

ple. That is now the subject of litigation and we will probably be supported in court, but not until after long and heart-breaking debate. Meanwhile, the political problems of the Garrison project and others are always at hand.

> The job is one of those for which there are no real winners: I consider it a good day if the conflicting constituencies are equally unhappy. I long ago gave up trying to make everybody equally happy. I keep plugging along, but it doesn't get any easier. That's a good sign, I think, since it reveals that we're having more and more impact on people and things — and that's what we're in business for.

In spite of all the new rules and rhetoric, then, "public funds are still being used to frustrate public values associated with public lands," in the words of Larry Jahn. Leopold's ecological conscience awaits a renewed burst of communication. I'm betting my student products will supply it. Thanks to Art Hawkins and his fellow flyway biologists, today's waterfowl journalists start 'way ahead of where I was on that depot platform thirty years ago.

Conservation and communication have had a long and honorable liaison. I'm pleased to have been a very small part of that partnership. No, I've never gone back to Day County, but they tell me if I did, I'd find some of those drained potholes restored to duck production — a tribute to sportsperson dollars and USFWS diligence. A dawn wind in spring once more stirs across greening wheat fields, over phalanxes of willows, across bog meadows heavy with dew, to dapple the waters of an ice-fringed prairie pond — then, out of some far recess of the Dakota sky comes the susurrant sound of waterfowl wings, and ducks are back in parts of Day County.

Prairie Marshes Will Not Die

Grady E. Mann

Conservation and communication have had a long and honorable liaison, and Clay Schoenfeld's 1949 *Field & Stream* article "Good-By Pot-Holes" served as a prime example of that contribution to the prairie wetland scene. Schoenfeld was in the first skirmishes of this prairie wetland conservation movement and ably directed the first needed public attention to it. His article, with its collecting reverberations, closed out prairie pothole region Wetland Era 1.

After his call to battle, Schoenfeld shifted to other missions. But his 1949 alarm had set the stage for prairie region Wetland Era 2 — an era spanning the period from 1950 to 1972. Schoenfeld continued to wonder what happened to the South Dakota potholes long after his initial publicity. In 1980, thirty-one years after publication of his historic article, he wrote: "I've never gone back to Day County, but they tell me if I did, I'd find some of those drained potholes restored to duck production — a tribute to sportsperson dollars and Fish and Wildlife Service diligence."

Yes, Clay Schoenfeld, I'm happy to report that should you return to the prairie zone of your earlier battles, that spring wind does blow across ice-fringed ponds. Teal, gadwall, and pintail continue their spring flights and drop into those prairie potholes. At the crack of dawn, prairie chickens boom with age-old calls across blocks of shallow wetland habitat. Winnowing jacksnipe, willets, plover, and a host of other species add their distinctive calls to the prairie scene. And with scattered wetlands adding diversity to the landscape, all is right with at least this part of the prairie world.

Wetland Era 2 left a vast network of preserved marshland blocks across the prairie pothole region of the Dakotas and western Minnesota. It was an era not without its share of bloodletting, but one with great

rewards — prairie wetlands set aside for this and future generations.

The switchover from widespread drainage of prairie marshes to conservation of prairie marshes did not come easily. Drainage contractors, many Department of Agriculture (USDA) officers, and prairie landowners were on one side. Prairie conservationists, sportsmen groups, and key personnel of the USFWS and state game departments were on the other.

In 1950, I landed on the front edge of Wetland Era 2. In 1972 I officially left it; but only after experiencing twenty-two years of interesting waterfowl field studies, surveys, wetland inventories, field observations, writing, radio work, staffing, and a touch of administration.

To describe highlights of Wetland Era 2, I've taken them as they happened. These bits and pieces hang in my memory, reminders of this interesting era, an era in which the USFWS played a major role. That role centered on technical wetland advice, followed by a widespread wetland acquisition program throughout the prairie pothole region.

Little time was wasted after the pot had been stirred with *Good-By Pot-Holes*. By the spring of 1950, a detailed USFWS waterfowl study was started in the Waubay Hills of South Dakota in the heart of Day County, the scene of Schoenfeld's first skirmishes in the drainage controversy. Objectives were to determine how prairie potholes were used by waterfowl throughout all parts of the breeding season, not by guesswork, but by intensive, accurate research methods.

Chuck Evans, a University of Minnesota wildlife management graduate, excellent waterfowl researcher, and former World War II pilot, was the leader of this field study. I joined him in June of 1950, and for this first season we made up a two-man crew. Tom Schrader and Warren Nord held the administrative strings in the Minneapolis regional office.

Twelve square miles of rolling pothole topography were included in the study block. Potholes for this block numbered between

300 and 400. In 1950 they were all, at times, wet. Every wetland had to be checked regularly for use, number of breeding pairs in the spring, and brood production throughout the summer until all duck broods were a-wing. It required work in the marsh from the crack of dawn till darkness, day after day. We lunched and rested in the shade of a windbreak for a couple of hours during midday. By the end of the season there was little question how the South Dakota prairie ducks used various types of some 400 potholes in this working waterfowl study block. As someone jokingly remarked, "You guys probably know what those ducks are going to do before they know themselves."

These studies were duly reported after two seasons of detailed field work. Key conclusions were that during the breeding season these prairie ducks required a varied complement of wetlands to fulfill their breeding season needs. Small shallow potholes attracted them to an area, and other shallow marshes provided an early season food source of aquatic invertebrates for breeding and egg laying. Deeper marshes provided food and cover habitat for the broods until they were ready to fly. Later, these biological principles were to serve as key planning blocks for a multi-million dollar small wetlands preservation program, a program bracketing some 50,000 square miles of prairie pothole country in the United States. This was a good example of the process of evolution in the field of waterfowl management.

This Waubay Hills Waterfowl Production Study of South Dakota was an intensive investigation within the U.S. prairie pothole region. On its heels, the USFWS launched a nationwide inventory of wetlands. This inventory rated various zones for waterfowl potential and typed the wetlands of these broad zones. From this inventory and other background information, the U.S. prairie pothole region was delineated as one of the most important areas for concentrating wetland preservation efforts. The next activity blossomed.

Another line of action came in 1954. That action was to zero in on the prairie pothole region — the region recently hitting the nation's limelight. Orders from the USFWS high command were to establish a small group of drainage liaison personnel. Their mission: to work directly as waterfowl biologists with the Soil Conservation Service (SCS) and other USDA agencies on prairie country drainage problems.

On a hot July day in 1954, to start this assignment, I landed at Fergus Falls, Minnesota, an interesting town of 13,000 on the western Minnesota prairie edge. Fergus Falls was to serve as the first office for this mission. When my wife and I arrived, we didn't know whether the assignment would last a month or much longer. As things turned out, the next move was to be some eighteen years later, this after a fruitful and interesting career working toward preservation and management of marshes of the prairie region.

Other personnel assignments followed quickly. Across the prairie pothole region this initial liaison assignment drew together a diverse group of waterfowl biologists. Ellison "Bull" Madden, a Purdue University and Michigan State graduate, landed at Devil's Lake, North Dakota; Bill Sweeney from Massachusetts and Ken Black from the state of Washington drew assignments at Sioux Falls and Watertown, South Dakota; Bob Panzner, wildlife management graduate from Michigan State, took charge of operations at Benson, Minnesota. I added my West Virginia background with graduate work at the University of Minnesota to round out a five-man field crew — a crew with considerable geographical diversity. If that diversity did not always promote agreement within our own ranks, it did, when the chips were down, lend strength and purpose to the overall prairie pothole preservation movement.

Burt Rounds, trained in New Hampshire and at Colorado State University, was assigned as coordinator for this group of field mavericks. His New Hampshire state motto was "live free or die," and this group, temporarily free of major administrative shackles, was not about to let those prairie marshes die.

This pioneering group of field drainage liaison personnel was soon bolstered with Milt Reeves, Clyde Odin, and Art Stone. This dedicated group had a mission to help save prairie potholes. For a short period it was a freewheeling organization, one given considerable leeway to explore ways to get a pothole preservation job done. These men were not exactly inexperienced at the rough and tumble game of conservation of natural resources. Several were World War II veterans. If blocked on one front, they shifted to other approaches that might be more effective. Pressures and politics were moved into the drainage pothole ballgame. In short, they pulled out the stops. They were dead-set against abandoning the land and water resources of the U.S prairie pothole region. There were a lot of people in this country who were interested in preserving wetlands, yet federal tax dollars were being used to drain them. It just didn't make good sense, particularly during this period, to drain valuable prairie marshes.

This early contingent of five drainage liaison personnel had to be viewed as pests by USDA officials. Official courtesies were extended to us, but underneath the formalities the liaison was an uncomfortable one. A case in point: a wetland speaker at one rural Minnesota meeting was introduced with: "And here is one of those guys from the Conservation Department who is going to tell us why we can't drain our potholes." Others were constantly on the hot seat at rural agricultural meetings.

We were officed with the SCS. Usually it worked out that we were between a couple of file cases, or behind them. But before the close of Wetland Era 2, in 1972, a nearly complete switch came with a change in the state-level administration. Though this would have been unbelievable earlier, I witnessed a single file of thirty SCS work unit personnel crossing a northwestern Minnesota field while their own staff of wildlife biologists showed this group various wetland types and explained their uses.

This reversal in attitude and approach had not come overnight. Nor, we should note, is it fixed in the prairie land ethic of the present or future. The switch, encouraging at the time, had taken about fifteen years of meetings, positive preservation programs, discussions, field trips, television efforts, radio programs, news releases, and political and personal efforts. This combination brought a change in attitude toward the prairie potholes. With reapportionment on the legislative books, city dwellers were being heard on how federal tax dollars should be spent in rural areas. There was a turning of the conservation tide. Rural officials began to think that it might be good to at least listen to the story of how other land and water resources of the prairie were benefitting the total society.

Washington office personnel soon began to tour the prairie pothole region. Ernie Swift, then executive director of the National Wildlife Federation, was a staunch supporter, who probably helped to ensure that the Federation kept an eye on this important resource. Ernie appeared frequently in the field, and he constantly had his finger on the pulse of this movement.

Tours by visiting USFWS dignitaries became the pattern. Some were successful in getting the wetland preservation points across; others failed. We should consider examples of both.

First, the bad news. Through political processes, we managed to arrange a tour for the assistant secretary of the USDA, a feat in itself. The tour covered a heavily drained western Minnesota pothole zone, one laced with ditches. From the air the ditched pattern looked like a spiderweb network across the prairie landscape. Everything was set. The drainage projects below had virtually all been funded with federal tax dollars, contrary to the intent of current USDA drainage regulations. These examples showed well from the air. The tour proceeded right on schedule. Pilot-biologist Don Ledin of the Minnesota Conservation Department flew in with the department plane, and we made a dry run of the tour area the day before the arrival of the assistant secretary. He arrived in town the night before the tour. But as fate would have it, Mother Nature dropped five inches of rain that same night onto the drained prairie tour area. By morning, this undulating prairie pothole topography looked more like a veritable inland seascape. This part of the prairie pothole drainage problem was completely hidden, "Not a major problem" was the essence of the official report . . . or so it seemed at that time.

Now the good news. Another wetland preservation tour for key Minnesota Soil Conservation administrators had been planned, this out of Benson, Minnesota. Bob Panzner, the southwestern Minnesota USFWS representative lined it out. This season had been particularly dry. The tour was to cover the excessive drainage and questionable land use of the uplands in the rolling hills northeast of Benson. Stop after stop on this tour showed drainage ditches that were questionable operations by current interpretations of the USDA regulations. One didn't have to use much imagination to see that these drainage operations were the consequences of poor resource management calls. About 11 A.M., the prairie wind picked up. By noon, the flag in front of the post office was straight out. The wind sock on the town airstrip was full-blown. By 1 P.M., we had a good blow going and with it a major dust storm reminiscent of the 1930s. Visibility dropped to about thirty yards. Grit from the eroding topsoil was in our teeth; the air was suffocating. The tour party remained in the cars. Scattered remaining marshes on the route appeared as sparkling oases on this blackened biological desert.

This was a success story despite the grim picture of resource management. Mother Nature showed again who had the whip hand. She was telling us on this day that dry years in the prairie are the rule, and those responsible for the management of the prairie resources should take heed. By 2 P.M. the top administrators had seen enough. They had enough sand in their teeth and dust in their lungs. Abruptly the tour was concluded with, "We'll have to get back to St. Paul to take care of some office details." Mother Nature had cooperated this day. These officials were convinced that changes had to be made. These two experiences, one bad, one good, were all in a day's work for the waterfowl field man.

In the early 1960s, additional tours of the prairie wetland situation were planned for several Washington USFWS officials. One ground tour cut through some of the best remaining Minnesota pothole range. What might be the future of the prairie pothole preservation effort? Signs on the Minnesota Conservation Department's wetland projects loomed up regularly through the cattails of the roadside marshes. Drainage ditches cut variable swaths across the gently rolling landscape. Prairie marshes that had, as yet, been spared the ditch, sparkled here and there. They seemed to bear a challenge for this seemingly uneventful tour. Lively calls of rails, bitterns, mallards, teal, and godwits cut through the calm of the prairie pothole region and further sparked speculation on this tour's outcome. This tour was to be fruitful.

Shortly after this pothole coverage, the historic moment arrived. It happened at the dining room table at Fergus Falls. James T. McBroom, key USFWS program coordinator, had with him a young representative from the Bureau of the Budget. A brief remark dropped at some point during the evening was, "We have to get some money for this prairie pothole preservation effort." A few months later, the badly needed legislation was passed. Public Law 87-383 was described as "an act to promote the conservation of migratory waterfowl by the acquisition of wetlands and other essential waterfowl habitat, and for other purposes." To carry this out, there was authorized to be appropriated for the seven-year period beginning with fiscal year 1962 a sum not to exceed $105 million. Funds were to be treated as an advance, without interest, to the migratory bird conservation fund.

From there on, the lone operator roles of the USFWS drainage liaison personnel faded

*Paul Errington, one of America's leading authorities on wetlands while he lived, wrote eloquently of the need to preserve marshes and their living systems in **Of Marshes and Men**.* USFWS photo by D. L. Leedy.

abruptly into history. The USFWS small wetlands program exploded into a full-scale preservation effort. Now came additional waterfowl biologists, appraisers, land buyers, clerks, engineers, vehicles, and equipment. Wetland Era 2 shifted into a higher gear.

Quickly, the 50,000 square miles of the prairie pothole region on this side of the Canadian border were mapped for wetland acquisition and easement effort. A biological waterfowl acquisition plan was laid. A framework was built, but results had to eventually materialize from lands now in private ownership. Marshes were to be acquired or placed under easement only from willing sellers.

For this example of waterfowl planning, administrators paved the way. Waterfowl specialists surveyed widely and established sound priorities, made decisions, and laid a waterfowl-pothole preservation plan in line with clear-cut objectives. From that plan, trained acquisition personnel systematically negotiated with landowners.

They moved rapidly so, as Les Pengelley quipped, they would not be classed with the zoologists who were still trying to name the Great Plains Grizzly long after it became extinct.

Planning for this project was essential. It seemed to us that it was certainly easier to

change a line on a map, in effect, than to shift a building after it was built. We didn't see why planning for waterfowl management should be any different.

Across the U.S. prairie pothole region those responsible did their planning in different ways. Each adjusted his procedures to drainage stages, topography, wetland concentrations, and wetland densities. With that responsibility for western Minnesota, I took to the air, township plat book in hand. Day after day, veteran Navy pilot Joe Dvorak cranked up his light plane, and systematically we flew a grid pattern, section after section, township after township, until all of the prime western Minnesota prairie pothole range had been completely mapped. Marshland acquisition priorities were then pinpointed and designated with appropriate symbols for 13,000 square miles of western Minnesota. Duplicate township plats with appropriate acquisition priorities served as the pothole preservation field plan for the negotiators. It was a plan with a biological base within the earlier-designated, most important segment of the prairie pothole region south of the United States-Canadian border. This waterfowl plan was not hit and miss. Mapped pothole concentrations on the plats were current as of that survey date. For a long time after that 13,000-square-mile aerial survey, I could not pass a light plane without my eyeballs screwing up a bit.

Negotiations for valuable marshes moved steadily for the next decade. Progress was made day by day, month by month. One example: within the nineteen-county, western Minnesota zone, by May 23, 1972, 854 excellent prairie-type, fee-purchased wetland management projects had been started through the combined efforts of the USFWS and the Minnesota Department of Natural Resources. Through careful planning, widely distributed wetland units had been practically patterned through the Minnesota prairie townships. Wetland easements in the vicinity enhanced the waterfowl capabilities of these entire zones. Such was the pattern throughout the top waterfowl zones of the Dakotas and Nebraska.

USFWS acquisition operations continued on a wide front in four states: Nebraska, North Dakota, South Dakota, and Minnesota. By April, 1972, 14,004 easement cases had been closed in these four states. Many of these easements represented better than two or three sections of top-quality prairie pothole country, with fifty to sixty potholes per square mile. By rough estimates, more than one-half million potholes and marshes were under tight easement control in the two Dakotas alone. The full impact of this wetland complex control could be seen when you scanned the wall-size status maps at Devils Lake and Jamestown, North Dakota, and Fergus Falls, Minnesota. These maps showed where this widespread distribution rested in the heart of the best remaining prairie duck production lands on this side of the border. The real impact hit when you related the mapped colors to the excellent marshes on the land.

Nearing the close of Wetland Era 2, several indicators of change began to appear. Wetland acquisition across the Dakotas and Minnesota were slowing, the cream having been skimmed from the readily available prairie wetland resource. Opposition was building against additional federal wetland purchases. These were anticipated trends of the times. By 1972, the stage was set for Wetland Era 3 of the prairie region. It was another interesting period, including continuing acquisition and easement of wetlands and stepped-up management of purchased projects. Widespread wetlands under easements were being kept under close surveillance. Closely checked easement violation cases were landing in the courts.

My official departure at the close of Wetland Era 2 prompted many pleasant reflections. There was a deep sense of accomplishment, an accomplishment that was now fixed on the prairie landscape. That prairie pothole preservation program represented combined efforts of a lot of interesting people: farmers, ranchers, private cooperators, biologists, negotiators, engineers, administrators, and office clerks who all helped to put it together.

It was a comforting thought at the close of Wetland Era 2 to know that marshes under control now and in the near future were the nucleus of plans for prairie waterfowl management on this side of the United States-Canadian border.

Yes, Clay Schoenfeld, your *Good-By Pot-Holes* bore fruit. It did give the USFWS "a public hook on which to hang a drive to get wildlife values considered more fully." Also there's been a solid touch of Aldo Leopold's ecological conscience spread across many parts of the prairie pothole region. That job is not yet done, but there are dedicated workers out there giving it their best.

This briefly describes one important prairie pothole conservation era. Those in that ballgame now and into the future will ensure that these potholes will maintain their rightful place in the sun. And when the ice and snow melt from the potholes in the spring, continuing vanguards of searching mallards and pintails will circle isolated shallow marshes, drop in, and start the age-old cycle again.

Marshes such as this one serve many purposes, benefiting both wildlife and mankind. USFWS photo by G. E. Mann.

Wetland Preservation In the Future

Carl R. Madsen

Like an Indian scout scanning the battleground from a prairie bluff, I got my first good look at the wetlands program in 1967. My first perceptions were of Grady Mann, a seasoned warrior in the fight to save prairie wetlands. He gave me his counsel: "Stick to principles, not emotions or personalities. Be consistent. You'll be in conflicts, but if you fight on principles, you can continue to deal with our adversaries on a level of respect."

Grady preserved wetlands for ducks *and* people. Prairie wetlands are not only the backbone of this continent's duck produc-

tion; they also provide habitat for resident wildlife and nongame species, while holding special values for people: runoff water retention, water storage and aquifer recharge, nutrient uptake and recycling, steam flow regulation, lake stabilization, and fish production. All of these values contribute to the recreational and economic well-being of those who live near wetlands. In many areas of the prairie pothole country, recreational values derived from wetlands are marketed at resorts, shopping centers, main streets, and service stations. The natural resources on which these industries depend are inseparably entwined with our agricultural enterprise and other business pursuits.

We seem to have a desire to live, work, and play in places that offer variety. Wetlands are one of the major contributors of diversity to

the prairies, a region of rich agricultural productivity.

When the "old-timers" began their wetland protection work, they fought an uphill battle against national, state, and local intentions to destroy wetlands and convert them to other uses. Today, we have national directives that clearly state the policy that wetlands are valuable and that their preservation is to be a national endeavor. This intent is expressed in a number of federal laws and policies, and is brought clearly into focus in the executive order on wetlands.

The federal government is limited in its powers to direct the activities of individuals, and rightly so. But many of today's land-use decisions are made by private individuals who are profit motivated and often short-sighted. Leaving decisions about wetland preservation or destruction up to these individuals invites the demise of precious and irreplaceable resources.

Our wetland preservation efforts on the prairies began and continue as a means for the federal government to influence land-use decisions by providing financial incentives, enforcing regulations, and purchasing land. While wetland acquisition has been successful in saving isolated parcels of waterfowl production habitat, it has not proved effective in preventing wetland losses on a broad scale. If that sounds like double talk, consider this: during 18 years of accelerated wetland acquisition in which many wetlands were preserved, the USFWS managed to purchase only a small percentage of the prairies wetlands that were present in 1962. Many more were drained. On the bright side, other wetlands still survive in private ownership. They are our challenge for the future.

Today wetland preservation means more than land acquisition. In the future especially, we'll have to deal with incentives to private landowners to keep wetlands on their land. We've seen a step in this direction through the U.S. Department of Agriculture's (USDA) Water Bank Program in which a landowner enrolls in a ten-year program to preserve wetlands and maintain cover around them. This program has enjoyed an increasing level of success and has often enhanced the quality of management provided to wetland communities. USFWS wetland easements are also directed toward maintaining wetlands on private land.

In the wetlands program we've seen a need for action. That action was taken by the Service and the states as they moved for acquisition of wetlands. We've also seen action by the USDA, which reversed its policies from subsidizing and encouraging wetland drainage to one of wetland protection; policy changes now prohibit the USDA from draining wetlands and resulted in establishment of the Water Bank Program. Some states have passed ordinances to regulate drainage and protect wetlands. Some eastern states, where wetlands have been most devastated, have some of the strongest wetland protection ordinances. We're probably a long way from that type of legislation in the prairies where we still have a relative abundance of wetlands and people who cherish their rights to do with their land as they wish. Historically, Americans usually don't protect their natural resources until those resources are threatened or scarce.

The wetland story is really typical of many past conservation issues. When our nation was one vast wilderness, no one sought to preserve a piece of it for the future. Our attitude then was to conquer, use, and divert that wilderness to other uses. As that wilderness shrank, we were able to gain support to preserve some national parks and a few other areas in their natural state. When the loggers went to the lake states to harvest the vast pine

forests, they thought very little of setting aside, preserving, and managing that resource for the future. The policy was one of cut out and get out; somehow, the pineries were expected to last forever. They, of course, did not. In spite of what seemed to be endless resources, we ended up with scars on the landscape, shattered hopes and dreams of everlasting prosperity, and ecological problems that have taken generations to work out. We face similar attitudes regarding the prairie wetlands. We're ruining this valuable resource at a rate that has led to many problems while a few have reaped short-term benefits. It is an attitude that can only be changed through understanding and education. We need more understanding of the fragility of our water resources and their relationship to our well-being, and education on how to use them wisely and capitalize on their long-term productivity.

In Minnesota, there is a new property tax incentive to maintain wetlands. In conjunction with all the other wetland preservation programs, the tax credit is another alternative for many wetland owners. This program, new in 1980, excludes all wetlands in agricultural areas from property taxes. Like churches, hospitals, and certain other property, wetlands are exempt from taxes. In addition, for an agreement to maintain wetlands in their natural state, a landowner receives a credit toward the net taxes due on the farm. The rate of credit is three-fourths of 1 percent of the value of an acre of nearby cropland for each acre of wetland preserved.

None of the programs now in effect can do the entire job needed to preserve wetlands on a large scale. It seems that what is needed is a variety of incentives, programs, and options whereby landowners can find incentives suitable for all kinds of outlooks and needs. This makes me wonder if we shouldn't have a single umbrella wetland protection mechanism that encompasses many options and has negotiable terms, conditions, and rates of payment, all in one program. There's a tendency in government to create administrative monsters by developing mutiple programs, sometimes with cross purposes, handled by many different agencies and organizations. It's no wonder that people get confused about the maze of options — even those who administer the programs. When problems arrive, perhaps we're too quick to look to government programs for solutions. You can count on one hand the ways our government can direct the use of private lands. We have legislation that restricts certain uses of the land. We have zoning that directs which uses of lands will be permitted in certain areas. We can influence land use through tax incentives and disincentives. We can direct land use by purchasing it or purchasing certain rights to land and using it for public purpose. All of these require the support of the people who own the land. It is not likely that a meaningful zoning ordinance can be passed to protect wetlands in areas where we are losing wetlands to private enterprise. This is because the very people who are developing and changing wetlands to serve their purposes are the ones who would have to pass the law to restrict their own activities. The same is true for prohibitive legislation and, to a lesser extent, tax incentives, disincentives, or subsidies.

What we've seen so far in wetland protection legislation is primarily federal action to put programs on the local level to address critical problems. This is most evident in the prairie pothole regions, where we've seen federal programs of one form or another aimed at protecting wetlands from private development. Although we are beginning to see local and state legislation to protect wetlands, it has been, for the most part, only in those areas where few wetlands are left.

Above all, we need education programs that will bring land ethics and stewardship to the people who make decisions about land uses. No element of land use, wetlands included, can be effectively treated individually without considering the many other facets of decision making that affect the land. How do we really go about establishing a land ethic? Obviously, it's not a matter of simply teaching a course in the school or

sponsoring a government public-relations program or publishing an informational leaflet about the value of wetlands. But through long-term approaches we can develop understanding of ourselves and our own relationships to the earth and its resources. When I say we, I mean those of us who work in the conservation business, those of us who live in urban areas, and those of us who live and work on the land.

Ultimately, the land resource and its values and relationships belong to all the people in this country. Some of us are stewards of that land for a short time. Others are users of the products of that land. But our whole society — and, indeed, the whole world — depends on the long-term continued productivity of the land, and we all have a very vital interest in seeing that the land is handled properly for the long-term benefit of people. Wildlife habitat diversity is one way to measure the long-term health of the land, and by preserving wildlife, we may enhance our own chances for survival.

It's not likely that as wildlife professionals we can maintain adversary relationships with landowners and successfully achieve long-term goals of maintaining widespread populations of wild animals. Our challenge for the future is to get beyond these adversary roles and to develop credibility and rapport with landowners. Our goal must be to communicate effectively and share concepts and ideas, knowledge about the land and its use. By cultivating good relationships with wildlife resources and wildlife habitats, we can help people institute a total land resource ethic.

It does not seem right to me that the only way we can maintain our natural resources, particularly our wetlands and associated wildlife populations, is through force of law, lawsuits, arrests, and convictions for those who violate one provision of the law or another. Our challenge must be to develop programs that will create attractive partnerships in preserving and developing wetlands and wildlife habitat for the long-term productivity of our land. It is very likely that our society will have to pay those who own land

in some way or another for the exercise of conservation rights, at least in the near future. Payments will probably have to be made for land-use rights, as long as owners have the attitude that "this is my land and I can do with it as I want."

We are a long way socially and politically from regulated land use in many parts of our nation, and that's probably a good thing. In many regions though, we are able to make incentive payments for certain land uses, especially for wetland preservation. Vehicles to reimburse landowners for use of certain rights to their land should be widely acceptable, easily available, and attractive to land users. This could be in the form of tax incentives or marketing credits through which a person could market the productivity of his land in some form that would give the landowner a just payment for the land-use rights that he provides for public benefit, foregoing income he might otherwise earn.

Reimbursement might be in the form of an income tax credit or a deduction where a landowner says, "I have maintained a certain number of acres of wetlands on my farm and have foregone the income from so many bushels of wheat that I might have grown here. The benefits from those wetlands were given to all the people of the nation. I will consider that a gift to those people and deduct a like value from my income, just as I would deduct a gift to any other charity."

We might develop a more widespread application of property tax credits for wet-

land preservation. If private land is used for public purposes — such as storing water for downstream flood protection, producing wildlife, or recharging groundwater — and most benefits accrue to all citizens, perhaps we should look for ways to share the tax burden so that all share in the cost of maintaining those public values on that private land.

If enough of us think of ways in which we can have large-scale applications or reimbursement and share the costs of maintaining public values on private lands, we can probably come up with a new package of incentives to maintain an active partnership between the landowner and those who would preserve public values through natural resource management on private lands.

The waterfowl manager of the future will have to be more efficient than his predecessors if he is to be successful. He will have greater demands placed on him for greater duck production and will be expected to do so on less land and water than has been done in the past. Where can he turn? So far, we haven't scratched the surface on wetland management for duck production. We have people we call wetland managers, but they don't truly manage wetlands, they manage the surrounding upland tracts. We need to develop techniques of manipulating water levels and water quality that will result in vegetative conditions and food production to benefit ducks. That will be a new level of management from what we've done in the past.

We've begun nest-cover manipulations, and here, too, we've just begun to tap the potential for maximum duck use and nest success. By some standards, we may think we're doing well now, but I believe time will show us that, as our skills develop, we can produce many more ducks per unit area than we have in the past.

The United States Congress, in the preamble to the Water Bank Act, clearly stated the values of wetlands and the intent of Congress to preserve those values. President Carter also stated those values and outlined a national policy for their preservation. An immediate need now is for state and local governing bodies to adopt similar statements of wetland values as they reflect local situations and the desirability of preserving them. When those statements of intent are developed, then ways and means to accomplish preservation can be developed. Statements of intent to preserve wetlands need not constitute endorsement of programs or agencies; they should merely stimulate action and initiate local efforts.

That, as I see it, is the real challenge for wetland preservation and management for the future. We have many issues surrounding our present programs. Many of our conflicts center around competition for land and its use. That competition will most likely be even more intense in the future. It was our central theme in the beginning of wetland preservation and will be our main challenge in the future. If we can put our human needs in perspective and find solutions to conservation problems, we can continue to enjoy the benefits that we receive from the wetland resources richly distributed throughout our prairie pothole country.

Saga of the Lake Erie Marshes

Karl E. Bednarik

Etienne Brule and his band of French voyageurs landed at the mouth of a southwestern Lake Erie tributary in what is now Ottawa County, Ohio, on All Saints' Day (November 1) in 1615. In honor of the day, Brule named the stream Toussaint Creek, the name which it still holds. Brule and his men on that day were looking across one of the finest and largest marshes in North America. This is the story of what has transpired since Brule first saw this rich marshland bordering Lake Erie in Ohio and Michigan.

Early records indicate that the western Lake Erie marshes, extending from present-day Vermilion, Ohio, to the mouth of the Detroit River in Michigan, bordered a vast wilderness encompassing 300,000 acres of marsh and swamp which teemed with wildlife. Southwest, the marsh became the "Black Swamp," a dense swamp forest that covered an ancient lakebed in northwestern Ohio. The higher portions were wet prairie rather than swamp or marsh, and were dotted with small groves of trees, probably burr oaks. These wider open areas were centered around Brule's Toussaint Creek and nearby Portage River.

The Lake Erie marsh region and the adjacent Black Swamp were the dwelling place of the Wyandot and Ottawa Indians. Ottawa or "Uttawa," an Indian word signifying trader, was applied to this tribe because of the commercial transactions with the early white settlers. The Indians' principal stock in trade was the furs and skins of wild animals.

Later the French, perhaps descendants of Brule's voyageur band, settled in this marsh country. Undoubtedly attracted by the abundant wildlife, these early settlers made their living hunting, trapping, and trading with the Indians. They lived in bark huts for many years, doing little or no clearing. Their chief source of income was from furs and bear grease. These Frenchmen were extremely jealous of their marsh homeland and forcefully defended it against other hunters and trappers.

The original marshes attracted vast flocks of migrating waterfowl. Located at a crossing point of two major flyways, they attracted ducks from eastern Canada and those coming from the western prairie provinces to winter along the Atlantic Coast. The beds of wild celery were particularly attractive to great numbers of canvasbacks, redheads, and scaups migrating southeastward to their wintering grounds on Chesapeake Bay.

The presence of these waterfowl concentrations was well known to the early trappers and settlers, and many became proficient market hunters. Old-timers still living near the marshes recall days when wagon loads of ducks were hauled to Port Clinton, placed in barrels, and shipped by train to Cleveland and other eastern cities.

Sportsmen were also interested in the duck marshes; as early as 1850, the marshes at the head of Sandusky Bay were surveyed for a shooting club. The Winous Point Club was chartered in 1854. The present-day Magee Marsh Wildlife Area was chartered as the Crane Creek Shooting Club from 1883 through 1903.

A 1793 writer described the Miami (Maumee) River, upstream from present-day Toledo, as being "near 600 yards wide and near the head of the Grand Rapids it resembles a meadow flooded over." He further described the river downstream as having little or no current and appearing "like a flooded meadow with long grass extensively across."

Describing this vast area of marshland, meadows, and prairies adjoining Lake Erie, a historian in 1815 claimed that it "cannot contain less than 300,000 acres." He explored the Maumee Bay to the Portage River area, noting that "the prairie grass was about seven feet high and so thick that it would easily sustain one's hat; in some places, a cat could have walked on it's surface." He also observed that "within the bosom of Miami (Maumee) Bay grow several thousand acres of *follie avione* [wild rice, wild oats]." This author made many references to the great number of waterfowl in the Portage, Toussaint, Swan, and other creeks containing an abundance of waterfowl food.

Another writer in 1837 presented descriptions of several extensive prairies, including the "Grand Maumee prairie from the Maumee River to the headwaters of the Portage River" and "low, level prairies stretching, when seen from some points, as far as the eye could see" between present Sandusky and Port Clinton.

In 1899, an early naturalist reported that "within the memory of men still living a wet prairie, covered with water during much of the year, occupied northwestern Erie County, close to Sandusky Bay."

Thanks to shooting club records and the memories of elderly marshmen, there are additional descriptions of a few marshes as they appeared near the close of the nineteenth century. From these sources, the following mosaic of the original marshes can be reconstructed.

On the shallow borders of the marsh, flooded only during periods of high water and without a protective cover of water in winter, stretched meadows of blue-joint grass, interspersed with patches of cord grass and various sedges. Shrubs, such as silky dogwood, elderberry, buttonbush, and swamp rose occupied drier sites. Cattail was probably the dominant vegetation on those portions of the marsh usually covered by shallow water. Large stands of reeds occupied similar areas, and bur-reed and bulrushes were common along the deeper margins. Where the water was deeper, wild rice, waterlilies, lotus, and spatterdock composed the emergent vegetation. In the waterways and deeper portions of the marsh, wild celery, pondweeds, coontail, and other submerged species of vegetation were plentiful.

These plant communities were not static, and their boundaries shifted as the lake level fluctuated over a period of years. Although this was largely a progressive shifting to water of optimum depth, certain communities decreased in size at the expense of others. At the Point Mouille Marsh, on the Michigan shore of Lake Erie, the years of low lake level from 1924 to 1938 allowed cattle to graze on sledges and grass where cattail had stood a few years previous. Between 1910 and 1944, the dominant emergent vegetation at Point Mouille changed from wild rice to cattail. During the winters of 1945-1946 and 1946-1947, and to a lesser extent in subsequent years, there was a large die-off of emergent vegetation, particularly cattail, on most of the Lake Erie marshes. This die-off was the result of high water in Lake Erie. At Winous Point, soft-stemmed bulrush replaced some dead stands of cattail. At the Magee Marsh, twenty miles east of Toledo, large stands of swamp loosestrife, an exotic species, replaced the once prevalent stands of cattail.

Few of the present-day marshes have retained their original characteristics. Drainage, siltation, land-fill, introduction of exotic plants and animals, and control of water levels by diking systems have contributed to the changes. The prairies and forests have long since been cleared and drained for agricultural and industrial use, or urban development, with only a few remnant marshes remaining of the once vast wetland habitat. Most of the remaining marsh has been maintained by private hunting clubs, USFWS, and the Division of Wildlife of the Ohio Department of Natural Resources.

Today the former marshes peripheral to the mouth of the Maumee River are industrial and railroad sites — iron ore and coal loading docks, servicing giant ore carriers and sea-going freighters, and three huge oil refineries. Once crystal clear, Maumee River and Maumee Bay are now coffee colored, the turbidity coming from topsoil runoff from farms in northeast Indiana and northwestern Ohio. The rich marsh observed by Etienne Brule in 1615 at the mouth of the Toussaint River now is the site of a giant, nuclear-fueled, electric-generating facility, with a 500-foot high cooling tower. In the same area

are found scores of summer and year-round cottages, as well as several boat marinas. Two private duck clubs, one of 2,500 acres and the other 500 acres, have preserved a remnant of the original marsh in that area.

Sandusky Bay — once crystal clear and full of submergent aquatic duck foods, attracted great concentrations of canvasback, redhead and scaup — is today also coffee colored due to agricultural topsoil losses within the Sandusky River drainage and a rough fish population that constantly stirs the muddy bottom. The submergent acquatics have disappeared, as have the diving duck concentrations. Despite the drastic changes in and around Sandusky Bay, the best waterfowl hunting, primarily for dabbling ducks, in Ohio occurs in the marshes owned by private duck clubs.

The fertile soils adjacent to the marshes are intensively cultivated. Drainage is vital to successful agriculture on the low, flat land. Soybeans, corn, wheat, and hay are the principal crops. A semi-marine climate afforded by the proximity of Lake Erie has encouraged the planting of orchards on better-drained soils, especially the Catawba and Marblehead peninsulas.

Under pristine conditions, the constantly changing water levels of Lake Erie played a major role in governing the flora and fauna of the marshes. Although most of the lake marshes were protected from severe wave action by a barrier beach, the numerous waterways dissecting the beach allowed lake fluctuations to control water levels in the marshes. This resulted in high water levels during the summer growing season, retarding temperature extremes and prolonging the season. The tempering effect of the lake retards growth of vegetation in spring and deters early killing frosts in autumn.

Lake Erie still plays a key role in determining how the marshes and adjacent cultivated lands are managed. A large, relatively shallow body of water at a mean elevation of 570.5 feet above sea level, Lake Erie water levels fluctuate greatly, due in part to seasonal and yearly differences in watershed

A nuclear reactor now stands near the site where Etienne Brule and his voyageurs first saw the Lake Erie marshes. Only a small remnant of this great marsh survives today. Photo by Aerial Surveys, Inc.

drainage, as well as short-period seiches caused by strong winds. A seiche occurs when persistent winds of strong velocity literally push the water from one end of the lake to the other. A severe storm on January 2, 1942, caused a difference of seven feet from mean level at each end of the lake, or a total difference of fourteen feet from one end to the other. Northeast winds often cause

seiches of two to three feet at the southwest end of the lake. When the lake is high, these seiches can inundate much of the lowland normally protected by dikes, profoundly affecting the natural vegetation of the marshes, land-use practices on the bordering lowlands, and consequent waterfowl abundance and use of the area. Annual fluctuations average one and a half feet from levels low in winter to high in summer. Besides these annual cyclic fluctuations, variations in precipitation within the Great Lakes basin cause changes in the lake level over a period of years. For example, Lake Erie levels varied by nearly five feet from February 1936 to June 1947. Lake levels have been above normal for the last eight years, a condition unequaled since 1860, when records were first kept.

In November 1972, a severe "northeaster" storm struck the southwestern shore of Lake Erie. Marshes were inundated with Lake Erie floodwater and dike systems were severely damaged. Subsequent storms in 1973 and 1974 destroyed most of the eroded diking systems. No water level control was possible, and little of the typical aquatic vegetation of a managed marsh remained. A 1974 wetlands inventory indicated Ohio's 30,000 acres of Lake Erie marshes had been reduced to 17,000 acres. The other 13,000 acres had been inundated by Lake Erie and Sandusky Bay due to the highest water levels ever recorded.

The unusually large amount of water reaching Lake Erie was the result of several factors: 1) a series of consecutive years of excessive rainfall on the upper Great lakes; 2) the discharge rate from Lake Erie through the Niagara River, though greater than normal, was not sufficient to keep Lake Erie within normal limits; and 3) a heavy runoff from northeast Indiana, southwest Michigan, and northern Ohio streams.

How to use and master the marshes and Lake Erie was a challenge to the early settlers, one that John Nicholas Magee accepted. The town banker in Elmore, Ohio, Magee was a colorful Irishman, short of stature and a go-getter. In 1903, he purchased the largest dredge around at that time — a floating steam-type, forty feet long and twenty-four feet wide, requiring a five-man crew to operate it.

Magee convinced the landowners along the lake that they should drain their lands to improve them for agriculture. After having constructed several miles of drainage ditches, Magee attempted to collect his fees for the work. Many of the landowners were unable to pay, so they had no alternative but to lose their lands by foreclosure. By the end of 1903, Magee had 1,110 acres adjacent to the Cleveland Club, a 1,600-acre tract which a group of wealthy Clevelanders had purchased earlier that year for hunting purposes. The following year, he purchased the club and annexed it to his other holdings, giving him title to 8,000 acres of marsh.

The new land baron began to use his giant dredge in earnest. He dredged a canal twenty-four feet wide and nine feet deep for four miles, throwing up a spoilbank fifteen feet high. All of this was done with the intention of draining the wetlands for truck farming. Magee, as many men before and since, failed to reckon with the forces of nature. In this case, mighty forces were present in the storm-tossed waters of spring "northeasters" that raged over the beach and inundated the newly drained lands. Several such episodes convinced Magee that his agricultural venture was too costly, so he decided to lease his lands for waterfowl hunting and trapping.

The Magee Marsh of 1905 was quite different from the Magee Marsh of 1980. Cattails formed a solid mass of vegetation, and wild rice, nonexistent in the marsh today, grew so profusely that duck guides had to beat the stalks down to lay out their decoys. Little wonder that the area was a good stopping point for waterfowl on their migratory flights.

Old hunters and trappers told me many interesting duck hunting episodes of bygone days on this marsh that would alarm most modern game managers. In the middle of the 1900s, it was common for two men to embark at dawn in a sixteen-foot duck boat and return at sunset with the boat loaded to the gunwales with ducks. Such a load would run from 125 to 140 birds.

The use of live decoys was common practice in that era. A pen of 300 "call ducks" was maintained for the use of the hunters. A hunter would use from ten to twenty-five live decoys in front of his blind. The guide would place a string around the duck's leg, then drop a one-half pound anchor into the water. The bird could move in a limited area, free to flap its wings and add its voice to those of the "Judas Birds," luring their wild brethren to the guns. A refinement was later introduced, a leather collar for the live decoys which made it easier to release the birds at the close of the shooting day. The guide would release the decoys from their anchors, and the birds would fly back to the clubhouse under their own power, seeking the corn bins in the duck pens. Many hunters enjoyed shooting at waterfowl silhouetted against a full moon.

The bountiful duck population enticed duck poachers to the marsh. The *modus operendus* was to scatter shelled corn in a shallow pond and permit the birds to feed freely for a day or two. Then the poachers placed a gill net near the marsh bottom over the baited area. The ducks, probing the bottom for the grain, poked their heads through the mesh of the nets, became entangled, and drowned. As many as 100 ducks would be taken in one night.

Legitimate duck hunting, poaching, trapping muskrats and turtles, and catching bullfrogs kept marshmen busy much of the year, but a few also had time for "moonshining" during the Roaring Twenties. Only the waterfowl who fed on the discarded fermented mash were aware of this hidden distillery. Some marshmen assisted busy rumrunners who ran the Coast Guard blockades to bring illegal whiskey from Canada. They operated discreet beacon lights along the marsh shore where the rumrunning boats unloaded their cargo on moonless nights.

Heavy financial obligations made it necessary for control of the marsh to pass from the Magee family to a group of receivers. For a number of years the Clevelanders who bought the land enjoyed the acme of duck hunting. A membership sold for hundreds of dollars. It has been stated that the average cost per duck taken was nearly $150. Despite this high cost, the fame of the Magee Marsh was such that an available membership was an eagerly sought prize.

In the 1920s, while marshes and potholes were being drained in many parts of the United States, marshes were being diked around Lake Erie. Each dike was an investment in ducks and hard cash. In this rich agricultural land it was more profitable to provide duck shooting than to raise corn. While the larger natural marshes readily attracted waterfowl, there was competition from the newfangled pickers who left a thin layer of yellow grain on the ground farther inland. Duck hunting was and is important to the local economy, involving hundreds of people employed as marsh caretakers, punters, cooks, waitresses, dragline operators, and managers. Millions of dollars have been spent to build miles of dikes, pump stations, boathouses, clubhouses, boats, and decoys.

A dark side of the history is that some marsh managers baited the marshes in an effort to provide club members of customers good shooting. Baiting was the practice of dispensing shelled corn or wheat on the marsh bottom in front of shooting blinds. Baiting continued to be a common practice around southwest Lake Erie long after it had been outlawed in 1934. Many arguments were presented by baiting advocates to justify their actions. Although natural feed and waste grain were abundant, the pro-baiters contended that "feeding," as baiting was called locally, was absolutely necessary to prevent starvation or at least to keep the birds in shape for reproduction. Helped by the baiting, bag limit violations on some marsh units were flagrant. In 1949, two years before the Magee Marsh became state property, two shooters in one day killed 180 ducks over a heavily baited shooting blind. The limit in 1949 was four ducks. With rigid enforcement by state and federal wildlife agencies, duck baiting has virtually been eliminated and over-bags are uncommon.

The economics of managing Lake Erie marshes primarily for waterfowl hunting and muskrat trapping is worth emphasizing because these marshes have been extremely expensive to maintain.

Marsh owners and waterfowling clubs, in an attempt to create or improve marshes, began to enclose them with dikes. By 1934, 30,000 acres of marshland were enclosed by 125 miles of dikes in Lucas and Ottawa counties. The average cost of marsh construction at that time was $150 per acre; $3 million was invested in marsh development by the end of that year. To offset these increasing costs, the marsh owners inaugurated marsh management.

The low water levels of the 1930s made it imperative that undiked marshland be impounded so that it could retain water. Approximately 100 privately owned pumping stations were put into operation to supply the marshes with much needed water. The average Lake Erie marsh in 1934 was eighteen inches above the level of Lake Erie. It is apparent that without diking some of the Lake Erie marshes would have passed out of existence during those drought years.

The 1940s witnessed a return of higher water levels, threatening the diked marshes. Dikes constructed to retain water within the marshes now were improved to keep out the rising waters. The Magee Marsh is a prime example of inundation and destruction by high water. Early maps, and conversation with former fur trappers having a half-century of experience on this marsh, reveal that a ten-foot high sandy knoll of the barrier beach on the lake side of the marsh extended 300 to 400 feet from the present shoreline. I know of a sunken well and the foundation of a fur trapper's cabin now sixty feet from shore under three feet of water. At the peak of the flooding, the lake absorbed a portion of the marsh.

Marshes located several miles upstream from Lake Erie, on the Portage River in Ottawa County, also provide evidence of the effects of rising water levels. In 1947 a group of waterfowlers constructed a new retaining dike along the river boundary line of the marsh; a berm of thirty feet wide was allowed to remain between the river and the dike. Observation of this dike in January 1952 showed that the dike had been breached in many places for several hundred feet.

Huge sums of money have been expended in a vain attempt to restrict the high water levels. In the 1930s, a duck club on Sandusky Bay bought tons of limestone to riprap the miles of dikes adjacent to the bay. By 1953, the riprapped dikes were under twelve inches of water.

On the majority of the marshes, some degree of water control is practiced. Marshes maintain their water levels in autumn by the use of sluice gates and pumps. Water is drawn down in the spring or summer by opening the sluice gates or dam spillways when the outside lake or river levels are low.

In September, all of the marshes begin pumping operations; some are pumped continuously twenty-four hours a day for three to six weeks to raise their water levels for the hunting season. The pumps vary in size from small, four-inch pumps driven by farm tractors to large twenty-four-inch diesel-driven pumps. There is also a thirty-six-inch, electric-driven pump, at the state's Magee Marsh Wildlife Area, which pumps 32 million gallons of water in twenty-four hours. In the course of a normal fall pumping season, the thirty-six-inch pump is operated twenty-four hours daily over a five-week interval to raise the water level on the 2,600 acre marsh eighteen inches. Pumping operations are an expensive feature of marsh management.

Water levels and their controls are basic to successful marsh management. Water level control, which is the key to successful marsh management, has several purposes. Pumping fresh or new water, to the depth desired prior to the waterfowling season, permits waterfowl to feed and provides access to the duck hunter. In addition, flooding enables muskrats to move freely under the ice so they can secure food. In shallow marshes, ice often freezes to the marsh bottom, making it impossible for muskrats that remain in dike dens to feed.

Marsh water level draw-downs permit an area to lie fallow. A period of dryness allows decomposition of vegetable matter. Water control can also be used to determine the type of vegetative growth. Mid-May or early June draw-downs expose the marsh bottom, thereby enhancing the growth of certain plants. Undesirable plants, such as loose-strife, which are tolerant of deep water, are eliminated by lowering water levels, while desirable plants such as cattails, bur-weed, and smart-weeds benefit by such practices.

The expensive task of salvaging the remains of one of the continent's greatest marshes is shared by private duck clubs, the state conservation departments of Ohio and Michigan, and the USFWS.

A study by the Mississippi Flyway Council, released in 1968, revealed that in the Lake Erie marshes Michigan had fifty-four duck clubs, while in Ohio there were sixty-three duck clubs. In Ohio, private duck clubs controlled 24,000 acres of wetland habitat, compared to 6,000 areas in state-federal wetland habitat. Thus, private clubs play a major role in perpetuating valued waterfowl habitat. In addition to providing hunting opportunities, private waterfowling clubs contribute materially to the waterfowl management effort in the Lake Erie marshes and the Mississippi Flyway by: 1) preserving, directly and indirectly, valuable habitat; 2) increasing the attractiveness of habitat through management, primarily water-level manipulation and vegetation control; 3) encouraging production of waterfowl; 4) aiding in waterfowl distribution, primarily by maintaining refuges and restrictions on daily and weekly shooting; 5) providing, in many areas, opportunities for a variety of recreational activities; and 6) investing substantial funds to maintain the quality of recreation. Private clubs complement and supplement state and federal programs aimed at preserving waterfowl habitat. Such investments would be difficult to match under public ownership.

All-time high Lake Erie levels in 1972, and subsequent storms in 1973 and 1974, destroyed many miles of dikes on 30,000 acres of private, state, and federal wetlands, reducing the marsh acreage to 17,000 acres by 1975.

Private duck clubs, such as the Winous Point Shooting Club, the Ottawa Shooting Club, and others, have spent in excess of $1.5 million since 1976 to restore and riprap new dikes, and install new water-control structure and marsh pumps in the Sandusky Bay area. Approximately 13,000 acres have been reclaimed from the high water devastation of 1972-1974.

Since 1976 the Division of Wildlife, Ohio Department of Natural Resources, has reconstructed twenty-seven miles of dikes, placed 39,000 tons of heavy armor rock along dike slopes, and constructed new control devices at a cost of $2.5 million to preserve 2,600 acres of wetlands at the Magee Marsh Wildlife Area.

Along southeast Michigan's Lake Erie shore, the Michigan Department of Natural Resources' famous Pointe Mouille State Game Area was virtually destroyed by the high Lake Erie water levels of the early 1970s. This 2,700-acre duck hunting marsh is now being restored through a far-reaching, cooperative program between the state conservation agency and the U.S. Corps of Engineers. The Corps was seeking a site to dispose Detroit River navigation dredge spoil. Working cooperatively, the Michigan Department of Natural Resources and the Corps have developed a program whereby the Corps has constructed a four and one-half mile long by 1,600-feet wide, banana-shaped, riprapped stone disposal containment island on the site of Pointe Mouilee's destroyed barrier beach. Each agency, working cooperatively, benefitted. The Pointe Mouille State Game Area will realize an additional 1,300 acres of restored marshland, for a total of 4,000 acres. The Corps has found a safe disposal containment site for heavily contaminated harbor dredge material. The "Big Banana" spoil-containment site cost the Corps $50 million. In addition, the state conservation agency, under the Title 150 program, will receive $800,000 for internal water-control structures, marsh pumps, and habitat restoration. Thirty-five percent of Michigan's Lake Erie marshes will have been restored under this imaginative, cooperative program.

In Ohio, the USFWS acquired about 8,000 acres of former duck club land, which evolved into two national wildlife refuges in

A typical view of the Upper Mississippi Refuge. Photo by A. M. Wetlach.

the 1960s: the Little Cedar Point National Wildlife Refuge and the Ottawa National Wildlife Refuge. Since 1976, the service has invested over $4 million in new dikes, water-control structure, and pumping stations.

Collectively, working toward the same goal, the private duck clubs and state and federal conservation agencies are doing an outstanding job in restoring and maintaining 30,000 acres of the former 300,000 acres of wetlands observed by Étienne Brule in 1615.

The Great River Refuge

William E. Green

The Upper Mississippi River Wildlife and Fish Refuge is the longest wildlife refuge in the continental United States, extending a distance of 284 miles along the Mississippi River from the Chippewa River in Wisconsin to the Rock River in Illinois. The refuge encompasses nearly 195,000 acres in parts of Minnesota, Wisconsin, Iowa, and Illinois, touching on twenty-six counties and two Corps of Engineer districts. The size of the refuge creates a number of special management problems. Its position, and the excellent habitat it provides waterfowl, makes this refuge one of the most important in the entire system.

The Upper Mississippi refuge was established by an act of Congress on June 7, 1924. Among the conservation groups providing stimuli for this legislation was the Isaac Walton League. League founder Will Dilg loved

A typical lock and dam on the Upper Mississippi. The pools above these dams hold flooded bottomlands that offer good habitat for dabbling and diving ducks. USFWS photo.

to fish on the Mississippi. One summer, when he and his son were fishing near the site of the present Whitman Dam, his son drowned. Dilg conceived the idea of establishing a national fish refuge in memory of his son, and enlisted the aid of the Isaac Walton League and other conservation groups for this purpose. At that time, there was no precedent for establishing a fish refuge. Inasmuch as there was a precedent for establishing a wildlife refuge, a compromise was made and the Upper Mississippi River Wildlife and Fish Refuge came into being.

I first came to the Upper Mississippi refuge on January 11, 1940, for a three-month training assignment as junior refuge manager. At the end of that time, the refuge biologist was assigned to Fort Peck refuge in Montana, and I took over his duties. Thirty-five years later, despite many changes in duties and responsibilities, and no longer a member of the refuge staff, I was still headquartered at the Upper Mississippi — and I

was still being trained!

During my first spring on the refuge, I had an opportunity to accompany a couple of "river rats" on a trip via refuge launch from Winona, Minnesota, to Guttenberg, Iowa, a round trip of 300 miles. These men were George Winslow (engineer-boatman), who had spent his entire life on the Mississippi River working with the Corps of Engineers and later with the refuge, and Howard Clark, who worked for several years for the Bureau of Fisheries Fish Rescue Station at Homer, Minnesota. Imagine, if you can, a mountaineer (from Colorado) who had never seen a big river spending several days with these old river men. Green, naive, and anxious to learn, I asked interminable questions — and got answers to every one. However, after the manner in which greenhorns are often treated, neither of my mentors permitted truth or accuracy to interfere with a good story. Years later I was still trying to sort out fact from fiction. It was a delightful trip.

Another memorable event during my first

year at the refuge was a three-month, tract-by-tract survey of Corps of Engineer lands from Winona, Minnesota, to St. Louis, Illinois, with a party consisting of F. M. Uhler, Patuxent Research Refuge; Robert H. Smith, then with the Section of Habitat Improvement for the Division of Wildlife Refuges, Washington D.C.; and Eugene Surber, from the Leetown, Virginia, fisheries station. The opportunity to work with these accomplished gentlemen gave me more insight into waterfowl and wetland management than any previous experience. It formed the base on which my career was built.

Among the jobs I did in my years with the Service was a series of waterfowl inventory flights along the Mississippi River and over other areas. This entailed low-level flying, usually well below the bluffs along the river. In the beginning I flew in Super Cubs. After doing this for several years, during which time the USFWS acquired better and presumably safer aircraft, someone in Washington decided that low-level flying was dangerous to our health and authorized hazardous duty pay!

The Upper Mississippi refuge is located in what was at one time the bottom of an inland sea, as evidenced by the flat tops of the bluffs on both sides of the river. The Upper Mississippi is a "driftless" area, where the last ice sheet split. As this ice sheet melted and receded, it formed glacial Lake Agassiz in northwestern Minnesota. Heavy flows from the melting ice flowed through the Minnesota River into the Mississippi River, and carved out the gorge which is now the Mississippi Valley. The Upper Mississippi refuge is bordered by bluffs averaging about 650 feet higher than the valley floor, from Lake Pepin, Wisconsin, to Clinton, Iowa. Below Clinton, the bluffs give way to more gradual slopes. Because the Minnesota and Iowa bluffs are primarily north or east sloping, snow does not melt off during the winter months, and because of the increased moisture, they are generally heavily timbered. By contrast, the Wisconsin bluffs are primarily south or west facing, and winter snows melt more rapidly. These drier conditions support less timber and grassier slopes, known as goat prairies.

A delta formed by the Chippewa River partially blocked the Mississippi Valley and formed Lake Pepin, immediately north of the Upper Mississippi refuge. This lake, thirty miles long and about five miles wide, has been very important to the ecology of the river below it, since it acts as a settling basin and almost a sewage lagoon for the Twin Cities and other population centers which over the years have dumped large quantities of raw sewage into the Mississippi River. Without the settling-basin effect of Lake Pepin, the Upper Mississippi River below the Chippewa River would be much more contaminated by pollution than it is today.

The Upper Mississippi enjoys ecological conditions not generally associated with its geographical location. It is situated primarily within the Alleghanian Life Zone, which extends about 300 miles up the Mississippi River, closely following the driftless zone. A wide variety of flora and fauna occurs on the Upper Mississippi. Not only does it have typical Alleghenian Life Zone species, but many Carolinian Life Zone forms intrude northward. In addition, many Canadian Life Zone species come in from the north, adding another facet to refuge diversity. Since the Mississippi River is the dividing line between many eastern and western subspecies as well, the area is an ecologist's dream.

Coincident with the forming of the river valley was the deposit of windblown soils. This has resulted in deep loess (windblown silt) deposits, and sand prairies have formed, scattered throughout the length of the refuge. Some of these sand prairies exhibit "blow-outs" normally associated with the western sandhills. On these scattered sand areas, forms of plant and animal life usually found much further west have persisted.

Some idea of the variety of species present can be gleaned from checking the refuge floral and fauna lists. The refuge herbarium boasts over 1,250 species of plants. This does not tell the whole story, because emphasis on the herbarium was concentrated on those species most important to wildlife and the management of the area. Thus, the herbarium represents only a portion of all plant species present.

Partial faunal lists include: 291 species of birds; 23 species of reptiles, plus 6 hypothetical; 12 species of amphibians, plus 3 hypothetical; 57 species of mammals, including 27 furbearers and larger rodents; an undetermined number of small mammals, as no effort has been made to identify this large group; 113 species of fish; and 60 species of mussels.

Shortly after the establishment of the refuge, land acquisition began. Approximately 87,000 acres were acquired by gradually buying out willing sellers.

In the early 1930s, the Corps of Engineers initiated the nine-foot channel project to facilitate movement of commercial vessels. In order that two government agencies would not be bidding against each other for the same lands, the refuge discontinued purchases until the Corps had obtained the parcels they needed. Arrangements were made under which the refuge agreed to make all refuge lands available to the Corps for use in the nine-foot channel project, with the understanding that when the nine-foot channel project was completed, all Corps lands not involved in actual structures would be made available to the refuge for wildlife management purposes. This was done in the St. Paul District by means of Executive Orders, giving the refuge essentially the same right as it would have on its own fee lands.

Subsequent to that, the Department of the Interior (USDI) became interested in other Corps lands south of Rock Island, involving lands in both the Rock Island and St. Louis Districts of the Corps of Engineers. These districts felt that lands should be made available under a general plan and cooperative agreement, rather than Executive Order. After long negotiations, such a general plan and cooperative agreement was formulated. This called for cancellation of all previous Executive Orders, so that all transfers of Corps lands would be handled under one instrument.

Although this resulted in large land transfers which enabled the USDI to establish the Mark Twain Refuge between Rock Island, Illinois, and St. Louis, Missouri, it complicated management of the Upper Mississippi.

The mixture of refuge- and Corps-owned lands under refuge administration has been confusing to the public. People tend to regard government land as government land, and don't understand why the refuge can permit some things on its own lands that aren't permitted on Corps lands, especially when the lands are adjoined.

Today nearly 110,000 acres administered by the refuge are Corps lands managed under cooperative agreement.

Within the boundaries of the Upper Mississippi refuge are thirteen locks and dams of the Corps of Engineers' nine-foot channel project. This series of locks and dams has changed the valley from a typical river to a series of lakes, and has greatly altered the character of the river.

Each pool has three distinct ecological zones. At tailwater, immediately below each dam, essentially natural river conditions exist with little effect of impoundment. The extent of this zone varies with each pool, depending on the length of the pool, but it usually ranged from one-quarter to one-third of the pool area. In the midsection of each pool, impoundment has raised the water levels moderately, and has resulted in excellent marsh and aquatic conditions. This varies from one-quarter to one-half of each pool, depending on variables such as length and slope. Immediately above each dam is an area where water levels were raised so high that marsh development has been limited. When first impounded in the mid- to late-1930s, excellent aquatic beds developed in these deeper water areas; in recent years, increased turbidity has militated against such growth because of decreased light penetration into the deeper water.

When the refuge was established, the river

Gatherings like this group of tundra swans and canvasbacks are a common fall occurrence on some pools of the Upper Mississippi Refuge where sago pondweed and other choice foods occur. USFWS photo by Luther Goldman.

bottoms were primarily wooded islands separated by deep sloughs. It was characterized by hundreds of small lakes and ponds scattered through extensive wooded areas. There were some hay meadows and other farming on the islands, but the bottoms were essentially wooded. Marsh development was limited to the shores of lakes and "guts" leading off the sloughs. Marsh flora was limited, with river bulrush making up the dominant habitat. These marshes often dried up completely by the end of the summer. Fish rescue work was a big activity, with crews netting fish trapped in bottomland lakes when the river receded.

The first pool connected with the nine-foot channel project was filled on May 29, 1935. The last pool on the refuge was filled in 1959.

This impoundment changed the river bottoms from an area of wide fluctuations in water levels, ranging from floods in the spring to drying out in the summer, to an area of semistabilized water levels, in which spring floods still occur but the bottoms do not dry out in summer. Fish rescue is a thing of the past. Former hay meadows and timbered areas are now in marsh, which offers habitat for furbearers and waterfowl.

For several years after the locks and dams were put into operation, there was a tremendous response to impoundment, and extensive beds of aquatic plants developed. Once the pools became permanently established, however, the normal deterioration associated with stabilized water areas gradually began, although for over thirty years conditions remained excellent.

Siltation from runoff of neighboring lands into tributary streams, combined with movement of spoil resulting from channel maintenance, have contributed to habitat deterioration. Many sloughs have silted to the point where small-boat navigation is difficult. Water circulation in these areas is limited or nonexistent. This stagnation of many backwater marshes has brought an accompanying reduction in the variety and abundance of vegetation.

Although this has been a gradual process, which started when the first dam was closed, it was not until the 1970s that people began to be alarmed. When the process reached the point where navigation by recreational boats was restricted, people were finally aroused. Many felt that the deterioration had taken place in a short space of time.

In the 1970s, the Great River Environmental Action Team was organized to study the problem. This team involved representatives from the various states, many governmental agencies, transportation groups, and the general public. As a result of their studies, a comprehensive plan for the management and protection of the Mississippi River is being developed.

Establishment of the pools, with resultant marsh and aquatic development on the Upper Mississippi refuge in the 1930s, coincided with drought conditions on the prairies. The vast expanse of waterfowl habitat along the Mississippi River offered excellent migration habitat during the drought. Each fall, thousands of waterfowl funneled into the river, and refuge "closed areas" accommodated large concentrations. Many birds entered the Mississippi Valley from tributaries leading to the northwest. Mallard populations especially swelled in numbers with each tributary, and the Louisa and Keithsburg units each recorded mallard populations of over 25,000 birds.

When the Fort Randall Dam on the Missouri River began holding large populations of mallards, numbers on the Mississippi and Illinois rivers correspondingly decreased. Despite this change in migration patterns, waterfowl populations on the Upper Mississippi have held up very well, with up to 35 million-days use recorded in the late 1970s compared to 16 million in the early 1950s.

One of the best-known mass migrations of waterfowl in modern times occurred during the Armistice (November 11) Day storm in 1940. Comparatively few ducks were present on the refuge prior to that storm. Armistice Day dawned bright and sunny, with little indication that by midday there would be an abrupt change in the weather. By noon, ducks started moving down the valley by the thousands, riding ahead of a storm front that pushed almost all ducks before it, plummeted temperatures, and brought high winds. By the next day when the storm had subsided, most of the ducks had moved south, and abandoned decoys and hunting equipment dotted the area. Over twenty-five hunters, ill-prepared for such weather or unwilling to stop hunting while the ducks were moving so well, lost their lives. Many hunters who survived spent the night in the bottoms under trying conditions. Never in the memory of hunters in this vicinity had so many ducks moved through in so short a time, or with such tragic effects on the hunters.

Another notable mass migration occurred on November 1-3, 1955. Refuge pilot Erwin Boeker and I had just finished a waterfowl survey of the Upper Mississippi, ending the survey at Savanna, Illinois, at about 10 A.M. on November 2. As we were returning to Winona at an altitude of about 1,200 feet, we suddenly found ourselves in the midst of thousands of ducks, all moving south — making our inventory obsolete before we had a chance to work up the data. This mass movement on November 2, 1955, was the heaviest single flight the refuge recorded, except for the Armistice Day movement in 1940.

There has been a change in species composition, however. While formerly puddlers far outnumbered divers, the trend has been for a reduction in puddlers and an increase in divers.

During the 1953-1960 period, mallards accounted for 37.5 percent of all duck use recorded on the Upper Mississippi, while canvasbacks accounted for only 2.5 percent and scaup about 13 percent. By 1975 mallards made up only 21 percent of total use, while canvasbacks had jumped to 14 percent and scaup to 23 percent. During the 1953-1960 period, wood ducks accounted for only 4 percent of total use, but increased to nearly 10 percent by 1975.

The change in use between puddlers and

divers is apparently associated with changing habitat conditions along the river. As previously stated, shortly after impoundment extensive marshes developed over substantial portions of each pool. In recent years, many of the marshes thinned out, leaving submerged aquatic habitat or open water. Change in use is also probably associated with deterioration of formerly excellent diver habitat elsewhere in the region, causing birds to shift their use to habitat remaining on the Mississippi River.

The Upper Mississippi River has become increasingly important to canvasbacks. While a small number of canvasbacks utilized the river even prior to the inception of the refuge, canvasback use was quite limited until about 1950. At that time, historic Wisconsin lakes such as Poygan, Butte des Morts, and Winneconne, harbored good concentrations of canvasbacks, as did the Illinois River valley. Gradually, use of these Wisconsin lakes declined, possibly because of siltation, pollution, or eutrophication. Something also happened to the fingernail clam population on the Illinois River and, in 1955, canvasback use there dropped radically.

Canvasback use of the Illinois River numbered about 80,000 birds in the early 1950s. But by 1955 only 15,000 were counted and only 2,500 in 1956. Since then, very few canvasbacks have used the Illinois River.

On the Upper Mississippi refuge, canvasback numbers did not exceed 20,000 until 1968, when buildups in Pools 7, 8, and 9 were first noted. Since then, peak populations on these pools have continued to grow, reaching 160,000 by the fall of 1975. This quantity represents a substantial portion of all canvasbacks remaining in the eastern United States.

Not only have peak populations built up on the Upper Mississippi refuge in recent years, but the length of time these birds spend on the refuge has also increased. In 1953, only 226,000-days use was recorded, while at present nearly 6.5 million days of canvasback use are recorded annually.

Despite this, one cannot help wonder whether the Mississippi Valley represents preferred habitat for those birds or whether it merely represents the best of what is left. At any rate, it emphasizes the current value of the Mississippi River to this species and to the flyway.

The Upper Mississippi refuge is basically a migration refuge and produces relatively few ducks. Wood ducks are the principal nesting species, with about 10,000 being raised on the refuge each year. Prior to flooding, the Corps of Engineers cleared all timber in the project boundary to a point three feet above normal pool levels. This eliminated much of the previously existing wood duck nesting sites. Accordingly, much of the actual nesting now takes place on the bluffs, up tributary streams, or in towns; but once hatched, the young move to the refuge where they are raised.

In recent years, the refuge has become important to migrating whistling swans, with as many as 10,000 using various portions of the refuge each spring and fall. Most swan use is found in the northernmost districts in Pools 4, 5, 7, and 8.

While the Upper Mississippi River has historically been an important migration area for waterfowl, prior to the establishment of the refuge heavy waterfowl fall use was often limited to a few days of the "flight." During this period, heavy hunting occurred throughout the area.

When the refuge was established, it was deemed unwise to attempt to close nearly 300 miles of the river to hunting. Consequently, a series of strategically located "closed areas" was established. Only about 20 percent of refuge lands are included in twelve closed areas. The remaining 80 percent of the refuge is open to public hunting on a first-come-first-served basis. Originally, closed areas were selected only on the basis of sufficient land ownership, but with the transfer of lands from the Corps, other aspects have been considered. The closed areas on the refuge were completely realigned in 1957 and have remained essentially unchanged since. It may now be time to reassess some of them in view of changing habitat conditions on the river.

The importance of the refuge to waterfowl hunters is evidenced by the fact that each year between 100,000 and 150,000 days of waterfowling takes place on the 150,000 acres of refuge lands made available for this purpose. Without the refuge, much of the bottomland would probably be in private ownership, and public hunting opportunities would be limited.

Hunters on the refuge have better-than-average hunting success as compared to most areas in the adjoining states. Nineteen species of waterfowl are harvested on the Upper Mississippi refuge each fall, with mallards, baldpates, blue-winged teal, wood ducks, and scaup being the principal species taken.

Duck hunters on the Mississippi take their waterfowling seriously. One fall I was checking hunters as they came back to a landing. One boat load of hunters came in quite late. One of their party had suffered a fatal heart attack in midafternoon, but since this was their day for going duck hunting, the rest had decided to finish the day's hunt before bringing in the body!

Trapping too, is an important recreational and economic contribution of the refuge. Each year, between 800 and 1,000 trappers take advantage of this opportunity. This, too, is done on a first-come-first-served basis. Each trapper is required to have a refuge permit and to affix a ten-cent tag to each trap, with a limit of fifty tags per trapper. Thus armed, the trapper can select where he wants to trap and can keep all his furs. Most other refuges assign trapping areas and take a share of the furs.

Muskrats comprise the bulk of the take, although mink and beaver are also important. Each year, about $150,000 worth of furs are taken by trappers using the refuge.

Beaver were almost extirpated from the Upper Mississippi at the time the refuge was established. In 1927-1929, beavers were live-trapped in northern Minnesota and Wisconsin and reintroduced on the Upper Mississippi. Given protection from then until 1948, the species became re-established, and some

trapping has been permitted since, with from 1,000 to 2,500 being taken each year. Nearly $500,000 worth of fur has been taken from the refuge since it was established.

The Upper Mississippi is an important wintering area for bald eagles, where each year several hundred congregate below the dams to feed on fish. The refuge also has a few nesting eagles, although only two different successful nests have been located so far. A few osprey also nest on the refuge, including one nesting on a powerline pole in Pool 6.

Cormorants once came through the refuge in flocks numbering in the thousands. Relatively few of these birds currently use the refuge. At one time cormorants nested in several places throughout the refuge in dead-standing timber. As this timber went down in the course of time, nesting became quite limited. However, construction of artificial nesting platforms have been tried successfully. In Spring Lake, Pool 13, the last cormorant nesting colony in the State of Illinois has been preserved by this method.

Canada geese use the refuge in spring and fall, with the largest concentrations now found in Pools 5, 7, 8, and 9. Birds in the Pool 5 group show some interchange with the Silver Lake concentration at Rochester, Minnesota. A few Canadas nest on the refuge, largely the result of captive flocks or local releases of young.

The Upper Mississippi is an important recreational area, with about 3.5 million visitor days recorded each year. Surveys of recreational use have identified at least twenty activities in which visitors commonly engage, ranging from fishing, hunting, trapping, and boating to camping, picnicking, bird watching, and relaxed loafing on the shores of the river.

When the states bordering the refuge passed enabling acts authorizing the government to acquire lands for refuge purposes, they retained their fisheries rights. Thus, the refuge is concerned with this resource only so far as it is compatible with other uses, and in assisting the states in the enforcement of fishing laws.

Nearly half of today's recreational visits to the refuge are for fishing in connection with other activities. Summer sport fishing accounts for the bulk of the activity, although ice fishing is also popular. Many commercial fishermen also use the river in both summer and winter. In the days of cotton nets, the presence of seine reels and tar vats along the banks of the river added to the scenic variety of the area. With the advent of nylon nets, few such scenes can now be found, as drying and treating nets is no longer essential.

At one time, clamming was an important industry along the Mississippi River. But the advent of plastics caused the demand for pearl buttons to drop off. Clamming has recently been revived, and several clamming outfits are now active on the river.

Boating ranks high in recreational use, either for its own sake or in connection with some other activity. Houseboats are common, and canoeing is increasingly popular.

Camping and picnicking are favorite activities, often in connection with boating or some other activity. On most weekends in the summer, the sand bars and islands along the main channel are packed to capacity.

Nature study and bird watching are widely pursued, often in connection with photography. During the migration periods for waterfowl and warblers, the river is an ideal place for birders.

Sightseeing ranks second to boating in recreational-use days recorded. The beautiful valley, nestled between scenic bluffs with winding sloughs and channels interspersed with islands, offer scenes that rival many other places in the world. In the summer, when lotus, water lily, and cardinal flowers are in bloom, thousands of people come to see them. In the fall, when waterfowl begin to concentrate and the leaves change color on the bluffs, the river presents unrivaled beauty.

I have travelled in over fifty foreign countries. While their scenic beauty may be different from ours, I am always glad to return to what the Mississippi Valley has to offer.

Thanks to the vision of Will Dilg, the Isaac Walton League, and other conservationists, the Upper Mississippi River Wildlife and Fish Refuge can hold this beautiful and ecologically important area in public trust for the benefit of all the people.

Cajun Country Marshes

Jacob M. Valentine, Jr.

A major portion of North America's waterfowl spends the winter in the bays, lagoons, marshes, and adjacent rice fields or pastures along the Gulf of Mexico. A vanguard of the blue-winged teal and pintails arrives in September, to be followed by a host of other duck and goose species later in the fall. Starting in February migrants leave the Gulf Coast, and most of them are gone by March or early April. Thus, for about half the year a large part of the waterfowl population depends on the Gulf Coast for its subsistence.

The Gulf Coast wintering grounds often play tricks on the birds returning after a few month's absence. Choice feeding areas in one year may be barren of food the next, due to natural forces such as droughts and hurricanes or to man's activities. Some effects are immediate; others are long-range. Some are good for the birds; others are disastrous.

Rather than dealing with the wide variety of habitats provided by the Gulf region, I shall restrict my remarks to the coastal marshes of Louisiana, known as Cajun Country. These vast wetlands are complex enough to illustrate the diversity of habitats that characterize the Gulf coasts of the United States and Mexico.

The Marsh Scene

For thousands of years, an immense fertile wetland covering more than four million acres, and teeming with fish, shrimp, crabs, oysters, and fowl, lay unspoiled and untapped by man. The early explorers and settlers avoided the marsh and traveled only on the rivers and bayous. Even the Indians plied the bayous, seeking food from the water and marsh edges. The Spanish Trail, which tracked from Florida to Mexico, followed the natural levees of ancient distributaries of the Mississippi River until it reached the prairies of southwestern Louisiana.

Three large marsh ecosystems, each formed by the Mississippi River and shaped and reshaped by the Gulf of Mexico, differ in size, age, and development. Within each ecosystem are gradations of elevation and salinities, two basic factors that determine marsh types. These types may be subdivided into broad categories: fresh, intermediate, brackish, and saline marsh. Plants, variable in their adaptations and tolerances to environmental influences, don't always fit into man's neat schemes; but for pragmatic purposes, these categories may be useful descriptions.

The active delta, found at the distributary ends of the Mississippi River, is the youngest and smallest region, covering one-third of a million acres. Overbank flooding has been reduced and most of the river sediments are being shunted out Southwest Pass into deep water. As a result, there has been little expansion of the active delta in the past thirty years. In the active growth stage of the delta formation, marshes were created between the minor passes. But as time went on and deposition diminished, these marshes began sinking; now open water dominates the marsh. The influence of the river is still strong, with most of the marsh water intermediate to fresh.

The inactive delta, which is the remains of extinct deltas of the Mississippi River, stretches from the Chandeleur Islands west to Vermilion Bay. These marshes total nearly 3 million acres, one-third salt marsh, one-third brackish, and one-third intermediate to fresh. Through subsidence and erosion, land loss is severe. On the east, the salt marshes are ragged fingers sticking out into Mississippi Sound following the course of old river passes. West of the Mississippi River, subsidence has been great, and large embayments such as Barataria and Terrebonne bays lie behind barrier islands, with names like Isles

Dernieres, Timbalier, Grand Isle, and Grand Terre.

The Chenier Plain marshes were formed on Pleistocene deposits. The marsh extends southward from the pastures and rice fields to the low dunes along the Gulf. Characteristic of the area are old beach ridges, known as cheniers, which parallel the coastline, forming natural levees and creating an immense marsh sump. Great estuarine lakes, such as White, Grand, Calcasieu, and Sabine, lie within the sump. The Chenier Plain extends from East Bay, Texas, to Vermilion Bay, totals over a million acres, and includes 800,000 acres of intermediate and fresh marsh combined, and 365,000 acres of brackish marsh.

Oil and Industry

For centuries after the Old World discovered Louisiana, the marshes lay pristine as a wonderland, or were an untamed morass, depending on one's point of view. Rivers and bayous were the principal means of transportation. Roads, scarce and primitive, generally followed the river banks well into the 1900s.

Beginning in 1901 when the first oil well was drilled near Jennings, the search for oil and gas brought great changes to coastal Louisiana. At first, the oil fields were developed in the upland, but with the development of marsh buggies and barge-mounted drilling rigs, oil companies and wildcatters moved into the marsh. Thousands of miles of canals were dug to move the drillers into the marsh and to transport the crude oil to the refineries.

The Intracoastal Waterway, an east-west navigation canal, cut through the upper marsh from New Orleans to Texas and beyond, and connected to the hundreds of waterways and bayous that flowed to the Gulf of Mexico. The Calcasieu Ship Channel, begun in the 1920s and widened and deepened several times, created a deep-water channel from the Gulf up through Calcasieu

Snow geese find the annual grass seeds highly attractive when a coastal marsh regains health after a sawgrass die-off. USFWS photo by J. M. Valentine, Jr.

Lake to Lake Charles. More recently, the Houma Navigation Canal was dug through the marshes of Terrebonne Parish into the inland town of Houma. The Mississippi Gulf Outlet, an immense ship channel completed in the 1960s, connects the Gulf to the Port of New Orleans.

The result of the digging of canals and navigation channels was that salt water penetrated the fresh and brackish marshes. Marsh vegetation died abruptly or changed slowly in response to the changes in salinities. The canals and dredged material physically destroyed the wetlands they occupied and disrupted natural drainage patterns. But they also provided access to the vast marshes for hunting, trapping, and fishing. The spoil-banks created habitats for deer, rabbits, and other mammals, as well as nesting and feeding cover for birds.

At first, canals and channels were dug with abandon with no thought to the effect on the surrounding marsh. Later, safeguards and mitigating measures were often incorporated.

Rice farmers on the prairie edge of the marsh soon found that salt water and irrigation did not mix. In 1951 the Corps of Engineers completed the Mermentau River basin by constructing locks and water-control structures on the Intracoastal Waterway near Vermilion Bay, at Calcasieu Lake, and on the Mermentau River. The basin converted a low salinity marsh into a 469,000-acre fresh marsh reservoir for irrigation, flood control, and navigation.

State Refuges

Edward A. McIlhenny can be credited as the father of the great system of state refuges in Louisiana. He ran the Tabasco Sauce fiefdom on Avery Island, but dabbled seriously in ornithology, horticulture, and wildlife conservation. He wrote articles on the snow goose and the Mississippi sandhill crane, a book on the alligator, maintained a living collection of exotic bamboos and other plants, and introduced the nutria. By the 1900s, plume hunters had nearly extirpated herons and egrets from Louisiana. Beginning in 1893 with a few captive snowy egrets, he created by 1910 a "bird city" of thousands of herons and egrets.

With Charles Ward of Michigan putting up three-quarters of the money, and McIlhenny the other quarter, they purchased 13,000 acres of marsh in 1911, now known as State Wildlife Refuge. The marsh, on Vermilion Bay and the Gulf, attracted thousands of snow geese. It contained a great gritting beach with the epithet "Hell Hole," doubtless named by some reef-stranded sailor or fisherman. Ward and McIlhenny also cooperated in securing the 75,000-acre Marsh Island Refuge for the state through a donation of the lands by Mrs. Russell Sage and the Russell Sage Foundation. A man of vision and fortitude, McIlhenny in 1913 risked $27,000 cash and a mortgage of $185,000 to buy 86,000 acres along the Gulf in Vermilion and Cameron Parishes. The New York Rockefellers were convinced by two DeForest brothers and McIlhenny that this marsh should be set aside as a state refuge, and in 1914 the Rockefeller Foundation purchased the lands now known as the Rockefeller Refuge. Under similar circumstances, the National Audubon Society acquired the 27,000-acre Paul J. Rainey Wildlife Sanctuary next to the State Wildlife Refuge.

The Pass á Loutre Waterfowl Management Area is a 65,000-acre tract of marsh located along the lower Mississippi River, just south of the Delta National Wildlife Refuge. Until 1921, the lands were owned by the state and leased for hunting and trapping. The Louisiana Wild Life and Fisheries Commission took it over in 1921 and maintained the Pass á Loutre Hunting Club, the only state-owned hunting club in the United States. From 1954 until 1969, when Hurricane Camille wiped out all of the facilities, it was operated as a nonprofit hunting club with lodging, guides, boats, decoys, and blinds furnished for a small fee. After 1969, the entire area was opened for public waterfowl hunting but without the frills.

National Wildlife Refuges

The great stimulus to the development of the National Wildlife Refuge System was the midcontinent drought when waterfowl hunters became concerned with the loss of breeding grounds in the prairies of Canada and the United States. The Great Depression and the need for stimulating the economy and putting people to work provided federal funds for acquisition of lands. In Louisiana, landowners who were going broke were ready to sell large marshes that were only used for waterfowl hunting or leased for muskrat trapping.

In 1930, when Alex Martin (USBS) visited the Orange-Cameron Land Company tract, which became the Sabine National Wildlife Refuge, he described the lands as an enormous open, freshwater marsh. The marsh had been a model muskrat farm, the largest in existence, but fur prices at the beginning of the depression were so low that the company was willing to sell. To facilitate trapping, the company had built 115 miles of canals and constructed water gates on the canals to regulate water levels. Except for the lakes, the entire area was covered with a luxuriant growth of marsh plants. White waterlily, pondweeds, milfoil, and widgeon grass were common in the lakes and ponds. Ducks, geese, and a great variety of marsh and water birds were abundant, and Martin considered the marsh one of the best if not the best migratory bird refuge prospect in the southern United States.

Lands that were to become part of the Lacassine National Wildlife Refuge were inspected by Bureau biologists Fran Uhler and W. F. "Koobie" Kubichek in 1934. In their report, they said that this rice region located near Bayou Lacassine held by far the greatest winter population of ducks in the state. The tract of land considered for the refuge, known as the Illinois Plantation, was described as a "notably unsuccessful rice plantation." The effect of the Depression was evident in the general state of disrepair of buildings and equipment, and the fact that no taxes had been paid for several years.

The area was well known as a major mallard and pintail concentration point, but a variety of other ducks also frequented the rice fields and marshes. The biologists considered the state refuges to be important for geese because they were located in brackish marsh not attractive to ducks. Several hundred acres of upland and 40,000 acres of marsh eventually became the Lacassine Refuge.

The Delta National Wildlife Refuge, a 48,800-acre wetland near the mouth of the Mississippi River, was purchased in 1937 from two nearly defunct hunting clubs, the Delta Duck Hunting Club and the Joe Leiter Club.

Drought has left emergent vegetation too high and remote from the water to be used by nesting canvasbacks and redheads. USFWS photo by A. S. Hawkins.

Waterfowl Management

Marsh management began with muskrat trapping and alligator hunting. The early managers of the large, privately owned marshes were innovative in seeking better means of transportation, coping with muskrat eat-outs, and controlling water levels. Narrow pirogue trails were dug by hand, dynamite, and plows. Larger canals for boats and barges were dug by dragline. Airboats and marsh buggies at first were quite primitive, but later became highly sophisticated. Water control devices ranged from crude wooded weirs on small bayous to earthen dams on the larger waterways.

Prior to the 1930s, marsh burning was used mainly to facilitate muskrat trapping and alligator hunting. Burning was controversial, and many trappers opposed it, but fires made walking easier and almost necessary for finding muskrat trails and gator holes. An unburned marsh with heavy cover was subject to lightning or accidental fires that might be disastrous. Burning became standard practice for cattlemen, trappers, hunting clubs, and refuges.

In 1914, W. L. McAtee published "Five Important Wild-Duck Foods," the beginning of food habits studies by the USBS. Later, Clarence Cottom headed the Food

Habits Section, which produced the classic work on waterfowl food habits by Martin and Uhler. Using the information on what ducks eat, federal and state refuge personnel began planting marsh and aquatic food plants in the marshes.

The memory of the Dirty Thirties, a reference to the drought and the economic disasters of that decade, convinced the administrators in Washington, who were mainly midwesterners, that permanent fresh water was the first priority in managing the southern marshes for waterfowl. Large impoundments were soon constructed by building levees and water-control structures. Lacassine Refuge built a 16,000-acre pool and Sabine Refuge, a 30,000-acre pool. The impoundments were designed to collect the abundant rainfall that averaged about sixty inches. Draglines dredged out levees from the marsh soils and control structures were built into the levees to allow surplus water to be drained off. Besides providing a permanent source of water, flooding was expected to kill or reduce sawgrass which was so dense and unattractive to waterfowl that it was considered a pest plant.

The Rockefeller Refuge, hitting the jackpot through oil leases, became the envy of federal waterfowl managers. With the great amounts of money they were able to spend, refuge administrators built an elaborate system of impoundments with much greater water control than found in the federal projects. The refuge was able to impound rainfall and brackish water, drain pools, and pump in water to flood annual grass and sedge food plants when the ducks arrived from the north. Pump-out during the spring created moist soil conditions ideal for the germination and growth of annual plants.

In the subdelta parishes where levees and impoundments were not practical because of unstable soils, weirs were built on canals and bayous to create semi-impoundments. These structures were designed to allow tidal water to flow over the weir, but precluded a complete drainage of the marsh and ponds on low tides. The result was more stable water levels, encouraging the growth of widgeon grass. The effect of the weirs on marine fish and crustaceans is moot and is being studied, but the beneficial effect on widgeon grass is generally accepted.

Winous Point Club member and punter on Lake Erie marsh in 1895. Photo courtesy of Karl Bednarik.

The People

First there were the Indians — Bayougoulas, Houmas, Chitimachas, and Attakapas — who camped on the lake and river banks, and fished, hunted, and gathered oysters and Rangia clams. Indian marsh settlements were scattered and were nearly gone when the white settlers arrived. A few still exist. The French and Spanish founded cities like Baton Rouge, New Orleans, and Belize, now buried under eight feet of mud somewhere on South Pass.

The settlers, a motley assemblage of nationalities, often settled in environments resembling their home country — fishermen on the coast, small farmers on the cheniers, bayous, and prairies. Those along the rivers acquired narrow tracts fronting the water but extending deep into the swamp or marsh. Each family dug a "trainasse" or pirogue trail from the high ground back into the marsh and water, much to the despair of the early game wardens.

In southwestern Louisiana, few rivers were suitable for navigation inland from the Gulf, but some boat traffic was possible through the passes into Sabine and Calcasieu lakes. Cheniers, which generally run parallel to the coasts, were settled in much the same way as the river banks of the subdelta marshes. Some cheniers like Grand Chenier and Pecan Island are many miles long but were isolated from the mainland and each other by the marsh. Travel was by boat on the Gulf and pirogue on the bayous, or by horse or foot on the ridges and beaches along the Gulf. The people lived insulated from the outsiders, subsisting on their small gardens, cattle, fish, and game. A few shot ducks for the market, but towns were far away so most everyone shot their own. Game laws were unknown or ignored, but after World War II, a new breed of game wardens soon convinced the natives that migratory bird laws were indeed on the books. The "Peanut Man," an undercover USFWS agent, caused so many arrests that the alleged market hunters had to be transported to justice by a fleet of buses.

The Swamp Land Act of 1849 gave Louisiana state over 9 million acres of swamp and marsh. After the Civil War and into the 1900s, northern speculators discovered the cheap marshlands of Louisiana, buying up huge chunks of it. The marsh was mostly worthless, but it was a time of national expansion and adventurism into lumbering, industry, and agriculture. In the subdelta marshes, thousands of acres were "reclaimed" by diking and pumping. A few crops were attempted, but soil deficiencies and excessive water made the lands unsuitable for agriculture. The soils oxydized and subsided, and when the pumping stopped, the lands reflooded, sometimes forming large lakes. Marshlands often changed hands or reverted back to the state for nonpayment of taxes and resold.

The fur industry developed in the early 1900s, first with free trappers, and later with the landowners leasing the lands for trapping, grazing, and hunting. Corporations like Louisiana Furs, Louisiana Land and Exploration, and the Orange-Cameron Land Company managed their lands with their own trappers and managers. Some companies were able to survive the economic disaster of the 1930s and became wealthy with the discovery of oil. Other marshes were purchased by groups of hunters and used exclusively for sport or combinations of business and pleasure.

During the muskrat heyday, Biological Survey biologists Vernon Bailey and Frank Ashbrook advised the embryonic state agency on fur mammals. Harry Oberholser, also with the Survey, published the first treatise on bird life for the Louisiana Department of Conservation in 1938. Alex Martin, L. E. Ekvall, Neil Hotchkiss, Bob H. Smith, Fran Uhler, W. F. Kubichek, and Charles Sperry made the early refuge acquisition reconnaissance. Later, J. Clark Salyer, Clarence Cottom, and Dick Griffith supervised management and operation of federal refuges. Civilian Conservation Corps (CCC), stationed in camps on the refuges in the mid-1930s, built dikes and weirs, fought pest plants, and planted duck food plants.

Waterfowl management in the 1930s was an infant art. Yankee feds were sent down to get rid of sawgrass, which in those days occupied several hundred-thousand acres; get duck food plantings going; and find out how many ducks and geese there were. Rumors still persist that some northern scientists visiting the coastal marshes in quest of data to round out their researches found the expense overwhelming, shook their heads in disbelief, and rushed home to continue their studies of their more familiar Walden Ponds. One who didn't leave was Johnny Lynch. He and Dick Yancey, then a young Louisiana biologist, laid out the first waterfowl transect system for counting ducks and,

445

with Ted O'Neil, studied the ecology of the muskrat. A consummate naturalist, Lynch received an honorary PhD from the marsh trappers, who referred to him as the "grass doctor." With a pilot's license in hand after World War II, he followed the geese and ducks from the Arctic Ocean to Mexico. He was a pioneer in the Canadian breeding duck surveys. In the winter, out of the Delta refuge, Abbeville, and Lafayette, he wrote on marsh ecology, the whooping crane, and waterfowl environments in Canada. He also devised a method of quickly and simply appraising goose productivity in the winter, when the geese were in large flocks in the marsh or rice fields.

Other refuge biologists and managers included V. L. Childs, Julian "Boy" Howard, Jack Perkins, Warren "Scudder" Bourne, Rudy Rudolph, Johnny DeLime, Claude Lard, and others. Budgets were skimpy for many years, so the refuge managers made do and scrounged as a way of life, an attitude that persisted long after "good times" came back.

There were the unsung heroes — the refuge patrolmen — like Johnny Mouton at Sabine, who told tales in Cajun-English of trapping and gator hunting with the Orange-Cameron Company. Johnny often guided visiting biologists, and later became the mechanic. He once diagnosed a motor problem: "I t'ink the DC was mixed up with the AC." Otis, his brother on the Delta refuge, despaired of breaking in one more refuge manager and teaching him the ways of the marsh and of the poachers who prowled at night. Otis crawled like a gator on the mud flats every spring for twenty years planting Delta duck potato.

Another hero was Johnny Gaspard on the Stanolind marsh, a natural-born ecologist who recognized the value of marsh plants like "jonc coupant," "roseau," "paille fine," and "grain evolee." After her husband died or ran off, "Madam Jim" donned bib overalls and raised cattle and her family on The Pines along Sabine Lake, and told bawdy stories to the game wardens, all the while scanning the company for a suitable husband for daughter Bebée.

Visiting feds, such as flyway biologists Art Hawkin, Ross Hanson, and Ed Willein, cooperated with state biologists in the winter counts of ducks and geese; Federal game agent-pilots like Joe Withers and Joe Perroux double-dutied as game wardens and waterfowl counters. State waterfowl biologists Dick Yancey, Mort Smith, Clark Hoffpauir, and Butch Bateman carried on the systematic aerial transect surveys over the inland and coastal marshes. In 1962 Art Brazda took on the duties of flyway biologist in the lower Central Flyway, including the Gulf Coast. State-sponsored studies by the Louisiana Wild Life and Fisheries Commission kept apace. The research and teaching of Dr. Leslie "Prof" Glasgow at Louisiana State University brought forth a nucleus of marsh managers and researchers like Bob Chabreck, Allen Ensminger, Clark Hoffpauir, Ted Joanen, and Larry McNease.

This fine North Dakota marsh was preserved in memory of J. Donald Smith. Smith, first as a member of the Minnesota Conservation Department and later as a pilot biologist for the USFWS, worked tirelessly for waterfowl until his tragic helicopter crash in 1967. USFWS photo.

Droughts

With the Gulf on one side and freshwater runoff on the other, it is natural that the Louisiana marshes should be dynamic and mutable. The broad marsh expanse and the adaptability and aggressiveness of marsh plants provide some stability. But man's intrusion in the form of channels, canals, and roads broke drainage patterns and allowed saline waters to penetrate far into the marsh. Coupled with natural phenomena such as droughts, hurricane saltwater surges, tropical rain storms, erosion, and subsidence, it is not surprising that ecological changes have and continue to occur.

The effect of droughts on vegetation and waterfowl is dependent on the season, tidal flooding, previous accumulation, runoff, and other factors. The severity is usually greatest during the spring and summer when evaporation is greatest. If a drought occurs in a marsh where tide water has been entrapped, evaporation can raise the soil salinity to lethal (for some plants) levels. Along the coast, a tropical storm often breaks a drought by dropping up to thirty inches of rain in a day or two.

Charles C. Sperry, reporting on duck food conditions in southern Louisiana in July 1925 for the USBS, said that former water-covered marshes were stock-grazed meadows where cars could drive. Freshwater plants died out and were replaced by salt-tolerant plants. Lakes and ponds were changed by salt tides, killing pondweeds, waterlilies, and wild celery. Sperry predicted that waterfowl would have slim pickings in southwestern Louisiana and complained that the severity of droughts would be lessened if the innumerable small canals and pirogue ditches used for trapping muskrats were separated from the larger canals and bayous to prevent drainage.

A drought in the early 1950s lasted on and off for five years. In 1951 several thousand acres of southern bulrush, cattail, and giant cutgrass died in the Big Burn marsh of Cameron Parish after a draw-down within the newly completed Mermentau Basin. Several thousand acres of sawgrass and cattail died in Vermilion Parish in 1952-1953 because of saltwater flooding and drought.

Temporary spring droughts that expose the soil for a few weeks may stimulate the germination and growth of annual waterfowl food plants. Most marsh and water plants, such as widgeon grass and waterlilies, survive dewaterings very nicely.

During the 1924-1925 drought, in the prairie marshes of Cameron Parish, fires burned deep into the accumulated peat, creating lakes and ponds that are still called the Big Burn and Little Burn — or Grand and Petit Brulee, in the Cajun vernacular. Fires of this magnitude are virtually eliminated now because the myriad of canals keep the marsh soils from deep drying.

During the 1930s through the 1940s, muskrats became so numerous that they had a profound influence on the marshes of southwestern Louisiana. John Lynch, Ted O'Neil, and Dan Lay in their study in the 1940s found that overpopulations of muskrats created eat-outs that reduced many marshes to a mucky quagmire. Thousands of acres were involved, and many of the damaged areas still remain as lakes and ponds throughout the brackish marsh. The muskrat population crash occurred in the early 1950s and has never fully recovered. I attribute the scarcity of muskrats in much of southwestern Louisiana during the 1950s and early 1960s to a long period of dry conditions when the threesquare sedges were in short supply. This dearth did not break until the late 1960s. Snow geese also caused temporary eat-outs, but these were less severe than those of the muskrat.

Nutria escaped from captivity at Avery Island, Vermilion Parish, in 1940. From there they multiplied and moved eastward into the Delta of the Mississippi and west into Texas. The population peaked in Vermillion and eastern Cameron by the mid-1950s, and by the early 1960s in western Cameron Parish. Harris and Webert studied the effect of the nutria on marsh vegetation from 1954 to 1956 and concluded that they had a distinct effect only on a few plants and were not the primary cause of the loss of emergent marsh vegetation. In 1961, I jumped to the conclusion that nutria had laid waste to several hundred acres of southern bulrush and big cordgrass on the Sabine Refuge. I later determined that high soil salinity induced by a drought was killing the plants. The nutria were only eating the roots of every plant as they became moribund. Nutria were at their peak at that time and were voracious in their appetites. By the late 1960s when precipitation returned to normal, bulrush and big cordgrass were again found in great stands throughout the refuge and surrounding marshes.

Floods and Hurricanes

During the 1940 flood, the freshwater marshes of southwestern Louisiana were inundated by rainfall for two months, destroying many acres of marsh vegetation. Hurricane Audrey, one of the worst storms in recorded history, struck the coast of Louisiana in June 1957, bringing extremely high tides over the marshes of Cameron and Vermilion parishes. The effect of deep flooding by salt water on sawgrass was almost immediate. By August 1957, most of the sawgrass in the Mermentau Basin was dead. In 1958, sawgrass outside of the freshwater impoundment at Sabine refuge was noted to be dying. By 1962 virtually all of the sawgrass of Cameron, Vermilion, and Calcasieu parishes had died. Hundreds of thousands of acres of marsh were left devoid of any plants. The mortality can be ascribed to the effect of the hurricane flooding and the summer droughts of 1960, 1961, and 1962, resulting in toxic salinities caused by evaporation with no dilution by rainfall, and possibly through other chemical changes in the soil.

Plant Succession

Within several years after the die-off, the vast bare marshes of Vermilion and eastern Cameron parishes sprang up into a luxuriant tangle of wild millet, fall panic grass, sprangletop, cypress, and setarias, creating a banquet for puddle ducks. The marshes around Grand Lake and White Lake became the concentration point for mallards, pintails, blue-winged teal, and gadwall. Aerial surveys conducted by Louisiana biologists Morton Smith and Clark Hoffpauir indicated a sudden population jump in certain species wintering in Louisiana as an aftermath to Hurricane Audrey. Few blue-winged teal wintered in Louisiana prior to 1957, but in the winter of 1957-1958, over 100,000 bluewings stayed in the die-off marsh and continued to frequent the area in the following years. The numbers of gadwall wintering in Louisiana, as reflected in the midwinter surveys, jumped from 127,000 in 1955 to over a million in 1965. Since 1965, wintering gadwall populations have fluctuated between a half-million to nearly a million birds, according to Louisiana biologist Hugh Bateman.

The most prolific waterfowl food seed producers are the annual grasses and sedges. These plants require open, moist soil sites. They are most abundant when the marsh goes dry, where cattle have trampled, or where muskrats or nutria have opened the dense perennial vegetation. There are perennials that also provide seeds for ducks, plants such as sawgrass, bulrushes, spike rushes, pondweeds, naiad, widgeon grass, and others. Prior to the die-off, rice and rice field weed seeds and perennial marsh plants ranked high in preference or availability for puddle ducks. After the die-off, mallard, pintail, and teal crops collected in 1961 by Glasgow and his students contained high percentages by volume of annual grass seeds, then abundant in the die-off marshes.

Nature abhors a vacuum. Annual plants pioneer open ground, but in time are inexorably overwhelmed by perennials. So it was in

A marsh on Sabine National Refuge in Louisiana starts to revegetate after a sawgrass die-off in 1960. USFWS photo by J. M. Valentine, Jr.

the sawgrass die-off marshes. In a study of plant succession (1958-1974), after the die-off on the Lacassine refuge, 86 percent of the marsh was open water in 1958. During the drought year of 1962, about one-half of the transect line was occupied by two annuals: mudbank paspalum and baldrush. By 1974, I found that over 80 percent of the line was occupied by bulltongue and white waterlily.

Plant succession was slower in the marshes of western Cameron Parish because of brackish and saline conditions. There are fewer plant species, and these are slow to colonize. In favorable sites, thousands of acres were covered by annual grasses and sedges, but as the years passed these marshes became dominated by saltmeadow cordgrass. There are large tracts, covering thousands of acres on the Sabine refuge and the area around Black Lake and Gum Cove that remain as open water. These marshes have been subjected to tidal flooding mainly through canals from the Calcasieu Ship Channel. Wave action and tidal scouring have deepened the ponded areas and are creating lakes where sawgrass and other marsh plants once grew.

On the sound side of the Chandeleur Islands lie marine meadows of turtle grass, manateegrass, shoalgrass, and halophila, where thousands of redheads and scaup winter. In 1969 Hurricane Camille, considered the most powerful storm to hit the Gulf, tore

the island chain to bits. The erosive power of the waves poured tons of sand over the grass beds. During the ten years after Camille, the northern islands were repaired by natural forces, and the grass beds, now smaller and confined to the area around North and New Harbor islands, have recovered. Despite the recurrent damage to the submerged food plants, the waterfowl populations do not seem to have been affected.

Atchafalaya Delta

A very exciting event, from a geological and biological point of view, is going on along the central Louisiana coast — not as dramatic as the Mount Saint Helens eruption, because it's quieter with no great explosions or aerial displays, but sensational nonetheless. The Atchafalaya (American Indian for "long river," and unpronounceable except by locals) River, a distributary of the Mississippi, threatened to take over the main river flow in favor of the shorter and steeper route to the Gulf. Geologist H. N. Fisk predicted this would happen by 1975, so a control structure was built by the Corps of Engineers in 1963 to limit the flow.

The Atchafalaya has been filling its basin for thousands of years, creating the largest river swamp in the United States. In the past sixty years, sediment has filled the lakes and deep channels have been established, carrying more and more sediments into the Atchafalaya Bay on the Gulf. From 1952 to 1962, sedimentation visibly increased in the bay. After the 1973 flood, the accumulation evolved into a definite emerging delta, nearly seven miles wide and forming over six square miles of new land. Some geologists predict that the bay may fill by the turn of the century and the area of new land could reach over 300 square miles in the next fifty years. Because accreted lands become state property, the Louisiana Department of Wildlife and Fisheries was able to set aside 125,000 acres of land and shallow water as the Atchafalaya Delta Wildlife Management Area. The lush growth of annual marsh grasses and sedges on the mud flats attracts thousands of ducks and geese, and the area is fast becoming a hot spot for hunting.

Effect on Waterfowl

What has been the effect of all the management for waterfowl and the natural and man-made changes in the environment? Most fluctuations in winter populations on the coast are determined by what occurs in the breeding grounds and on the migration routes farther north. The short-stopping story of the Canada goose is well known, but mallards and snow geese are also being delayed or stopped by attractive conditions north of Louisiana. The distribution of ducks and geese on the coast is influenced by local conditions. Heavy fall and winter rains will spread the birds, and conversely a drought will concentrate them. Waterfowl have traditional feeding and resting places, but if they're not suitable, the ducks and geese can always move around in the vast marshes or move on to Texas, Mexico, or South America. Some ducks, like the ring-neck, are quite specific in their requirements, but in general, there's a place for all.

Soon after completion of the impoundments on Rockfeller Refuge, the duck use increased nearly sixfold. Lacassine Pool, ideally situated between the marsh and the rice fields, attracts about a half-million ducks and a hundred-thousand geese. The out-size Sabine impoundment has only been mildly successful in attracting ducks, possibly because of the excellent feeding habitats surrounding it.

The Canada goose, once abundant throughout the coast, now rarely exceeds a few thousand, while the white-fronted goose appears to have increased from a few thousand in the 1950s to 60,000 in the 1970s. The center of its range is around the Lacassine refuge. Large flocks of snow geese use their traditional brackish marsh feeding grounds, but many remain along the rice belt. The flock in the Mississippi River Delta that once numbered several hundred-thousand now is down to less than 80,000, probably due to changes in their breeding grounds.

The mottled duck, a close relative of the mallard, nests throughout the coastal marsh, between Mexico and Florida. McIlhenny, commenting on the changes in bird life in southwestern Louisiana over a sixty-year period, said the mottled duck nested "sparingly" until about 1905 when fur trapping and gator hunting began in earnest. When raccoon, mink, and alligator numbers were reduced, the mottled ducks increased.

The fulvous whistling duck returns to the state in late spring, nests in the rice fields in summer, and usually leaves before the first frost. Flocks of several thousand often stage at Lacassine in late summer. A few blue-winged teal, mallards, and ruddy ducks have been found to nest.

Millions of migrant puddle ducks winter or stop-over in the marshes, with the majority found in southwestern Louisiana. The upper freshwater marshes adjacent to the rice fields are particularly attractive to mallards, pintail, and teal, but ducks may be found in every corner of the coastal marshes. During the bonanza years in the 1960s, when the sawgrass die-off areas were producing heavy

Draglines can be used both to create and destroy marshes.

seed crops, rice field use dropped off. Later in the 1970s, Alain Tamisier, a French waterfowl biologist studying the diurnal activities of green-winged teal and pintail at Lacassine, found that thousands of these species were roosting all day long in the pool and flying north into the rice fields at night to feed. My own food habits studies earlier in the same area indicated that during dry years when annual grasses were abundant, mallards and pintails ate much less rice than during wet years when the annuals were scarce.

Over 700,000 scaup winter in the large estuarine lakes and bays and in the Gulf waters, mainly in the subdelta marsh. Canvasbacks number but a few thousand and are found mainly in the lower Atchafalaya Swamp lakes, but may also be found scattered in small flocks from the Chandeleurs to Texas. Some 70,000 ring-necked ducks winter in Louisiana with a large portion found in the pool at the Lacassine refuge. Redheads, numbering 20,000 to 30,000, find the marine grass beds off the Chandeleur Islands to their liking.

East of Louisiana in coastal Mississippi and Alabama, the marshes were formed in the estuarine deltas of the Pearl, Pascagoula, Alabama, and Tombigbee Rivers. Inland refuges in Tennessee, Mississippi, and Alabama have short-stopped the great mass of puddle ducks that formerly came to the coast. Diving ducks, scaup, and redheads, still come in large numbers to the sheltered bays of Florida panhandle.

Beyond Sabine Lake in Texas the marsh becomes a narrow strip that totals over a half-million acres along the Gulf. The coastal prairie, now converted to rice culture behind the marshes, supports a tremendous number of ducks and geese. Up to 500,000 lesser snow geese, and several million ducks winter in the marshes and rice fields of Texas. The estuarine waters of Texas harbor the largest concentration of wintering redhead ducks in North America.

©M. Anderson

Persistent Problems and Issues

Some problems in waterfowl management have been with us for a long time and, despite great efforts to solve them, show little sign of going away.

One problem is the way that ducks and geese can eat up crops carefully planted and tended by men before those crops can be harvested. It is hardly a new problem. A newspaper in the Minnedosa, Manitoba, area remarked in 1904, that "ducks have been working on the unthreshed barley stocks in large numbers, and farmers for once were not averse to sportsmen coming on the fields to keep the ducks moving."

The problem has grown worse, partly because waterfowl management has tended to concentrate the birds. This chapter reflects the dimensions of this problem as it has occurred in Canada and the United States.

Another problem that won't go away is waterfowl disease, particularly lead poisoning. As we saw in the portrait of Alexander Wetmore in Chapter 3, a great deal was known about lead poisoning in the early 1900s. More Game Birds in America, the group that preceded Ducks Unlimited, published a pamphlet in 1931 that called attention to the seriousness of the problem. Half a century later, the problem is still with us, both as a major waterfowl disease and as a divisive political issue.

Canada geese are the focus of another sort of problem — actually a case of management being too successful. The big birds seemed doomed in at least one flyway until management efforts reversed the tide of their fortunes. While bird numbers have soared, they have brought a whole new set of problems that seem at least as thorny as the original problem of ensuring the continued existence of the species. The case history of Canada goose management in the Mississippi Flyway rounds out this discussion of persistent problems.

No Room For Ducks

Bill Burton

Winter was reluctantly relaxing its grip on the endless prairie when I looked down from the jetliner five miles above the heart of the Canadian "duck factory" where most of North America's ducks breed.

The factory was at a standstill that clear and bright afternoon in March, though nature was gearing up for duck production in ways not obvious from my distant vantage point. I knew the remaining ice and snow was melting grudgingly in the cool early spring. The rains of the previous fall had been quickly followed by below-freezing temperatures that created an almost-perfect frost seal in the earth. As the snow and ice melted, rivulets flowed down the gradual slopes toward countless potholes.

The frost seal is essential to carry water to the potholes and sloughs. In years when it does not form, much of the spring-melt water quickly seeps into the earth and never reaches the potholes. These depressions, most of which were created by the great glacier, are essential equipment in the Canadian waterfowl factory. They must be filled with water when the birds return from their wintering grounds south of the Canadian border. The sunlight glistening on water here and there made it obvious that many of the potholes were filling, but the ducks were late because the winter had been harsh in much of North America.

On the frozen ground below there was more to see. There were huge black rectangles bordered by white snowdrifts that fed the rivulets and creeks. The black was rich soil, plowed and fertilized the previous fall in preparation for spring planting, mostly wheat. The farmers, restless after the long winter, were undoubtedly anxious to start work.

Restless, too, were the raccoons and other predators cooped up in the long, thin, ugly scars sandwiched between the black fields and the sloughs. Some more fortunate predators were about to rouse themselves from their dens in the many abandoned farm buildings. I was worried about those abandoned buildings, but I was even more disturbed by ominous parallel scars on the prairie. They tell much of the story about the future of our waterfowl hunting.

Where those scars mar the earth there once was brush and trees. Heavy earth-moving equipment had uprooted and pushed the growth down to create more acres of tillable land. The trees and other debris were then pushed into long, narrow rows and burned in smouldering fires the likes of which I have seen many times in summer time small-plane survey flights with the USFWS over the duck factory. The smoke is often visable for many miles. The flames gradually die out and leave rows of charred tree trunks, brush, roots, and clotted earth. The newly cleared land goes into production to help pay for the new equipment needed to "tame" even more land. The trees are vanishing that helped to hold snow and moisture for the spring runoff, retarded erosion, provided habitat for upland gamebirds and big game, and broke the monotony of the prairie. And these unsightly burned strips also provide winter dens and shelters for those that prey on waterfowl and eat their eggs.

There was a time when a man would drive miles in this rather barren country merely to see a raccoon. Now there are too many of them. The raccoon isn't a prairie native. It had no haven during the long frigid winters until farmers started bulldozing, burning, and abandoning their buildings to live in town.

These Canadian farmers are businessmen, though many of them still live in close association with nature. Some were probably looking across the prairie for the first duck or goose of the spring migration. To them, the first sight of waterfowl is a harbinger of spring — a signal to return to the land with elaborate farming equipment that would have been beyond their wildest dreams only a few years ago.

But by fall many of these same prairie-

Bill Burton is an outdoor writer whose concerns about waterfowl have led him to the Canadian nesting grounds many times. Photo courtesy of Bill Burton.

province farmers will be worrying about birds. Fattening themselves for the long southward migration, waterfowl often hit hard-pressed farmers where it hurts most — in the wallet. Crop and depredation are ugly words heard with increasing frequency on the prairies where most of North America's ducks nest and where many birds (mostly geese) that breed farther north stop to feast during the massive fall flights.

Not long ago, feeding ducks and geese were ignored in the wheatlands. No more. Hungry waterfowl often make the difference between a good year and a fair year for farmers. In an exceptionally wet fall, when the wheat lies in the fields a long time because it cannot be harvested until it is dry, waterfowl depredation can mean the difference between profit and loss.

In the Manitoba countryside I was flying over, 90 percent of the ducks nest on private land controlled primarily by grain farmers. Those farmers have the choice of climbing down from the tractor seat to move ducklings or nests out of the way or of running right over them. They also decide whether or

not to plow around a vital slough on their land or go straight through it with their new heavy equipment, breaking the ground seal with the plow and adding another waterfowl nesting site to their tilled land. Each tillable acre counts, and every nest or pothole drained represents fewer birds to eat their wheat.

These men do not take pleasure in driving living things off their land. Most of them are considerate, hard-working people with a heritage of appreciation for wildlife, but they are also practical businessmen who must compete for survival in a cost-conscious local and world grain market. They can tolerate only so many federal, provincial, and local governments' organized sportsmen. Ducks Unlimited (DU) and others involved in waterfowl programs can study, work, talk, and plead but the continued existence of most North American ducks depends on the cooperation of the Canadian prairie farmer.

They have their own side of the story to tell, and I flew to the duck factory to hear it. For two weeks I drove across the wheatlands to interview farmers and those who deal with them. Before leaving the prairie provinces, I came to realize that the long-range outlook for most of the waterfowl is more ominous than I had imagined.

Elmer Kure was a farmer in Alberta's Red Deer county for thirty years before turning the farm's operation over to one of his sons. He now works full time ten months a year as director of environmental relations for the Alberta Fish and Game Association. The other two months he spends fishing.

Kure spelled out his "lay-it-on-the-line" approach to current waterfowl problems at the recent Third International Waterfowl Symposium sponsored by Ducks Unlimited. He made it obvious that he appreciated the sentiments of both farmer and sportsman.

He urged waterfowl authorities to place more emphasis on managing people and the land instead of wildlife — and to get on with it quickly and overcome the current trend to "use up resources, rather than use them." Nor did he pull any punches in insisting the time has come to start paying farmers for feeding waterfowl.

When I visited Kure and Tony Ferguson, who is president of the Alberta Fish and Game Association, in Edmonton, both emphasized the importance of the Canadian farmer above all else in the effort to save waterfowl. They are not certain the fight to save huntable numbers of ducks will be won.

"If we are to have ducks and other wildlife breeding and surviving in farm country, we will need to cultivate a positive attitude among our farmers on whose land they live," Kure stressed. "Lest you think we can buy enough land in agricultural areas to serve wildlife interests, let me set you straight. If it were not for a few carefree, inefficient farmers, and some very conservation-minded ones, we would be out of both habitat and wildlife by now.

"The politics of producing food today wields a heavy stick, and we are going to have to compete with farmer's interest at the level he best understands, his pocketbook."

Hunting rights, as such, cannot be sold in Canada, where it is taken literally that wildlife is a public resource. And this means,

contend Kure and Ferguson, that the farmer will have to be compensated "by the acre, not by the gun, if we are going to see any significant concern by landowners for wildlife."

They maintain the biggest problem is a lack of concern for wildlife at the political level.

Lack of political clout has put the fight for wildlife into a rear-guard action, Kure lamented. He said, "On the one hand, wildlife is a headache to the farmer — he gets nothing out of it — and on the other hand, no real budget is available to actually pay the farmer to preserve habitat."

Prime land for waterfowl and other wildlife is usually priced out of consideration, requiring that management projects become more dependent on marginal agricultural lands. Sometimes they are more valuable for wildlife, other times not. Yet farmers always ask, "What are you going to do with the ducks that result from that cover you're improving. Who's going to feed them?"

What does feeding cost? Estimates vary, but it is substantial. A 1973 Saskatchewan report by Ross MacLennan, since named superintendent of wildlife for that province, which is first in North American duck production, cites an average of 3.4 cents per duck per day. This is based on information available from 1965 to 1971, when agricultural costs were about half of that today.

In Delta, Manitoba, H. Albert Hochbaum estimated it cost an average of thirty dollars to raise a duck. The farmer provides food for a "waterfowl crop" reaped by sportsmen mostly in the United States, he observed. Hochbaum, a native of Colorado and now a Canadian citizen, was director of Delta Waterfowl Research Station for more than thirty years and is now author-in-residence there. He is active in waterfowl research.

MacLennan now estimates prairie Canada depredation losses average one percent of the grain crop in a normal year, and much more than that in a bad year, such as 1977 when crops, mired for weeks in wet fields, beckoned ducks, geese, cranes, and other birds.

A concentration of pintails in rice fields at Colusa National Wildlife Refuge in California in December 1954.

If a normal-year loss of $6 million was shared by all 70,000 Saskatchewan farmers, it would figure out to a rather inconsequential $100 a farm. (One farmer may own two or more farms.) But the depredation problem is not that simple.

Not only are some years much worse, but crop losses vary considerably from farm to farm. The average loss for a farm invaded by fowl is $1,000, and losses of $2,000 to $5,000 are not uncommon in a normal year.

Fall-feeding ducks, a potential estimated at 10 million to 12 million, can consume or trample beyond harvest 12 million pounds of grain a day. Mallards, pintails, and sometimes baldpates are the worst offenders. Sandhill cranes number only between 200,000 and 250,000, yet they create losses equal to that of twice their number in ducks because of high trampling damage. These estimates are for Saskatchewan alone.

In a short, fourteen-day harvest 168 million pounds of grain can be lost, MacLennan said. Under unusually wet harvest conditions, depredation can take up to 840 million pounds. The formula is simple. The loss reflects the number of birds and the number of days the crops are exposed to them.

The depredation problem spread out of control when farmers turned to the swathing method of harvest, by which grain is cut in strips, then left to dry and ripen in windrows. Under ideal sunny and dry conditions, it can be harvested a week to ten days later. Rains and boggy fields can delay the harvest for as long as ten weeks. Every day the wheat lies swathed, it is vulnerable.

Ed Begin, executive director of the Saskatchewan Wildlife Federation, summed it up aptly: "Let a farmer watch his grain going into the hopper under sunny skies, and he doesn't mind that flight of ducks feeding on the other side of the field. He'll get to it before much is lost. But, let that same farmer stand on his porch as ducks feed on his crops day after day in the rain and he's in trouble. Every day costs him more."

There are many techniques for scaring off waterfowl, but none have been effective over the long run. Moreover, the farmer and his family are usually too busy at this time of year to spend time trying to chase off ducks, geese, and cranes.

Tom Motta, president of the Saskatchewan Wildlife Federation, told me in his Moose Jaw office, "We have listened with horror while agricultural organizations have openly talked about the massive poisoning of ducks. The landowner who once climbed down from his tractor to move an imperiled nest now goes out of his way to run over it."

MacLennan's sympathy with the farmers of his province was very apparent when we talked in his Regina office. At that time the federal government's five-year depredation-payment program to farmers was about to expire. Officials in Ottawa had announced an improved payment plan, but only on a one-year basis, and the superintendent of wildlife considered the plan far too little compensation, even for one season, taking current farming costs into consideration.

Basically the proposal would have provided continuance of payments up to $25 an acre for crop losses, but increased the total available from $1 million to $2.8 million a year to be divided up between Alberta, Saskatchewan, and Manitoba. MacLennan considered the plan an insult to farmers, as did the farmers and others I interviewed.

Crop production costs alone average from forty to fifty dollars an acre — that's just the farmer's investment in fuel, fertilizer, seed, and other expenses; not to mention time, taxes, payments on equipment, and the loss of anticipated profit. Compensation formulas vary by province, and there are special insurance plans financed primarily by hunter revenue to help defray losses. Under some plans farmers must preregister and pay a small advance fee to become eligible for compensation. And, of course, bureaucratic red tape is involved, and so are accompanying delays.

In 1977 calamity befell the program in Saskatchewan. It went broke and was closed down by MacLennan on September 22, even before the rains started. Damage complaints came from everywhere, he said, some as high as $10,000 — and there was no money to pay them off.

"Unless we get increases in acreage payments, we will bow out of everything to do with waterfowl," he told me.

As I write this (in 1978), Paul Naftel, assistant director of Wildlife for Saskatchewan, informs me the federal government revised its offer under a complicated plan that would compensate farmers for the cost of production to a maximum of 75 percent of their loss or fifty dollars an acre — whichever is the lesser of the two. Details, he said, had not been completely worked out, nor was the plan validated by signatures. It was based on a one-year period, although a definitive clause was being inserted to make possible a long-term agreement.

Also included were provisions for lure crops, under which the government buys standing crops or pays to have them grown in specific areas of high depredation and flight concentrations to lure the birds away from the farmers' fields. Lure-crop costs would be split evenly between federal and provincial governments.

Offhand, this would appear to solve much of the depredation problem that has been so visible it has overshadowed many other disturbing aspects of a deteriorating waterfowl picture. Yet doubts were being raised as final revisions were being worked out.

Motta told me the new plan represented a "big step forward, but not a giant step." In his dealings with farmers, he has found the need for a long-range program with built-in funding to guarantee success of a plan through changing governments and priorities.

The question of how long financially hard-pressed provincial and federal governments could underwrite the program was being asked. Kure and others had said that for every farmer who filed a depredation claim there was at least one who didn't. Increased maximum payments will undoubtedly prompt more claims, for which the individual farmer payoff might well be double under the new formula. Also to be considered is that in many areas the depredation problem spreads.

One speculates whether the time will come when United States hunters will be asked to underwrite part of the depredation plan, and what the response might be. Currently, spokesmen for Ducks Unlimited and provincial wildlife organizations play this down, but farmers and individual hunters hint strongly of the need for assistance and of the obligation of American hunters who take 70 percent of the continental bag.

Americans can justifiably point to many accomplishments, says Ducks Unlimited, which has become the catalyst for wetlands conservation projects without which habitat and birds would be far worse off than today. Yet, realistically, all contributions of the American hunter in Ducks Unlimited's forty-year history would just about cover one severe year's depredation loss in Saskatchewan. The USFWS' duck-stamp program has taken in $200 million since the first stamp was issued in 1934, a sum that would offset little more than depredation losses for two severe years in the western provinces. That is the magnitude of the depredation problem.

DU's policy is not to participate directly in depredation compensatory programs, but to continue use of its funds along the traditional path of improving habitat. Yet effects of depredation are felt by DU.

Both Bernie Forbes, DU's Saskatchewan manager, and D. S. Morrison, executive director of Canadian Operations, addressed the increasing responsibility expected of their organization for increased waterfowl resulting from habitat improvement projects. And, of course, there are the farmers who want to know who's going to feed the ducks reared on the sloughs they allow to be placed in the custody of DU.

Gone are days when a DU representative with pencil and brown paper outlined a project while leaning against the fender of a pickup, an idling tractor motor sputtering nearby. The farmer signed, and a water-control structure was installed before summer's end.

The farmer now asks questions and is more reluctant to grant exceptionally long-term easements. Water and other environmental changes must be approved by the government, and often the agreement is officially recorded. Simplicity has given way to complications brought on by changing times and a multitude of regulations. The project probably won't be started until the following year or later.

Much of the prairie country seems so endless, so filled with sloughs, that one cannot conceive the possibility that the day might come when waterfowl will no longer be available in huntable numbers. Yet the transformation continues. Consider the following: Changing patterns in rural life have resulted in many more holdings of 1,200- to 3,500-acre farms, rather than the traditional quarter-section farms of 160 acres. Larger farms usually mean more expensive and elaborate equipment, which in turn demand more efficient operation to pay for equipment and expansion. Efficiency too often requires utilization of every available acre.

Not only has farm equipment become more expensive, but it is now capable of tilling marginal land — including sloughs — that was safe from the old equipment. When a pothole's water level drops, the hole often loses some of its sloping bank to the plow. If it goes dry, the whole impoundment is tilled.

As in the United States, many of the farmers' sons have returned from college to take over the farm. With their business training, they realize the necessity of efficiency, and they convince dad of the merit of saving fuel and time by plowing through the slough rather than around it.

Agricultural-assistance programs help finance drainage projects that the farmer with heavier and more efficient equipment now has the means to accomplish. And thanks to the time-saving aspects of that equipment, he has the time to clear and burn more land. Clean farming practices remove scrub brush and other marginal habitat vital not only to waterfowl, but to other wildlife. Predators

thrive in such circumstances.

The trend to larger farms has resulted in an exodus from the countryside to the towns and cities. Even many who farm the larger tracts now live in the towns nearby to enjoy municipal services and conveniences. Their absence from the farm at nighttime, holidays, and over the winter often diminishes their closeness to the land and its wildlife. Some of the traditional association is gone, and eventually the farmer becomes unaware of the gradual changes.

Soaring land prices make owners carefully weigh the merits and drawbacks of any long-term easements for wildlife management on their land.

More and more muddy, worthless-to-waterfowl, man-made watering holes take the place of natural potholes for livestock and other farm-water-supply purposes. The deep watering hole can hold much more water per surface area than the shallow slough, which becomes no longer useful.

Increasing demand for power brings more hydroelectric projects involving dams, which "starve" once-productive marshes below them. As the marshes wither and dry, the huge impoundments created above the dam fill with water of little use to nesting waterfowl. However, they complicate the depredation problem by serving as staging areas for massive flocks of marauding fowl. Nearby farmers suffer crop depredation.

Rising meat prices spur interest in beef production among cattlemen who, as in this country, are influential in obtaining special privileges on government land. Overgrazing often results on government and private land as beef production is stepped up on both leased public and private lands. Unreasonable grazing pressure removes essential cover vegetation from the edges of potholes. The cattle have full bellies, and so do predators that can now locate hens, their eggs, and ducklings.

Improved road systems have drainage ditches that farmers often utilize to drain sloughs to increase agricultural production. Usually this is legal, provided their do-it-yourself project doesn't flood a neighbor's land.

There is also the matter of what hasn't happened — the absence of a widespread and prolonged drought. Retired DU chief biologist Bill Leitch has observed that more stable water conditions with intermittent short-term dry spells since the duck depression days of the 1930s has caused many of today's farmers to forget the value of potholes to hold moisture and provide water for livestock. The value of small patches of trees and brush to retard wind and soil erosion is also overlooked.

There's hardly a farmer left managing the soil who remembers what the dry days were like and how much they needed the things they're removing today, Leitch said. Add to this the shift in farmer thinking about hunting, wildlife, and hunters.

Thankfully, aggressive hunter-farmer relations programs have in some cases slowed down antihunter or "don't really care about hunting" sentiment. But the time, money, and personnel needed to carry out programs the individual hunters should do themselves would be much more profitably spent in the fight to save wetlands and other areas vital to waterfowl, other wildlife, and man himself. Provincial wildlife federations currently carry much of the burden of farmer relations.

The future of waterfowl hangs in the balance of what direction we take in the next couple of years and the accomplishments gained within the next decade. Currently, we are buying time piecemeal, and it is expensive. It will cost much more to buy the future of the resource on a long-term basis. The question is whether those who enjoy flights of waterfowl are willing to pay, not only in money, but in sacrifices.

Rachael Carson wrote *Silent Spring*. Will someone, sometime not long after the year 2000, write *Silent Fall?*

They've Got to Eat Someplace

Clinton H. Lostetter

"Get rid of those damn ducks before I go broke and lose the ranch." Such statements of indignation came from people with a real problem during my early days in California. As duck crop-damage problems grew during the latter days of World War II and the post-war period, farmers demanded crop-damage relief, I was assigned by the USFWS to deal with these waterfowl depredations. My work began in 1946 and continued for nearly twenty years.

I realized then, and time has certainly shown us, that there is no one solution to waterfowl crop-damage relief. The basic reason for bird damages is the shortage of habitat on which these creatures can sustain themselves during migration stopovers or on wintering grounds. When agricultural and other users of the land and water take the natural wetlands away from waterfowl, especially from ducks, a conflict basic to the bird's survival is bound to occur — they've got to eat someplace.

How did this situation come about? Well, as happens to many wild animal populations whose numbers fluctuate over a period of time, the birds exceeded the carrying capacity of their habitat. It began in the 1930s and 1940s when there were several catastrophic outbreaks of botulism (duck sickness) in northern California and in California's San Joaquin Valley. This sickness claimed tens of thousands of ducks during the early fall. These were mostly pintails, mallards, and teal, the potential breeders for future fall flights. Crop damages from migratory waterfowl during those years were relatively minor in the Pacific Flyway since large acreages of irrigated cereal crops had not yet been developed. At that time, the philosophy accepted by many farmers (even if they didn't like it) was that the presence of migratory wildfowl was a part of the natural system.

Mount Shasta provides a spectacular backdrop for this Pacific Flyway waterfowl concentration at Tule Lake National Wildlife Refuge. Crop residues in nearby grain fields provide much of the feed for these waterfowl hordes. USFWS photo by E. J. O'Neill.

Following those early duck sickness die-offs, waterfowl numbers wintering in the Pacific Flyway, especially ducks, began to build up. Their recovery was accelerated by the end of the drought on their northern breeding grounds in the late 1930s, fewer losses from botulism, and a decline in hunting pressure during World War II. These factors, coupled with a decrease in their habitat on their southward migration and wintering grounds, forced the birds to go looking for food. For survival, these opportunistic creatures learned to eat cereal grains of many types, especially rice, and other agricultural crops that were handy. But this was only the beginning!

In the Pacific Flyway at various times of the year, waterfowl made assaults on green grains in eastern Washington, Oregon, and California; ripening barley or wheat in Wash-

ington and southern Oregon; and rice in California's Central Valley. Even wigeons, which weren't selective, would eat sizeable amounts of alfalfa. The young, tender stems were a favorite food of these night marauding ducks in the Imperial Valley of California. During the early winters of 1943 and 1944, wigeons descended onto fields of commercial head lettuce and devoured up to forty acres in a few nights. Also, in the early 1950s these ducks attacked cabbage crops in the Sauvie Island area, near Portland, Oregon, and close to Oregon's State Wildlife Management Area. During the early 1950s several crop-damage incidents by Pacific black brant occurred in the "Pecho" area along the Pacific Ocean, south of Morro Bay, California. Brant came up from the sea for their daily rations of young barley and peas. Similar incidents took place during this time at Tomales and Humboldt bays in California, where brant selected cattle pastures and feed for grazing in the vicinity of their concentration areas. This sudden shift in the brant's feeding was believed to be due to the lack in the nearby bays of eelgrass, their normally preferred food.

We observed these problems; now what could we do about them? Because migratory birds were involved, the USFWS was held primarily responsible and accountable by farmers and farm organizations for waterfowl crop depredations. A few of the flyway's state game departments also took some responsibility, as will be shown later. At many meetings, tempers of farmers flared. During the 1940s and early 1950s, as ducks cleaned up hundreds of acres of marketable crops, many wild statements were cast about on both sides of the controversy. Farmers' shouts ranged from "the only good duck is a dead duck" to "what good are those damn ducks anyway." Some of the "feds" countered with "the ducks were here first" or "go ahead and shoot 'em, we'll let the courts decide who's right." Needless to say, these charges and countercharges did little to help achieve solutions to the basic problem of crop-damage control; but they helped release tension at the forums, which later resulted in beneficial relationships when the underlying problem of providing habitat for waterfowl were addressed.

From the many, and sometimes rough, local duck-damage meetings, the heads of wildlife agencies concerned with refuges and management areas got "the word" that they needed to give farmers relief from crop depredations. Through the stormy 1940s the USFWS director, Dr. Ira N. Gabrielson, strongly supported the idea of acquiring and managing areas for the potentially depredating ducks to feed and rest on. At this time, the Service assigned Everett E. Horn to coordinate efforts to abate the duck-damage problems. He was an early advocate of federal and state participation in the management of habitats to preserve the resource and control crop damage. In the early 1950s Seth Gordon, California's director of Fish and Game, actively forwarded the state's acquisition and development program for waterfowl management areas in strategic locations. The California Farm Bureau Federation also supported the acquisition and development of waterfowl feed areas in localities adjacent to areas sustaining serious duck damages.

The concept of agency-managed feeding and resting areas for migrating ducks has proven to be a beneficial program for minimizing duck depredations of cereal grain crops, as well as providing a place for sportsmen to harvest a crop of birds after the damage period is over. During the early 1950s, the Service established national wildlife refuges, and several other states in the flyway acquired and managed areas for waterfowl on their migration and wintering grounds. Washington and Oregon were the leaders, followed by Idaho and Montana.

Many other approaches besides providing feeding and resting areas are still an integral part of the program for controlling waterfowl depredations. Among the important ones are waterfowl hunting regulations, wildfowl flock management, area management, and species management, particularly with farmer and sportsmen input. In local areas where crop damages are significant and other control methods have proven unsatisfactory, the USFWS has issued special permits, or "depredation orders," that authorize the legal taking of migratory birds that are causing or about to cause serious crop damages. Partly because of the duck population build-up in the Columbia Basin in the late 1950s and attendant increased depredations, certain counties in eastern Washington, northern Oregon, and western Idaho were granted special hunting regulations that provided longer seasons, later shooting hours, and more mallards in the bag. The rapid increase in acreages of cereal crops (field corn and wheat) in the basin, brought about by the reclamation of thousands of acres of high desert lands, attracted more ducks (mostly mallards) to winter there. The greater duck numbers were cause for concern. Resultant

This flooded field on Gray Lodge Wildlife Area in California attracted many ducks in October 1975. Photo by J. B. Cowan.

longer hunting seasons and larger mallard bag-limits have been in effect in the basin for about twenty-five years. This has greatly reduced the late fall and winter crop damages to field corn, yet the harvestable supply of mallards allowed during the regular season has not, in my opinion, been jeopardized, nor has the sustained breeding potential of this population.

At times "bonus" ducks, those ducks surplus to the huntable population, were allowed in the bag-limit regulations. In California, during the 1950s, bonus pintails and wigeons were additions to the regular daily bag. During the years of this regulation adjustment, pintails were the chief offenders damaging the valuable rice crop in California's Central Valley.

As the planted watergrass (millet) and rice "lure" crops on federal and state waterfowl management areas in California became increasingly more effective in attracting and feeding ducks, the severe losses to ripening rice declined. The need for bonus ducks diminished as a better balance in the fall and wintering habitat increased in favor of the ducks. Bonus birds also helped the crop depredation program in another way, because managers developed a better relationship with the rice farmers who feed waterfowl

after their crops are harvested.

The potentially serious crop depredation problems that can flare up in the Columbia Basin of Washington or in the Central Valley of California are given consideration at the annual hunting regulations meetings of the Pacific Flyway Council. Of particular significance is the approximate beginning date of the rice harvest in the Sacramento Valley as it may affect the opening hunting-season dates on state and federal wildlife management areas. The opening in California of state and federal public waterfowl hunting areas is now deferred until about 50 percent of the rice is harvested. These management areas first serve to hold potential depredating ducks from commercial rice crops, and afterwards provide hunters with sport harvest opportunity.

The short-lived Pacific black brant depredation problem of the early 1950s brought about a consideration for changing regulations. From 1949 through 1953, brant appeared to move away from their normal diet of eelgrass, a food that occurred in the shallows of California's northern bays. I observed damages by grazing brant to young barley and pea fields and special pasture lands that included trefoil clovers. With some discouragement by the rancher and conservation officers, the birds were easily scattered. It was at this time (1953) that consideration was given to changing the brant hunting season, which normally began in November, to a season starting in January or February, ostensibly in order to help the farmers' crop damage problem. The bird crop-damage problem was relatively minor; but it served, for better or worse, as a rationale for harvesting brant during parts of January, February, and March on their northward flight. This change in the hunting season, I feel, was prompted by unusual brant depredations, but the previous hunting framework has nevertheless not been restored. Wintering brant along the Pacific Coast of the United States have dramatically declined in numbers since 1958, due in part I believe, to man's increased disturbance of their wintering and migration stopover areas. We also may have been too eager to harvest these birds when they were vulnerable as they headed north to their Alaska and northern Canada breeding grounds. Numbers of brant wintering in Mexico have remained relatively stable.

Development of the USFWS' Tule Lake and Lower Klamath national wildlife refuges, along the northern California and southern Oregon borders, is perhaps the best example of multipurpose waterfowl management in the western United States. This refuge complex was once a multi-thousand-acre natural marsh. These refuges have existed as such for about fifty years in spite of encroachment by reclamation projects. The remaining wetlands and farmed grain lands attract over six million ducks and 600,000 geese at times during the fall. The complex acts as a funnel through which pass much of the flyway's southward and northward waterfowl migrations.

As we have seen in many areas of the West, the nation's need for more agricultural land accelerated the draining and damage of many native wildfowl habitats. So it was in the Pacific Flyway following World War II. As the squeeze on duck habitat increased through dredging, draining, and diking, so did the threat and actual damage to cereal grains by waterfowl increase at Tule Lake and Lower Klamath. With decreases in their native habitat, it's no wonder that ducks moved over to the farmers' grain crops to feed. This was "good pickin's" for ducks to hop over the refuge's dike and feed on the farmer's table. There was a clear need to establish suitable feeding and resting areas on federal agency lands to help hold the ducks off the farmers' crops.

After numerous bureaucratic battles and after several attempts, an effective lure-crop program got under way on service lands. Presently in the Klamath Basin the USFWS does some grain farming; other fields are sharecropped by local ranchers. Since the 1940s and 1950s, the heavy barley crop losses to ducks are a thing of the past. August-arriving migrant ducks soon adapt to areas where they can feed unmolested on refuge crops. With a minimum of farmer harassment, ducks soon learn where their next meal should come from.

The Tule Lake complex of feeding and resting areas also serves as an important checkpoint or holding area that delays the southward duck migration into California's Sacramento and San Joaquin valleys. This detainment helps in preventing depredations to maturing rice in these valleys. This is especially important as more rice is planted nearly every year (in 1979 over 500,000 acres were planted). It should be mentioned here that many pintails also migrate down California's coast and enter the Central Valley and southern California at several places. As has been shown, the better the waterfowl habitat, the better the ducks' chances for survival. At the same time, better habitat provides better crop-damage protection and the opportunity for orderly hunter harvest of this renewable resource.

Another real help in lessening California's rice crop-damage problem has been better crop growing practices, improved rice varieties which mature earlier and have shorter stems, plus farmer "know-how." Improved handling of irrigation water and increased land leveling left fewer open water areas.

Attempts to solve waterfowl depredation problems date back many years. Here S. J. Carpenter is shown firing aerial bombs to frighten ducks from rice fields near Maxwell, California in 1918. Photo courtesy of the Smithsonian Institution.

Weed control and thicker-sown and improved rice strains add up to increased yields that are less attractive to raiding ducks. California's 1979 rice crop yielded a record 6,400 pounds per acre.

A knotty problem of duck damage to ladino seed clover was a real headache for several years (1949-1954) in California's western Glenn and Colusa counties. During the crop's final irrigation, ducks moved in, especially wigeons, and had a good feed, mainly damaging the clover by trampling. You know that money talks, and at that time clover seed was over $130 per hundred weight — high enough to raise real concern, yes! The howls and complaints on duck depredations were directly proportional to the market price of clover seed, or so it seemed. Very few complaints about duck depredations on ladino clover have been heard since the 1950s outbreak.

In most of the former acute crop damage areas of California, Oregon, and Washington, the farmer seems to have become aware of potential crop depredations and has taken steps to help himself. His crop protection efforts, when he is near a habitat management area, have brought this once irritable annual problem under routine control. Favorable farmer attitude has a great deal to do with cooperation and acceptance of a sensible and practical waterfowl management program. The USFWS still has depredation control problems around, as well as a few unhappy farmers.

The strategic location of waterfowl management areas for duck feeding, in relation to natural flyways, is very important in attracting waterfowl and minimizing depredations. Also important are the timing and type of planting. The plantings of cereal grains, watergrass, and certain moist soil foods as lure crops should be timed to mature when most needed to keep ducks off the farmers' crops.

Lure crops are especially effective at holding ducks when the farmer herds or harasses ducks from his crops before large flocks become established. A feeding pattern of ducks, and geese too, in a field becomes difficult to change when thousands of birds have their feeding habits well formed. In many of the duck concentration areas of Washington and California, ranchers use a variety of scaring devices, including shotguns, exploding shell crackers fired from shotguns, and various fireworks noisemakers. In some instances, automatic exploding acetylene gas guns are used to frighten birds from a limited area. In spots where ducks are stubborn, a farmer may employ several shotgun-armed herders to scare the birds away. In the large rice fields of the Sacramento and San Joaquin valleys, it was common practice years ago to use small airplanes to herd ducks from the paddies to official feeding areas, or to other feed and water areas on private lands. Sometimes the pilots dropped exploding simulated hand grenades or fired shotguns for effect. Some herding from aircraft is still done in California when ducks congregate in fields. The herding of geese is much more effective when they have been continually harassed from a field.

A scare device in the form of revolving searchlights was effectively used years ago in the Imperial Valley of California to keep night feeding wigeons out of alfalfa fields. The light, sometimes eighteen inches in diameter, was set up in fields where crop damage was expected to occur. Wigeons are finicky at what stage of growth they like alfalfa, preferring succulent plants about eight inches high. I have observed many wigeon-damaged fields that resembled a bowl haircut. In the late 1940s and early 1950s, large World War II antiaircraft searchlights, mounted on high towers, were used to frighten ducks from the larger barley fields in the Klamath Basin. Few of these lights are used now.

At present, most farmers with potential waterfowl crop-damage problems do their own harassment and protection. The self-help program has become a part of farming operations. Most of the long-time farmers realize that their crop depredations can be lessened if they take appropriate action soon enough. It shouldn't be overlooked that during the late 1940s and through the 1950s, the USFWS provided farmers with free rifle grenade flares and signals, obtained from the military, for their crop protection. During those years, over 300 tons of pyrotechnic frightening devices were used to herd potential depredating ducks and geese.

During the war years of the 1940s when the ducks were devouring rice, alfalfa, and other crops in California's Central and Imperial valleys, suggestions were made to feed ducks on private duck clubs to help solve the crop-damage dilemma. The merits of club feeding were debated in the 1940s and into the early 1950s. Finally, after much jockeying and politicking, in 1953 the California Game Commission began issuing permits to feed waterfowl on private duck hunting clubs. This ostensibly was a measure to help cut down duck depredations. The USFWS did not openly approve this duck club "out-of-sack" feeding program, as it was believed contrary to federal regulations under the Migratory Bird Treaty Act. But the service did allow this feeding, under state control, to continue as an experiment for crop depredation abatement. In 1954 the club feeding program really got into gear when the state issued about 145 permits to feed. The next year the number of permits dropped to about 110; in the following years, through 1979, the number of permits dwindled to 35. Over the past twenty-five years numerous studies were made and reports written about California's duck club feeding program and its possible benefit for waterfowl crop-damage relief. Conclusions reached in all instances indicated that this type of feeding had a negligible effect in controlling duck depredations. In 1954 and again in 1957, I was assigned to review this club feeding program and concluded the entire program, however well intended, had little or no effect in abating duck depredations to cereal crops in the fall or to alfalfa crops in the late fall and winter. Other member states of the Pacific Flyway Waterfowl Council over the years have shown little interest in the duck club feeding idea, in spite of periodic fall and winter crop damage threats from migrating and wintering waterfowl.

Although not classed as waterfowl, the coot or mudhen does commit a variety of crop depredations in parts of the Pacific Flyway, especially in California. Damages generally occur during spring and winter. In the spring they may cause considerable damage to newly seeded rice in the Sacramento and San Joaquin valleys. As the first shoots of rice come up through the shallow water, coots nip off the tender shoots, root and all. This is a real cause for concern of many rice growers whose rice paddies may attract several thousand coots at a time. When this type of damage is extensive, the field must be quickly reseeded or there will be no chance to get a crop off at harvest time. Considerable herding and limited killing of coots may take place to protect rice seedlings. To abate crop damages the USFWS has issued special depredation orders for affected counties in California. Coots, as do some ducks and geese, like the fairways of a golf course, which are especially inviting when a pond or lake is close by for easy access. Coots also traverse and sometimes feed on golf greens, where their droppings are not at all welcome and definitely constitute a hazard to putting. Damages sometimes occur to young grain plants and pastures. I have observed fields of young cauliflower plants that coots have repeatedly damaged.

Early management efforts to cope with wigeon depredations included the Service's feeding of cull lettuce and chopped alfalfa. This supplemental feeding had some limited success in holding wigeons from alfalfa fields during their wintering in the Imperial Valley of California in the mid-1950s. At times during the 1940s and early 1950s the USFWS declared special orders allowing the taking of wigeons in crop-damage areas.

During the late 1940s and early 1950s several railroad carloads of barley were shipped each year from the USFWS' Tule Lake refuge in northern California to areas in the Sacramento and San Joaquin valleys for early fall feeding of pintails and mallards. During the mid-1950s, up to four carloads a year of barley, sorghum, and red oats were transferred from the government's Commodity Stabilization Service to the Fish and Wildlife Service for feeding depredating ducks. The objective was to keep these ducks

off fields of maturing commerical rice. Also at this time, in the early fall, out-of-the-sack feeding of grain was carried out with the cooperation of a few private landowners and duck hunting clubs in the Grasslands area near Dos Palos, California, because there was available water. It must be made clear here that this supplemental feeding in no way compromised the USFWS' enforcement of the waterfowl hunting regulations. The feeding for depredations control ended well before the hunting season began, so there would be no chance of violating the federal baiting regulations.

Another development in the supplemental duck feeding program came about with the use of aircraft to spread grain over flooded duck clubs in the Grasslands from August to mid-September. Flooding was done at little expense to the California Fish and Game Department or to the USFWS. Part of this water was purchased by the Grasslands Water District and part was diverted drain water from the rice fields. This initial flooding also exposed weed seeds and other foods at a period when rice crops were vulnerable to duck damages. Excellent cooperation among the rice growers; the Grasslands Water District and its chairman, J. Martin Winton; the California Fish and Game Department; and the USFWS made this operation highly successful. This supplemental feeding program ended in the mid-1950s when the newly acquired state and federal waterfowl management areas began to provide water, feed, and a place to herd the ducks at critical times.

The role of private duck clubs, especially in California, in providing wetland habitat should not be overlooked. Individually they may be small, but in the aggregate they are important contributors in perpetuating the resource. Of the approximate 550,000 acres of state, federal, and private lands for waterfowl in California, about 175,000 acres are wetlands on private property. Many look upon clubs as a group with special privileges that connote something underhanded or evil because they shoot ducks. The fact is that they supply water, the critical ingredient for duck survival in the early fall, as many of the clubs flood their lands for the coming hunting season and attract early migrants and locally raised ducks. In both the Sacramento and San Joaquin valleys, this early flooding takes some of the depredation pressure off of rice crops. Progressive flooding brings out numerous insects and seeds for waterfowl. Birds taken care of on club lands, however many, are not feeding on ranchers' crops. Thus, the privately owned habitat helps reduce the depredation problem. The foregoing remarks are in no way a contradiction of my earlier comments about the effect of club feeding permits that California has issued for twenty-five years. The results of each of the duck clubs' management operations have to stand on their individual merit.

The dynamics of waterfowl populations and shifts in migration patterns can also affect crop depredations. For example, the latest Pacific Flyway winter waterfowl surveys indicate that the once relatively large wintering wigeon population in California's Imperial Valley no longer exists in the numbers that formerly caused alfalfa and lettuce damages. It appears that greater numbers of this species are now wintering in the Mexicali Valley of Baja California, Mexico, where an increase in irrigation development has likely induced a wigeon migration pattern shift. For Imperial Valley alfalfa growers this is good news, as from 1943 to about 1965 the wigeon crop-damage problem was a big headache.

This discussion has been mainly about duck depredations along the Pacific Flyway, but we should also consider crop damages caused by geese, even though they are far less serious and more localized. Very seldom now does the wintering flock of Great Basin Canada geese cause crop damages to young grain in the Imperial Valley of California. Presently, local depredations take place to young grain by these geese in San Diego County on crops adjacent to reservoirs and inviolate bird congregation areas.

In Douglas County, near Wenatchee in Washington, Canadian geese may cause damages to young grain in the late winter and early spring. In Oregon's Willamette Valley, during the late winter period, dusky Canada and lesser Canada geese may cause depredations to young grain and rye grass. This former flock has built up from about 10,000 in the early 1950s to about 23,000 in the late 1970s. Three nearby USFWS refuges have planted grain crops to attract them. This is good, yet these geese frequently forage on outlying private lands. The dusky goose population increase attests to the effectiveness of the refuge complex and somewhat stringent hunting regulations. Of course, population gains are also due in part to the dusky's successful reproduction on their Copper River delta, Alaska, breeding grounds. The number of crop depredation complaints in the Willamette Valley is currently not serious: some of the land owners employ scare devices to solve or moderate their problems. On Sauvie Island, near Portland, the number of goose crop-depredation complaints appears to be increasing and soon may reach a level sufficient to cause administrators and managers serious problems. Within the past ten years lesser Canada gesse have come into the valley and co-mingled to now numerically surpass the duskys. Although this mixed flock of Canada geese has been cropped by sport hunters, their wintering populations continue to increase. It would seem highly inadvisable to let the Willamette Valley flock build up so large that the overpopulations would bring on more serious crop damage, as was the case with "short-stopping" Canada geese at Horicon, Wisconsin, years ago. More recently the large honkers have become established as both breeding and wintering birds in the valley. I understand that management plans for this Willamette Valley goose flock propose limiting the posthunting season population from 20,000 to 25,000 for each of the duskys and lesser Canadas.

In the Skagit area of western Washington, lesser snow geese threatened pasturelands and cereal grain crops during and following World War II. At times their spring grazing damages were considerable as they competed with livestock for forage and aggravated the weed problem. Earlier in the year geese frequently uprooted many seedling grain plants from the soft soil. To help solve this problem, the Washington Game Department, with USFWS support, promoted and maintained an attitude of tolerance toward the geese by farmers and landowners. To minimize crop damages many scare devices were used, but propane gas exploders proved the most practical. The state promoted subsidizing winter wheat and rye plantings by paying the farmer for some or all the cost of the seed. On the state's Skagit Wildlife Management Area, two goose pastures, totaling fifty acres, have been planted.

In British Columbia, Canada, depredations from lesser snow geese have been limited to the Fraser River estuary. Here propane exploders have proven effective in alleviating most crop damages. In the Fraser Delta and Skagit areas, farmers appear to have become tolerant of these geese, possibly because they feel assured that effective relief is available when needed. Winter counts of lesser snow geese indicate a mean of 18,700 birds on the Skagit and 2,630 on the Fraser Delta during comparable twenty-four year counts. A large increase in snow geese using the Skagit area could cause an expected increase in crop depredations. The deltas of the Skagit and Fraser rivers appear to be meeting the habitat needs of lesser snow geese adequately for the present. Unfortunately, severe weather conditions that force the geese to move to the fields also are likely to move most of them from the Fraser to the Skagit; hence, the potential goose crop-damage threat.

Legislative and congressional actions that authorize programs and funds are of great significance to waterfowl management in the Pacific Flyway, especially to California's recurring duck depredation problem. Federal funds in the World War II days of duck crop damages were hardly enough to do much, but they were a start and pointed out the dire need for funding depredation relief.

Migratory Waterfowl Hunting Stamp (duck stamp) funds were used at first, even though they were inadequate to acquire some lands for resource preservation and crop damage control. In the late 1940s, California Congressman Clarence Lea introduced legislation authorizing federal land purchases in California. Properties acquired by the USFWS beginning in 1948 have provided for waterfowl management, crop depredation control, and, where possible, public hunting on federal areas operated in cooperation with the California Department of Fish and Game. In the early 1950s, duck stamp funds became more widely used; and in 1961, the Accelerated Wetlands Acquisition Act funded more waterfowl habitat by advancing funds from future duck stamp income.

During the early period of duck crop depredations in California, the Fish and Game Commission was limited in authority and funds to acquire lands for waterfowl management. In 1949 the California Wildlife Conservation Board stepped up the allocation of funds for the acquisition and development of state waterfowl management areas. Areas first selected were in rice growing country and heavy duck depredation locations. Wildlife Conservation Board funds are obtained from the state's share of parimutual money from horseracing, as provided by the legislature. Lands acquired by the Conservation Board are turned over to the Department of Fish and Game for management.

We have seen that ducks and geese are a resource that provide enjoyment for millions of Americans, whether they be sportsmen and hunters, bird watchers, or everyday citizens who feel good just knowing the waterfowl resource exists as a part of their national heritage. This feeling includes many of the farmers who sometimes become irate at ducks or geese for taking crops; they, too, often like to see the birds around. I like to think that wildlife administrators and managers, along with their farm friends, have really grown to discover they can get along together with the mutual problem of crop depredations. A long-time Sacramento Valley rice grower, Ernest Hatch, said to me recently when asked about the "old rough days" of duck damage, "Things are going along really quite well. I think we've all got a handle on the situation, but the farmer has to do his part to help protect himself."

As long as birds fly and go through their annual migration and evolution, and as long as farmers farm their lands, both will want to survive. Birds and farm crops are products of the land. There is bound to be some conflict when these two competing forces want to use the same piece of land and water at the same time. The tolerance of man to waterfowl and their potential depredations will continue to present challenges. This discussion has been a progress report to let you, the reader, know the situation is quite well in hand for the birds, as well as their custodians. Yet neither party can be complacent over the gains made.

Lead Poisoning: A Tragic Waste

Frank C. Bellrose

A foot-high stack of papers and reports on lead poisoning attest to the amount of effort that has been expended on this problem in waterfowl. Most of the studies point to the deleterious effect of shot ingestion.

Although a majority of the investigations have been made during the last two decades, the history of lead poisoning is long. According to two researchers writing in 1930, J.C. Phillips and F.C. Lincoln, the March 1894 edition of *American Field* carried a note on lead poisoning in waterfowl that stated that this disease had been known for twenty years. That same year, *Forest and Stream* carried articles by George Bird Grinnel and E. Hough on the assumption that lead shot in gizzards produced a poisoning of waterfowl.

The first experimental evidence that the ingestion of shot pellets produced lead poisoning was provided by Alexander Wet-

more. He dosed penned wild ducks with various amounts of number 6 lead shot, which resulted in mortality. A dose of six number 6 shot invariably resulted in fatalities, and two to three pellets caused some deaths. Wetmore was induced to make experiments on lead poisoning by finding dead mallards and pintails whose gizzards contained between fifteen and forty pellets each. He was on the Bear River marshes in Utah during the summer of 1915-16 to study western duck sickness, then an unknown disease but later diagnosed as botulism. Early in his investigation, Wetmore astutely determined that not all the dead ducks he found were victims of western duck sickness.

During the next three decades there was sporadic reference to lead poisoning in waterfowl. More Game Birds in America was concerned about waterfowl losses from lead poisoning. In 1931 the group declared, "A study should be made of the number of waterfowl killed by lead poisoning. If the losses of ducks from this cause are as large as many believe, an attempt should be made promptly to solve the problem." In 1935, M. D. Pirnie discussed the occurrence of this disease in Michigan and reported on experimental studies conducted at the Michigan Agricultural Station. One conclusion of the experimental studies was that there was a "wide variation in the susceptibility of mallard ducks to lead poisoning."

The first attempt to determine on a national basis the extent that lead shot was ingested by waterfowl was made by J. E. Shillinger and C. C. Cottam in 1937. Analyses of 8,377 gizzards of fourteen species of ducks disclosed lead shot in 8.1 percent, with some species containing an average exceeding ten pellets. The analyses pointed out that shot ingestion was particularly high among bay diving ducks.

A solution to the problem of lead poisoning in waterfowl was promulgated as early as 1936 by R. G. Green and R. L. Dowdell. They proposed a shot composed of lead and magnesium that would either disintegrate in the water or in the gizzard upon ingestion.

Frank C. Bellrose, who has studied lead poisoning problems for many years, examines lead poisoned diving ducks picked up on Rice Lake, Illinois, in 1972. Photo by George Arthur.

Unfortunately, later work on this type of shot pellet indicated that there were some serious flaws in its performance.

During the 1940s there were eleven papers reporting on some phase of investigations concerning lead poisoning in waterfowl. Many papers reported the local occurrence of lead poisoning, and several investigators initiated laboratory studies. F. E. W. Alder reported on the amount of lead found in the tissues and bones of afflicted Canada geese. E. L. Cheatum and D. Benson tested the effect of lead poisoning on egg fertility. Their experiments led to the conclusion that there were no appreciable differences between dosed and control birds in the fertility or numbers of eggs laid.

A loss of 2,000 mallards from lead poisoning near Grafton, Illinois, in January 1948 attracted the attention of officials from the nearby Western Cartridge Company (now a division of Olin Industries, Inc.). Once Frank

C. Bellrose had confirmed to the company's satisfaction that the loss was indeed from lead poisoning and not starvation as had been presumed, Charles H. Hopkins and Ray Holmes of Western Cartridge Company expressed an interest in pursuing an investigation of the problem. The upshot was that the Illinois Natural History Survey and Western Cartridge Company agreed to an investigation of the lead poisoning problem with two major objectives: to determine the importance of lead poisoning as a mortality factor in waterfowl, and to develop possible solutions to the problem with emphasis on developing a nontoxic shot.

James S. Jordan was employed to participate in the investigations. Several papers reported on the findings of this study, which extended over a period of five years. The first evaluated the effect of diet and considered various alloys. Lead, not the antimony or the arsenic added to shot pellets, was determined to be the agent that produced the toxemia condition caused by ingestion of shot pellets. All tested alloys of lead proved to be toxic. A later paper further evaluated the influence of diet on survival of ducks dosed with lead shot.

The importance of lead poisoning in wild waterfowl populations was evaluated by Bellrose on the basis of (1) the incidence and magnitude of known die-offs from this disease, (2) the occurrence of lead shot in waterfowl gizzards obtained during the fall and early winter, (3) band recoveries of mallards dosed with lead shot and those not dosed (controls) to appraise the mortality resulting from several shot-dose levels, and (4) experiments with penned wild waterfowl given various doses of lead pellets and fed a variety of diets.

This study concluded that mallards in the Mississippi Flyway suffered an annual population loss of 4 percent from lead poisoning. A comparison of mallard mortality in the field with laboratory findings of mallards and other ducks produced an estimation that from 2 to 3 percent of all waterfowl in North America succumbed to lead poisoning. The same paper suggested that iron shot pellets offered a possible solution because they were nontoxic to waterfowl. Experimental shooting of stationary duck targets with both lead and iron shot showed that iron pellets were as effective as lead except at maximum ranges.

The first formal action on the lead poisoning problem was taken by the planning committee of the Mississippi Flyway Council. They reviewed several aspects of the problem from 1962 to 1965 and issued a report entitled "Wasted Waterfowl" that urged "finding a substitute for lead which is non-toxic to wild waterfowl when ingested and is acceptable to the industry." In this report Art Hawkins reviewed the occurrence of known lead poisoning outbreaks in the four flyways, concluding that "lead poisoning is a serious problem and one worthy of considerable effort to solve."

One way to solve the problem was through the use of iron shot that Winchester-Western had previously experimentally manufactured. To test iron versus lead shot more effectively, E. J. Mikula analyzed results of controlled shooting of flying game-farm mallards at Nilo Farms. He determined that at ranges up to forty yards, one ounce of number 2 iron shot yielded results similar to or better than one and a quarter ounce of number 4 lead; but beyond that range, the ballistic curve fell rapidly. Mikula proposed developing higher-velocity loads for iron shot to increase its killing range.

At the urging of conservationists, the Sporting Arms and Ammunition Manufacturers Institute decided to further investigate the development of a nontoxic shot pellet in 1966. It engaged the services of the Illinois Institute of Technology to explore metals, alloys, and other substances that might be useful. USFWS agreed to test the experimental products provided by the Institute at its Patuxent Wildlife Research Center.

Results of the testing were reported in three papers by Irby et al., Grandy et al., and Longcore et al. The crux of their findings was that the several alloys containing lead were as toxic as the commercial pellets. Tests of several types of iron shot showed that mortality did not differ significantly from the lead-free controls. One number 4 lead shot ingested by eighty pen-reared mallards caused an average mortality of 19 percent.

Evidence continued to mount that lead poisoning caused serious losses in waterfowl and that iron (steel) shot appeared to be the only feasible substitute. Consequently, in 1970, the International Association of Game, Fish and Conservation Commissioners passed Resolution number 17 requesting that the USFWS begin the transition from lead to steel shot for waterfowl hunting. The National Wildlife Federation in 1972 petitioned the Secretary of the Interior to promulgate a regulation requiring the use of steel shot by waterfowl hunters as a means of reducing lead poisoning losses.

In response to these pleas, the Secretary of Interior announced in 1972 that the USFWS would seek an early solution to the problem.

Nathaniel P. Reed, as Assistant Secretary of the Interior for Fish and Wildlife and Parks, requested representatives of ammunition manufacturers, the waterfowl flyway councils, and conservation organizations to meet with him in Washington, D.C. Representatives from these groups formed a Steel Shot Coordinating Committee and requested that the USFWS pursue two lines of investigation: a further evaluation of the importance of lead poisoning in waterfowl, and the effectiveness of steel shot in bagging and crippling waterfowl.

USFWS researchers took a new approach in evaluating the importance of lead poisoning. They sought to achieve this objective by analyzing the lead content of wing bones with samples drawn from the annual "wing bee" — wings submitted by hunters and used to determine the species, sex, and age composition of the waterfowl harvest each year.

Almost 4,200 wing bones were analyzed for their lead content. Mallards composed about half of the sample and black duck wings from the Atlantic Flyway; pintail wings from the Central and Pacific Flyways; mottled duck wings from Florida, Louisiana, and Texas; and diving duck wings from a few states made up the remainder. Wing bones of mottled ducks contained the highest levels of lead, whereas those of mallards, black ducks, pintails, redheads, and canvasbacks contained intermediate concentrations.

The report of this study concluded that "the 1972-73 wing-bone survey demonstrated that lead occurs in the bodies of some immature ducks at levels that indicate high exposure over an interval of only a few months. Information now available suggests that much of the lead found in wing bones originated from ingested lead pellets."

The initial effort to test the comparative performance of lead and steel shot was conducted with a unique automated facility at the Patuxent Wildlife Center. Restrained game-farm mallards were mechanically conveyed past an electronic firing point so that each moving target was centered in the shotshell pattern. A total of 2,010 target ducks were used at ranges from thirty to sixty-five yards and at two different angles. Test results indicated that one-ounce steel loads were very similar to one-and-a-quarter-ounce lead loads in bagging or crippling ducks.

E. Kozicky and J. Madson, Conservation Department, at Nilo Farms conducted an experiment similar in design to that by Andrews and Longcore. Aim error was again eliminated as a variable. This test utilized one-and-one-eighth ounce of number 4 steel and one-and-one-half ounce of number 4 lead with a filler or buffer added to the lead load. The lead load bagged at a higher rate and crippled at a lower rate than the steel load, and the differences were more pronounced than in any previous or subsequent test.

R. L. Cochrane conducted a more rigorous reexamination of the same ducks shot previously at Nilo Farms. He found a slight difference between number 4 lead and steel shot in the proportion of ducks bagged up to fifty yards; but from fifty to eighty yards, lead shot appeared to be increasingly more effective. Lead shot was more effective than steel in computed crippling losses at forty yards and similar at fifty and sixty yards, but steel produced fewer cripples at seventy- and eighty-yard ranges. The performance of number 6 steel shot was examined in these tests and it was found to be less lethal than number 4 steel shot and number 4 lead shot.

However, Cochrane recognized that the Nilo and other experimentally controlled shooting tests were not comparable with shooting waterfowl in the wild. He pointed out that the ranges used in experiments represented only the extremes of ranges used by hunters and not the frequency of ranges used in shooting waterfowl in the wild. Further, the distribution of hunter "miss" distance is unknown, and hunters do not center their target duck perfectly. Cochrane concluded that "the only way an unbiased estimate of the crippling rate of steel and lead shot can be made is by intensive, well-controlled field tests involving actual hunting conditions."

J. M. "Frosty" Anderson examines victims of lead poisoning found near the Lake Erie marshes after a hunting season.

In a more sophisticated version of Mikula's study, R. H. Nicklaus examined flighted game-farm mallards shot with lead and steel pellets at the Max McGraw Wildlife Foundation. He concluded that there was no significant difference in the total number of crippled ducks resulting from the use of lead or steel shot. The ducks were shot at ranges from thirty-eight to fifty-four yards.

The effectiveness of lead and steel shot loads were tested at public shooting grounds across the United States during the seasons of 1973-74 and 1974-75. Voluntary participation by hunters provided with free unmarked lead and steel-shot shells formed the basis of the test conducted on both state and federal areas. Observers recorded the number of shots fired and the number of waterfowl dropped and unretrieved.

Over 11,000 rounds of lead and steel shot were fired at ducks and geese in this unique test. Results slightly favored lead loads, with

240 birds bagged for each 1,000 shots with lead versus 230 birds bagged for each 1,000 shots with steel. Rates of crippling were close: 16.6 percent of the downed birds were unretrieved with lead and 18.9 percent with steel. The differences in bagging and crippling were not statistically signficant.

During this period of testing the effectiveness of steel shot, the Canadian Research Council considered the problem at the request of the Canadian Wildlife Service. The council suggested using a shot composed of both lead and iron and produced experimental samples of such a shot in its laboratory.

G. C. Sanderson and J. C. Irwin conducted a series of toxicity tests in the new mixture using five number 4 shot with varying contents of steel and lead. They used USFWS guidelines for mortality, weight loss, and other physiological affects resulting from shot ingestion as a threshold of toxicity. At the five-shot level of ingestion, they reported that the shot could not be composed of more than 40 percent lead because a higher proportion of lead in the tested shot resulted in rapidly escalating symptoms of lead poisoning.

No extensive tests have been conducted with a lead-steel shot to determine its ballistic characteristics. It has been produced in very small quantities. The practicality of its manufacture seems to be an issue, and low-cost production of such a shot may be difficult to achieve.

Because of the small sample of geese in the initial evaluation of lead-and steel-shot tests on wild waterfowl, the USFWS has placed further emphasis on testing the comparative performance of lead and steel loads on geese. USFWS and the Oregon Institute of Technology conducted tests on white-fronted, snow, and cackling geese at Tule Lake in 1977 and 1978. These tests over two seasons revealed that one and one-half ounce lead loads bagged 16.8 geese per 100 shots, whereas one and one-eighth ounce steel loads bagged 15.6 geese per 100 shots. Lead loads crippled 40.7 geese for every 100 bagged, while steel loads crippled 35.8 geese for every

100 bagged. In this test three shot sizes in lead were compared to three shot sizes in steel.

Similar shooting tests involving the larger interior Canada goose were conducted at the Union County public hunting area in southern Illinois during the 1978-79 hunting season. Hunters shot at an average range of forty-six yards, requiring 3,204 shells to bag 618 geese. Both lead and steel were loaded in three-inch shells, with the lead load at one and seven-eighth ounce and steel at one and one-fourth ounce. For every 100 shells fired, they bagged 19.5 geese with number 2 lead, 17.9 with number 1 steel, and 20.7 with BB steel. In the same order, crippling losses per 100 bagged were 35.8, 30.5, and 27.4.

The early concern that steel shot might not perform well against geese is unmerited. All testing in the field between the two loads to date has shown little difference in either bag or the crippling loss.

The apparent superiority of the buffered lead loads when compared to steel loads at Nilo Farms in 1973 was investigated further in 1979. A duck shooting test was conducted jointly by the USFWS and the Missouri Conservation Department, utilizing hunters who volunteered to participate at the Schell-Osage Wildlife Management Area in Missouri. Approximately 2,000 ducks were bagged under actual hunting conditions. The lead loads out-bagged the steel loads slightly: 20 per 100 shots fired to 18 per 100 shots fired, while the crippling rates were nearly identical at 4.7 per 100 shots for steel and 4.5 per 100 shots for lead. This test demonstrated in a dramatic way the importance of conducting comparisons of shot shell performance under actual hunting conditions rather than laboratory conditions.

To implement research findings into management, the USFWS issued a proposal in July 1974 titled "Draft Environmental Statement Relating to the Use of Iron (Steel) Shot for Hunting Migratory Birds in the United States." This draft was circulated for comment among federal and state environmental and conservation agencies; waterfowl flyway councils; private, national, and state conservation organizations; and the interested business community.

After receiving and taking cognizance of the comments in 1,045 letters on the draft, the Service issued "Steel: Final Environmental Statement Proposed Use of Steel Shot for Hunting Waterfowl in the United States." This report was sent to the Council on Environmental Quality, and notice of availability of the statement to the public was published in the *Federal Register* in January 1976.

In an effort to ease the transition from lead to steel shot, the USFWS decided to start the implementation of steel shot in 1976 only on those Atlantic Flyway shooting grounds that had heaviest deposits of lead shot. Prior to announcement in the *Federal Register,* USFWS personnel met with Atlantic Flyway state directors at Hershey, Pennsylvania, on April 27, 1976, to present initial recommendations for selecting problem areas for the 1976-77 hunting season.

Rules on the use of steel-shot shells for hunting waterfowl during the 1976-77 season were published in the *Federal Register* on July 28, and an amendment exempting gauges smaller than 12 was published in the *Federal Register* on September 13, 1976. At that time, steel shot was being produced in 12-gauge shells only.

The *Federal Register* for April 27, 1977, announced a proposal for steel-shot zones during the 1977-78 season in thirteen states of the Atlantic Flyway and in eleven states of the Mississippi Flyway. Steel-shot zones were expanded in 1978. According to the *Federal Register* (February 28, 1978) the USFWS proposed zones in thirteen states of the Atlantic Flyway, eleven states of the Mississippi Flyway, three states in the Central Flyway, and five states of the Pacific Flyway.

The final steel shot ruling for the 1978 season contained descriptions of zones in thirty-two states. However, at that time an amendment was introduced to the USFWS appropriation bill restricting expenditures of funds for enforcement of the steel shot regulation without prior approval from each state in question. This amendment became law for the first time in October 1978 and remained in effect through 1983.

Many state administrators, even if they favored the use of steel shot, were unable to withstand the pressure placed upon them by hunters opposed to steel shot. This pressure was especially evident when a neighboring state did not support the steel shot regulation.

Failure to implement the steel shot regulations disregards the accumulating evidence on the importance of lead poisoning in waterfowl and the value of steel shot as a solution to the problem. It ignores the findings of the U.S. District Court for the District of Columbia, which reviewed the evidence for lead poisoning in waterfowl and the use of steel shot as a solution. In hearing the suit by the National Rifle Association of *America* vs. *Kleppe,* the court declared that the USFWS nontoxic shot regulations are the most "reasonable, viable, and meaningful alternative to end the lead poisoning problem." Moreover, the court considered the proposed issue of leaving the lead poisoning problem to state regulations, concluding that "only a few states have taken positive steps in specific locations, and lead poisoning continues to be a problem, some of the reasons for which are beyond the control of the State."

The future of the steel shot regulations and the joint state-federal program to reduce lead poisoning among waterfowl is uncertain at the time of this writing.

Waterfowl Get Sick, Too

Milton Friend

Waterfowl, like other birds and animals, are subject to a variety of problems that can be broadly categorized as disease. I'm certain none of you are surprised by this statement, for you have heard about such problems as lead poisoning, avian botulism, avian cholera, DVE (duck virus enteritis), and perhaps other diseases. However, general awareness of the existence of disease and concern for the number of birds being lost is the extent of recognition and perspective usually afforded these problems.

To many waterfowl enthusiasts, disease outbreaks represent random displays of Mother Nature's cussedness. They seem to occur without warning, are often locally devastating, and then vanish like the smoke from a fire. Lost in this perspective is the insidious nature of many diseases and their drain on our waterfowl resource. These outbreaks are not random events; instead, they represent the end result of a chain of biological interactions. Stated more simply, disease outbreaks don't just happen! In some instances disease problems are a direct result of man's actions.

Disease problems in waterfowl are no more stable than the world we live in. However, changes taking place often do not become apparent until they result in a major biological event, such as a catastrophic die-off or a series of die-offs. During the remainder of this presentation the changing role of avian cholera — its past, present, and future — as a disease problem in North American waterfowl will be used to illustrate the transition of a disease from an unknown entity to one of national prominence.

The Past

The study of disease of wildlife is of rather recent origin, with the exception of rabies and a small number of other diseases directly affecting man and his domestic animals. Therefore, it is difficult to trace with much certainty the origin of specific disease problems. In the early days of settlement, existing disease problems could have easily been hidden by the vastness of wildlife habitat across the continent, the sheer numbers of wildlife, and the relatively small human population available to make observations. Nevertheless, there is a rather rich documentation of historical waterfowl observations that are useful in helping reach some conclusions.

History tells us, for example, that in my grandfather's lifetime "wide marshes and uncounted lakes, ponds, potholes, and rivers teemed with ducks, geese, and other fowl. Adventurers and settlers as they moved westward saw great flights of birds, flocks of a size and of kinds beyond the power of most of them to describe but within the power of all to appreciate as sources of meat and pleasure." History also tells us that lead poisoning was known to cause losses among waterfowl in Texas since about 1874, that avian botulism rose to national prominence in 1910 as a cause of waterfowl mortality in the Great Salt Lake region of Utah, and that aspergillosis was probably responsible for a large die-off of scoters (species unknown) on Burlington Bay, Lake Ontario, in 1875. Therefore, we can state with certainty that observations of mortality from disease have been reported for more than 100 years in North American waterfowl. We also know that in many instances investigations were carried out to determine the causes of this mortality and that accurate diagnoses were made.

Avian cholera, fowl cholera, or pasteurellosis has been recognized as a distinct disease for almost 200 years. It was first studied in the United States in 1880, but was described as causing losses of chickens, turkeys, and

Milton Friend examines wood duck botulism victims at Horicon Marsh. USFWS photo.

domestic geese in Iowa as early as 1867. We can conclude then that this disease was present in the United States for at least three-quarters of a century prior to the first report of its presence in North American waterfowl in January and February of 1944. At that time avian cholera was diagnosed as the cause of mortality in waterfowl wintering in the Texas Panhandle and San Francisco Bay area of California.

There is no evidence that avian cholera was present in wild waterfowl at either location prior to these outbreaks; there are indications, however, that it was not present. Phillips and Lincoln provide the best compilation of waterfowl disease problems of a half century ago in their book *American Waterfowl, Their Present Situation and the Out-*

look for their Future., published in 1930. They noted that although fowl cholera was a common disease in domestic poultry, losses in domestic ducks did not appear to be serious. They went on to state that "we do not have a single well-authenticated case of its occurrence among wild North American waterfowl. It should be watched for, however, as it is a virulent, usually fatal, and highly infectious disease." Their prophecy has unfortunately come to pass with a vigor that is probably beyond what they anticipated.

Another indication of the absence of avian cholera in wild waterfowl prior to 1944 is failure of investigators reporting die-offs during the next few years to make reference to its existence in previously undocumented die-offs. In their 1946 paper, Quortrup et al., stated their report represented the first authentic record of pasteurellosis in wild ducks.

If we accept 1944 as the beginning of avian cholera as a disease problem in wild waterfowl, we might ask where it came from. I believe the answer is domestic poultry. The first outbreak in waterfowl in California occurred immediately following an avian cholera die-off of domestic fowl in that area. Investigations in the Texas Panhandle disclosed that avian cholera frequently occurred in chicken flocks in the immediate vicinity of the 1944 outbreak. Further, it was found that instead of burning the diseased carcasses, the usual procedure was to discard them along the highways. This practice provided a potential bridge for disease transmission through contamination of the environment. A link between infected poultry and wild waterfowl has also been identified in Maine.

The 1940s and 1950s

California Department of Fish and Game records disclose twelve additional outbreaks of avian cholera in that state during the 1940s, with the greatest loss estimated at 40,000 waterfowl during the winter of 1948-49. The number of outbreaks during the 1950s increased to twenty-three and the number of countries or other areas involved increased from nine to fifteen. The greatest loss reported for any single location during the 1950s was 6,000 birds.

Avian cholera also persisted in the Texas Panhandle during the 1940s and 1950s. When reporting on this disease in 1951, Petrides and Byrant stated that waterfowl losses in that area had occurred annually since the first loss of 307 ducks in 1944. The heaviest losses during that period were an estimated 36,000 during the winter of 1947-48. This was exceeded during the 1950s by a loss of more than 60,000 waterfowl at the Muleshoe National Wildlife Refuge during the winter of 1956-57.

There are no reports of avian cholera in wild waterfowl in other areas of North America during this era. The disease appeared to be restricted to California and Texas and to be localized rather than generally distributed within these two geographical states. Therefore, while local interest was high, avian cholera could not be considered widespread, and was not generally accepted as a major waterfowl disease problem of a national perspective.

The 1960s

In 1963 American eider ducks *(Somateria mollissima)* breeding off the coast of Maine became the first recognized waterfowl victims of avian cholera in the eastern portion of the United States. More than 70 percent of the 146 nests tallied on Goose Island had failed, and a similar proportion of nesting female eiders died from the disease. Losses also occurred on two other nearby islands. Speculation about the origin of the disease included domestic poultry or refuse from international shipping. No link between the Texas or California sources of avian cholera is apparent, nor is it likely that there was any.

AVIAN CHOLERA IN WILD WATERFOWL

1944 – 1980

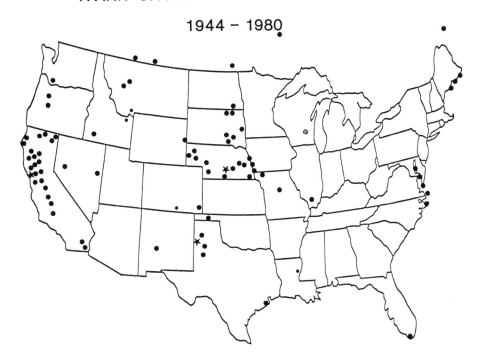

The distribution of avian cholera in wild waterfowl is shown on this map. The original outbreak sites in Texas and California are marked with stars; dots represent separate locations where the disease has appeared since then. USFWS photo by M. Friend.

This outbreak off the coast of Camden, Maine, was an unrelated event probably precipitated by exposure to poultry viscera or other tissues containing virulent *Pasteurella multocida* bacteria.

Later that year avian cholera struck lesser snow geese and other waterfowl wintering at the Squaw Creek National Wildlife Refuge in Missouri. Approximately 7,000 carcasses were collected and burned during the outbreak, which persisted into early 1964. That summer nesting eider ducks were again victimized, this time on islands in the St. Lawrence River in Quebec. The final outbreak occurred outside of California and Texas during the 1960s in the Florida Everglades. This was also the first avian cholera epizootic ever recorded in wintering waterfowl along the Atlantic Flyway.

The 1960s then saw avian cholera appear in both the Mississippi and Atlantic Flyways for the first time in wild waterfowl. While only a single outbreak was reported in the Mississippi Flyway, the multiple outbreaks in the Atlantic Flyway were an indicator of more to come.

The 1970s

The early 1970s witnessed a major outbreak of avian cholera among oldsquaw, white-winged scoters, other ducks, Canada geese, and whistling swans on Chesapeake Bay. This outbreak began in February 1970 and lasted until April of that year. The Wildlife Management Institute estimated the loss at 88,000 birds, making this the largest avian cholera die-off on record.

That summer, avian cholera reappeared in American eider colonies off the coast of Maine. Dr. Howard Mendall of the Maine Cooperative Wildlife Research Unit, writing about the outbreak in the unit's quarterly report, indicated that "total mortality was greater than that of the 1963 occurrence, which was the last recorded evidence of the disease in Maine" (in wild waterfowl). He also noted that eiders and scoters are associated on the Maine coast during spring migration, giving rise to speculation that the disease in eiders that summer may have been related to the Chesapeake Bay outbreak.

Another major avian cholera outbreak occurred in the Atlantic Flyway in February 1975. This time the location was Back Bay, Virginia. However, perhaps the most significant outbreak since those of 1944 took place in Nebraska's Rainwater Basin, where an estimated 25,000 waterfowl died. It is the location of this outbreak rather than the number of birds lost that is of significance. South-central Nebraska is a major staging area for spring migrants, including most of the midcontinent population of white-fronted geese. This species accounted for most of the loss, comprising approximately 35 percent of the total.

This was the first confirmed outbreak of avian cholera in wild waterfowl in Nebraska, despite speculation in the literature that previous waterfowl die-offs along the Platte River in 1950 and 1964 might have been due to this disease. A review of correspondence between individuals involved in these outbreaks provides strong evidence that the 1964 die-off was not avian cholera and creates serious doubt that this was the cause of the 1950 die-off. Dr. Louis Locke of the Patuxent Wildlife Research Center in Laurel, Maryland, in an April 13, 1964, memorandum to Mr. Robert Wheeler of North Platte, Nebraska, concluded from his examination of birds submitted for necropsy that "In view of our inability to recover the bacteria of fowl cholera by mouse inoculation; our failure to demonstrate fowl cholera organisms in blood smears; and, the lack of typical cholera lesions, I believe that cholera was NOT responsible for these losses."

Dr. Wayne Jensen of the Bear River Wildlife Disease Laboratory at Brigham City,

Utah, also examined specimens from the 1964 and other waterfowl die-offs in Nebraska. In a letter of December 27, 1978, to Dr. Sarah Hurley of the National Wildlife Health Laboratory, Madison, Wisconsin, he recalled the waterfowl die-offs of the 1960s in Nebraska, noting that no isolation of *Pasteurella multocida* had been made by anyone. He also noted, "We had a considerable amount of experience with the disease in Texas by that time, so I don't believe we were unsuccessful simply because we didn't know how to go about it."

Outbreaks of avian cholera have occurred in the Rainwater Basin each spring since 1975. This area, the Central Valley of California, and the Texas Panhandle must now be considered as focal points for this disease. Next on the list of important events in the progression of this disease was diagnosis of its occurrence in lesser snow geese, Ross' geese, and other waterfowl in 1977 in Saskatchewan. This problem has also reappeared in the same general spring staging area each year since then.

The final phase for completing the disease cycle occurred during the summer of 1979 when a massive outbreak of avian cholera occurred in lesser snow geese breeding colonies along the west shore of Hudson Bay. Estimates of mortality are highly variable depending on the source, but most likely were in the tens of thousands of geese. Information provided by Dr. Kent Brace of the Canadian Wildlife Service disclosed losses occurring in the vicinity of the Maguse River, Eskimo Point, McConnell River, and Wolf Creek, Northwest Territories. The die-off was described as being "extensive and widespread." Eskimos reported "dead geese all over the land," and elder Eskimos were saying that "the dead geese at McConnell River have brought arctic fox all the way from Baker Lake," a direct line distance of approximately 250 miles.

Our perspective of avian cholera as a disease of waterfowl changed drastically during the 1970s, especially during the second half of the decade. No longer could this disease be viewed as a problem primarily restricted to California and Texas. It now had to be viewed as a disease on the march, one that was expanding its distribution and its impact.

The Present

The present situation is best summarized by examining the known distribution of this disease in North American waterfowl. It is readily apparent that much of this distribution is of recent origin and occurred during the period of July 1979 through spring of 1980. The avian cholera outbreak in snow geese on the breeding grounds appeared to perpetuate itself through a series of additional outbreaks in the Mississippi and Central Flyways from Manitoba south to Texas. Interactions with snow geese may have been responsible for the first reported epizootic of avian cholera in Canada geese at the Horicon National Wildlife Refuge in east-central Wisconsin.

The 1980 March-April outbreak in the Rainwater Basin was the largest ever occurring in that area. Estimates of waterfowl loss ranged between 70,000 and 100,000, thereby establishing this outbreak as one of if not the largest avian cholera die-offs ever recorded. Nearly 31,000 carcasses were picked up and burned. White-fronted geese comprised 21 percent of this mortality.

Avian cholera has now succeeded in establishing itself as a significant disease problem of North American waterfowl. It is widely distributed, occurs during all seasons of the year, kills greater numbers of waterfowl than ever before, and reoccurs in all four flyways. It has taken less than forty years for this disease to change in perspective from an unknown problem in North American waterfowl to one of the more devastating diseases we are currently faced with — and will continue to be faced with in the future.

With today's greater hunting pressure and loss of habitat, diseases of ducks and geese must be watched more closely than formerly. USFWS photo by M. Friend.

The Future

The perspective for future generations of waterfowl is not bright considering the track record of this disease both in wild and domestic birds. Three separate pathways appear to be operating in the spread of avian cholera among wild waterfowl. In the west, California is the focal point, and movement of waterfowl northward through Freezeout Lake, Montana, is the apparent route involved in the spread of avian cholera to spring staging grounds in Saskatchewan. Ross' geese are at high risk because losses occurring in California now are being compounded by the presence of avian cholera on their spring staging grounds. The progressive southward movement of avian cholera in California is expected to continue and will undoubtedly result in future epizootics from this disease on wintering grounds in Mexico.

A separate pathway is involved in the Central and Mississippi Flyways. Lesser snow geese appear to be an important vehicle for the spread of this disease. However it is the white-fronted goose that is at greatest risk. The midcontinent population of this species is confronted with continued shrinkage of habitat in its spring staging areas in Nebraska. The resulting dense concentrations are especially vulnerable because of the ease with which avian cholera is transmitted from one bird to another. We are virtually in a position of "having all our eggs in one basket." Unless this dangerous condition of concentrated birds can be alleviated, catastrophic losses from avian cholera are likely.

The spread of avian cholera within the Atlantic Flyway is not as easily visualized, nor does the disease appear to be as firmly established in wild waterfowl in that portion of the country. The role of domestic poultry as a source for outbreaks cannot be ignored, and was suggested as the initial source of the disease in eider colonies off the coast of Maine. This disease is common in domestic waterfowl being raised on Long Island, New York. White Pekin flocks are often visited by their wild "cousins," thereby providing a suitable pathway for exposure to avian cholera and the initiation of future outbreaks. It is likely that the frequency of this disease in the Atlantic Flyway will continue to increase in future years.

Conclusions

Disease is a growing menace for our waterfowl resources. It is increasing in importance, diversity, and distribution. And if current trends continue, disease is likely to become a limiting factor for populations of some of our more popular waterfowl species. The preceding discussion traced the evolution of just one disease problem, avian cholera. Many other exist. Duck plague, or duck virus enteritis (DVE), and other diseases yet to be discovered are "waiting in the wings" for their chance at center stage. Therefore, it behooves all of us to reflect on a statement appearing in *Waterfowl Tomorrow* sixteen years ago: "If we really want to save our waterfowl, we must prepare now. We must expand and use fully our experience and knowledge of ways to manage waterfowl. We need new, imaginative approaches to preservation, utilization, and management. Yesterday's answers may not meet the problems and requirements of tomorrow."

We are all aware of some general perspectives for the future of waterfowl. Among them looms continued losses of habitat and increased demands for utilization of the waterfowl resource that is dependent upon this ever-diminishing habitat. As noted in *Waterfowl Tomorrow*, "Once there were about 127 million acres of wetlands in the United States. Drainage had reduced our area of wetlands to about 82 million acres in the 1950s." Accelerated drainage since that time has reduced this figure even further. Just in the prairie pothole country of the north-central states, more than a million acres were drained between 1943 and 1961.

No longer are we likely to record observations such as were made by Capt. Howard Stansburgy on the Bear River marshes of Utah in 1849 when he described waterfowl concentrations before him: "Thousands of acres, as far as the eye could reach, seemed literally covered with them, presenting a scene of busy animated cheerfulness, in most graceful contrast with the dreary, silent solitudes by which we were immediately surrounded."

Unless we "expand and use fully our experience and knowledge of ways to manage waterfowl" the "scene of busy animated cheerfulness" described by Capt. Stansburgy is likely to be replaced with frequently reoccurring masses of dead and dying waterfowl due to disease. We will never eliminate disease. However, it is within our power to prevent losses from being excessive. This can only be done by addressing the problems head-on. It cannot be accomplished by letting Mother Nature take care of these problems for us.

Birds dead from "duck sickness" (avian botulism) at the mouth of the Weber River in Utah, September 1914. Photo courtesy of the Smithsonian Institution.

Newly hatched Canada goose and young at Agassiz NWR. USFWS photo by Ralph Town.

Canada Goose History

Karl E. Bednarik

The story of the Mississippi Valley Population of Canada geese in the past thirty years covers some of the worst moments and some of the brightest events in waterfowl management. From an all-time low in 1946, the population climbed to an all-time high three decades later. But this gain has not come without problems, many of which apply to goose management in general and are seemingly unavoidable.

In the late 1940s, Canada goose problems in the Mississippi Flyway centered around the Horseshoe Lake, Illinois, goose flock. High kills coupled with unfavorable public-

ity gave goose hunting a bad name while creating many problems for the state of Illinois and the USFWS. Biologists reported that, in 1945, 2,100 geese were killed in the first two days of shooting. Approximately 275 geese per hour — five a minute — fell to the hunters' guns in twenty-two and a half hours. The opening-day kill equalled the total 1938 season for Horseshoe Lake. In 1946 the Mississippi Flyway was closed to goose hunting by presidential proclamation. The closure of an entire flyway was the first of its kind in the history of Canada goose management.

By 1953, three major goose management areas in southern Illinois (Horseshoe Lake, Union County, and the Crab Orchard National Wildlife Refuge) were functioning smoothly and apparently with sufficient con-

Karl Bednarik (left) and John Koerner of the Ohio DNR place a neck band on a goose. Birds so marked can be easily identified during their travels. Photo by Ohio Wildlife Cooperative Unit.

trol over the goose harvest to prevent a recurrence of the 1945 two-day slaughter. In 1953, however, a high kill of geese occurred, causing a temporary setback in population growth. In 1957 the kill again increased in southern Illinois and coincided with a sharply increased harvest at Horicon, Wisconsin, thereby setting the stage for a goose-harvest quota system. The goose harvest in southern Illinois was brought under control in 1959, and Horicon Marsh became the major problem area in the Mississippi Flyway. In 1942, few if any Canada geese stopped at Horicon Marsh, but by 1975 as many as 250,000 Canada geese spent time there during the fall migration.

In 1956 a Canada Goose Committee was formed in the Mississippi Flyway Council's Technical Section. The committee attempted to define the problems as they were understood at that time and to develop a plan of action for future Canada goose management. Canada goose management guidelines were developed and incorporated in the Mississippi Flyway Management Plan in 1958. These guidelines were updated in 1965. The stated objective was "to distribute Canada geese throughout the Mississippi Flyway in order to supply as many portions as possible with reasonable recreational opportunity of the highest possible quality." To realize the objective, a number of management aspects had to be considered:

(1) Improving distribution and utilizing recreational opportunity by developing a wider choice of stopping places.

(2) Managing by subunits and individual flocks.

(3) Setting quotas consistent with production.

(4) Obtaining better utilization of potential nesting grounds.

(5) Reducing waste from various causes.

(6) Improving the quality of recreation provided by Canada geese.

By then, the Canada geese *(Branta canadensis interior)* that used various parts of the Mississippi Flyway had been defined into four populations for management purposes, each having fairly well-defined breeding grounds, migration routes, and wintering grounds. Each population could include separate "flocks" associated with specific concentrations north of the primary wintering grounds.

The Mississippi Valley population is perhaps the best defined of any group of geese. Its principle breeding range extends from the western James Bay area, along the Hudson Bay lowlands, and north to the Cape Tatnum area in Ontario. The migration area extends west of the Mississippi River and east to central Michigan and northwestern Ohio, with the majority of the birds moving into southern Illinois, northern Kentucky, and several Mississippi River counties in Tennessee where most of them spend the winter. Formerly, they wintered on sandbars of the Mississippi River and adjacent bottomlands south to the Mississippi Delta.

The Eastern Prairie Population occupies a rather broad band adjacent to and west of the Mississippi Valley Population. The breeding range of these geese merges with that of the Mississippi Valley Population in the Cape Tatnum area north of the Hudson Bay lowlands, extending west from the Hudson Bay coast to Churchill, Manitoba. They migrate through Manitoba and Minnesota enroute to the wintering area, which for most of the birds is Swan Lake and vicinity in Missouri. Formerly, they wintered from Arkansas to Louisiana.

The Tennessee Valley Population breeds in the southern James Bay region (the Harricanaw River area between Quebec and Ontario; the Moose and Kwatobohegan rivers, Ontario; and the Twin and Akimiski islands, Northwest Territories). The population migrates through central Ontario, eastern Michigan, Indiana, Ohio, western Pennsylvania, and Kentucky to winter in the Tennessee Valley (Tennessee, northern Alabama, and western North Carolina).

The fourth population of Canada geese occurring in the Mississippi Flyway are local nesting populations of giant Canada geese *(Branta canadensis maxima).* By 1950 the giant Canada goose was believed to have been extirpated in North America for three decades. The giant Canada goose breeding range formerly extended south from the Dakotas and Minnesota to Kansas, Kentucky, Tennessee, and Arkansas. Dr. Harold C. Hanson, Illinois Natural History Survey, weighed and examined several hundred large Canada geese of a wintering population at Rochester, Minnesota, in 1962. He realized that the Rochester flock was *Branta canadensis maxima,* proving that the giant Canada goose was not extinct as had been commonly believed by taxonomists. Local flocks of giant Canada geese have been re-established in Ohio, Ontario, Wisconsin, Missouri, and Michigan. Establishment efforts are now under way in Kentucky, Tennessee, Mississippi, Louisiana, Illinois, Indiana, and Iowa. Ohio has supplied Kentucky, Tennessee, and Mississippi with goslings imprinted to elevated, overwater nesting structures. A newly established flock in the Appalachian hill country of southeast Ohio originated from surplus stock from metropolitan Toronto, Ontario.

The Mississippi Flyway Council Canada Goose Committee hoped through proper management to achieve a distribution pattern consisting of many stopping places located between northern nesting areas and southern wintering grounds, with a smooth-flowing migration down the Mississippi Flyway so that each population would spread its benefits throughout its traditional range. After many failed attempts to move geese from newly adopted winter terminals, the plan was modified to state that flocks firmly attached to a wintering range must be managed where they have chosen to remain.

Most Canada geese now winter north of their ancestral winter range, and the lower reaches of the Mississippi Flyway have few Canada geese. A phenomenon called "short-stopping" developed as new habitat for the geese was created in the midsection of the flyway. The short-stopping syndrome developed as follows: Originally, a population of geese nested in Canada, migrated southward through the United States, and wintered along the Gulf Coast, arriving there by early December. All along the migration route, they were harassed by gunners whose constant shooting kept the birds moving, which at the same time depleted goose numbers. To protect the geese, waterfowl managers developed a series of refuges along the migration routes. Large areas were acquired, suitable foods were planted, and decoy flocks were established on refuges. The geese responded beyond all expectations, and the flocks increased. Hunters were happy, except those farther down the line now deprived of their goose hunting. The "haves" demanded more of the same because they reaped the dividends of intense management on and around the refuge areas.

To combat the short-stopping syndrome, managers developed a "stepping-stone" refuge concept, hoping to get the geese to spill over from one area to the next and finally leading them to their ancestral wintering area in the deep south. But the geese did not respond. More and more geese chose to accept the fine facilities provided farther north. Meanwhile, farther south the process of destroying the tradition was hastened by the intensified gunning pressure against the fewer geese that still attempted to complete their migration. When it became apparent what was taking place, it was too late to reverse the trend, although several southern states closed the Canada goose hunting season. For all practical purposes, a new wintering terminus has been created many miles north of the traditional wintering grounds. Waterfowl biologists, however, are still reluctant to admit defeat. The Mississippi Flyway Council's goose management plan still recognizes the total historic flyway, but continues working toward this goal because Canada geese are so popular with people at both ends of the flyway and because large investments have been made in the development of wintering areas in the Deep South. It is extremely frustrating and embarrassing to have these areas untenanted by Canada geese.

A typical case history is that of the Eastern Prairie Population of Canada geese. Twenty-five years ago this population wintered from Arkansas southward. Now most of these geese winter in Missouri, with indications that some would remain even farther north. Attempts have been made to dislodge these birds from their recent midflyway wintering grounds, but with only limited success.

Between 1953 and 1965 hundreds of Canada geese were trapped on midflyway terminals, crated, and trucked to the lower Mississippi Flyway. The objective was to increase the flow of Canada geese to the Deep South. It was hoped that the birds that were moved to new, attractive wintering areas would return to these areas in subsequent years. Several methods were used to induce the birds to accept their new wintering areas: 1) direct releases of full-winged birds, 2) release of birds whose primary feathers had been pulled so they would remain until the northward migration started, and 3) holding young birds in pens until they attained breeding age prior to release. Analyses of 20,734 transplants indicated that this was not an effective method of extending the wintering range of Canada geese to more southerly locations.

Short-stopping of Canada geese is not confined to the Mississippi Flyway. It is also evident in the Atlantic and Central flyways.

Modern goose management techniques have changed the entire goose situation in the Mississippi Flyway. As a result of the ample nesting grounds; productive, sound breeding stocks of geese; a restrained and managed harvest; and a good food management effort on state and federal refuges, the Canada goose population of the Mississippi Flyway has reached an unprecedented level. However, in the process of concentration and building, we have changed goose distribution patterns and sacrificed goose hunting traditions. More people bag more geese more easily than ever before, but some of the challenge of hunting a truly wild bird has been lost. The Canada goose — which in song, poetry, and the minds of waterfowl hunters has been the symbol of wildness — in recent years more often acts anything but wild in and around many refuges. Even their feeding habits have been modified. Formerly a bird of open places so they could see danger approaching, they now drop into standing corn to feed without hesitation on some refuges. Most goose hunting is now confined to the vicinity of the few concentration areas where success is fairly certain. The skill formerly required is no longer needed in many situations. Often goose management becomes mostly people management. One of the major decisions still facing the Mississippi Flyway Council in this decade is whether to accept these changes or to try to alter them.

©F.L. Jaques

Epilogue

Harvey K. Nelson

During a recent October eve, on a rustic, little-traveled grouse trail, I paused to inhale a familiar musical yodeling which stirred my memory. The swans came into view in the V-formation I expected, brilliantly etched against the clear blue sky now washed with pinks and reds of sunset. Racing against winter, these great white birds would soon reach their Chesapeake Bay wintering grounds after brief stopovers in the Saginaw Valley of Michigan and in the Lake Erie marshes of Ohio, where I had studied and admired them earlier in my career.

As the swans and their whistling faded into the twilight, I wondered what sights and sounds of waterfowl would be available for our children to relish at the turn of the century, a mere two decades away.

Even at the beginning of the present century, some writers expressed their concern about the future of waterfowl. Inroads on wetland habitat already had begun, but greater, more immediate worries were market hunting and an absence of regulations with the means to enforce them. Apparently just in time, in 1916, inspired leadership both in Canada and the United States brought management order from the impending chaos of extirpation with the signing and implementation of the Migratory Bird Treaty Act.

The improved situation was short-lived, however. During the early 1930s, drought spread across the prairie pothole region of the United States and Canada, mercilessly showing the hand-in-glove relationship between wetlands and prairie-nesting ducks. Also demonstrated by this unprecedented drought was the high recuperative powers of these ducks when favorable habitat conditions finally returned. The lesson learned was that as prairie wetlands go, so go many populations of the principal species of ducks.

The duck crisis of the 1930s also served notice that the waterfowl resource was not to be taken for granted. It became evident that too little was known about these birds to manage them properly. Again, leaders with great dedication and foresight stepped forward to muster public support for action programs that produced results. The story of these developments has been told on the preceding pages.

Adverse conditions in the form of drought, drainage, general deterioration of habitat, disease, and pollution afflicted waterfowl with increased frequency as the century unfolded. It speaks well for the adaptivity and resilience of the waterfowl resource that populations held up so well under these circumstances. Species that nest in northern

491

areas above the inhabited and developed agricultural areas, especially Arctic nesting geese, have experienced more stable conditions and even expansion. But severe tests may lie ahead.

The human population increase in North America and worldwide affects the water-fowl situation both directly and indirectly. For every person here at the beginning of this century, there will be three or four people by the year 2000. At first there was room to spare and a few extra people made no noticeable difference to the vast habitat base that supported waterfowl populations. But now the squeeze is on. Demands for food, energy, and places to live are increasingly having adverse effects on the habitats required by waterfowl for survival.

Places once considered immune from agricultural or industrial development, even the far northern hinterlands, have proven vulnerable as energy needs increase. Agriculture not only provides for increasing food and fiber needs at home, it is our primary balance-of-payment commodity in foreign trade. Agricultural products also are increasingly utilized toward our goal of attaining energy independence. Meanwhile, rural lands are being reduced at the rate of 3 million acres per year by industry, roads, airports, urban sprawl, and other competing users. Severe erosion of fertile soils exerts additional pressure on the remaining cropland base. Water has become a resource of steadily increasing value as the demands of many human uses mushroom. It appears inevitable that during the remainder of this century, land and water, including waterfowl habitat, will be subjected to pressures far greater than any experienced to date.

With signals such as these on the horizon, how will the managers and supporters of the waterfowl resource react? Against such odds will they be able to protect an investment involving millions of acres, millions of dollars, millions of birds and people, and a century of deep dedication by many people?

Methods used in the past to maintain waterfowl populations at huntable levels may not be adequate in the future. As room for waterfowl diminishes, the remaining space becomes more valuable and must be managed more efficiently. On public lands suitable for high waterfowl production, low success rates of nesting birds should no longer be tolerated, and appropriate steps must be taken to increase nest success and duckling survival. On private lands, which currently produce a major share of the duck crop and will continue to do so, greater understanding and cooperation between landowners and waterfowl managers must be achieved. This meeting of the minds is not likely to happen in the absence of reasonable economic incentives. With competition for the land and water shared by waterfowl and farmers becoming even keener, positive and convincing reasons — including acceptable financial incentives — will be needed before farmers can be expected to accept any inconvenience resulting from the presence of wildfowl.

The role of the hunter becomes increasingly significant when the bird supply becomes limited by habitat restrictions. Questions regarding the sharing of the resource in an equitable manner take on new meanings. The qualitative aspect of the sport also becomes more important, and waste through such causes as lead poisoning or illegal activities becomes less tolerable. It seems likely to me that hunting regulations such as those of recent years will seem archaic as we approach the next century, much as we all favor more simplified and stable regulations. Yet, there may be some acceptable solutions.

Early in the decade of the 1980s, both Canada and the United States are expected to unveil waterfowl management plans providing an operational blueprint for the remainder of this century. These will, hopefully, be cemented into an International Waterfowl Management Plan for North America. They will recognize the rapidly changing conditions and provide for the contingencies envisioned here. Having spent more than thirty years of my professional career working with migratory bird problems in North America, there is little question in my mind that by the mid-1980s, waterfowl managers and agency administrators must focus on the remaining opportunities and strategies to achieve the desired minimal habitat preservation goals in Canada, the United States, and Mexico. They must also strike a balance between the interest groups that enjoy and use migratory birds and those that produce and feed them. Hunting must be kept in proper perspective, for without sportsmen's support many of the present funding sources could wither away. We must all consider the merits of more intensive management on remaining habitats to maintain present populations levels, including closer monitoring of the impact of hunting on certain populations. We must develop programs to encourage the willing support of private landowners and private hunting clubs. More intensive management requires more emphasis on research to better understand the interactions of the multiple factors involved. We should also be directed toward economic considerations as to where we are likely to obtain the greatest dividends during the next twenty years. We can ill-afford to give this effort anything but our best shot!

As long as the vision and dedication exhibited by those featured in this document live on, the courtship flights of mallards and swan music will continue to grace our lives in the years ahead as it has in the past. We can and we must make it happen.

About the Contributors

The Editorial Committee

Rossalius C. Hanson *(A Career Hard to Beat)* retired in 1980 from USFWS, where he spent over thirty years in work related to wildlife management and piloting aircraft. The last twenty-five of those years were served as Mississippi Flyway Biologist-Regional Pilot. He has flown waterfowl surveys as far north as the Arctic Ocean in Canada and south to Guatamala. He graduated from the University of Minnesota and served in World War II as a naval aviator.

Arthur S. Hawkins *(The U.S. Response, Portraits: Aldo Leopold, Mississippi Flyway)* retired from the USFWS in 1972 but returned as a rehired annuitant through 1980. He served for nearly two decades as Mississippi Flyway Representative. Before that he was a Flyway Biologist and Assistant Supervisor in Management and Enforcement. Most of his summers in that period were spent on Canadian assignments. Before and shortly after World War II he headed the Section of Wildlife Experimental Areas of the Illinois Natural History Survey. In addition to authoring several articles on wildlife, he served as a technical reviewer for *Waterfowl Tomorrow* and *Ducks, Geese and Swans of North America.* His undergraduate studies were at Cornell University and his MS degree was received from the University of Wisconsin (Madison).

Harvey K. Nelson *(Epilogue)* has, since 1979 been Regional Director for the USFWS, North Central Region. He returned to Minnesota, his home state, after serving in Washington, D.C., as Associate Director from 1975 to 1979. His duties there included supervising USFWS's major programs, including the National Wildlife Refuge System, migratory bird management, wildlife law enforcement, animal damage control and fishery resources for portions of that time. Before moving to Washington in 1974 as Deputy Associate Director, he was Director of the Northern Prairie Wildlife Research Center from its inception in 1963. He has been involved with migratory bird research and management in North America most of his professional career of 33 years with the USFWS. He graduated from the University of Minnesota, has an MS degree from Michigan State University, and continued graduate work at George Washington University.

Henry M. "Milt" Reeves *(Portraits, J. N. "Ding" Darling, Portraits of Goldman and Gillham, Duck Banding Methods, USFWS Operating Branches)* joined the USFWS in 1954 as a U.S. Game Management Agent. During the past twenty-seven years he has worked in several branches, including service in Management and Enforcement, River Basin Studies, Refuges, and Research. In Region 3 he was Assistant Regional Supervisor (technical) in Management and Enforcement. In 1967 he joined the Migratory Bird Population staff at Patuxent Research Center. Since 1976 he has been in Washington as Chief, Branch of Operations. In this capacity he provided orientation to Brazilian and Venezuelan wildlife officials on the U.S. migratory bird program, with emphasis on banding. He represented the USFWS in meetings with Mexican and Bahamian officials on migratory bird topics, Three summers were spent in Canada on survey and banding assignments. His graduate and post-graduate degrees are from Utah State University. He retired in 1983.

The Authors

C. Edward Addy *(Eastern Canada)* was Atlantic Flyway Representative for the USFWS at the time of his retirement in 1972. He served as secretary of the Atlantic Flyway Council through 1979. His waterfowl experience in eastern Canada and the Atlantic Flyway states covered more than three decades. Addy was a charter member of the Black Duck Committee, the predecessor of the Atlantic Flyway Council. His graduate degree is from Virginia Polytechnic Institute.

John W. Aldrich *(Taxonomy's Contribution)* was for thirty-two years Ornithologist and later Staff Specialist in Classification and Life Histories of Birds in the Division of Wildlife Research, USFWS, in Washington, D.C., before retirement in 1973. Since then he has been a Research Associate in the Division of Birds at the Smithsonian Institution, Washington D.C. He is the author of over 120 articles and technical papers on wildlife. He is a graduate of Brown University and holds a Ph.D. degree from Case Western Reserve University.

John M. "Frosty" Anderson *(Winous Point Club's Contribution)* was superintendent of the Winous Point Club near Port Clinton, Ohio, for nearly twenty years. He has served as consultant for the USFWS, the CWS, and various game departments. Since 1966, he has been director of the Wildlife Sanctuary Department, National Audubon Society. He is a graduate of Ohio State University.

John N. Ball *(A Pilot)* retired from the USFWS in 1968. He joined the Biological Survey's Branch of Refuges in 1934. After serving as naval pilot and flight instructor from 1941-1946, he returned to the USFWS and held various administrative positions involving wildlife refuges, aircraft maintenance and safety, and civil defense. He graduated from the University of Pennsylvania.

James C. Bartonek *(Pacific Flyway)* has been with the USFWS since 1965, working entirely on migratory bird management and research problems for the Northern Prairie Wildlife Research Center, then the Alaska Area, and, since 1977, for the Office of Migratory Bird Management as Pacific Flyway Representative. His biological experience began with five seasons as a seasonal aide and, later as a graduate student working on upland game, waterfowl, and waterfowl habitat in Utah. He spent six seasons conducting research on ducks in Manitoba and the Northwest Territories and ten years working on a variety of problems confronting migratory birds in Alaska. He served with the U.S. Army in Korea, taught high school in Utah, and was an Adjunct Professor of Wildlife Management at the University of Alaska. Born and raised in Utah, Bartonek's education includes B.S. and M.S. degrees from Utah State University and a Ph.D. degree from the University of Wisconsin.

Karl E. Bednarik *(Saga of the Lake Erie Marshes, Canada Goose History)* is Supervisor of Wetlands Wildlife and Director of the Crane Creek Wildlife Experiment Station for the Ohio Department of Natural Resources. He has had thirty-two years of waterfowl and furbearer experience and has been actively involved in the Mississippi Flyway Council's technical section for twenty-six years. He has a graduate degree from Ohio State University.

Charles H. Bell *(Delta Waterfowl Research Station)* is retired President and Chairman of the Board of Directors of General Mills, Inc. He is a trustee and member of the Executive Committee of the North American Wildlife Foundation.

Frank C. Bellrose *(One State's Contribution, Lead Poisoning: A Tragic Waste)* has spent over forty years in waterfowl studies as Wildlife Specialist for the Illinois Natural History Survey. Author of numerous technical articles, he is best known for his prize-winning book, *Ducks, Geese, and Swans of North America.* He graduated from the University of Illinois and has an honorary Sc.D. degree from Western Illinois University.

Warren W. Blandin *(Atlantic Flyway)* joined the USFWS as Atlantic Flyway Representative in 1974 after serving eight years as Chief of Wildlife Research in the Massachusetts Division of Wildlife. Before that he was research biologist for the South Carolina Wildlife Resources Department. He had degrees from the University of Massachusetts, University of Michigan, and a Ph.D. from Clark University. He died in 1982.

Arthur R. Brazda *(The Bush)* is a Flyway Biologist with USFWS, having joined the Service in 1957. Before that he was a state big game biologist for Nevada and North Dakota. He flew fighter planes for the U.S. Navy in World War II before returning to school and graduating from Montana State University.

Walter J. Breckenridge *(Back's Great Fish River)* is Emeritus Director of the James Ford Bell Museum of Natural History in Minneapolis, Minnesota. He retired in 1970 after serving as Director from 1946-1970. Before assuming that post, he was Preparator and Curator at the museum, joining in 1926. During the period 1955-1970 he made several trips to the Arctic. His wildlife paintings have appeared at many art exhibits. He holds the Arthur A. Allen award for outstanding contributions in ornithology. For several years he has been a member of the National Audubon Society's Audubon Wildlife Film lecture series. His undergraduate studies were at the University of Iowa and his Ph.D. came from the University of Minnesota.

George V. Burger *(Max McGraw's Legacy)* has been general manager of the Max McGraw Wildlife Foundation, in Dundee, Illinois, since 1966. He is active in the Mississippi Flyway Council's Technical Section and was formerly a member of the Atlantic Flyway Technical Section while manager of Wildlife Management at Remington Farms, on Maryland's eastern shore. Burger has authored over 100 technical and popular articles on waterfowl and upland game, as well as a book, *Practical Wildlife Management.* Since 1966 he has written a monthly column on conservation in *Sporting Times* magazine. He holds a Ph.D. in wildlife management from the University of Wisconsin.

Bill Burton *(No Room For Ducks)* has been outdoor editor of the Baltimore *Sun* since 1965 and is also a freelance writer and columnist for numerous regional and national outdoor life magazines. He conducts television and radio shows on the subject. Burton has made extensive tours of waterfowl breeding grounds in the midwest and Canada on eighteen occasions. He attended Goddard College and the University of Alaska.

Samuel M. Carney *(Estimating the Harvest)* is Chief, Section of Waterfowl Harvest Surveys, in the Office of Migratory Bird Management of the USFWS station at Patuxent Wildlife Research Center. He has had twenty years of experience working with surveys and their analyses. His graduate degree is from Michigan State University.

F. Graham Cooch *(Canadian Connections)* is Senior Scientist, Migratory Birds Branch, CWS. He has had a varied career with the CWS; as a student from 1947 to 1954 he worked from Alberta to Labrador, to James Bay and Hudson Bay, and in the Mississippi and Central Flyways. He has been Arctic Ornithologist, Staff Specialist Migratory Birds, Chief of Populations and Surveys Division, and Senior Scientist while serving with CWS. His research interests are broad, but his major contributions have been with snow geese, based on his pioneering work in the Canadian Arctic. He graduated from Queen's University and has a Ph.D. from Cornell University.

Leon D. Cool *(Foreign Service For a Game Management Agent, Pothole Hopping in Old 724)* is semi-retired in Montana. Starting as a lumberman, he had a hitch in the horse cavalry and was a trick rider in a "wild west" show before becoming a U.S. Park policeman. After service with the U.S. Coast Guard in World War II, he joined the USFWS as a pilot-game management agent until he was called back into the Coast Guard during the Korean conflict. Afterward, he went into private business but traveled since then from the Amazon to the Arctic.

Walter F. Crissey *(Calculators and Ouija Boards)* was serving as Senior Scientist in the USFWS when he retired in 1975. He was associated with wildlife research for more than forty years and with waterfowl population studies from 1947-1975. He was closely involved with surveys of waterfowl breeding and wintering areas. As a pilot-biologist, he helped collect the data, and as a statistician and administrator he analyzed the data, interpreting it for hunting regulations. He is a graduate of Cornell University.

Charles D. Evans *(East of Hudson Bay, Ground-Air Coordination)* joined the Branch of River Basin Studies of the USFWS in 1951. In 1953 he became Mississippi Flyway Biologist, transferring to the Atlantic Flyway in 1955. He returned to River Basin Studies in 1961, first in Washington then in Alaska, where he worked on the Rampart Dam proposal and other development projects, including the Trans-Alaska pipeline. In 1972 he retired from USFWS to serve as Resource Biologist with the University of Alaska's Sea Grant Program. He now is with the University's Environmental Information and Data Center. A graduate of the University of Minnesota, he holds a M.S. degree from that school.

Philip A. Du Mont *(The Darling-Salyer Team)* retired from the USFWS in 1972 after over thirty-seven years entirely in the National Wildlife Refuge program. Phil has been interested in birds for over sixty-two years. His field work has taken him to all fifty states, Mexico, several South American countries, to Europe, and to the upper half of the East African coast. He spent sixteen months collecting for three museums in Madascar and was one of the first biologists to do research on the albatross-airplane problem on Midway Islands.

Milton Friend *(Waterfowl Get Sick, Too)* is Director of the USFWS's National Wildlife Health Laboratory (NWHL) in Madison, Wisconsin. Prior to joining the USFWS in 1971, he was employed by the New York State Conservation Department as a research biologist until becoming Chief, Section of Pesticide Wildlife Ecology. He has served as the first and only Director of the NWHL since its inception in 1975. He is a graduate of the University of Maine and holds degrees from the University of Massachusetts and the University of Wisconsin. A past president of the Wildlife Disease Association, he has authored approximately fifty papers in wildlife disease and wildlife management.

Kenneth E. Gamble *(Mississippi Flyway)* has been the Mississippi Flyway Representative for the USFWS since 1973. Before that he served as Assistant Project Leader and Project Leader of statewide Dove Research Project for the Texas Parks and Wildlife Department from 1968-1973. While in graduate school at the University of Wisconsin, from 1963-1966, he studied the life history of the musk duck in Australia under a Fulbright scholarship. His undergraduate work was at Murray State in Kentucky and Utah State University during the period 1959-1962, followed by two years of military service.

Fred A. Glover *(Ducks and Dogs)* has been environmental consultant for more than three dozen clients since he retired from the USFWS in 1972, following twenty-five years of service. He spent ten years in Washington, D.C. helping to plan, organize, and conduct waterfowl surveys and banding projects. In 1964 he left Washington to become leader of the Colorado Cooperative Wildlife Research Unit. Before joining USFWS, he was head of the Wildlife Department at Humboldt State College. He holds a M.S. degree from Penn State University and a Ph.D. from Iowa State University.

William E. Green *(The Great River Refuge)* retired from the USFWS in 1975 after spending thirty-five years as Biologist on the Upper Mississippi National Wildlife Refuge. He is recognized as a national authority on marsh management and has authored many papers on that subject. From 1965-1969 Bill served as director of the FWS Refuge Manager Training Academy in addition to his other assignments. His undergraduate degree is from Colorado State University and his M.S. and Ph.D. degrees are from Iowa State University.

Henry A. Hansen *(From the High Latitudes)* retired in 1979 after thirty-one years of research and management at both the federal and state levels. Prior to retirement he was the USFWS administrator for the Pacific Islands. From 1972 to 1977 he was Deputy Regional Director of all USFWS programs in Alaska. Before that he served for eight years in Washington, D.C., as Chief of the Branch of Management. He also worked eight years, starting in 1948, for the State of Washington before joining the USFWS. He graduated from Iowa State University.

Laurence R. Jahn *(Origin and Role)* is Vice-president of the Wildlife Management Institute in Washington, D.C. He served as the Institute's north-central field representative for eleven years prior to his move to Washington, D.C. Before that he was wildlife research biologist for ten years with the Wisconsin Department of Natural Resources. Jahn has authored numerous papers and reports and has served on countless committees, boards, and task forces as an officer or member. Among his contributions of international scope: past president of the Wildlife Society; chairman of the annual North American Wildlife and Natural Resources Conference; and secretary-treasurer of the North American Wildlife Foundation. He has three degrees from the University of Wisconsin, including a Ph.D.

G. Hortin Jensen *(Alligator Airboats),* before his retirement in 1975 following thirty-four years of service, was Flyway Biologist for the USFWS, based at Brigham City, Utah. Jensen's work took him to western Mexico, Alberta, and the Northwest Territories of Canada. He holds a graduate degree from Utah State University.

Cyril Kabat *(Origin and Role)* directs the Bureau of Research of the Wisconsin Department of Natural Resources. From the date of its establishment in 1952, he served as Wisconsin Representative both on the Mississippi Flyway Council and its technical section through 1959. He participated as an advisor to Ernest Swift, Wisconsin's first voting member. His graduate degree in wildlife management is from the University of Wisconsin.

William H. Kiel, Jr. *(Manitoba's Duck Factory)* is director of the Wildlife Department of King Ranch, Inc., which he joined in 1962. He also has been a member of the Graduate Faculty at Texas A and M University since 1967. From 1958-1962 he worked as project leader of mourning dove studies for the USFWS, based at Patuxent Wildlife Research Center. He received a M.S. degree in wildlife management in 1953 from the University of Wisconsin. His undergraduate studies were at Texas A and M University.

James G. King *(Pre-Statehood Alaska, Making Like a Bird)* has lived in Alaska since 1949. In 1951 he joined the USFWS as Stream Guard on Kenai Peninsula, following which he became an Enforcement Agent stationed at Fairbanks, a position he held for eleven years. In 1962, Jim became the first Refuge Manager at the Clarence Rhode National Wildlife Refuge on the Yukon Delta. From 1964 to date, he has been supervisor of Alaska Waterfowl Investigations. He has a degree from Washington State University. He retired from the USFWS in 1983.

Daniel L. Leedy *(Cooperative Wildlife Research Units)* is Wildlife Research Director, Urban Wildlife Research Center, Inc., Ellicott City, Maryland. During his career with the USFWS (1945-1963), he served as Leader, Ohio Cooperative Wildlife Research Unit, Biologist in Charge of the nationwide Cooperative Wildlife Unit Program, and Chief, Branch of Wildlife Research. Before his retirement in 1974 from the U.S. Department of Interior, he served in the Bureau of Outdoor Recreation as Chief, Division of Research and Education and Senior Scientist. His advanced degrees, including a Ph.D., are from Ohio State University.

William G. Leitch *(Response of the Private Sector, Recollections of a Stump Sitter)* retired from Ducks Unlimited (Canada) in 1977 after thirty-eight years of service with that organization. A native Manitoban, he served as Chief Biologist for twenty-six years and authored the book, *Ducks and Men,* which recounts the forty-year story of Ducks Unlimited's work for waterfowl in Canada. His career with Ducks Unlimited was interrupted for over four years while Bill served in the Royal Canadian Air Force during World War II. He holds a M.Sc. degree from the University of Manitoba.

Frederic Leopold *(Recollections of a Duck Hunter)* retired in 1975 as president of the Leopold Company, manufacturers of office furniture in Burlington, Iowa. He has always been a careful observer of wildlife as well as a skillful hunter whose meticulous field notes would do credit to a professional wildlife biologist. For forty years he has studied wood ducks nesting in his back yard, where nearly 5,000 ducklings hatched from over 450 successful nests. In relation to his wood duck studies he has given countless illustrated lectures at schools, civic group meetings, and before technical groups. At present, his voluminous wood duck field notes are at Cornell University being analyzed.

Clinton H. Lostetter *(They've Got to Eat Someplace)* joined the USFWS in 1946 and retired in 1973 after over thirty-one years of federal service. Before and for a short time after World War II, he worked for the Minnesota Conservation Department. Much of his work with the USFWS was in western states, particularly in California, coordinating state, federal and private activities related to waterfowl depredations control. He graduated from the University of Minnesota's School of Agriculture.

Jessop B. Low *(Cooperative Wildlife Research Units)* was leader of the Utah State University's Cooperative Wildlife Research Unit before he retired in 1974, after thirty years at the same location. Before joining the USFWS he was Waterfowl Biologist for the Illinois Natural History Survey for two years; Assistant Professor in the Department of Wildlife Science at Utah State University for one year; and Waterfowl Supervisor for the Utah Division of Wildlife Resources for one year. An avid researcher himself, he directed the research of about seventy-five M.S. and Ph.D. candidates in waterfowl biology and wetland ecology. He has authored many publications on waterfowl, upland game birds, and big game animals. His Ph.D. degree was awarded by Iowa State University.

John J. Lynch *(A Field Biologist, Voyages of the Flapjack, Winter Productivity Appraisals)* retired from the USFWS in 1972 but returned for a year on special studies and worked intermittently through 1977. His waterfowl career started in 1936 when he served as Biologist on federal refuges from the Dakotas to Louisiana. He was one of the pioneers in breeding ground surveys from the Arctic to the Prairie Provinces of Canada. He has published numerous articles on both the breeding grounds and wintering grounds of waterfowl. He holds two degrees from Rhode Island College. He died in 1983.

Carl E. Madsen *(Wetland Preservation — The Future)* is a Wildlife Biologist with the USFWS, stationed at Fergus Falls, Minnesota. Since 1967 he has served in a number of positions in Migratory Bird Management and Habitat Preservation. He has a B.S. degree from the University of Wisconsin (Stevens Point) and a M.S. degree from Michigan State University.

Grady E. Mann *(Prairie Marshes Will Not Die)* was formerly USFWS Wetlands Program Supervisor for western Minnesota. As a consultant, subsequent to his retirement in 1972, he has served on major wetland management policy projects in Saskatchewan and in Minnesota. He graduated from West Virginia University, with a postgraduate degree from the University of Minnesota.

Gerald W. Malaher *(A Surveyor, Manitoba Joins the Team)* retired from the directorship of the Manitoba Wildlife Branch, Department of Mines and Natural Resources. His involvement in natural resources conservation began in 1927. He has travelled widely in the far north. Since retirement he has been actively involved in conservation issues and has served on the board of directors of Ducks Unlimited (Canada). He is a graduate of the University of New Brunswick.

William H. Marshall *(A Teacher)* retired in 1978 after thirty-three years at the University of Minnesota, where he advised many students who are now waterfowl biologists in the USFWS and state game departments. Before coming to Minnesota he was a biologist with the USBS in Utah and Idaho and with the Forest Service in California, Arkansas, and New England. He is a graduate of the University of California and holds advanced degrees from the University of Michigan.

Larry Merovka *(A Federal Game Warden)* retired from the USFWS in 1965 after serving twenty-five years as Regional Supervisor of Law Enforcement, stationed at Albuquerque, New Mexico. Appointed U.S. Deputy Game Warden in 1924, Larry became a U.S. Game Warden in 1929. His territory, which had been Missouri and Illinois, became western Tennessee and northern Mississippi and Alabama. In 1933 he moved from Memphis to New Orleans and was placed in charge of federal game law enforcement for Louisiana. There he remained until 1940. He received many honors for his outstanding contributions to game law enforcement.

Harvey W. Miller *(Central Flyway)* is Central Flyway Representative, stationed in Denver, Colorado. Before becoming Wildlife Biologist for the USFWS he was waterfowl project leader for the Nebraska Game, Forest and Parks Commission. He was Nebraska's technical representative for the Central Flyway Waterfowl Council. He is a graduate of Colorado State University.

Ernest L. Paynter *(Saskatchewan's Part in the Early Program)*, until his retirement, was Director of Wildlife of the Province of Saskatchewan. First as a Saskatchewan farmer and later as a conservation leader, he has been closely associated with both agriculture and wildlife management. His several honorary memberships and offices held in both agricultural and wildlife organizations attest to this dual relationship. Paynter has a degree in agriculture from the University of Saskatchewan.

Matthew C. Perry *(The Patuxent Team)* is a wildlife research biologist for the USFWS at Patuxent Wildlife Research Center, in Laurel, Maryland. His research has mostly been conducted on the canvasback, with emphasis on this bird's food habits and nutritional requirements. He is presently enrolled as a Ph.D. candidate at the University of Maryland.

Harold S. Peters *(Surveying the Atlantic Flyway)* retired from the USFWS in 1958 after thirty years of government service. Starting his career as an entomologist, he became Cooperative Wildlife Research Unit Leader at Alabama Polytechnic Institute in 1935. Two years later he was appointed Atlantic Flyway Biologist, a position he held until 1947 when he became Mourning Dove Study Coordinator. During the late 1930s he had considerable experience in the eastern Arctic. Peters authored a book in 1951, *The Birds of Newfoundland,* one of his more than 200 publications. He learned to fly in 1938 and pioneered the use of airplanes by USFWS. From 1948-1952 he pioneered in waterfowl surveys of the West Indies. For seven years after retirement he was Field Biologist for the National Audubon Society, and has led many nature tours throughout the world. He is a graduate of Ohio State University.

George B. Saunders *(The U.S. Team)* is a Wildlife Biologist now retired from the USFWS. His experience in fish and wildlife investigations covers more than thirty years, half of which was spent as Flyway Biologist in the Central Flyway. He initiated waterfowl surveys in Central America. On waterfowl investigations in Canada he worked mostly in Alberta north to the Athabasca Delta. He is author of many articles on waterfowl and white-winged doves. His Ph.D. degree is from Cornell University.

Clarence A. "Clay" Schoenfeld *(Welcome Back Potholes)* is Professor of Journalism and Mass Communication at the University of Wisconsin (Madison), where he links three fields — mass communication, environmental studies, and higher education administration. He has authored two journalism texts and numerous articles interpreting environmental problems and situations to the reader. He is author or editor of twelve books on conservation, and is founding editor of the *Journal of Environmental Education.* An avid hunter and outdoorsman, Schoenfeld is well known by readers of sporting magazines. He holds degrees from the University of Wisconsin.

Allen G. Smith *(Duck Studies in Alberta)* retired from the USFWS as a Wildlife Research Biologist. Most of his career was spent on studies related to waterfowl in the Central and Pacific Flyways, especially in Alberta and the Bear River Marshes of Utah. His studies of a pothole area in Alberta spanned nearly two decades. He earned a graduate degree from the University of Connecticut. He died in 1980, shortly after completing his article for this book.

Robert H. Smith *(Exploring James Bay by Canoe, From Tundra to Tropics)*, until he retired in 1968 was Flyway Biologist, first in the Mississippi and later in the Pacific Flyway. He has surveyed waterfowl in most of the major waterfowl nesting, migrational, and wintering areas between Central America and the Arctic islands. He joined the USFWS in 1936, serving as biologist on the White River in Arkansas and Sabine Refuge in Louisiana before spending three years in Washington, D.C., on the Refuges administration staff. Returning to the field in 1942, he spent the next twenty-five years exploring the waterfowl habitats of North America. He graduated from Dartmouth College.

Victor E. F. Solman *(The Canadian Response, Portraits, The Canadian Team)*, following work as a weather forecaster with the Royal Canadian Air Force during World War II, served as Limnologist for first the National Parks Bureau and later the CWS. He was appointed Chief Biologist with the CWS in 1949. In 1962 he became Superintendent, then Staff Specialist with the CWS. He has been a member of numerous scientific organizations in several countries and has authored over 200 articles in the wildlife field. Among his several degrees is a Ph.D. from the University of Toronto.

David L. Spencer *(Beyond the 48)* spent most of his thirty-plus years in the USFWS in National Wildlife Refuge work, serving as supervisor of the Alaskan National Wildlife Refuges for twenty-six years. He studied forestry and wildlife conservation at Pennsylvania State University, the University of Michigan, and the University of Wisconsin. He was working with the Missouri Conservation Commission on wild turkey studies prior to World War II. He served as a Navy pilot during the war, later working with the Wyoming Fish and Game Department before joining the USFWS in 1946. He is now with the Arctic Environmental Information and Data Center of the University of Alaska as a resource consultant, where he works with two other ex-USFWS people: Dave Hickok and Chuck Evans.

Jerome H. Stoudt *(Duck Nesting Studies)* is a retired Wildlife Research Biologist of the USFWS who spent nearly forty years in the study and management of waterfowl. Starting in Minnesota, he extended his studies westward into the Dakotas and northward throughout the pothole region of Canada. Canvasbacks were his specialty. He received a M.S. degree from the University of Minnesota.

Peter Ward *(Delta Waterfowl Research Station)* is director of the Delta Waterfowl Research Station in Manitoba. Except during World War II years, when he served as bomber pilot for the RCAF, he has been nearly a life-long resident of the Great Delta Marsh, where, during his boyhood, his father managed the Bell property. An accomplished wildlife artist, he has traveled extensively, visiting many of the important waterfowl areas of the United States and Canada.

Jacob M. Valentine, Jr. *(Cajun Country Marshes)* is a native of Racine, Wisconsin, who served in the U.S. Army in Louisiana, Australia, and New Guinea (1941-1945). He received a B.A. and an M.A. from the University of Wisconsin, Madison, where he majored in zoology, botany, and wildlife management. In 1950, he entered the USFWS and has held the position of Refuge Manager at Slade National Wildlife Refuge, North Dakota (1950-1955); Chincoteague National Wildlife Refuge, Virginia (1955-1958); South Florida National Wildlife Refuges (1958-1960). His most recent position, before retirement, was Gulf Coast Management Biologist for Refuges, which covers the states of Louisiana, Mississippi, Alabama, and Arkansas. He has written papers on the cattle egret, marsh ecology, alligators, and the Mississippi sandhill crane.

*USFWS refers to U.S. Fish and Wildlife Service, the Bureau of Sport Fisheries and Wildlife, and/or the Bureau of Biological Survey. CWS refers to the Canadian Wildlife Service.

Special Thanks

The reproductions of paintings and sketches that grace the pages of *Flyways* have been generously donated by the artists listed below. Dr. H. Albert Hochbaum also permitted the use of many of the line drawings from his book, *To Ride the Wind*. Their contributions add significantly to the general theme of the publication, and reflect the desire of the wildlife artist fraternity to foster a greater public appreciation of our wildlife heritage.

These illustrations are copyrighted and cannot be reproduced without prior permission of the individual artist.

M. Anderson	L. Kouba
W. Breckenridge	D. Nelson
H. A. Hochbaum	C. Pearson
F. L. Jaques	R. Plasschaert
J. Killen	J. Raedeke
W. J. Koelpin	H. Tollas

Index

F

Fairchild, Cliff, 362
Feast, C.N., 383, 393-94
Federal Aid to Wildlife Restoration Act
 (Pitman Robertson or PR Act, 1938),
 355-56, 360, 362, 373, 392-93, 396-97
Federal Migratory Bird Law
 (Weeks-McLean Act), 4, 348
Feitz, Earl, 42
Ferguson, Roy, 50, 160
Ferguson, Tony, 456
FFA, *see* Future Farmers of America, 340
Findlay, John, 273
Fish and Wildlife Coordination Act (1934), 354
Fisk, H.N., 449
Forbes, Bernie, 459
Franklin, Sir John, 90
Fred, E.B., 410
Freeman, George, 319-20
Freeman, Wynn, 305
Fretwell, C.L., 119
Friend, Milton, 478-84, 500
Friley, Charles Jr., 359
Frison, T.H., 343
Frost, Jack, 339
Froves, 397
Furness, M.J., 119
Furniss, O.C., 125
Future Farmers of America (FFA), 339-40

G

Gabrielson, Ira N., 52-53, 86, 98-99, 112, 215,
 310, 356-57, 362, 377, 409, 463
Gale, Robert, 330
Gamble, Kenneth E., 388-92, 500
Garrat, Tom, 184
Gaspard, Johnny, 446
Gavin, Angus, 240-41
Geis, Aelred D., 93, 205, 258, 339
Gilbert, Paul T., 394
Gildersleve, Delbert, 397
Gillett, Francis G., 353-54
Gillham, Charles E., 36, 41, 119, 122, 124,
 134-42, 177, 230, 304, 330, 360, 362
Giltner, L.T., 82
Gimby, Dick, 197
Glading, Ben, 382, 395, 397-98, 402
Glasgow, Leslie, 446, 448
Glass, Floyd, 318
Glover, Fred A., 51, 271-78, 305, 316, 500
Godfrey, W.E., 305
Goldman, Edward Alphonso, 95-97, 122, 125,
 129-30
Goldman, Jacob, 96
Goldman, Luther C., 95, 125
Goldman, Luther J., 56, 90-91, 95, 98, 119, 122,
 125, 127, 129-34
Goldsberry, Jim, 197
Gollop, J. Bernie, 242, 273, 275, 306
Goodrich, David W., 41
Gordon, Seth, 42, 102
Gottschalk, John S., 383
Grayknife, John, 240
Green, R.G., 471
Green, William E., 299, 431-39
Greenwalt, Lynn, 407, 410-11
Greenwood, Ray, 340
Grennan, Sgt., 57
Grey, Douglas, 46
Grey, Hugh, 406

Griesa, T.E., 81
Griffith, Dick, 445
Grinnell, George Bird, 347, 406, 471
Grooms, Steve, iii
Groves, Frank, 397, 399
Gruener, Carl, 277
Gunderson, Millard F., 82-83
Gunn, Cecil, 322
Gutermuth, C.R., 305, 377, 381, 393

H

Hallock, Charles, 4-5
Hamilton, Bill, 330
Hammond, Jay, 51
Hammond, Merrill, 305, 389
Handley, Charles, 254
Hansen, Henry A., 293, 295, 362-71, 500
Hanson, Chuck, 332
Hanson, Harold C., 189, 252-53, 312
Hanson, Rossalius C., ii-iv, 51, 196, 201-02,
 251, 296-300, 315-16, 320, 446, 495
Harkin, J.B., 4, 10-11, 161
Harmic, Jay, 388
Harper, Francis, 102, 215
Harris, D.B., 50-51, 447
Harris, John, 58
Harris, R.D., 306-07
Hart, George, 201
Hart, Robert N., 396
Hartwell, Art, 316
Haskell, William S., 4, 347
Hatch, Ernest, 471
Hawkins, Arthur S., ii-iv, 2-9, 103-06, 122, 178,
 194, 227, 229-30, 236, 239, 243, 246-47, 258,
 273, 304-07, 309-10, 312-13, 316, 329-30,
 343-45, 380, 388-92, 406, 410, 446, 473, 495
Hawkins, Arthur S. "Tex", iii, 304
Hay, Eduardo, 96
Hayes, Chuck, 272
Hayes, Hellen, 306
Hearne, Samuel, 90, 181, 319
Hedlund, Harvey, 51
Hennessey, T.S., 304
Henry, Alexander, the Younger, 321
Henry, Cordy, 305
Henshaw, H.W., 87
Hewitt, D.C., 10
Hewitt, Gordon, 4
Hewitt, O.H., 215, 304, 306
Heyward, A.C., 42
Hickey, Jim, 51
Hickey, Joe, 246, 305
Hickson, Officer, 65-68
Hine, Ruth, 390
Hoar, Crosby A., 52
Hochbaum, H. Albert, 177, 305, 312, 321, 324,
 327, 330, 456
Hoffpauir, Clark, 446, 448
Hoffus, Gordie, 318
Holmes, Oliver Wendell, 5, 349
Holmes, Ray, 472
Hooper, Dave, 231
Hoover, Herbert, 32
Hopkins, Charles H., 472
Hopkins, Harry, 111
Hopkins, Joe, 272
Horn, Everett E., 463
Hornady, William T., 347
Horner, Charles, 307
Hotchkiss, Neil, 85, 114-16, 119, 123, 127,
 155, 445

Migratory Bird Hunting and Conservation Stamps (Duck Stamps)

1934-35 Mallards by Jay N. "Ding" Darling*
1935-36 Canvasbacks by Frank W. Benson
1936-37 Canada geese by Richard E. Bishop
1937-38 Greater scaups by J. D. Knap
1938-39 Pintails by Roland Clark
1939-40 Green-winged teal by Lynn Bogue Hunt*
1940-41 Black ducks by Francis L. Jaques
1941-42 Ruddy ducks by E. R. Kalmbach
1942-43 American widgeons by A. Lassel Ripley
1943-44 Wood ducks by Walter E. Bohl
1944-45 White-fronted geese by Walter A. Weber
1945-46 Shovelers by Owen J. Gromme
1946-47 Redheads by Bob Hines
1947-48 Snowgeese by Jack Murray
1948-49 Buffleheads by Maynard Reece
1949-50 Common goldeneyes by Roger E. Preuss
1950-51 Trumpeter swans by Walter A. Weber
1951-52 Gadwalls by Maynard Reece
1952-53 Harlequin ducks by John H. Dick
1953-54 Blue-winged teal by Clayton B. Seagears
1954-55 Ring-necked ducks by Harvey D. Sandstrom
1955-56 Blue geese by Stanley Stearns
1956-57 American mergansers by Edward J. Bierly
1957-58 Common eiders by Jackson Miles Abbott
1958-59 Canada geese by Leslie C. Kouba

1959-60 Labrador retriever with mallard by Maynard Reece
1960-61 Redheads by John A. Ruthven
1961-62 Mallards by Edward A. Morris*
1962-63 Pintails by Edward A. Morris
1963-64 Brant by Edward J. Bierly
1964-65 Nene geese by Stanley Stearns
1965-66 Canvasbacks by Ron Jenkins
1966-67 Whistling swans by Stanley Stearns
1967-68 Oldsquaw ducks by Leslie C. Kouba
1968-69 Hooded mergansers by C. G. Pritchard
1969-70 White-winged scoters by Maynard Reece
1970-71 Ross' geese by Edward J. Bierly
1971-72 Cinnamon teal by Maynard Reece
1972-73 Emperor geese by Arthur M. Cook
1973-74 Steller's eiders by Lee LeBlanc
1974-75 Wood ducks by David A. Maass
1975-76 Canvasback duck decoy by James L. Fisher
1976-77 Canada geese and brood by Alderson Magee*
1977-78 Ross' geese by Martin R. Murk*
1978-79 Hooded merganser by Albert Earl Gilbert*
1979-80 Green-winged teal by Kenneth L. Michaelsen*
1980-81 Mallards by Richard W. Plasschaert*
1981-82 Ruddy ducks by John S. Wilson*
1982-83 Canvasbacks by David A. Maass*
1983-84 Pintails by Phil V. Scholer
1984-85 American wigeons by William C. Morris
*Reproductions used in this publication.

Trade and company names mentioned in this publication are for informational purposes only. They do not imply U.S. Government endorsement of products.

Copyright Restrictions

The text of this book is in the public domain and may be reproduced. Permission to reproduce contributed illustrations must be obtained from individual artists.

As the Nation's principal conservation agency, the Department of the Interior has responsibility for most of our nationally owned public lands and natural resources. This includes fostering the wisest use of our land and water resources, protecting our fish and wildlife, preserving the environmental and cultural values of our national parks and historical places, and providing for the enjoyment of life through outdoor recreation. The Department assesses our energy and mineral resources and works to assure that their development is in the best interests of all our people. The Department also has a major responsibility for American Indian reservation communities and for people who live in island territories under U.S. administration.

☆ U.S. GOVERNMENT PRINTING OFFICE: 1984 — 667–157